FOSSIL MEN

FOSSIL MEN

MARCELLIN BOULE

*Late Director, French Institute of Human Paleontology, and
Professor, French National Museum of Natural History*

HENRI V. VALLOIS

*Director, French Institute of Human Paleontology; Professor,
French National Museum of Natural History; Director, Museum
of Man (Paris)*

THE DRYDEN PRESS · NEW YORK

Authorized translation of Les Hommes Fossiles *by*

MICHAEL BULLOCK

Fellow of The Royal Anthropological Institute

ILLUSTRATIONS FOR THE COVER

Front: *Painted panel from Minateda, Spain (see p. 324).*

Back: *Engraved equine type* (Equus hydrunticus) *from Levanzo, Italy, and reproduced from* Breuil: *Four Hundred Centuries of Cave Art (Centre D'Études et de Documentation Préhistoriques, Montignac, Dordogne).*

4. The Fontéchevade discovery, which, complementing that made at Swanscombe, has proved the former existence in Europe of a phylum parallel to that of Neandertal and independent of it.

All these facts and many others, the fruit of research doggedly prosecuted in all parts of the world by the scientists of all nations, prove that human palaeontology has lost none of its momentum. Larger and larger rents are beginning to appear in the veil that has long concealed our origin. If much is still lacking, we must recognize without false humility that much has already been gained. It is the sum total of the knowledge thus obtained, set out as far as possible in terms of the material evidence and without leaving the solid ground of scientific objectivity or indulging in overbold hypotheses or idle speculation, that this book is intended to present. May it arouse the reader's interest in a science that is one of the most enthralling of all, because its subject is the origin and earliest history of our kind.

H. V. VALLOIS

PREFACE TO THE FIRST EDITION

BARELY a century and a half have elapsed since the prime question of the origin of Man was raised from the regions of dreams and fiction to the domain of science. Zoology and Comparative Anatomy first sought to solve it by methods soon found to be inadequate. Later, Palaeontology became established as a separate science, having as its object the retracing of the history of beings of former ages, and since that time the highest hopes have been raised that this new science would reconstruct for us our own history.

During the second half of the nineteenth century, after the ever memorable discoveries of Boucher de Perthes in the ancient alluvials of the Somme, and of Édouard Lartet in the caves of Périgord, research in Human Palaeontology was consistently carried out. The advances made in the last twenty years are so striking that the 'problem of fossil Man' has become a universal subject of discussion among the general public, even more so perhaps than in professional scientific circles. From the very moment of its announcement each new discovery relating to our distant ancestors becomes the subject of numerous articles in the daily press or popular reviews; the substance of the articles could be easily criticized, but they bear clear witness to the lively and justifiable curiosity of the people. From all quarters comes a demand for a book which will give an account at once detailed and synthetic of our present-day knowledge of fossil Men.

In France there are already certain valuable works of this nature, such as Hamy's *Précis de Paléontologie humaine*, G. de Mortillet's *Le Préhistorique*, E. Cartailhac's *La France préhistorique*, S. Reinach's Catalogues of the Saint-Germain Museum, Déchelette's *Manuel d'Archéologie préhistorique*, and the like. But, these works are either too old, or else they present only the archaeological aspect of Human Palaeontology.

In foreign lands, where interest in all that touches upon prehistoric studies is no less keen than in France, there have appeared many popular works in which the items of text and illustration have been largely drawn from French publications. Some of these have been written by pure geologists, some by archaeologists obviously unacquainted with biological problems, and others, by medical men or anthropologists, are too exclusively anatomical. Each has its merits, but none deals with the subject in all its fullness, that is to say in all its manifold aspects.

In writing in my turn this work on the *Elements of Human Palaeontology*, I make no claim to more perfect achievement, but I have aimed at achieving something different. For close on forty years, from the time when I took up the science under the fond guidance of my very dear friend, Émile Cartailhac, I have never ceased to be interested in the natural history of Man. The variety of my researches, and the editing for twenty-five years of the journal *L'Anthropologie*, have perhaps placed me in a less unfavourable position than more strict specialists for gathering together the facts now acquired by the various branches of the science.

A few years ago, after having described at length the now famous skeleton from La Chapelle-aux-Saints, I tried to bring into focus the present state of our knowledge of Human Palaeontology. The copies of the memoir containing this attempt, of which too few were published, were soon exhausted; and besides it included a mass of technical evidence not easily grasped by readers insufficiently versed in the subject.

On several occasions I have discussed fossil Men in the course of my Museum lectures; but such a method of diffusing knowledge is very limited, and my audiences and friends have urged me to publish these lectures in a form readily accessible to all naturalists and even to all educated persons who may wish to peer into the mysteries of the past. Hence the origin of this book, which attempts to sum up the main achievements of a science still young, in the establishment and development of which France has taken a preponderant part.

*   *   *

Fossil Man is revealed to us by two classes of relics, by two sorts of evidence. The first consists in the presence, in the heart of geological layers, of bones contemporary with these layers and more or less fossilized, like the bones of extinct animals with which they are often mingled. The second comprises various objects bearing traces of deliberate handiwork, that is to say, the products of human industry.

The latter evidences are much the most numerous, since they are most resistant to the various agents of destruction. They are to be met with in innumerable localities in almost all parts of the world. They provided the first proofs of the high geological antiquity of Man, and thereafter served as a basis for the establishment of a classification of prehistoric times. Above all, they reflect the intellectual and moral outlook of the oldest communities of Mankind.

The bone evidences, more friable and less easily preserved, are much more rare. Yet it is the scientific study of these alone that, bringing to our ken the chief anatomical characters of our most remote ancestors, is capable of throwing some light on their origin, on their zoological descent and their physical evolution, that is on the genealogical history of human beings or Hominians, the highest group of the Primates.

Although these two kinds of information both bear on Human Palaeontology, although they should co-operate in establishing a History of fossil Man, and are consequently inseparable, they belong to two somewhat different schools: for one is more zoological in nature, the other more archaeological.

With the second of these two points of view I shall deal much more briefly than with the first.

* * *

I have endeavoured to write this work with complete detachment of mind, confining myself exclusively to scientific ground. In my anxiety to avoid attributing conclusive value to any but positive facts, I have not hesitated to strew my text with more marks of interrogation than of affirmation; and this I have done in the belief that thus I may best advance science, and at the same time show most consideration for my readers.

Nevertheless, I am quite aware of my temerity. It is probable, indeed it is to be hoped, that almost as soon as my book is published, it may be already behind the times. Palaeontological researches multiply on every side; new evidences will soon be brought to light, and we may expect them to be such that, if they do not controvert, they will at least modify our present theories, and present under unforeseen aspects the problems which engage our attention.

It cannot well be otherwise, considering the extreme poverty of our evidence. Our researches have as yet been directed upon but tiny portions of the habitable globe, and the European region, the only one which we are beginning to know, cannot be regarded as a centre of appearance or of dispersal. It is but an appanage of the Eurasiatic Continent, which through all time has been a great laboratory of life. In this appanage, this blind-alley, the history of the early human races cannot present an aspect of continuous and regular evolution: it is rather made up of intermittent contributions brought by successive waves of far-distant origin, from vast Asiatic and African territories of which our knowledge is still very scanty and vague.

This book is, then, only a provisional attempt to bring the subject into focus. I am far from regarding it as a true *History* of fossil Man: the writing of such a history will be possible in the distant future. This work, which I have sought to render concrete by means of accurate and abundant illustrations, will none the less serve a useful purpose of its own. While satisfying so far as possible the justifiable curiosity of the general public as to the present aspect of the problem of our origin, it will, I hope, be of service to students and professional workers. It is with the second class of readers in view that I have given a large choice of bibliographical references, in order to aid more advanced study and to permit of references to the sources of information. I may be excused for particularly recommending the thirty volumes of *L'Anthropologie*.

To me it is a source of much gratification that this work should appear at the same time as the official inauguration of an establishment which forms the finest instrument for research till now available for prehistorians, the *Institut de Paléontologie humaine*, founded in Paris by a great patron of science, H. S. H. Prince Albert I of Monaco.

MARCELLIN BOULE

1921

CONTENTS

Chapter Three

LIVING PRIMATES AND FOSSIL MONKEYS

Chapter Four

THE PROBLEM OF TERTIARY MAN

Chapter Five

THE PREHOMINIANS
PITHECANTHROPUS AND SINANTHROPUS

Chapter Six

THE MEN OF THE LOWER PLEISTOCENE AGE

Chapter Seven

NEANDERTAL MAN (*HOMO NEANDERTALENSIS*)

Chapter Eleven

THE FOSSIL MEN OF AFRICA

Chapter Twelve

THE FOSSIL MEN OF AMERICA

Chapter Thirteen

GENERAL CONCLUSIONS

Index 527

LIST OF ILLUSTRATIONS

Fig.   *Page*

Fig.

INTRODUCTION

Les Hommes Fossiles has always ranked, and will doubtless long continue to rank, as the most comprehensive and authoritative general work on human palaeontology. This able translation by Michael Bullock will be greatly welcomed by all students of the subject in the English-speaking world. Popular interest in the evidences on the ancestry of man has greatly increased in recent years, and the orderliness and simplicity with which the relevant facts are set out in this work will ensure that it will be widely consulted and appreciated.

With the general reader in mind it may be appropriate to introduce *Fossil Men* by briefly reviewing the growth of knowledge in this field.

Human palaeontology is a very young science. One hundred years ago there were extremely few people in the world who had thought about the possibility that man had evolved from lower animals. Even the idea that man had existed in the time of extinct animals such as mammoth had not been generally accepted when my grandparents were at school. Commenting on some human bones alleged to have been found with remains of 'diluvial' animals in the Rhine Valley, the great French scientist Cuvier said in 1823: 'All the evidence leads us to believe that the human species did not exist at all in the countries where the fossil bones were found, at the period of the upheavals which buried them.' During the next twenty years excavations in the caves of the Midi of France, in Devonshire and in Belgium revealed deliberately shaped or cut bones of animals now extinct in those regions, and these evidences were accepted by a few pioneer workers as proof of man's geological antiquity. In 1829, Tournal, in the Department of Aude, was convinced that 'Geology, in supplementing our brief history, will at length awaken the pride of man by revealing to him the antiquity of his race . . .' Yet this question was still the subject of bitter dispute thirty years later. The controversy began to simmer again in 1846 when Boucher de Perthes, French customs official, announced that he had found in the ancient gravels of the Somme near Abbeville flints worked by 'antediluvian' man. 'In spite of their imperfection', he said, 'these rude stones prove the existence of man as surely as a whole Louvre would have done.'

Yet the majority of geologists and archaeologists were frankly scornful of his claim. In the autumn of 1858 the English palaeontologist Hugh Falconer visited the Abbeville pits, and was followed in the spring of 1859 by the geologist Joseph Prestwich and the archaeologist John Evans. On returning to England, Prestwich read a paper at a meeting of the Royal

Society announcing their acceptance of the claims made by Boucher de Perthes. This announcement had a decisive effect on advanced scientific opinion throughout the world. The year 1859 stands as one of the turning points in the history of human thought: the high antiquity of man was established almost simultaneously with the publication of *The Origin of Species* by Charles Darwin. The antiquity of man continued to be doubted by scientific diehards for a decade or two. As Max Planck once remarked: 'A new scientific truth does not triumph by convincing its opponents, but rather because its opponents die, and a new generation grows up that is familiar with it.'

With the growing acceptance of the antiquity of man, and with evolutionary ideas well to the fore, a fossil human skull discovered in 1856 at NEANDERTHAL near Dusseldorf was soon acclaimed as helping to lessen the gap separating man from the apes. In 1864 the anatomist William King referred this skull to an extinct species of man: *Homo neanderthalensis*. Few of his contemporaries were prepared to go quite so far. Thomas Huxley, in his memoir on *Evidence as to Man's Place in Nature* (1863), hailed the skull as supporting the idea of man's close relationship with apes, but he cautiously regarded it as an extreme variant of the existing type, rather than as representing a separate species. Many others followed Rudolf Virchow, who considered that the skull was that of an imbecile. Not until the end of the century was the idea of Neanderthal Man as a separate species generally adopted. (Now, remains of more than fifty Neanderthal Men are known.)

The antiquity of our own species *Homo sapiens* was and still is much disputed. The Moulin Quignon jaw from the Abbeville gravels (1864) and the Galley Hill skeleton from the Swanscombe gravels (1888) were claimed to indicate that our species had a vast antiquity, far greater than that of Neanderthal Man. Methods of relative dating applied to these specimens eventually proved them to be later intrusions into the deposits which contained them. On the other hand, the antiquity of the truly fossil *Cro-Magnon* skeletons, like the cave drawings of the same period, were at first *un*justifiably doubted.

When Darwin wrote *The Descent of Man* (1871), scarcely any palaeontological facts were yet available to support the theory of man's animal origins. I think it is not too far-fetched to suggest that Darwin's memoir led indirectly to the discovery of the first concrete proof that man has been subject to evolutionary change—Dubois's discovery of the JAVA SKULL. Eugene Dubois was a young army doctor who had been greatly influenced by reading Darwin's works, and he resolved that he would himself make some contributions to the knowledge of fossil man. His resolve ultimately led him to carry out official excavations in the ancient river gravels at Trinil in Java, which resulted in the discovery of the skull and thigh-bone of *Pithecanthropus erectus, a Man-like Species of Transitional Anthropoid from Java* (1894). Thus he launched the idea, now widely held, that in their earliest evolutionary stage men had skulls approximately of the Java type. Curiously enough, Dubois became, as it were, his own opponent. Having discovered the earliest man, he fought doggedly throughout the rest of his life to maintain that *Pithecanthropus* was not early man but a giant man-like *ape*.

The Trinil material was tantalizingly incomplete, and for many scientists it was inadequate as confirmation of Darwin's view of human evolution. I have sometimes wondered whether it was a misguided impatience for the discovery of a more acceptable 'missing link' that formed one of the strands in the tangled skein of motives behind the Piltdown Forgery (1912). As many readers will know, the founder author of *Fossil Men* was originally one of the strongest opponents of the view that the Piltdown jawbone belonged to the same creature as the human braincase. At first he had no doubt that the jawbone was that of a fossil ape; but he wavered in this view when pieces of a second Piltdown braincase were found at another site in association with a molar tooth like one of those in the original jawbone.

Fortunately for the reputation of human palaeontology a series of important discoveries largely based on scientific foresight were made in China and Java between the two world wars; and these added considerably to our knowledge of the *Pithecanthropus* stage of human evolution. The further discoveries in Java were due to Professor G. H. R. von Koenigswald (Utrecht). The discovery of the closely related PEKING MAN ('*Sinanthropus*') was an achievement resulting mainly from efforts of the Swedish geologist Gunnar Andersson, the Austrian-born palaeontologist Otto Zdansky and the Canadian anatomist Davidson Black, who in 1927 boldy originated the name *Sinanthropus pekinensis* on the basis of a single fossil molar tooth from excavations at Chou-kou-tien. Portions of more than a dozen skulls of this new type of man were eventually brought to light through systematic excavations at the same site by Dr. Wen Chung Pei. The thoroughness with which they were described by the late Dr. Franz Weidenreich in *Palaeontologia Sinica* mitigates the tragic loss of all this material through an abortive attempt in December 1941 to send it for safe keeping in the U.S.A.

The Chou-kou-tien researches illustrate the advantage of geological, palaeontological, anatomical and archaeological disciplines all being combined in the study of fossil man. Perhaps the most outstanding aspect of our knowledge of Peking Man is the archaeological one, for the Chou-kou-tien excavations provided unquestionable evidence that he was a tool-maker, a regular fire-user, a meat-eater and almost certainly a cannibal. To the more conservative students of human evolution, at first it seemed possible that '*Sinanthropus*' had not been responsible for any of these activities, but was a sub-human being that had been the victim of a higher type of true man with cannibalistic habits. The evidence was eventually seen to be overwhelmingly on the side of the simpler explanation. Before the end of the nineteen-thirties there was no longer any question that hominids of the *Pithecanthropus* group were capable of such essentially human cultural activities as making tools and using fire. The difference between the Java and Peking types was regarded by some investigators as no more than specific.

The gap between these earliest known men, dating from the end of Lower Pleistocene times, and the Neanderthal group of the Upper Pleistocene was still largely blank. The HEIDELBERG jaw found in 1907 was possibly an intermediate type; the STEINHEIM skull found in Middle Pleistocene river gravels near Stuttgart in 1932 also helped to bridge the gap. The discovery of the SWANSCOMBE skull of similar age in 1935-6, and of the FONTECHEVADE skulls of the Last Interglacial age in 1948 led to a revival of the idea that primitive *Homo sapiens* came into existence during Middle Pleistocene times, and evolved independently but parallel to the Neanderthal type. Professor Vallois is the leading exponent of this view. Other authorities doubt if it is possible to distinguish 'pre-sapiens' from 'pre-neanderthalensis', and consider that both *H. sapiens* and *H. neanderthalensis* arose from a generalized type (cf. Steinheim skull) which combined features of both. The Neanderthal group may have developed their aberrant characteristics in Western Europe under conditions of isolation due to advances of ice, while their more progressive contemporaries to the east and south-east gave rise to *Homo sapiens* (e.g. Cro-Magnon Man) who spread into Western Europe and replaced the more specialized Neanderthalers about 30,000 years ago. The human remains found in the Mount Carmel Caves, and studied in great detail by the late Sir Arthur Keith and Professor T. D. McCown, have a considerable bearing on this problem, for they show a variation from *H. neanderthalensis* to *H. sapiens*, such as one might expect on the fringes of the Neanderthal territory close to the focus of the emergence of the Cro-Magnon group of *H. sapiens*.

In southern Africa and the Far East the 'presapiens-neanderthalensis' amalgam gave rise to regional variants such as Broken Hill Man (discovered in 1921), Florisbad Man (1932), Saldanha Man (1953) and Solo Man (1931-2).

The question of the earlier transition, from *Pithecanthropus* to *Homo*, may be solved as more remains of '*Atlanthropus*' come to light in North Africa. The three mandibles and portion of parietal bone found at Ternifine, Algeria, by Professor C. Arambourg in 1954-5 in association with stone hand-axes and cleavers indicate that the earliest Acheulian tool-makers had some of the characteristics of Peking Man. The Swanscombe skull with features of *Homo sapiens* was associated with a later stage of the same culture. Unfortunately we have no information about the jaws of Swanscombe Man. As 'ideas' are communicable between men of different physical types, it should not be assumed that all Acheulian hand-axe makers were of the same 'species' or lineage.

Central Asia was at one time favoured by palaeontologists as the probable cradle of the human stock—the Hominidae—largely on the basis that a variety of apes were living in the Himalayan region during Middle and

Upper Miocene times when the rising of the mountain ranges would have caused a restriction of tropical forests on the north side, and so perhaps favoured the emergence of a ground-dwelling type of ape. However, discoveries in central and southern Africa, particularly since the second world war, have thrown new light on the pre-human stages of Hominoid evolution, and have underlined the wisdom of Darwin's comment (1871): it was 'probable that Africa was formerly inhabited by extinct apes closely allied to the gorilla and chimpanzee, and as these two species are now man's nearest allies, it is somewhat more probable that our early progenitors lived in the African continent than elsewhere.'

Through the researches of Sir Wilfrid Le Gros Clark, Dr. L. S. B. Leakey and Dr. A. T. Hopwood, we know that a considerable variety of higher primates (e.g. three species of PROCONSUL) lived in the Lake Victoria region at the beginning of the Miocene period, and may well have been adapted to various ecological niches ranging from rain forest to savanna. The desiccation which affected large areas of central Africa during Late Miocene and Pliocene times would have favoured the survival of any apes that were adapted to savanna. Those which had learnt to scuttle on two legs through tall grass in efforts to reach the shelter of trees in a region where forests were dwindling would have been well on the way to becoming Hominidae.

One of the most outstanding events in the history of human palaeontology was the recognition by Professor Raymond Dart that the fossil skull found in 1924 during quarrying of limestone at Taung in Bechuanaland represented a young individual of an ape-like group on the verge of humanity. He named this creature AUSTRALOPITHICUS ('Southern Ape'). Subsequently, through the energetic researches of the late Dr. Robert Broom and his successor Dr. J. T. Robinson (and through further collecting by Dart and his colleagues), numerous Australapothecine remains came to light in the cave and fissure deposits of the Transvaal. These specimens included several adult skulls and portions of hip-girdles, fragments of limb-bones and a vertebral column. Studies of all this material confirmed Dart's view, and showed that although these creatures were of simian appearance and had brains mostly no larger than those of typical apes, they had essentially human dentition, and walked upright in approximately human fashion. They were of pygmy size. The associated animal remains indicated that they lived in open country similar to the veldt of today.

Scientific opinion has been sharply divided on the question of the geological age of the Australopithecine remains (estimates have varied from Middle Pliocene to Upper Pleistocene); and on the question as to whether the creatures should be regarded as a lineage of apes that at a late date forsook the forests and became adapted to living in open country, thereby closely paralleling Man, or whether they represent part of the ancestral stock of Man. Some palaeontologists consider that there is little difference between these two interpretations. It is arguable that in either case the Australopithecines qualify as Hominidae rather than as Pongidae.

At the time of going to press it is reported that stone tools have been found in association with *Australopithecus* at Sterkfontein. If this is confirmed, the question will be raised as to whether the tools were made by *Australopithecus*, or by a higher type of Hominid who hunted the latter. If it is eventually proved that the Australopithecines were tool-makers, it is doubtful if the small size of their brains could any longer be counted as good enough reason for excluding them from the 'human' category.

It is now generally agreed that the oldest known specimens of *Australopithecus* date from the second half of the Lower Pleistocene, and therefore are probably too late geologically to be ancestral to *Pithecanthropus*. However, earlier members of the same genus living further north and as yet undiscovered may well have been ancestral.

We have seen again and again that the problems of man's ancestry require for their solution a combination of several scientific disciplines: geology, prehistory, anatomy and palaeontology. Scientists capable of competent research in more than two of these fields of knowledge are rare, and becoming rarer; but the founder author of this book was one of those talented people.

Marcelin Boule, who published the first edition on *Les Hommes Fossiles* in 1921, had an unequalled grasp of human palaeontology in all its manifold aspects. He was unusually well qualified to attain distinction in this field. He began his scientific career under the aegis of the distinguished prehistorian Émile Cartailhac; for a time he was deeply absorbed in the study of geology, and wrote several geological treatises, on the central massif and volcanoes of France; eventually he veered to palaeontology and wrote many monographs on Pleistocene mammalia, in the course of which work he became a gifted comparative anatomist. For some years he was assistant to Albert Gaudry, who he succeeded as Professor of Palaeontology at the Natural History Museum in Paris, in 1903, and while there he made a masterly study of the skeleton of Neanderthal Man found at La Chapelle-aux-Saints (Corrèze). He was appointed the first director of the Institut de Palaeontologie Humaine, established in Paris in 1914 through the generosity of Albert I, Prince of Monaco.

After passing through two editions *Les Hommes Fossiles* was revised in 1946 and again in 1952 by Professor H. V. Vallois, who succeeded Boule as Director of the *Institut*, and serves also as professor in the *Muséum national d'Histoire naturelle*. To the world at large Professor Vallois is perhaps best known as the Director of the *Musée de l'Homme*, which ranks as the greatest museum devoted to anthropology in the world. He is author of many scientific reports on early human remains, and is an authority on 'race'. One of his major contributions to science has been his investigation of the so-called *Pre-sapiens* skulls from Fontéchevade. As co-editor of *L'Anthropologie*, and co-author of *Fossil Men* he is doing a great service in the communication of knowledge about the nature and origin of our own species.

KENNETH P. OAKLEY

CHAPTER ONE

HISTORICAL SUMMARY

By virtue of a supreme biological law, Mankind as a whole has had to pass through the same phases of intellectual and physical evolution that today characterize the development of each individual human being. In the beginning, the child is beguiled with tales or songs of marvels: poetry is the first instructress. Later, his faculties of observation and reason awaken: he is drawn to truth, and poetry gives place to science.

In the same way, Mankind had in its infancy no other source of information regarding the 'supreme question' of its origins than fairy tales, legends and stories of the miraculous. Then human intelligence developed. A few outstanding minds gave birth to brilliant hypotheses. Next dispassionate observation, freed from all preconceptions, played its part. Finally, but only in later centuries when the reign of science began, there dawned some rays of truth.

Our knowledge of Man's existence on the earth in prehistoric times is a conquest of modern science.

FIRST PHASE: FROM ANCIENT TIMES TO THE RENAISSANCE: SIMPLE IMAGINARY VIEWS

Neither in ancient times nor in the Middle Ages does there seem to have been expressed any but imaginary conceptions of the origin of Mankind. In the Greek poets and philosophers of the pre-Christian era, vague references occur bearing on the low estate of the first Men. And so also in the Latin poets; everyone is familiar with the oft-quoted verses of Lucretius:

> Arma antiqua manus, ungues dentesque fuerunt,
> Et lapides, et item sylvarum fragmina rami,
> Et flammae atque ignis postquam sunt cognita primum,
> Posterius ferri vis est, aerisque reperta.
> Sed prior aeris erat, quam ferri, cognitus usus.[1]

Similar views were expressed by Horace, Pliny, Strabo, Diodorus and others. They were not purely intuitive, for we must not overlook the

---

[1] The passage is thus rendered in English by Creech (1714):
'And RAGE not furnish'd yet with SWORD nor DART;
With FISTS, or BOUGHS, or STONES the Warriours fought;
These were the only WEAPONS Nature taught:
But when FLAMES burnt the trees, and scorch'd the Ground,
Then BRASS appeared, and IRON fit to wound.
BRASS first was us'd.'

persistence of very ancient traditions nor what was known of savages and backward peoples, of which there were many on the confines of the known
world of that day. Herodotus wrote of Ethiopians dressed in the skins of
lions and leopards and armed with bows and arrows tipped with pointed
stones; Strabo of the wretched condition of the 'Ichthyophagi' dwelling
on the shores of the Red Sea and the 'Elephantophagi' in the interior;
Tacitus of the Finns, who possessed no weapons save pointed bones, sharp-
edged stones, and so forth. In any case, these views do not seem to have
been based on accurate interpretations of ancient objects or monuments,
for even though—in addition to the bronze arms of Homer's heroes—
stone axes and weapons, called ceraunia (from the Greek $\chi\epsilon\rho\alpha\nu\nu\delta s =$
thunder), were well known, their origin and real significance were unrecognized. They were regarded as produced or hurled by lightning, and
extraordinary powers were attributed to them (Fig. 1).

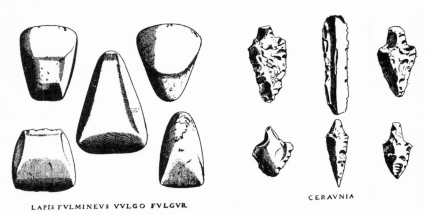

LAPIS FVLMINEVS VVLGO FVLGVR   CERAVNIA

1 Thunderbolts, figured by Mercati in his *Metallotheca*

These primitive ideas became widespread: with slight variations they
have persisted to our own day in the popular superstitions of almost every
country.[2]

And yet it is to a reasoned study of these ancient objects, it is to archaeology,
that we owe the first positive, concrete facts concerning the great antiquity
of Mankind.[3]

SECOND PHASE: FROM THE 16TH TO THE 18TH CENTURY

With the Renaissance, scientific curiosity awoke and a contact with nature

[2] Cartailhac, É., *L'âge de pierre dans les souvenirs et superstitions populaires* (Paris, 1878).

[3] See for the whole of the first part of this Historical Summary: Hamy, E. T., *Précis de
Paléontologie humaine* (Paris, 1870). *Id.*, 'Matériaux pour servir à l'Historie de l'archéologie
préhistorique' (*Revue archéologique*, 1870). Evans, Sir John, *Ancient Stone Implements* 2nd
Ed. (London, 1897). Cartailhac, É., *La France préhistorique* (Paris, 1889). Daniel, G., *A
Hundred Years of Archaeology* (London, 1950).

was regained that had been lost since the time of the Ancient Greeks. Two great artists, Leonardo da Vinci and Bernard Palissy, propounded correct views regarding fossils. Meanwhile various authors—e.g. Agricola (1558) and Gesner (1565)—described or figured polished stone axes and arrow-heads, but only as oddities. They still considered these objects, together with so many other 'fossils', as sports of nature, of which they gave more or less quaint explanations.

MERCATI AND THE TRUE NATURE OF CERAUNIA

At the end of the 16th century, Michael Mercati, whose writings were not published until 1717—more than a century after his death (1593)—proclaimed, if he did not discover, the true nature of the so-called thunderbolts or *ceraunia*: 'Most men', he says, 'believe that *ceraunia* are produced by lightning. Those who study history consider that they have been broken off from very hard flints by a violent blow, in the days before iron was employed for the follies of war. For the earliest men had only splinters of flint for knives.' And in this connexion he quotes the lines of Lucretius.[4]

2 Portrait of Mercati. Reduced from an engraving in the *Metallotheca*.

In 1636 Boetius de Boot, indifferent to 'being taken for a madman', repudiated the commonly accepted ideas. But he believed that he was dealing with implements of iron transformed into stone through the process of time.

Aldrovandus in 1648, Hassus in 1714, A. de Jussieu in 1723, the Jesuit Lafitau in 1724, and Mahudel in 1730, compared the old stone weapons of our countries with the stone weapons of living savages, notably the American Indians, and so initiated an excellent working method based on comparative ethnography, at the same time 'delivering the death blow to the erroneous beliefs regarding *ceraunia*'.

SEQUENCE OF PREHISTORIC AGES

In 1750, Eccard, after excavating old German burials, established a succession of different prehistoric ages; and in 1758 a learned magistrate named Goguet published a very well documented and searching work on *The Origin of Laws*, in which he declared that a Stone Age had been followed by an Age of Copper and Bronze, and then by an Iron Age. Later this classification was firmly established and developed by the Danish archaeologists Thomsen and Worsaae.

[4] Mercati, M., *Metallotheca, opus posthumum* (Rome, 1717) p. 243.

Thus the hesitating science of the 18th century arrived at the same ideas as the ancient poets and philosophers; but these ideas were now based on the observation of material evidences. The realm of fiction and fantasy had been abandoned, in order to enter that of rational knowledge.

Nevertheless, although it was recognized that the historic civilizations had been preceded by uncivilized or crudely barbarous periods, the great antiquity of these primitive times was not suspected. The theories had first of all to be accommodated to the demands of biblical chronology. The new idea of Mankind beginning in a state of primitive destitution seemed incompatible with the idea of the physical and moral perfection of the terrestrial paradise. Hence arose those heated discussions, those fierce battles of words, that today seem to us so naïve or ridiculous—especially when we consider, as Cartailhac pointed out, that the most widely differing opinions regarding the date of the creation of Man did not diverge by more than 1,500 years.

Buffon, who first suspected the immense duration of geological time—although he still sought to interpret the Scriptures 'soundly'—was familiar with the stones 'which were believed to have fallen from the clouds and to have been formed by thunder, but which are really only the first relics of the art of Man in a state of nature'. Yet, to his mind, the epoch of Man was only the seventh and last of his 'Epochs of Nature', much later than the fifth epoch characterized by the remains of the Elephant, the Rhinoceros and the Hippopotamus, which he found in the superficial soil.[5]

THIRD PHASE: MAN DATES FROM A GEOLOGICAL PERIOD
PRIOR TO THE PRESENT EPOCH

With the 19th century, Natural History sprang into sudden life and vigour. To the new sciences of Geology and Palaeontology it fell to throw light on the great antiquity of Man. Up to that time it had been a question only of objects dating no further back than modern geological times, objects that today are known as *Neolithic*. But now attention had to be turned to stone implements much more ancient, found in the very heart of formations dating from a geological period preceding the *modern* epoch and marked by the presence of remains of animals no longer existing today.

As early as 1715, Conyers, a pharmacist and antiquary of London, had found near that city, in the gravels of a former river and near the skeleton of an elephant, a flint worked in the manner now known as Acheulean. Bagford, a friend of Conyers, made the suggestion that the flint was a weapon used by a Briton to kill the elephant, which had been brought over by the Romans in the reign of the Emperor Claudius!

In 1797, another Englishman, John Frere, made a similar discovery at Hoxne in Suffolk. He collected some dressed flints at a depth of thirteen feet from a deposit containing bones of large extinct animals (Fig. 3). He

[5] Buffon, *Époques de la Nature* (Paris, 1778).

gave his find a much more accurate interpretation than Bagford, declaring that it must certainly belong 'to a very distant period, much more remote in time than the modern world'. This observation, of a perspicacity bordering on genius, passed unnoticed. It was brought to light again by John Evans only after the memorable struggles of Boucher de Perthes, of whom John Frere must be considered the fore-runner.[6]

19TH CENTURY: CUVIER

In 1823 a French geologist, Ami Boué, presented Cuvier with a human skele-ton exhumed near Lahr, on the banks of the Rhine, from an ancient mud or loess also containing remains of extinct animals. This discovery was rejected by the celebrated palaeontologist. 'All the evidence leads us to believe', he wrote, 'that the Human Race did not exist at all in the countries where the fossil bones were found at the period of the upheavals which buried them.'[7]

3 One of the flint weapons found by Frere at Hoxne, Suffolk. Half natural size. Facsimile of a figure published by Sir John Lubbock.

The great naturalist has often been reproached for these words; but it is easy to excuse him.[8] Cuvier had, as a matter of fact, examined all the material sent from various quarters as remains of 'antediluvian Man'. Some were really human bones—those from Cannstadt, from certain German caves, from Lahr and from Guadeloupe, for example—but no accurate observation, no conclusive geological evidence justified the assertion of their extreme antiquity. As for the other remains, Cuvier had recognized that the bones from Belgium were those of elephants; from Cerigo, fragments of a cetacean; from Aix, remains of a chelonian; from Oeningen, the skeleton of a salamander (the famous *Homo diluvii testis* of Scheuchzer) (Fig. 4), and so on. Such statements were well calculated to render him sceptical—all the more so as not the least trace of any fossil Ape had yet been discovered. Cuvier prudently added: 'But I do not wish to conclude that Man did not

---

[6] Evans, Sir John, *loc. cit.*, p. 573. John Frere's account is to be found in *Archaeologia*, Vol. XIII, 1800, p. 204.

[7] 'Discours sur les révolutions de la surface du globe', in *Recherches sur les ossements fossiles*, 4th Ed., Vol. I, p. 217.

[8] Cartailhac, É., 'Georges Cuvier et l'ancienneté de l'Homme' (*Matériaux pour l'Hist. nat. et primitive de l'Homme*, 1884, p. 27).

exist at all before this period [that of the 'last upheavals of the globe']. He might have inhabited certain circumscribed regions, whence he repeopled the earth after these terrible events; perhaps even the places he inhabited were entirely swallowed up and his bones buried in the depths of the present seas, except for a small number of individuals who carried on the race.'

Cuvier died in 1832, just at the time when a spate of discoveries were imminent. 'Perchance, had he lived', wrote de Quatrefages, 'he would have repeated the words he addressed one day to his fellow-worker Duméril: "My dear friend, we have been mistaken." '

TOURNAL AND SCHMERLING

About the year 1830, as a matter of fact, several naturalists in the French Midi, Tournal in the Department of Aude, Émilien Dumas, de Christol and Marcel de Serres in the Departments of the Gard and of Hérault—continuing researches that had been started in France, in 1810, by the Périgourdin Jouannet,[9] and in Britain, in 1820, by Buckland and McEnery—excavated the deposits accumulated in the grottoes and caves of their respective regions. There they found human bones, associated with numerous remains of animals belonging to species that had migrated or become extinct: bears, hyaenas, reindeer, and others, the bones of which sometimes showed traces of cutting instruments. So clearly did Tournal recognize the importance of these observations that in 1829 he had no hesitation in writing ' . . . Geology, in supplementing our brief history, will at length awaken the pride of Man by revealing to him the antiquity of his race; for henceforth it lies in the power of geology alone to help us to some knowledge of the period when man first made his appearance on the globe.'[10] These words assuredly mark a great step forward.

5 Portrait of Tournal

Again, the Belgian author Schmerling published in 1833 an important work entitled *Recherches sur les ossements fossiles des cavernes de la province de Liége*. In this he not only demonstrated the co-existence of Man with the Rhinoceros, Bear, Hyaena, and other animals, but further, he entitled his final chapter: 'Relics worked by the hand of Man'. These relics consisted of shaped bones, and in particular of an arrow-head and some flints. 'Everything considered', he wrote, 'it must be admitted that these flints have been cut by the hand of Man, and that they have been used to make arrows or knives . . . Even if we had not found human bones in circumstances strongly

[9] Cheynier, Dr. André, *Jouannet, grand-père de la Préhistoire* (Brive, Imprimerie Chastrusse, 1936).
[10] *Annales des sciences naturelles*, XVIII, 1928, p. 258.

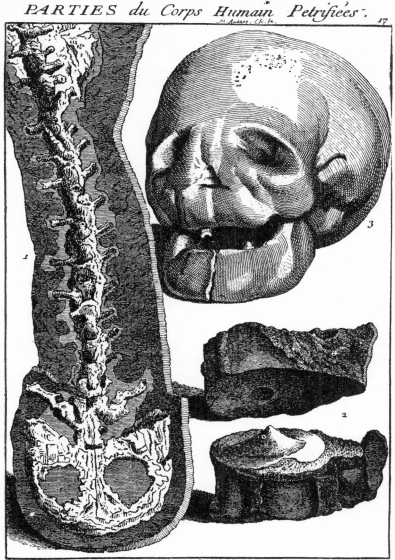

PARTIES du Corps Humain Petrifiées.

Aux depens de M.ᵉ Dargenville le fils, Conseiller du Roy,
Maitre ordinaire en sa Chambre des Comptes.

4 Remains mistaken, even in the eighteenth century, for those of Fossil Man. Facsimile of an engraving from *Oryctologie* by d'Argenville (1755)

1, Section of a salamander found in a Miocene deposit in the neighbourhood of Constance and described by Scheuchzer as that of a 'Human Witness of the Deluge' (*Homo diluvii testis*); 2, So-called 'Petrified vertebrae from the back of a Man': in reality vertebrae of a fossil reptile, the Ichthyosaurus; 3, Modern skull in a pathological condition (hyperostosis) which may still be seen in the Anthropological Gallery of the Musée de l'Homme, Paris.

supporting the assumption that they belonged to the antediluvian period,[11] proof would have been furnished by the worked bones and shaped flints.'

Some years later, in 1840, Godwen-Austen, continuing McEnery's studies of Kent's Cavern in England, arrived at the same conclusions.

Proof of Man's geological antiquity was thus firmly established by these pioneers; but that is not to say that it was accepted by professional scientists, except perhaps by Constant Prévost.[12] To Boucher de Perthes belongs the merit of impressing it upon the learned world and of giving it common currency as well.

BOUCHER DE PERTHES

Boucher de Perthes (1788–1868) was Controller of Customs at Abbeville.[13] He was a learned and prolific writer in diverse fields, a great lover of antiquities, and 'accustomed from childhood to listen to talk of fossils'. Having devoted himself to the collecting of all sorts of ancient human remains, he had, towards the end of 1838, the good fortune to find in 'diluvial beds' the 'first diluvial axes', which he submitted to his fellow-members of the Société d'Émulation d'Abbeville. In 1846 he published the first volume of his *Antiquités celtiques et antédiluviennes*, entitled *De l'industrie primitive ou des arts à leur origine*. In this work, Boucher de Perthes declared that the ancient alluvial soils—*diluvial* as he called them—in the suburbs of Abbeville contained many stones worked by 'antediluvian Man', buried at various depths along with bones of large animals belonging to extinct species.[14] 'In spite of all their imperfection', he says, 'these rude stones prove the existence of Man as surely as a whole Louvre would have done.'

This assertion, although founded on minute observations and excellent evidence, at first met with the utmost disfavour. 'Contradictions, jeers, scorn, were unsparingly heaped upon the author', wrote M. de Saulcy. 'He was regarded as a dreamer, as a kind of visionary, and the scientific world, priding itself on its detachment, allowed him to talk without further concerning itself with the facts for which he was forcefully claiming an entry into the realm of the exact sciences.'[15]

Far from losing heart, Boucher de Perthes continued, with fine perseverance and good nature, to combat this systematic and often sarcastic

[11] A hundred years later, Charles Fraipont proved that the skulls found by Schmerling were really those of fossil men ('Les Hommes fossiles d'Engis', *Archives de l'Institut de Paléontologie humaine, Mémoire* 16, Paris, 1936).

[12] Gosselet, A., *Constant Prévost* (Lille, 1896), p. 165.

[13] See Ledieu, A., *Boucher de Perthes, sa vie, ses oeuvres* (Abbeville, 1885).

[14] For the genesis of this view, see the critical and well documented study by L. Aufrère, *Essai sur les premières découvertes de Boucher de Perthes et les origines de l'archéologie primitive (1838–1844)* (Paris Staude, 1936).

[15] In Meunier, Victor, *Les ancêtres d'Adam* (Ed. Thieullen, Paris, 1900). This failure was probably due in part to the fact that Boucher de Perthes associated with true primitive implements, as if they were of the same significance, other stone *figures* or *symbolic* stones which were only 'sports of nature' and which are now recognized as of no account. But how was it possible at that time to separate the tares from the wheat?

opposition. Soon the learned world split into two camps. The first included several independent naturalists, among them A. Brongniart and Constant Prévost, who, without committing themselves, encouraged Boucher de Perthes. In the second and by far the largest camp, that of the diehards, with Élie de Beaumont at their head, were to be found scientists in the highest official positions, disciples and suc-cessors of Cuvier, whose scruples they exaggerated; this group denied the state-ments of de Perthes without even consider-ing them. 'Before the intervention of British geologists and archaeologists had deprived this great question, raised and solved by a Frenchman, of its wholly French bearing, for so long the entire French Academy of Sciences followed the lead of its Permanent Secretary, like a flock of sheep on the heels of the shepherd.'[16]

6 Portrait of Boucher de Perthes, from a lithograph

In 1854, Dr. Rigollot of Amiens, having found in the sand-pits at Saint-Acheul, 'axes' similar to those from the gravels of Abbeville, was the first to give his whole-hearted support to the views of Boucher de Perthes, which he had hitherto strenuously opposed. The previous year a distinguished naturalist of the Midi, Dr. Noulet, had brought forward favourable evidence when he announced the existence at Clermont, near Toulouse, of an 'alluvial deposit containing re-mains of extinct animals, mingled with stones shaped by human hands.'

In 1859, after repeated study of the facts on the spot, several distinguished British scientists—the palaeontologist Falconer, the stratigrapher Prestwich, the archaeologist John Evans, the anatomist Flower, and the great geologist Lyell, who soon afterwards published his famous book *The Antiquity of Man proved by Geology*—all clearly and decidedly adhered to the theory.[17]

The same year Albert Gaudry, a palaeontologist then at the outset of a brilliant career, went to Amiens to study the deposits and carry out excava-tions. Having resolved never to leave his workmen, he himself succeeded in extracting 'nine axes', along with teeth of a large ox, from the diluvium at a depth of 14 feet, and at a level which, a short distance off, had yielded up rhinoceros, elephant and hippopotamus bones[18] (Fig. 7). Gaudry's evidence made a deep impression on the minds of certain independent scholars, but opposition persisted in the Institute, which clung to the old

[16] Meunier, V., *loc. cit.*, p. ix.
[17] For an account of this intervention, see Falconer, H., *Palaeontological Memoirs*, Vol. II, p. 596; Prestwich, 'On the Occurrence of Flint Implements, associated with the Remains of Extinct Mammalia' (*Proc. Roy. Soc.*, 1859).
[18] Gaudry, A., 'Contemporanéité de l'espèce humaine et de diverses espèces animales aujourd'hui éteintes' (*Comptes Rendus de l'Acad. des Sciences*, 3rd October, 1859).

conception of the deluge and had absolute faith in the chronology of the Bible, according to which the creation of the world dated no farther back than 4,000 years before Christ. This opposition was carried to such a point that on May 18, 1863, a geologist in the highest official position, Member and Permanent Secretary of the Academy, Élie de Beaumont, went so far as to say: 'I do not believe that the Human Race was contemporary with *Elephas primigenius*. M. Cuvier's theory is born of genius; it is still unde-

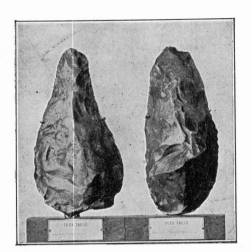

7 Two of the flints obtained by A. Gaudry from the gravels at Saint-Acheul. About one-third natural size. Now in the Palaeont-ological Gallery, French National Museum of Natural History.

molished.'[19] He even wondered if the dressed flints were not of Roman origin. . .[20]

Academic immortality is but a senile illusion. Permanent Secret-aries pass away and their names fall into oblivion. But the names of Boucher de Perthes and his glorious predecessors, John Frere, Tournal, Schmerling—all of them possessed of the same creative inspiration—will forever shine in the firmament of Science.

Science had taken a tremendous step forward with the discovery that, beyond the limits of History stretched a vast Prehistory, which is finally lost in the obscurity of geological time. Henceforth the origin of Man became a problem for palaeontology, on a par with the problems of the origins of the animals. The impulse had been given; a new science, that of 'Human Palaeontology',[21] was on the point of being definitely established.

ÉDOUARD LARTET

Édouard Lartet, who was born and died in Gers (1801–1871), was the chief founder of this new science. Originally a lawyer by profession, he awoke

[19] *Comptes de Rendus l'Académie des Sciences*, May 18, 1863.

[20] The persistence of this injurious influence, which continues even to our own day in a more or less feeble and unconscious form, is shown by the following facts: At the death of Boucher de Perthes his works were withdrawn from sale by decision of his family and sold for waste paper. Some years afterwards, Victor Meunier wrote his book *Les Ancêtres d'Adam, Histoire de l'Homme fossile*. The book was printed in 1875, but was never published. It gave an account of the 'martyrdom' of Boucher de Perthes, and the publisher, afraid of incurring the displeasure of the Academy, suppressed the whole issue. In 1900 the firm of Fischbacher published a new edition edited by A. Thieullen, a warm admirer of Boucher de Perthes. It is a work of great interest.

[21] The expression is due to Serres—'Notes sur la Paléontologie humaine' (*Comptes Rendus de l'Acad. des Sciences*, XXXVII, 1853, p. 518).

to his true calling on seeing a molar tooth of a Mastodon found by a peasant from his village. His interest aroused, he read Cuvier's works, studied osteology, and devoted himself to the investigation of the fossil bone-remains that were so abundant in the ground about his family estate. From 1834 onwards he explored and made famous the rich beds of Sansan, which date from Mid Tertiary times. There he discovered, among other strange forms entirely new to science, remains of an Anthropoid Ape, an ancestor of the modern Gibbons, which he named *Plio-pithecus.*

P. Fisher, author of a biography of Édouard Lartet, points out the importance of this discovery from the point of view of the question of fossil Man: 'Cuvier, in an illuminating and necessary criticism of alleged bone-remains of Man and contemporary Monkeys of extinct species, exposed their lack of authenticity. He accordingly inferred that Monkey and Man were late in appearing. "What astonishes me", he said, "is that, amongst all these mammals, the majority of which have their congeners still living in the warm countries, there is not a single Quadrumana; and also that there has not been found a single bone, a single tooth of a monkey, even of any extinct species. Neither is there any Man: all the

8 Édouard Lartet, from the only portrait made during his lifetime and for which we are indebted to his son, Louis Lartet.

bones of our species that have been collected along with those I have referred to were present by accident." '

'By thus associating the date of Man's appearance with that of Monkeys', continues Fisher, 'Cuvier prepared the way for the great reception accorded to the discovery of the Sansan Ape, and it could be foreseen that the discovery of a fossil Ape would be followed by that of fossil Man.'[22]

The perspicacity of Étienne Geoffroy Saint-Hilaire did not err. Cuvier's distinguished adversary had pointed out 'the important bearing on natural philosophy' of Lartet's discovery, which was destined 'to inaugurate a new era of knowledge relating to human life.' But, he added, 'the hour of philosophical research has not yet struck.'

Even in 1845, Lartet boldly admitted the possibility of Tertiary Man. 'This corner of ground', he said, speaking of Sansan, 'once supported a population of mammals of much higher degree than those here today. . . Here are represented various degrees in the scale of animal life, up to and including the Ape. A higher type, that of the human kind, has not been found here; but we must not hastily conclude from its absence from these

[22] Fischer, P., 'Note sur les travaux scientifiques d'Édouard Lartet' (*Bull. de la Soc. géolog. de France*, 2nd Ser., XXIX, p. 246).

ancient formations that it did not exist. . .' These were prophetic words.
It is almost as though Lartet had 'a presentiment of the important part he
was to play later in the scientific discussion concerning the co-existence of
Man with the large Quaternary mammals.'

About the year 1850 É. Lartet went to Paris to continue his researches.
He settled near the Museum, attracted by its scientific treasures. In 1856
he described the jaw of the new Anthropoid Ape, *Dryopithecus*. Three years
later he published a comprehensive monograph on the fossil Proboscidians.
But his writings on the animals of former times constantly led him back to
the great problem of fossil Man. He followed with great sympathy and
interest the efforts of Boucher de Perthes.

On March 19, 1860, É. Lartet sent to the Académie des Sciences a note
on the occurrence of Man in Western Europe entitled: 'Sur l'ancienneté
géologique de l'espèce humaine dans l'Europe occidentale'. The Académie
has been accused of refusing to print this memoir, and the fact is that only
the title appears on p. 599 of Volume L. of the *Comptes rendus*. For the text,
reference must be made either to the *Archives des Sciences de la Bibliothèque
universelle de Genève*, or to the *Quarterly Journal of the Geological Society
of London*, which received it with enthusiasm.[23]

Now this memoir was of cardinal importance. Together with a description of
the celebrated cave of Aurignac, which the author had just excavated, it contained certain suggestions of the greatest significance, which were renewed
and developed the following year (1861) in the *Annales des Sciences naturelles*
under the title: 'New researches on the co-existence of Man and the large
fossil mammals regarded as characteristic of the last geological period'.[24]

It seems that even from the time of his first purely geological writings,
É. Lartet had been an opponent of the cataclysmic theory of the world's
development. It required a great deal of independence and true courage
to challenge a theory held by the scientific pundits. This courage he showed,
a fact which sufficiently explains the hostile attitude of Élie de Beaumont.

In 1858, in his note 'On the Ancient Migrations of Mammals of the
Present Period'[25] he had already assailed the idea of deluges or other catastrophes. 'The day is perhaps not far distant,' he said, 'when the erasure of
the word *cataclysm* from the vocabulary of practical geology will be proposed.'
Or again: 'It is an abuse of the technical language of science to use such
high-sounding expressions as *upheavals of the globe, cataclysms, universal
disturbances, general catastrophes*, and so on, for they immediately give an
exaggerated significance to phenomena geographically very limited. . . . The

[23] 'It was too soon to announce these truths to the Académie des Sciences; it did not understand that, in refusing to publish the forecast of É. Lartet, it was placing itself in the backwash
of geological and anthropological progress, and that a day would come when it would be a
cause for deep regret to find in a foreign publication seven pages so creditable to French
science, rejected by the Institute of France.'—É. Cartailhac, *in litt.*

[24] 'Nouvelles recherches sur la co-existence de l'Homme et des grands Mammifères fossiles
réputés caractéristiques de la dernière époque géologique.'

[25] 'Sur les migrations anciennes des Mammifères de l'époque actuelle.'

great harmony of physical and organic evolution on the surface of the globe has in no case been affected. Aristotle perfectly understood these alternating movements of the earth, which have at different times changed the relations of continents and seas; he knew equally well how to reduce to its proper regional proportions the Deucalian Deluge, exaggerated and embellished by poetic fiction. Apparently this great naturalist also had to combat the fantastic ideas of the cataclysmic philosophers of his time, and the severe reproach he flung at them, might just as well, after 2,000 years, be applied to certain of our geologists or palaeontologists of the present day: "It is absurd, on account of small and transitory changes, to invoke the upheaval of the whole universe".[26]

The memoir contains another new and suggestive idea. The history of Man, like that of animals or like any geological history, is a continuous story which calls for a chronological method. 'If it were possible to establish that the disappearance of the animal species considered characteristic of the last geological period was successive and not simultaneous, a means would be discovered of establishing, at one and the same time, the relative chronology of the unstratified fossil deposits and their time relations with those diluvial beds whose geognostic bearings are well defined.' Lartet accordingly put forward a provisional 'palaeontological chronology', which made it possible, for the first time, to classify the strata in which traces of fossil Man had so far been found. 'Thus, in the period of Primitive Man we shall have the Age of the Great Cave Bear, the Age of the Elephant and the Rhinoceros, the Age of the Reindeer, and the Age of the Aurochs; much after the manner recently adopted by archaeologists in their divisions of Stone Age, Bronze Age, and Iron Age.'

This classification could not be perfect; but its actual existence was of great value, in that it asserted the geological nature of the problem of Man's existence, showed how far back in the past the history of our ancestors must be sought, and set up some milestones on the long journey. So a broad path was thrown open to investigators. In his eulogy of Lartet, Hamy very rightly remarked: 'Aurignac converted to the doctrine of the antiquity of Mankind adherents who were all the more valuable because they translated their convictions into productive activity.'

Soon after, in 1864, É. Lartet discovered the famous engraved mammoth of La Madeleine, where one of our remote ancestors had himself inscribed, in a delightful manner, conclusive proof of his geological antiquity (Fig. 9). Along with Christy, an Englishman, he undertook an investigation of the deposits of the Vézère Valley, the fame of which is now world-wide. As a result he succeeded in revealing the astonishing artistic culture of the Men of the Reindeer Age. The work in which so many fine discoveries were to have been described and expounded was unfortunately never completed.[27]

---

[26] 'Ridiculum enim est, propter parvas et momentaneas permutationes, movere ipsum totum' (γελοιδον γαρ, etc., Aristotle, 1, I, Chap. II).

[27] Lartet, É., and Christy, H., *Reliquiae aquitanicae: being contributions to the archaeology and palaeontology of Périgord* (Paris, 1866-1875, 1 vol. in 4to with 102 plates).

In 1869 Lartet was chosen to succeed d'Archiac in the Chair of Palaeontology at the French National Museum of Natural History. He was then sixty-eight years of age, and he died some months later, without having delivered his first lecture.

If we have spoken at length of Édouard Lartet, it was, first, from admiration for so independent and disinterested a man of science; secondly, to show the outstanding part which, through him, France played in the creation

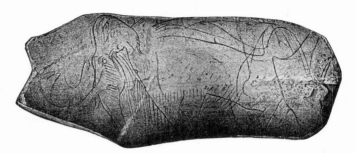

9 Fragment of ivory from La Madeleine bearing an engraving of a mammoth. One-third natural size. From the plate by É. Lartet. The original is in the Palaeontological Gallery, French National Museum of Natural History

of the new science of human palaeontology; and finally, because the achievement of this illustrious Frenchman has not always been properly understood. To the public at large he has remained unknown, and official science has not appraised him at his true worth. And yet the passing of the years only adds to the fame of Édouard Lartet.

ÉDOUARD LARTET'S SUCCESSORS

Lartet's example was followed in France by numerous scholars and investigators—P. Gervais, de Vibraye, A. Milne-Edwards, Louis Lartet, Piette and others—while in Belgium Dupont resumed and completed the work of Schmerling; and in Britain, where the good fight had also been fought, Lubbock, John Evans, and Boyd Dawkins published extremely valuable works on Prehistory.[28]

In 1864 Gabriel de Mortillet founded a special review for the purpose of recording the day to day progress of the science—the *Matériaux pour l'Histoire naturelle et primitive de l'Homme*—which he soon placed under the able and liberal editorship of Émile de Cartailhac. G. de Mortillet revised Lartet's classifications, taking particular account of the archaeological standpoint. With a lucidity that brought them within the grasp of every

[28] Lubbock, John (later Lord Avebury), *Prehistoric Times* (London, 1867, 7th Ed. 1913). Evans, John, *Ancient Stone Implements* (London, 1872, 2nd Ed. 1897). Dawkins, W. Boyd, *Cave Hunting* (London, 1874); *Early Man in Britain* (London, 1880).

investigator, he grouped the innumerable facts of a science at whose birth he had been present and to whose growth he had largely contributed.

Prehistorians were not slow in organizing their own reviews, their museums and their international congresses, at which general questions were discussed, or plans drawn up for integrating the work done in various countries—for discoveries were now being made in every continent. And so we come, step by step, to the present day, when researches in prehistoric archaeology have become the fashion and everyone rummages through the most venerable of our archives—too often, alas, with an utterly inadequate scientific training.

*   *   *

Thus arose the science of Prehistory or Prehistoric Archaeology, a science that draws its information from all sorts of objects which, though themselves purely material, nevertheless cast a tolerably bright light on the intellectual and moral character of the Men concerning whom history is silent.

THE BONES OF FOSSIL MAN

In the meantime what progress had been made in research regarding the physical and zoological characteristics of Man himself? What steps had marked the progress of Human Palaeontology in the strict sense of the term, the sense in which it is mainly used in this work?

After the discovery by Ami Boué, in 1823, of a human skeleton in the loess of the Rhine Valley—a discovery whose significance Cuvier, as we have seen, utterly repudiated—there followed a barren period. Every find of human bones was now regarded *a priori* with suspicion. But when the extreme antiquity of Man had been demonstrated by the dressed flints and proved by geology, discoveries of human bones seemed more natural and became increasingly frequent.[29]

From the beginning of the 19th century to the present day more than two hundred such finds have been recorded. Human palaeontology would thus seem to have been provided with material sufficient to enable it to reach great results and frame important conclusions.

REVIEW OF THE DISCOVERIES

Unfortunately all these discoveries are far from being of equal value, because of uncertainty regarding the age or even the authenticity of many of them. It is very easy to fall into error in dealing with such material. In many a place the earth is but human dust. Nothing, alas, is more common in superficial soils than the skeletons of our fellows. Of course, the physical characters of the bones vary according to the date of their burial; and the burials of historic times present features that would scarcely deceive a practised eye. In the case of prehistoric burials or Quaternary bone-remains

[29] See Quatrefages, A. de, and Hamy, E. T., *Crania ethnica: Les crânes des races humaines* (Paris, 1882). Part One: *Races humaines fossiles.*

the important factor of fossilization comes into play: that is to say, the physical and chemical transformation of a bone which has lost its organic substance, become permeated with mineral matter, and so grown more dense. But this factor is not decisive: the degree of fossilization may vary according to certain conditions of the environment, independent of age. Appeal must then be made to the conditions of the soil deposit, to geological and palaeontological criteria. When a discovery is made, however, a competent observer is rarely on the spot, ready to make the necessary investigation. At the present day, now that the attention of an enlightened public has been directed to such events and their importance is understood, the assistance of professional scientists is usually invited; and several recent discoveries have also been made following upon systematic excavation conducted by experts. Formerly this was not the case, for then the geology and the palaeontology of the Quaternary formations had barely been outlined. Many human skulls and skeletons, carelessly exhumed without scientific investigations, have been placed in museums, where anthropologists study them without sufficiently enquiring into the record of remains the origin and exact bearings of which cannot now be accurately determined.

As the question of age is a factor of prime importance in palaeontology, scientific accuracy demands a courageous elimination of all those osteological evidences the high antiquity of which is not assured. After close scrutiny of all the discoveries recorded up to the present day, we retain for consideration in this book only those whose authenticity and age are beyond dispute. Here it is better to err through excess rather than through lack of prudence.

The story of these discoveries, which form the foundations of human palaeontology, will be given in the following chapters in order of the age of the relics disclosed, that is, in their respective chronological order. For the present, we wish only to indicate briefly the main steps of progress up to the present day.

THE NEANDERTAL DISCOVERY

The first and one of the most important stages centred in the discovery, in 1856, of the famous brain-pan or cranium at Neandertal in Rhenish Prussia. This object was examined in succeeding years by various naturalists. With its considerable dimensions, its receding forehead, its enormous orbital ridges and its flattened brain-box, the skull presented an extraordinary appearance (Fig. 10). Schaaffhausen in Germany, and Huxley in England, declared it 'the most bestial of all known human skulls', and emphasized its simian or monkey-like characters.

This happened at a time when the scientific world was in a state of effervescence. Evolutionist ideas had begun to spread. Lamarck, who, long before Darwin, had not hesitated to attack the formidable problem of the origin of Man, and who conceived it as occurring through the modification of a

Quadrumane, had been forgotten before he had even been understood or appreciated. But now Darwin published *The Origin of Species*, Boucher de Perthes began to gain ground, and Albert Gaudry made public the results of his first researches on the transformations of fossil mammals; Broca founded the Société d'Anthropologie de Paris, and Huxley wrote his celebrated memoir on the *Evidence as to Man's Place in Nature* (1863), which was followed soon after by Carl Vogt's excellent *Vorlesungen über den Menschen* (1863).

The Neandertal skull, by reason of characters obviously of low type, and a conformation resembling that of the skulls of certain large Apes, supported the evolutionist theory: in the eyes of philosophic naturalists it appeared to be a sort of primitive form lessening the depth of the gulf which now separates the Apes from Men.

But this interpretation was not to the liking of anti-evolutionists of the old school. The scientific value of the skull was disputed and denied. As it had been found by workmen, geologists and palaeontologists took exception to the obscurity of its origin. Eminent anthropologists, among them Virchow, regarded it as a pathological

10 The Neandertal skull-cap, seen full face and in profile. One-third natural size. Photographs of a cast.

specimen or the skull of an idiot. I shall say nothing of the zealous and often foolish intervention of the defenders of religion, in a debate to which religion could only contribute arguments, animated by sentiment, tradition or prejudice. It was an intervention of this kind which provoked the famous epigram of Huxley, that it was better to be a perfect Ape than a degenerate Adam.

Just at this time there occurred the notorious episode of the jawbone of Moulin-Quignon. In 1863, Boucher de Perthes, desirous at all costs of discovering the fossil bones of the Man who had dressed the flints of Amiens and of Abbeville, found a human jawbone in conditions which stirred up lengthy polemics and caused floods of ink to flow. It would indeed seem as if on this occasion the famous and worthy archaeologist had been the victim of a fraud.[30] The English scientists who had so emphatically

[30] The discussions aroused by this discovery have been well summarized by A. Vayson in his book *Les Fraudes en Archéologie préhistorique* (Paris, 1932), pp. 65–101.

supported his views regarding the dressed flints, refused to believe in the authenticity of the jawbone; and one of them, John Evans, pronounced upon it a *Requiescat in pace*, of which the echoes have not yet died away. This, clearly, was not calculated to add to the credit of the new theory.

LA NAULETTE

But in 1865, Éd. Dupont, in the course of scientific explorations organized by the Belgian Government in the caves of that country, found a human lower jaw in one of the excavations on the left bank of the Lesse, the *Naulette pit* (Fig. 11). The circumstances of its deposit left no loophole for criticism. Now this jaw, taken from a deep bed, where it lay along with bones of the Mammoth, Rhinoceros, Reindeer, etc., differed from the jaws of all modern Men in one important character which struck the observer at first glance, the absence of a chin. Here again was the stamp of the Ape, associated none the less with other characteristics which were purely human. One was tempted to associate the jaw from La Naulette with the Neandertal skull, as belonging to a similar lowly type.

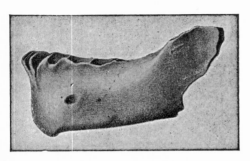

11 The jawbone from La Naulette. Three-quarters natural size. After de Quatrefages and Hamy.

CRO-MAGNON

In 1868, Louis Lartet, following with distinction in his father's footsteps, described the rock-shelter of Cro-Magnon on the banks of the Vézère, in the Dordogne, from which several human skeletons had already been obtained. On this occasion the skeletons presented all the features of modern Man; so much so indeed, that their great antiquity was not acknowledged by most anthropologists, who could not bring themselves to abandon their preconceived notions and to throw so far back into the past the physical type of *Homo sapiens*. So it was also with the skeleton found in 1872 by Rivière in one of the caves of Grimaldi (Fig. 13). The 'Mentone Man' closely resembling the Cro-Magnon type, was considered to be Neolithic. The geological bearings were, however, perfectly definite.

On the other hand, far too much importance was laid on some skeletons obtained, about the same time, from more or less ancient and more or less disturbed river deposits of the Seine, at Clichy, Grenelle, and elsewhere.

In 1870 Hamy[31] published a summary of the state of the science at this

[31] Hamy, E. T., *Précis de Paléontologie humaine* (Paris, 1870).

time, in a book which may still be consulted with profit. In the following year, Darwin,[32] tackling the great problem of the descent of Man, published a work in which palaeontological facts do not and could not as yet play any but a secondary part, but in which the famous naturalist expounded in all its bearings the theory of the animal origin of Man, formerly precisely stated by the great Lamarck.[33] To this theory the German naturalist Haeckel had just given his strong support in his *Generelle Morphologie der Organismen* (Berlin, 1866).[34]

About the same time, Broca[35] published some excellent studies on the comparative morphology of Apes and Man, and thus placed his great craniological knowledge at the service of human palaeontology. During the years 1873 to 1882, de Quatrefages and Hamy contributed to this

12 E. T. Hamy, from a photograph

branch of science a great work,[36] in which descriptions of the principal cranial types of modern Man were preceded by long systematic discussions on all the fossil or pseudo-fossil evidences then known.

THE SPY MEN

13 'Mentone Man', found by Rivière. Anthropological Gallery of the Musée de l'Homme.

The year 1887 was marked by an interesting discovery of two human skeletons in a cave at Spy in the province of Namur. This was an event of considerable scientific importance, fortunate in two respects: first, in that the Quaternary Age of the deposit, investigated by

[32] Darwin, C., *The Descent of Man* (London, 1871).
[33] Lamarck, *Philosophie zoologique* (1809), I. p. 337.
[34] See also Haeckel, E., *The History of Creation* (1st Eng. ed., London, 1875; 3rd, 1883). *The Evolution of Man* (Eng. ed., London, 1879). *Our Present Knowledge of the Descent of Man* (1898).
[35] Broca, P., 'L'ordre des Primates' (*Bull. de la Soc. d'Anthrop. de Paris*, 2nd. Ser., Vol. IV, 1869).
[36] Quatrefages, A. de, and Hamy, E. T., *Crania ethnica*.

geologists, was not open to question; secondly and especially, because the Spy skulls resembled in every way the Neandertal skull. The hypothesis of the pathological nature of the latter was definitely destroyed by the fine report of Fraipont and Lohest, which helped to confirm the opinion of those who believed in the actual existence of an ancient human type very different from, and of lower nature than modern types.

PITHECANTHROPUS

This opinion was notably strengthened some years later, in 1894, by the work of Dubois on the remains of *Pithecanthropus*, discovered in Java in 1891. In a succeeding chapter we shall discuss this famous fossil at some length; it is sufficient at present to state the indisputable fact that the skull-cap of *Pithecanthropus* really embodies a morphological type ideally inter-mediate between the skulls of Anthropoid Apes, such as the Chimpanzee or the Gibbon, and a human skull.

These fine discoveries instigated others. A positive fever took hold of investigators; and excavations carried out in almost every part yielded many evidences, but of very unequal value.

KRAPINA, GRIMALDI, MAUER

Amongst the most important of the later discoveries, first in order of time must be mentioned that at Krapina in Croatia, which brought to light many human remains of Neandertal type.

Next come the results of the important explorations undertaken by the Prince of Monaco, Albert I, in the Grimaldi Caves. Several human skeletons were exhumed in the Grotte des Enfants: some belonged to the Cro-Magnon type, the Palaeolithic age of which was here definitely established; while another, the most ancient, revealed to Professor Verneau the existence of a different type, of negroid character, the 'Grimaldi type'.

In 1907, a new fact of prime importance was brought forward. Up to that date, the Man of the oldest dressed flints was known only by the products of his handiwork—no authentic relic of his skeleton had been obtained. Then Schoetensack described a jawbone found in the ancient gravels of Mauer near Heidelberg. And this jawbone, very much older than those from La Naulette, Spy, or Krapina, presented a still more primitive appearance.

NEW DISCOVERIES OF NEANDERTAL MEN

In the course of systematic excavations carried out in France between 1908 and 1911, the Abbés Bouyssonie and Bardon, Capitan and Peyrony, and Henri Martin, recovered from human habitations deep in the caves and shelters of La Chapelle-aux-Saints in the Department of Corrèze, La Ferrassie in the Dordogne, and La Quina in Charente, several skeletons and portions of skeleton belonging to Men of the Neandertal type. The finds made more recently at Weimar and Steinheim in Germany (1914–1933), in the Crimea (1924), in Galilee (1925–1935), in Italy (1929–1939), in Hungary (1932), and in Siberia (1938–1939), have enlarged the area of geographical distribution and the limits of variation of this human form, which is of such great interest on account of its primitive characters.

Human palaeontology has thus been furnished with records of exceptional value, which have enabled us to gain a fuller knowledge of this ancient type than we possess of many modern savages.[37] This *Homo neandertalensis* will form the subject of one of the longest chapters of this volume.

THE PRESAPIENS

Being chronologically antecedent to *Homo sapiens* of the Upper Palaeolithic, Neandertal Man was long regarded as his ancestor. Time and again, however, various discoveries have led to the supposition that other Men—already possessing the general characteristics of *Homo sapiens*—lived parallel with, or even prior to Neandertal Man. It looks as though this group was the ancestral stock from which sprang Modern Man, while the Neandertalians were merely a collateral branch that remained without issue. But the various discoveries assigned to this *Presapiens* group were open to criticism on a number of counts. The discovery at Piltdown, Sussex, in 1912—the subject of prolonged controversy—finally proved worthless. More recent finds, however—such as those made at Swanscombe in 1936 and 1955, and above all the find at Fontéchevade, Charente, in 1947—have provided a definite affirmative answer to the question of the existence of *Presapiens*.

FOSSIL MAN OUTSIDE EUROPE

Up to the present we have spoken almost exclusively of Europe. This is a very small section of the globe, but relatively little is yet known about the rest of it from the point of view that interests us here.

Nevertheless, during the last thirty years, our knowledge has made some notable advances, not only from the standpoint of prehistoric archaeology, as we shall see later, but also from that of palaeo-anthropology.

Thus the continent of Asia, whose cardinal importance in the history of the Hominians is becoming increasingly evident, has yielded—in addition to the more or less Neandertaloid skeletons from Galilee and Siberia already noted—various human remains of more recent date, and especially the interesting skulls found near Peking belonging to the creature that has been dubbed *Sinanthropus*.

Java has given us the so-called Wadjak and Solo skulls and a whole series of new *Pithecanthropi*; Australia the skulls from Talgai, Keilor and Cohuna, which are more primitive in character than those of the present Australian aborigines. But the continent of Africa, above all, has been the site of a growing number of discoveries: in North Africa the mass of skeletons found

[37] Boule, M., 'L'Homme fossile de La Chapelle-aux-Saints' (*Annales de Paléontologie*, 1911–1913).

in a cave near Bougie; in the Sahara, the Asselar skeleton; in East Africa, the Oldoway and Kenya skeletons; in South Africa, the very curious cranium from Broken Hill, the Boskop skull, and the skeletons from Tzitzikama, Springbok and elsewhere, which introduce us to a race of Proto-Bushmen or Proto-Hottentots. And, finally, this continent has seen the vitally significant discovery, by Dart and Broom, of numerous remains belonging to a group of Anthropoids, the Australopithecinae, so manlike in certain features that many writers do not hesitate to classify them as human. The problem that has already arisen once in connexion with *Pithecanthropus* arises afresh, and in an even more emphatic manner, in relation to the Australopithecinae.

Even the New World, where investigations for so long proved fruitless, has yielded during recent years traces of a Man who, if not fossil, is at least sub-fossil and allows us to form some idea of how this continent was first peopled.

The facts outlined below, by showing all the progress that has already been made, prove that as soon as systematic exploration is carried out in all parts of the globe with adequate material resources, new discoveries will be forthcoming. It is hardly necessary to stress the importance these will have. Our present knowledge of Human Palaeontology is largely based on finds made in Europe. The archives still buried in the heart of the other continents certainly contain a great deal of information, as yet unknown, that will add materially to our knowledge of the human story.

Rather than seek to revive the importance of the odds and ends of old bones, collected in past times without sufficient scientific guarantees, upon which many authors still dwell with too great satisfaction, we must now devote ourselves to making new explorations, with all the care, the precaution, and the scientific method now incumbent upon palaeontologists and anthropologists having a true understanding of the problems to be solved.

CHAPTER TWO

TIME RELATIONS OF EARLY MAN

RELATIVE CHRONOLOGY

THE GEOLOGICAL ERAS

CHRONOLOGY is the basis of all genealogy, and it is therefore important, before entering upon the history of fossil Man, to see how the evidences relating to our distant ancestors can be arranged according to the order of their relative antiquity. For this, some idea of geology and general palae-ontology is indispensable.[1]

The history of the earth falls into several Eras:

        (1) The Archaean
        (2) The Primary
        (3) The Secondary
        (4) The Tertiary
        (5) The Quaternary

The *Archaean* Era, by far the longest, corresponds to the formations deposited in the primitive seas of the globe. Under the influence of central incandescent masses and of mechanical processes resulting from their contraction, these deposits have been subjected to innumerable transformations, which have caused the fossils they must once have contained to disappear almost entirely.

The succeeding Eras are characterized by the development of certain groups of organisms, and they are distinguished from one another owing to great changes in the physical world, such as upheavals of mountain ranges, alterations in the distribution of lands and seas, and so on.

The *Primary* or *Palaeozoic* Era begins with the formation of the first deposits in which fossils are well preserved. At that time living things belonged to the lower groups or types of the organic world: the animals comprised only Invertebrates and, just towards the end of the Age, some Fishes and certain primitive four-footed creatures.

The *Secondary* or *Mesozoic* Era is marked by an advance in the animate world. It is the Age of Reptiles, which were then much more numerous, more varied, and more powerful than at the present time.

The *Tertiary*, or *Cainozoic* Era, shows fresh progress. The great Reptiles

---

[1] Boule, M., *Géologie* (11th Ed., Paris, Masson, 1935). This short work is very elementary. For greater detail see Gignoux, M., *Géologie stratigraphique* (3rd Ed., 1943); Boule, M., and Piveteau, J., *Les Fossiles, Éléments de Paléontologie* (Paris, Masson, 1935).

have disappeared, and their place has been taken by the more highly-organized animals, Birds and especially Mammals.

Finally, the *Quaternary*, *Anthropozoic* or *Psychozoic* Era, which still

GEOLOGICAL ERAS	Thickness of Deposits	Duration in Years	REIGN
QUARTERNARY	600'	500,000	of MAN
TERTIARY	12,000'	10,000,000	of MAMMALS
SECONDARY	18,000'	15,000,000	of REPTILES
PRIMARY	100,000'	74,500,000	of FISHES
ARCHÆAN	?	?	?

14 Diagram of the general succession of the Geological Eras, their relative duration (estimated according to the thickness of the corresponding formations) and their principal palaeontological characters

lasts, is characterized by the reign of the most highly perfected of Mammals, Man.

The appearance and the development of the great zoological groups have thus followed in order of degree. Invertebrates appeared before Vertebrates, and amongst the latter, the lowest, the Fishes, came first, then the Batrachians or Amphibians, then the Reptiles, the Birds and the Mammals.

The diagrams (Figs. 14 and 15) show that the importance of each Era is

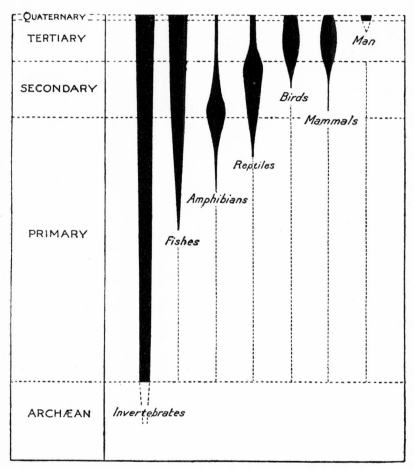

15 Diagram showing the development and distribution in time of the Invertebrates as a whole, of the various classes of Vertebrates, and of Man

in close relation to the depth of the corresponding formations, and therefore in close relation to its duration.[2]

One is struck by the disproportion between these Eras. The following

[2] The figures placed in the third column (duration in years) are purely hypothetical. Only their relative values need be considered. From the absolute point of view their proportion alone need be borne in mind. Further, we probably ought to compute by hundreds, rather than by tens, of millions of years.

figures, although only very approximate, will give some idea of it. If the figure 1 be taken to represent the thickness of the Quaternary formations, or the duration of the corresponding Era, the duration of the Tertiary Era must be represented by 20, of the Secondary Era by 30, and of the Primary Era by 150. And it is probable that the Archaean Era corresponds to a lapse of time equal or superior to that which separates us from the beginning of the Primary Era!

THE TERTIARY ERA AND ITS MAMMALS

Man, a mammal, could not appear before the Tertiary Era, for the mammals of the Secondary Era were small and very primitive animals. The more highly-developed types of mammals of the Tertiary Era are not all of the same antiquity. We must, therefore, examine the divisions of the Tertiary Era, as well as the relative development of mammals in general, and more particularly of the most highly organized group, the Primates, of which Man is the most perfect type.

Geologists divide the Tertiary Era into four great Periods:

(1) As regards mammals, the EOCENE PERIOD, the most ancient, possessed only Marsupials (*Didelphia*), or else primitive placental mammals of synthetic types, presenting such a mixture of characters that it is often impossible to classify them in any of the now existing Orders. Certain strange Pachyderms of rather large stature became extinct in early times, without leaving any descendants. Other groups evolved and advanced. All had small brain capacity.

(2) During the succeeding OLIGOCENE PERIOD, a striking process of differentiation led mammals in the direction of the types of modern times. There are yet no Horses, no true Ruminants, no true Proboscidians, but certain forms show very distinct tendencies towards these different groups. No genus of Oligocene mammals has, however, survived to our day.

(3) In the MIOCENE PERIOD, which followed, the process of differentiation ended in the establishment of the now existing families, and many of the genera obviously appear to be the direct ancestors of those of our own day.

(4) In the last period, called the PLIOCENE, there appear side by side with the ancient genera numerous genera still living, the species of which can often be recognized as the ancestors of the species now surrounding us.

Finally, during the Quaternary Era, we are aware of the existence, together with several extinct species which have not survived to our times, of a great number of forms identical with the present-day species, or, at least, ancestral varieties of them.

Considering the Primates in particular—that is to say, the zoological group to which Man belongs—we see that they make their first appearance in the Eocene Period in the form of the lowest types—the Lemurs and Tarsiers. The Oligocene Period presents the most ancient Tailed Monkeys; and in the Miocene and Pliocene Periods appear numerous Anthropoid

Apes.[3] So far as present knowledge goes, fossil Man is only known in the Quaternary Era. Here, also, we thus have a continuous progression: Man, the most highly perfected of the Primates, is also the last-comer.

The Quaternary Formations

No very great difficulty would be likely to arise in indicating the chronological order of discoveries made in Tertiary deposits, for their succession is well established. The task is more difficult and much more delicate in relation to Quaternary formations, which are rich in human remains. It demands more precision, and we must therefore deal with this subject in some detail.

The classification of Quaternary times may be based:

(1) On the study of the formations and of their relative positions (Stratigraphy).

(2) On the study of fossils (Palaeontology).

(3) On the study of human relics (Prehistoric Archaeology).

The Quaternary deposits are numerous and of varied character. The last to be formed, they cover all the others and are themselves covered only by humus. For this reason they are often called 'superficial soils'. A complete acquaintance with them is indispensable to the study of human palaeontology. They may be classified as follows:

I. Deposits of marine origin.

II. Sedimentary deposits of continental origin.
  { Glacial formations.
  { Alluvial deposits of plains and valleys.
  { Cave deposits.

III. Deposits of volcanic origin.

Marine Deposits

Marine deposits are of relatively little importance from our point of view. In Europe, at the end of the Tertiary Era, the Pliocene seas already possessed —apart from Italy—approximately the configuration of the seas of the present day. In the Quaternary, the differences were even slighter. Nevertheless along certain coasts there are to be seen old littoral strands or ancient beaches, one above the other, denoting oscillations in the sea-level greater than used to be supposed.[4]

The theory has been advanced that these are signs of a single, progressive fall in the level of the sea that took place in a series of sudden drops from the uppermost Quaternary beaches to the present sea-level. This hypothesis is an almost childish over-simplification. In reality, the various marine deposits that are today above water all testify to the alternation of advances

---

[3] For a more detailed account, see Chap. III.

[4] In flat or relatively flat countries, invasion by the sea during Quaternary times covered comparatively large areas on several different occasions, notably in Belgium, Holland, North Germany, Finland, the Aralo-Caspian region of Russia, etc.

or *positive* movements on the part of the sea (transgressions) with recessions
or *negative* movements (regressions). The former diminish the land area: the
latter increase it.

The malacological fauna contained in these old beaches alternates between
a fauna that is 'colder' than the nearby modern sea, a 'warmer' fauna exhibit-

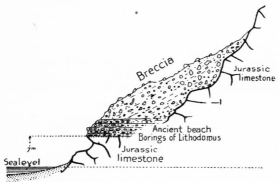

16 Geological section of the
shore of the Mediterranean at
the headland of Grimaldi. An
ancient sea-beach, containing
shells of warm seas, is almost
23 feet higher than the level
of the present sea. It bears
breccia or fallen debris, also
Pleistocene, but of a later
period.

1M : 3·28'

ing sub-tropical elements, and a fauna that is identical with the one existing
today (Fig. 17).

A sort of rhythm analogous to the glacial rhythm, which we are about
to discuss, may therefore be observed. Geologists who have dealt with

17 Shells from Quaternary marine deposits in France.

To the left, a *Strombus* of warm seas
(*Strombus bubonius*). To the right, a
species from cold seas (*Mya truncata*).
One-third natural size.

these problems have underestimated the importance of the negative movements, the consequence of which was to enlarge the territory occupied by
primitive Men.

DEPOSITS OF GLACIAL ORIGIN

The study of fossil shells indicates gradual cooling of the last Tertiary seas.
In the Upper Pliocene layers Arctic species extend as far as the Mediterranean. It is therefore not surprising to observe that by the end of the
Tertiary Era—that is to say, at a date when the Pyrenees were still young,
when the Alps had just effected their greatest thrust, and when the formation
of the great volcanoes of Central France was nearing completion—these
mountains were covered by glaciers much larger than the largest modern
glaciers of the Alps.

Under the influence of causes not fully understood, these glaciers—like those of the Asiatic and American mountain ranges—underwent an extraordinary development at the end of the Pliocene and during the Quaternary Era: their thickness may have exceeded 3,000 feet.[5] From the summits they reached the plains, where they extended vast distances from their

18 Sketch showing the extent of the Quaternary glacier of the Rhone Valley contrasted with the present-day glacier.

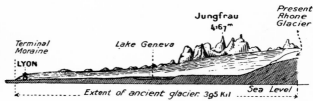

IM : 3·28'

starting points, dispersing or accumulating all along their tracks enormous erratic blocks and immense moraine deposits (Fig. 18).

In the northern countries of Europe the same phenomenon occurred on an even larger scale. Rivers of ice flowed in all directions from the heights of Scandinavia until they merged into one continuous sheet, similar to the *Inlandsis* of modern Greenland but far vaster. On one side, these streams of ice, overflowing the North Sea, came into contact with the glaciers that covered most of the British Isles. On the other side, they spread over Denmark, Holland, Germany and Russia, whose soil is still covered with moraines and erratic blocks of Scandinavian origin (Fig. 19). The glaciers advanced northward into the Kara Sea, and joined up with those from Spitzbergen, Novaya Zemlya and the Northern Urals. North America had an even vaster covering of ice with an average thickness of 6,000 feet.

The advance of the glaciers was progressive from the Pliocene Period onwards, but this progression was not regular. There were numerous oscillations, increasing in amplitude until they reached the *maxima*, after which contrary but analogous movements of diminution and recession took place, the whole phenomenon having the structure of a sinusoidal curve. The most important of these oscillations are termed *glacial* and *interglacial phases* respectively. There is little agreement as to the number of these phases, because of the difficulty often experienced in distinguishing simple oscillations, more or less local and of slight importance, from true glacial periods that are more general and a great deal longer. Thus the number of these periods varies even more according to different geologists than according to the countries. J. Geikie defined six for the British Isles. Penck and Bruckner counted four in the Bavarian Alps, which they named the Günz, Mindel, Riss and Würm phases. In most of the mountain chains and massifs of France, as in all other countries, traces of three main glacial phases have

[5] This development is not peculiar to the later geological periods; it followed all the great upheavals of mountain chains, at all periods and in every country. We now know that vast glacial fields existed during the Cretacean, the Permian, the Silurian, and even the Archaean Ages.

been clearly distinguished, the oldest dating from Pliocene times, while the two others are Quaternary (see Fig. 28). They are separated by two inter-glacial phases, the later of which—easily recognized everywhere—is by far the most clearly characterized.[6]

In intertropical regions the glacial phases seem to have been represented

19 Map of during the maximum Glaciation.

by *pluvial* phases, during which a more humid climate caused parts of these regions (the Sahara, for example) to lose their character of more or less barren deserts.

The moraine formations, as one would naturally expect, contain neither fossils nor human remains; they cannot then be of direct interest in the study of palaeontology, but they contribute to it valuable data regarding the climatic conditions of Quaternary times, and sometimes help us to establish useful stratigraphic relations.

[6]   General works on glacial geology: Penck, A., and Bruckner, E., *Die Alpen im Eiszeitalter* (Leipzig, 1909). Antevs, E., *The Last Glaciation* (New York, 1928). Woldstedt, P., *Das Eiszeitalter* (Stuttgart, 1929). Wright, W. B., *The Quaternary Ice Age* (2nd Ed., London, 1937). Flint, R., *Glacial Geology and the Pleistocene Epoch* (2nd Ed., New York, 1928).

ANCIENT ALLUVIAL DEPOSITS

Away from the bed of a stream or tidal river and up the sides of the valley are to be found, above the flood-plain, areas of varying size arranged in terraces covered with gravel, silt or rolled pebbles (Fig. 20). These alluvial deposits have been laid down in Quaternary times by floods, due either to

20 Outline across the valley of the Gar-onne at Toulouse.

1M : 3·28ʰ

an extraordinary increase in rainfall, or to the rapid melting of the glaciers. As each valley shows formations disposed in terraces at several levels, it

21 An old sand-quarry at Chelles (Seine-et-Marne)
There may be clearly distinguished two sets of alluvial deposits occupying the bottom of the Marne Valley and resting uncomformably one upon the other (along the line X X). The lower set is of Chellean age. The upper set, cutting into the former, is of more recent age, Acheulean or Mousterian. (Phot. d'Acy).

may be concluded that the hollowing out of the valley was not continuous, but was subject to periods of cessation, followed by new activity; here is a phenomenon of periodicity parallel to, and often correlated with that of the glacial phases.[7]

[7] These features must be explained chiefly by changes in the general slope of water-courses in consequence of movements of the earth's crust or to displacements in the line of the sea-shore, either in a positive or in a negative direction, as we have stated above in con-nexion with ancient marine beaches now above sea-level, which may often be observed towards the mouth of rivers with ancient alluvial terraces.

In general, *these alluvials are the more ancient the higher the level they occupy.* Those which cover the high plateaux in France generally date from the Pliocene Period. Their components, exposed for a very long time to the action of atmospheric agents, are much changed and partially decomposed. The middle terraces of the rivers of France and their large tributaries belong to the beginning of Quaternary times, and the lower terraces to more recent periods. Thanks to this altimetrical arrangement, it is generally possible to establish the relative age of the relics yielded by these alluvials, such as the bones of animals, the bones of Man, or the products of Man's industry.[8]

A serious source of error—into which prehistorians have fallen in the past and still continue to fall—arises, however, from the alterations undergone by these gravels, which are constantly undermined, displaced or swept away by the streams themselves. Often, indeed, in ancient alluvials at a definite level, the presence of elements derived from all the older levels may be observed. An imported fossil must be distinguished from a fossil contemporary with the layer in which it is found. It must not be forgotten that *the true age of the alluvial deposit is that of its most recent fossils.*

MUD, PEAT-BOGS, CALCAREOUS TUFAS

In many countries, particularly the north of France, Belgium, Germany and the whole of Northern Eurasia, the ancient alluvials are covered with

22 Shells of land molluscs from loess
    Left, *Helix hispida*. Right, *Pupa muscorum*

silts (or *loess*), due either to the transport of dust by the wind, or to the violent rush of rain down the slopes, but most often to both causes together. These muds contain shells of land molluscs (Fig. 22). They are of the utmost importance in our study, because of their wealth of human fossil remains of all kinds. We cannot apply to them the rule laid down above with regard to alluvials and take their altitude as a basis for establishing the relative ages of the layers. The muds form a kind of cloak cast over the sides of the valleys and their alluvial formations (Fig. 23); these may belong to different periods, but owing to their continuity, *the muds may actually be contemporaneous on the plateaux and in the bottoms of the valleys.* Ignorance of this fact has led many prehistorians, on occasion, into unfortunate mistakes.

I shall merely mention the *peat-deposits*, which—in France, at any rate—

[8] It must be noted that the rule is not absolute. Certain valleys, like that of the Marne at Chelles (Fig. 21), may have been completely hollowed out even below their modern channel since the Lower Pleistocene. New alluvials, due to change in the general gradient of the streams, may then have filled up the bottom of the valley, superimposing themselves upon the older alluvials, and occupying a higher altitudinal level than they did.

generally date from a relatively recent period, and consequently do not possess the same interest for us. But it must be added that a study of the vegetable matter which has formed these peat-deposits, and notably of the

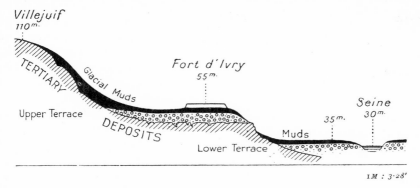

23 Geological section near Paris, to show the disposition of the Pleistocene muds, extending from the summit of the plateaux to the bottom of the valley, whilst the ancient alluvials are clearly deposited in terraces

grains of pollen belonging to forest species, has enormously contributed to our knowledge of the climatology and chronology of post-Palaeolithic times. We shall return to this point in Chapter IX.

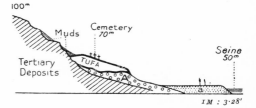

Calcareous tufas, deposited by springs charged with carbonate of lime (encrusting springs), often contain imprints of plants, remains of invertebrates, and bones of mammals, which give us valuable information relating to climatic conditions. Certain of these tufas have even yielded human relics, such as La Celle-sous-Moret, near Paris (Fig. 24),

24 Geological section of Pleistocene tufas at La Celle-sous-Moret (Seine-et-Marne). The tufas, with warm flora, rest on Pleistocene alluvials, overlaid at one point by muds containing a cold fauna. A, Pleistocene alluvials. *a*, Recent alluvials.

Cannstadt and Taubach in Germany, and others.

SCREES AND DEBRIS

The debris on the slopes is due to the disintegration of the underlying rocks of a region. These accumulations may belong to any age, for the influence of the atmospheric agents to which they are due has been exerted at all times, but the most ancient have been destroyed, and the great majority hardly date beyond Quaternary times. They are particularly common and extensive in territories outside the range of glacial action, where, in a way, they take the place of moraine deposits (Fig. 16, p. 34). The accumulations of detritus of which they are composed may contain all kinds of fossils and traces of ancient human settlements.

Linked with these accumulations of debris—rather than with direct glacial formations—are other more or less confused and chaotic-looking terrains formed, outside glacial territories, either by the abrupt breaking up of melted snow (névés), or by the sudden thawing of superficial soils saturated with water and resting on a subsoil that remains frozen (solifluxion). These processes, acting upon 'moving soils', which have long been known, have recently become a fashionable subject of discussion for prehistorians, who have drawn unwarranted, and often highly improbable chronological conclusions from them. It must not be forgotten that, while these processes are most powerful and effective in Arctic countries or in the mountains, they may be observed at the present time in the countries of Europe—even those with a minimum of broken and uneven ground—following periods of hard frost and sudden thaws. And we are not living in the Ice Age!

When these accumulations of detritus, instead of forming talus-screes on the outer slopes, fill up fissures or cavities hollowed out in the solid rock by natural agencies, agglomerates containing angular fragments are formed, known by geologists as *breccias*. They are often composed of bones of animals, and in such cases are termed *bone-breccias*. If the fissures or cavities thus filled attain any considerable extent or depth, they afford examples of every gradation up to bone-caves and -caverns.

BONE-CAVES AND -CAVERNS

In regions formed of calcareous rocks riddled with subterranean cavities,

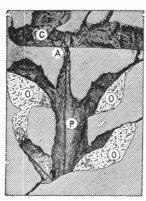

25 (left) Section of a bone-pit in the Gargas Cave (Haute-Pyrénées).

C, bottom of cave; A, entrance to pit; P, O, clay which yielded skeletons of bear, hyaena and wolf, now in Palaeontological Gallery of National Museum of Natural History, Paris.

26 (right) Rock-shelters at Bruniquel (Tarn-et-Garonne), inhabited during the Reindeer Age.

the play of atmospheric erosion and the progressive hollowing of the valleys has established communications between these caves and the outer air. Through the openings thus produced, fierce torrents have carried in earth, pebbles, bones of animals, and so on. Further, the caves became the dens of lions, bears, and hyaenas; thither the wild beasts brought their ⹁rey,

27 The Grimaldi Caves
Photograph taken about 1870, before the construction of the railway

and there left their own dead bodies (Fig. 25). Finally, they often served as habitations for the men of these times.

From our point of view, two kinds of subterranean caves may be distinguished: first, caves serving as dens, the deposits of which contain mainly animal remains, and second, the habitations of cave-dwellers. The latter did not penetrate so far into the interior of the earth's crust, and sometimes they only occupy the entrance of the deeper caverns. Often, indeed, they are only simple shelters under overhanging rocks (Fig. 26). In such cases the cave deposits are formed chiefly by human agency, cinders from hearths and kitchen debris, in which are mingled products of man's industries and sometimes even the bones of the ancient inhabitants themselves.

All these remains of Quaternary times have been gradually buried under depths of rubble, so that the deposits in the interior of grottoes or caverns now form, for the naturalist, archives as valuable as they are time-honoured. The more such deposits lend themselves to detailed and stratigraphic analysis, the more exact is the information they yield regarding the ancient stages of the Human Race in any given country; and in this connexion may be mentioned the Cave of Mas d'Azil, in the Pyrenees, and the Grimaldi Caves, near Mentone (Fig. 27).

VOLCANIC FORMATIONS

Volcanic countries are very often rich in fossils. The dense streams of lava, ejected at burning heat, do not of course contain them, but the lava-flows are generally poured into the depths of the valleys, and cover the contemporary alluvials. These alluvials and all their palaeontological content have thus been, in a sense, sealed up and preserved from all outside interference, and are most valuable for chronological study.

Volcanic discharges, cinders and lapilli, may bury the dead bodies of animals; they are often swept along and redistributed by water, in association with all kinds of debris scattered over the surface of the soil, and with it are deposited further on as stratified layers of volcanic tufas. *Pithecanthropus* was found in a layer of this nature.

CLASSIFICATION OF QUATERNARY TIMES:

STRATIGRAPHICAL METHOD

Even the detailed study of these different geological formations would not in itself be sufficient to enable us to establish a correct chronology or classification of Quarternary times.

The *stratigraphical method*, which is, in general, the most certain and the most precise, is here more difficult of application than in the preceding geological Eras. The Quaternary deposits, indeed, varied as they may be, are isolated or placed side by side, rather than superimposed. In short, we have only local and limited successions, each representing only a fraction of the duration of Quaternary times.

Marine formations, so important to consider in preceding Eras, are now reduced in extent, difficult to co-ordinate as between one country and another, and especially difficult to correlate with the continental formations, which are by far the most interesting from the point of view of human palaeontology. A few neophytes have been taken in by the deceptive simplicity of chronologies of the Quaternary Era based solely on these marine deposits; but, by overlooking serious difficulties, attempts to establish time relations on this basis have led to conclusions that are sometimes ludicrous and to a nomenclature whose success with less lazy-minded investigators was inevitably only transitory.[9]

Many geologists and prehistorians ascribe a preponderant role to glacial formations in classifying Quaternary times. The present authors cannot contradict them in principle, since one of them was among the first—half a century ago—to believe in and apply this method. Unfortunately, here too, we lack a firm chronological framework, for experts are unable to agree about these formations. The systems they have proposed range from a

---

[9] The most remarkable, and at the same time the most worthy, conversion is that of M. Gignoux in *Géologie stratigraphique* (3rd Ed., 1943) pp. 616–617.

classification that accepts only one single Ice Age to another that claims half a dozen. Divergence of opinion in the various countries is no less when it comes to assigning such and such a moraine formation to such and such an Ice Age. This diversity of views throws into sharp relief the difficulties of applying such an uncertain chronological system. It should make us cautious. During recent years, some prehistorians unfamiliar with the difficulties of geological problems have succeeded by this means, and with the aid of a more or less fallacious 'typology', in constructing unacceptable chronological edifices on shaky, and sometimes non-existent foundations.

The ancient alluvial deposits in valleys may be more fruitful in precise information, for they are often rich in fossils and products of human industry. But they must be studied under rigorous scientific conditions, which, up to the present, has not always been the case.

These old fluviatile deposits are more or less closely linked with the glacier formations on the one hand and the marine sediments now above sea-level on the other. These links have become increasingly clear since geologists have grasped the full importance of a theory whose origins go back almost a century and which has been developed by various workers, notably the late Professor Wilhelm Ramsay, of Helsingfors.[10]

It occurred to geologists that the quantity of water stored up in the form of inland ice and mountain glaciers must have caused the level of the sea to drop by a distance varying with the circumstances. Calculations showed that this fall might have been around 600 feet at the maximum glaciation and about 300 feet during the last period. This recession, or negative movement of the sea, corresponding to a glacial phase, resulted in a lowering of the level of the beds of the rivers that flowed into it and caused them to deepen their valleys. When, during an interglacial phase, the water of the glaciers was released and restored to the sea, the level of the latter rose and the rivers filled their valleys. Thus—contrary to what many geologists used to claim—alluvial terraces and old marine beaches correspond to interglacial, not to glacial phases (Fig. 28).

It is worth adding that this law, apparently so straightforward, may be upset by the intervention of other processes resulting from the elasticity and movements of the earth's crust, which is never entirely static. This shows, once again, all the difficulties involved in questions of this kind.

QUATERNARY FOSSILS AND THE METHOD OF PALAEONTOLOGY

The *palaeontological method* also has its weaknesses. There are no longer marine fossils so widely distributed as were the Graptolites of Primary, the Ammonites of Secondary, and the Nummulites of Tertiary times. And, moreover, the marine invertebrates of the ancient Quaternary raised beaches

[10] Ramsay, Wilhelm, 'Changes of Sea-Level resulting from the Increase and Decrease of Glaciations' (*Fennia*, 52, No. 5, 1930). See also: Daly, A., *The Changing World of the Ice Age* (1934).

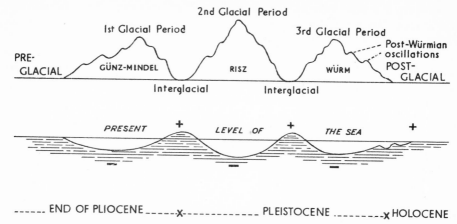

28 Diagram showing the parallels between the Glacial and Inter-Glacial Periods (above) and
the positive and negative movements of the sea (below)[11]

cannot afford much help, for all the Quaternary invertebrates present a
degree of specific development closely resembling their modern state.

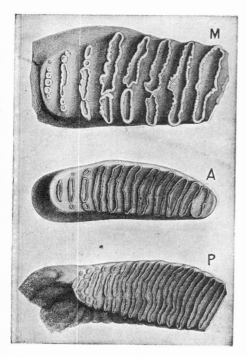

The Quaternary plants were
identical with the plants of today.
They were too greatly influenced by
topographical conditions to permit
of their being used successfully to
elucidate the problems of chronology. But they furnish valuable
information regarding climate. For
it has been found that, in one and
the same region, certain layers contain species of warm climates, whilst

29 Molar teeth of the three principal
species of fossil elephants found in
France.

M, Southern Elephant (*Elephas meridionalis*): the tooth is very broad, the
enamel plates are thick and widely
separated. A, Ancient Elephant (*Elephas antiquus*): the tooth is narrow, the
enamel plates are less thick but again
widely separated. P, Mammoth (*Elephas primigenius*): the tooth is broad,
the enamel plates are much more numerous, more compressed, and less thick.

[11] Most modern geologists are agreed in also placing in the Quaternary the Günz-Mindel
Period or Periods; see p. 49 below.

others yield species of cold climates. It is permissible to suppose that the latter date from a glacial phase, while the warm flora corresponds to an interglacial phase.

The study of fossil vertebrates, particularly of mammals, is of great assistance. The Quaternary species are usually so closely akin to the modern species that it is often difficult to distinguish them. But there are also some extinct species: the Ancient Elephant (*Elephas antiquus*), the Mammoth

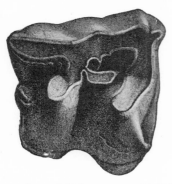

30 Upper molars of *Rhinoceros mercki* (left), and of *R. tichorinus* (right). Three-quarters natural size

(*Elephas primigenius*), Merck's Rhinoceros (*Rhinoceros mercki*), the Woolly Rhinoceros (*Rhinoceros tichorhinus*), the Sabre-Toothed Tiger (*Machairodus*), the Cave Bear (*Ursus spelaeus*), and others. These animals are capable of furnishing excellent chronological data, for their extinction was not simultaneous. Thus of the three species of fossil Elephants in Europe, easily distinguished by their molar teeth (Fig. 29), *Elephas meridionalis* became extinct before *Elephas antiquus*, and the latter before the Mammoth. In the same way the Woolly Rhinoceros persisted longer in Europe than Merck's Rhinoceros (Fig. 30).

Side by side with these forms which are now extinct, there is a fairly large number of species still alive, but no longer inhabiting our part of the globe; they are species which have *migrated*, and these are equally useful for study. At the present day the mean temperature of our regions is less high than it was during the warmest period of Quaternary times, and it is less low than during the coldest period. So that, following Lartet's example, the Quarternary mammals may be divided into two groups: a *warm-climate group*, which migrated to the south; and a *cold-climate group*, which migrated to the north. The principal animals of the southern group are the Hippopotamus, which could live only in a country where the rivers do not freeze; the Cave Lion, which differed from the modern Lion only in its slightly larger build; the Cave Hyaena, which exactly resembled the Spotted Hyaena of Central Africa, although it was also somewhat stronger in build; the Panther; the Porcupine, and the Barbary Ape.

Among the animals of the northern group, which now live only in polar regions, must be mentioned the Blue Fox, the Glutton, certain Rodents such as the Lemming, the Musk-Ox, the Reindeer, the Great Snowy Owl, and birds of the *Lagopus* genus.

The Reindeer deserves special mention. This Ruminant, which cannot now live in a wild state in a degree of latitude lower than 60°N., was remarkably widespread throughout the whole of France at a particular epoch of Quaternary time, called on that account the *Reindeer Age*. At the same time, the Ibex and the Chamois, now confined to the high peaks of the Alps and the Pyrenees, frequented the lowest plains of France.

Excellent fossil remains of all these animals have been obtained, but they must be made use of with judgment. The geographical distribution of animals had already become so complex during Quaternary times that each region might have, and indeed did have, its own peculiar fauna; and this renders the synchronizing of deposits far from each other a task of much delicacy. Finally, we know that changes of climate have led to migrations of faunas, so that a species need not belong to the same age in two different localities.

Other species are found almost everywhere at all levels, and are therefore without significance as chronological data. These include the Horse (initially in a wild state); the Pig; the Primitive Ox or *Urus*, the ancestor of our Cattle; the Aurochs, the ancestor of the European Bison; the Roe Deer; the Red Deer; the Wolf; the Common Fox; the Brown Bear, and others.

THE ARCHAEOLOGICAL METHOD

For the establishment of the chronology of Quaternary times, a third method is available, the most ancient of all, the *archaeological method*. It is based on the study of human industry, which has developed and changed, becoming by degrees more and more perfect; the least destructible of its products, implements of stone, are everywhere widespread.

31 A Palaeolithic *dressed* axe, and a Neolithic *polished* axe. One-third natural size

Thanks to them, it was early recognized, as we have seen, that an age of stone preceded the age of metals. And in the Stone Age an older or *Palaeolithic* phase can be distinguished, during which Man did not know how to work or fashion stone except by shaping it through repeated blows; and a more recent or *Neolithic* phase during which Man had learned to fashion stone by another process, by wearing it down through friction and polishing it (Fig. 31).

Further, in each of these phases a succession of periods has been determined, characterized by different forms of objects or implements. Archaeologists have thus arrived at results of great interest to science. But classifications of this kind can have only local significance, for, even at the present day, very different industries may be contemporaneous in different regions. Taken to extremes, this method, which lacks universal application, may lead to serious mistakes.

Many archaeologists adopt the principle that industrial progress began at a single centre, from which it spread, coming last to those countries farthest removed from this centre of origin. 'To our minds', writes Capitan,[12] 'the savage who, a few hundred thousand years ago, dressed his flat, oval implement (the Chellean hand-axe) in Southern Africa must have been in contact—either himself, his ancestors, or his descendants—with the savage who fashioned exactly the same implement on the banks of the Thames.'

It is extremely difficult to share this opinion, especially in so far as it concerns primitive stone artefacts, which are very simple in conception and correspond to the same exceedingly low degree of civilization. It is much more reasonable to explain them as spontaneous and independent inventions. It seems to us much more likely that these earliest tools and weapons were the inevitable and constant outcome of human actions dictated by the same elementary needs and exercised upon the same stone material. What we see here are trends that converge along paths predetermined by the unity of the human spirit in all places and at all times.

In any case, the distinctions made by 'typologists'—distinctions of great subtlety applied to the earliest stones used or dressed during periods of extreme antiquity—could not possess any general chronological value, even if the hypothesis of a single point of origin be accepted: the diffusion of the new invention from one end of the world to the other, from Paris to the Cape of Good Hope or vice versa—supposing it to have been materially possible—would involve an immense period of time, and hence an enormously complicated sequence of chronological stages.

This was also the opinion of that excellent archaeologist and naturalist Jacques de Morgan, who complained that many prehistorians attached too much importance to the morphology of dressed flints, in these words: 'As if two different men could not have dressed a pebble in the same fashion without having consulted together beforehand. They (prehistorians) attribute extraordinary excursions to the ancient peoples, as though there had been a Cook's Tourist Agency in those days.'[13]

Each method thus has its merits and its defects, and each is insufficient

[12] Capitan, L., *La Préhistoire* (2nd Ed. revised and brought up to date by M. Faguet, Paris, 1931).

[13] *L'Anthropologie*, XXXVIII, 1928, p. 336.

by itself. Certain classifications established by pure geologists incur the grave reproach of not taking sufficient account of palaeontological and archaeo-logical facts and of seeing everything in terms of a single phenomenon, itself not fully understood—whether it be the glacial or the marine phenomenon. Classifications based solely on fossils can serve only for the major divisions and must necessarily vary with the different regions of the globe. In appealing to archaeological facts exclusively, prehistorians have come to make a much greater number of stages in the series of prehistoric times and to establish a more detailed chronology. Unfortunately, such classifications, initiated or perfected by Lartet, Gabriel de Mortillet, Piette, Cartailhac, Breuil, and others, can only be applied *a priori* to restricted areas of our continent alone. Archaeology is incapable of establishing with certainty synchronisms or time-correlations at great distances; for the human factor—after a certain primitive stage has been passed—becomes increasingly mobile, changing, and varied in its manifestations. Archaeological aspects tend to be local, rather than to show sequences of ethnographical facts having general and contemporaneous significance. The idea of *facies* should play as important a part in prehistory as in geology.

PROPOSED GENERAL CLASSIFICATION OF QUATERNARY TIMES

In 1888 one of the present authors proposed a classification of Quaternary times based on the use and correlation of the three kinds of data.[14]

The discoveries made since, in all parts of the world, have modified the main lines of this first attempt, which a kind colleague described as 'epoch-making in its day'. We now know that the Quaternary Era has gone on much longer than was thought fifty years ago. It has embraced at least three glacial epochs, together with the periods between them. This has extended an immensely greater distance into the past the duration of the oldest prehistoric industries. But the principles on which the proposed classification was based have lost none of their value.

First, we must call upon facts of a geological and palaeontological order. They have a more general significance and bearing than ethnographical facts, because they are independent of human action, and because they dominate it. It therefore falls to geologists and palaeontologists to establish the great divisions of Quaternary times, since these are of geological signi-ficance; and it is within the limits fixed by them that prehistorians may, in their turn, make subdivisions of an archaeological and of a more localized nature.

A first problem is the delimitation of Tertiary and Quaternary times, a problem the more difficult to solve because no great physical or biological fact can be appealed to in order to establish a division between them. In reality the Tertiary Era still exists in every respect. It would certainly be best

[14] Boule, M., 'Essai de Paléontologie stratigraphique de l'Homme' (*Revue d'Anthropologie*, 1888 and 1889). This classification only applied to Europe. Any attempt at a universal classi-fication would have been premature.

to suppress the term 'Quaternary' in our classifications, and to include it in the Tertiary under another name, *Pleistocene*, as a Period analogous to the Pliocene, Miocene, and other Periods which preceded it.

Apart from this—the most rational view of the matter, which, however, does not seem likely to be readily adopted—we may either consider the Quaternary Era as starting with the age of *Elephas meridionalis*, as we formerly thought, or immediately after this epoch, which would then remain in the Pliocene, and this is our present opinion. In any case, the matter is of little importance from our present point of view. Problems of grouping are somewhat arbitrary, for they represent only mental conceptions; what must be established is the succession of events and the synchronism of the phenomena.[15]

We will leave in the Pliocene the fauna that includes *Elephas meridionalis*, which is found in formations terminating a geological cycle and denoting a topography, and sometimes even a geography, somewhat different from those of Quaternary times. It is possible that this epoch was marked by a very old glacial extension (*Günzian* of Penck's system) of which the moraines, few in number and barely visible, appear to merge with the alluvial deposits now covering the plateaux between existing valleys. The chief fossils characteristic of these alluvials of the plateaux and other contemporary formations are: *Elephas meridionalis*, *Hippopotamus major*, a Giant Beaver, *Trogontherium*, large Cervidae, *Machairodus*, and others.

Various fossil-bearing deposits, notably in raised terraces of modern valleys, correspond to the first hollowing-out of these valleys with which the Quaternary Era opens.

The Quaternary Era comprises the *Pleistocene* Period[16] and the *Holocene* or *Modern* Period. The Pleistocene of geologists corresponds exactly to the *Palaeolithic* of archaeologists, the Holocene to the *Neolithic* and the Ages of the *metals*. A transitional phase or period between the two is now distinguished—the *Mesolithic*.

Geological Divisions	*Archaeological Divisions*	
	Period of the Metals	Iron Age
Holocene Period	Neolithic Period	Bronze Age
Quaternary Transitional		Copper Age
Era phase	Mesolithic Period	
Pleistocene Period	Palaeolithic Period	

[15] Going even further, Haug, in his *Traité de Géologie* (1911), made the Quaternary Era begin much sooner, claiming that its commencement was marked by the sudden appearance in Europe of three genera: *Elephas*, *Equus* and *Bos*. Thus the upper phase of the Pliocene, the Villafranchian, is included in the Quaternary. This view was long disputed. Many geologists have returned to it today following discussions raised at the last International Congress of Geology in 1948 (*L'Anthropologie*, LIII, 1949, p. 144).

[16] The term 'Quaternary' is often used as synonymous with 'Pleistocene'. This is erroneous, since it mistakes the part for the whole; but the term, nevertheless, has passed into current use.

Table

Geological Divisions			Geological Phenomena and Formatio
QUATERNARY	HOLOCENE OR RECENT		Recent alluvials Peat mosses Climate almost as today
	PLEISTOCENE	Upper	RETRO- AND POST-GLACIAL PHASES Marine transgression Upper cave deposits Upper part of the loess Climate first cold and dry; regime of tundras then of steppes
		Middle	LAST GREAT GLACIAL PHASE (Würmian) Marine regression Internal moraines Maximum cave deposits Loess. Alluvials only at low levels Climate cold and moist
		Lower	GREAT INTERGLACIAL PHASE Marine transgression Middle and lower terraces Calcareous tufas Temperate climate PENULTIMATE GREAT GLACIAL PHASE (Rissien) Maximum marine regression External moraines Ancient loess Principal hollowing of valleys VERY LONG INTERGLACIAL PHASE Alluvials of the high terraces ANTEPENULTIMATE GLACIAL PHASE (Mindelian) Alluvials of the plateaux Pre-glacial continental deposits
TERTIARY	PLIOCENE	Upper	End of the Pliocene sedimentary cycle Günz glaciation ?

uaternary Times

Palaeontological Characters	Archaeological Divisions			Fossil Men	
ecies now found in the ne country mestic animals	METALS		Iron Bronze Copper	HOMO SAPIENS	
teppe Fauna EINDEER AGE	NEOLITHIC MESOLITHIC (Transition Period)			Race of CHANCELADE	Fossil HOMO SAPIENS
undra Fauna	PALAEOLITHIC	Upper	MAGDA-LENIAN		
IAMMOTH AGE				Race of CRO-MAGNON	
ephas primigenius hinoceros tichorhinus			SOLU-TREAN		
ge of the ANCIENT LEPHANT			AURIG-NACIAN	Race of GRIMALDI	
ephas antiquus ephas trogontherii ppopotamus amphibius inoceros mercki		Middle	MOUS-TERIAN	HOMO NEANDERTALENSIS	
		Lower	ACHEU-LEAN	PRESAPIENS and PRE-NEANDERTALENSIS	
			CHEL-LEAN		
e of the JUTHERN LEPHANT			PRE-CHEL-LEAN	HOMO HEIDELBERGENSIS	
phas meridionalis inoceros etruscus				PITHECANTHROPUS	

Divisions of the Pleistocene Period:

Lower Pleistocene

The Pleistocene Period may be divided into three ages corresponding to as many stages.[17] The following are their main characteristics, to which we shall return at greater length when dealing with the fossil Men of each of these stages.

The *Lower Pleistocene* comprises two glacial extensions (Penck's *Mindelian* and *Rissian* phases) with the two corresponding interglacial phases. Of these extensions of the ice-sheet, the second seems to have been the most important, and its moraines (called 'external') extend furthest from the mountain centres. At the same time, the level of the sea was greatly reduced. This recession resulted in a progressive hollowing-out of the valleys to depths that were sometimes greater than those they have at the present time.

The two interglacial phases—the first of which, separating the Mindel and the Riss glaciations, was particularly long—were accompanied by marine transgressions and are marked by a fauna composed of elements indicating a warm climate: *Elephas antiquus*, an animal that seems to have been adapted to forest life; *Rhinoceros hemitoechus* and later *Rh. mercki*;

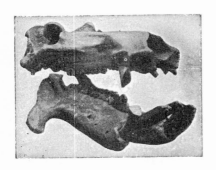

32 Skull of fossil hippopotamus, about one-tenth natural size. Palaeontological Gallery of French National Museum of Natural History, Paris.

Hippopotamus (Fig. 32), Monkeys, and so on. The Sabre-Toothed Tiger and the Trogontherium had disappeared at the beginning of this Period, and the two glacial phases are characterized by a fauna that is in part new: *Elephas trogontherii*, and the Woolly Rhinoceros (*Rhinoceros tichorhinus*). Remains of all these animals are found especially in the alluvials of the middle terraces of the modern hydrographic system and, occasionally, in the deepest and oldest deposits of caves.

The deposits of this period have also yielded the most ancient stone instruments unanimously accepted as authentic—notably the amygdaloid flints. Archaeologically speaking, these are the *Chellean* and *Acheulean*,

---

[17] The classification adopted here has been established with special reference to the needs of human palaeontology. Very different classifications have been advanced from the point of view of pure geology, and many writers now include in the Upper Pleistocene the whole of the last Ice Age, while some even place in it the last Interglacial Period. Similarly, the Mid Pleistocene is extended as far back as the penultimate glaciation.

names derived from the localities of Chelles, in the Department of Seine-et-Marne, and Saint-Acheul, near Amiens, which have now been universally adopted.

It was a long time before there was any certainty that remains of Lower Pleistocene Man had been discovered. Certain finds can now be confidently attributed to him. Apart from a jawbone that has been dubbed *Homo heidelbergensis*, all these discoveries look to us like forerunners of the two great human groups that succeed one another during the ensuing epochs, Neandertal Man and *Homo sapiens*. It is to the Pleistocene, too, that we must assign a group of extremely primitive forms from the Far East, *Pithecanthropus* and *Sinanthropus*, for which has been created the significant term *Prehominids*.

MID PLEISTOCENE

The Mid Pleistocene is characterized, from the geological point of view, by the return of a cold climate and those great glacial developments which have left the best-preserved moraines, situated, as a rule, within the limit of the moraines of the preceding glacial extension and therefore known as *internal moraines* (*Würmian* phase of Penck). It is also characterized by the formation of fresh alluvial sheets, sometimes superimposed upon those of the Lower Pleistocene, but most often situated below the level of the latter, and forming terraces *lower* in relation to the *middle* terraces. This is the period of the principal deposits of cave debris, and of the formation of great masses of mud or loess in France, for both these deposits have a similar origin.

It is also the period of the last hollowing out or filling up of the valleys, of the penultimate sculpturing of the surface configuration of the present day.

The fauna is very different from that of the Lower Pleistocene. The Hippopotamus is no longer found in France. The Ancient Elephant is replaced by the Mammoth (Fig. 33). Merck's Rhinoceros persists a little longer, and is succeeded by the Woolly Rhinoceros which, as we know, was

33 Skeleton of mammoth from Beresovka (N.E. Siberia). In Leningrad Museum. Height 10 ft. 8 in.

adapted, like the Mammoth, to the rigours of a glacial climate. In France the Mid Pleistocene saw the reign of the great Carnivores: the Bear, the Hyaena and the Cave Lion (Fig. 34). It corresponds fairly exactly to the archaeological period called *Mousterian*, after the Le Moustier Cave in the Dordogne.

In the cave-deposits of the Mid Pleistocene were found many human bones, sometimes almost complete skeletons, which revealed a prehistoric

34 Exhibit of Quaternary Carnivores in the Palaeontological Gallery of the French National Museum of Natural History

From left to right: skeleton of cave hyaena; three skeletons of cave bears; two skeletons of cave lions; in the right foreground, cave wolf.

type very different from modern man, namely Neandertal Man (*Homo neandertalensis*), which we shall study at length, from French material of exceptional importance.

The Mid Pleistocene was of far shorter duration than the Lower Pleistocene.

UPPER PLEISTOCENE

The Upper Pleistocene has no clearly defined characters from the geological or stratigraphical points of view. The deposits corresponding to it present a topography and hydrography very much resembling those of the present day, but, especially towards the end of the period, they were contemporaneous with a drier climate. In the caves the deposits are principally formed by relics of Man, cinders from hearths and kitchen refuse.

In spite of some forward movements of the ice, gradually decreasing in importance, but considered by certain authors as glacial phases, this Period marks the general retreat of the great glaciers of the preceding Period; it is, therefore, often distinguished as *Post-Glacial*, though *Retro-Glacial* would be a better term.

The fauna is still essentially that of the Mid Pleistocene. The large species are the same (Mammoth, Woolly Rhinoceros, and so on), and in this respect the Mid and Upper Pleistocene may be regarded as forming one geological unit, as distinct from the Lower Pleistocene. But the stratigraphy of the caves generally allows of the recognition of several successive layers enclosing slightly different faunas. It is impossible, however, always to affirm that these differences are not due to the interference of Man. His intervention must certainly have brought to the settlements, to the exclusion of many others, the bones of certain animals which perhaps could not have come there by the simple play of natural causes.

The Reindeer is accompanied first by a very cold fauna, known as the fauna of the *tundras*, because it contains the principal members of the fauna of

35 Modern Reindeer

the frozen and desolate countries which bear this name today, such as the Musk-Ox, Glutton, Blue Fox, Lemming, Snowy Owl, and others, whose remains are found in association in certain layers of the Arctic peat-bogs. Then comes a less cold fauna, indicating a climate and habitat similar to those of the Russian and Siberian steppes, and including the Saiga Antelope, Prairie Squirrels, Jerboas,[18] and others, whilst our low plains are invaded by the Chamois, the Ibex, the Marmot, and, everywhere abundant, those large ruminants, the Bison and Great Extinct Ox. But the Reindeer (Fig. 35) is always the dominant species throughout the whole Period, which has long been known as the *Reindeer Age*.

Archaeology has been of special service in enabling a very clear line to be drawn between the two great Periods of Mid and Upper Pleistocene.

[18] See various works by Nehring, A., notably *Über Tundren und Steppen der Jetzt-und Vorzeit* (Berlin, 1890). Also Pfizenmayer, E., *Les Mammouths de Sibérie* (Paris, 1939).

The distinction between the Mammoth Age and the Reindeer Age, first made by Lartet, is justified much more by archaeology than by palaeontology. It crops up again in the almost parallel terms of Mousterian and Magdalenian, invented by G. de Mortillet. Modern prehistorians are agreed in dividing the Palaeolithic into the *Lower Palaeolithic*, comprising the Chellean and the Mousterian Periods, and the *Upper Palaeolithic* or Reindeer Age, thus affirming the archaeological and anthropological individuality of two periods difficult to distinguish by the resources of geology and palaeontology alone.[19]

Ethnography goes even further, and allows of the introduction into the Reindeer Age, or Upper Palaeolithic, of several divisions of real importance, at least for Western Europe. The names given to these are: *Aurignacian* (from Aurignac in the Haute-Garonne, where there is a grotto explored by Lartet), *Solutrean* (from Solutré, Saône-et-Loire), and *Magadalenian* (from La Madeleine, in the Dordogne).

The fossil Men of these periods are fairly numerous and very different from Neandertal Man. They have already the characteristics of Modern Man (*Homo sapiens*), from whom they cannot be distinguished except on the ground of race or of ancestral variety.

HOLOCENE

Certain deposits, typified by those in the grotto of Mas d'Azil (Ariège) and which are becoming daily more numerous and varied, correspond to a period called *Mesolithic*, which, as we shall see later, presents all the characteristics of a transition from Pleistocene to Holocene.

The *Holocene* Period,[20] the duration of which has been relatively short and in which we are at present living, is marked by the final retreat of the glaciers, an improvement in the climate, the localization of rivers in their present valleys, the complete extinction of the great beasts enumerated above, the emergence of the modern fauna, and the gradual perfection of human civilizations.

It comprises the archaeologists' Neolithic Period and the Age of Metals. It is of comparatively little interest from the standpoint of human palaeontology, which in this period is already confronted by the modern races.

[19] The geological expressions Upper, Middle and Lower Pleistocene should not be absolutely confounded with the archaeological expressions Chellean, Mousterian and so on. The latter can only have a local or regional significance, while the former should be, in principle at least, of universal application. It will be useful to employ, as the case demands, one or other of these two nomenclatures, in order to avoid confusions which prehistorians often make.

[20] If we were writing here exclusively as geologists we should not accept the term Holocene period; we should rather consider it as the last *epoch* of the Pleistocene Period; but prehistory justifies the importance given to this division.

ABSOLUTE CHRONOLOGY

RELATIVE AND ABSOLUTE CHRONOLOGY

Relative chronology, which we have just been studying, is distinct from absolute chronology. The latter must furnish dates in units of time—years, centuries or millennia. History has its absolute chronology, which, it may be said, is the more determinate or precise as it deals with events more or less close to us. On every hand there arises the demand for an absolute chronology for prehistory. The first question asked by the public at large, in connexion with any prehistoric fact, has to do with its date.

Now we must honestly admit that, in the present state of the science, it is almost impossible in most cases to answer such a question.[21] The temerity with which certain writers, without sufficient reservation, present figures which are all the more fallacious because their very detail suggests precision, makes an unfortunate impression on the minds of scientists aware of our ignorance. We would not for a moment suggest that the problem may or must remain unsolved, for no one can fix a limit to the progress of the human mind. But we hold that the first duty of the scientist is to respect the confidence of those who come to him in good faith, and to set before them only such facts as are sufficiently well established.

In order to satisfy as far as possible the curiosity of our readers, which is after all quite legitimate, we shall briefly summarize the results of the leading attempts at establishing a definite chronology, and shall draw from these results such conclusions as seem to be most reasonable.

There is no need to dwell here upon the estimates of the ancient writers, of biblical legends, of the Chaldean, Egyptian or Chinese traditions and chronicles, and others, which in this matter cannot be considered reliable.

DIFFERENT METHODS OF TIME ESTIMATION

Since the great antiquity of Man was scientifically established, men of science have constantly striven to translate it into figures. They have conceived all kinds of time-measuring methods, based on astronomy, on geology, and even on biology.

In principle, astronomical methods ought to be most satisfactory, since astronomy has given us our units of time. The difficulty is to discover a geological event which can be correlated at once with the antiquity of Man and with a measurable astronomical phenomenon. It was believed to have been found in the development of the glaciers, which were attributed either to variations in the eccentricity of the earth's orbit (that is to say, to differences in the distance of the earth from the sun) or to variations in the obliquity of

[21] Thanks to certain historical dates furnished by Chaldaea and Egypt, and to archaeological comparisons established step by step, satisfactory results have been obtained for the Ages of Metals in the West (see Chap. IX). But these Ages only represent the end of our prehistoric era. What we are discussing here relates to an infinitely more remote past.

the earth's axis (precession of the equinoxes). As astronomy can calculate
the dates of such periodic variations, it should be enough to choose from
among the dates those which correspond to the variations most favourable
for the establishment of glacial climatic conditions, in order to know the
absolute age of the Glacial Period and, in consequence, the age of the Men
contemporary with this period.

Thus, according to the English astronomer Croll, the Glacial Period
began with the last great cycle of eccentricity in the earth's orbit (corresponding to the maximum distance of the earth from the sun, that is, to a maximum
of coldness) 240,000 years ago; further, it lasted 160,000 years and came to
an end 80,000 years ago. According to Lyell, the Great Glacial Period
coincided with an older period of great eccentricity, and this would make it
date back to 800,000 years ago.

This theory has been attacked alike by astronomers, physicists and
geologists. It has not been proved that the Glacial Period or periods were
related to the astronomical phenomena in question; and we shall see that
there are excellent reasons today for believing that the end of the Glacial
Period did not date so far back as was believed by Croll and Lyell.

It will be enough merely to mention a few attempts at time-estimation
based on palaeontology and the phenomena of organic evolution. It was
believed that a numerical appraisement could be made of the periods corresponding to changes undergone by the fauna of a country through extinction,
transformation or the appearance of species. The hints thus obtained are
altogether vague and indefinite; they have, however, the merit of impressing
on the mind the idea of the immensity of even the most recent geological
times, when we learn, for example, that the changes which have taken place
in the animate world since the end of the Palaeolithic Period are imperceptible or insignificant.

The geological methods of estimating are more numerous, and almost
all depend upon much the same principal: A geological phenomenon is
selected, the effects of which can be measured throughout a unit of time—
that is, the rapidity of whose progress in the present period, or throughout
a lapse of time determined by historical data, can be gauged. From this
result, by simple rule of three, the time may be calculated necessary to
produce effects conforming to the prehistoric period the date of which we
desire to discover. If we know, for example, the absolute value of the time
required for the deposition of a certain thickness of alluvium, it will be easy
to estimate the time required for the deposition of a greater mass of alluvium,
the formation of which corresponds to a definite geological or archaeological
period.

Unfortunately, conditions are far from being so simple as this. The
first difficulty lies in really knowing what we wish to measure, especially
in the case of events the beginning and end of which it is impossible to
determine with exactitude. The expressions we must necessarily employ,
such as the 'beginning' or 'end' of the Glacial Period, the 'date of Man's

appearance', and those serving to designate the divisions we make in the succession of the ages and of the events correlated with them, are perforce very vague; they correspond to no absolute reality, for such abrupt divisions exist only in our minds.

Further, the duration of the same event may have varied in different countries. It is clear for example, that the Glacial Period came to an end much sooner in France than in Scandinavia.

Another, and still more serious objection is that geological methods of time-estimation depend on an assumption of the permanence and unbroken regularity of natural processes; and this is extremely improbable. In any event, in the majority of cases it is impossible to make allowance for the counteraction of destructive forces, which may have worked in inverse ratio to the constructive forces, weakening, diminishing and sometimes annihilating the effects of the latter.

But whether these criticisms be justified or not, and their significance is evident, investigators have turned their attention to all kinds of natural accumulations. They have examined, in their turn, the peat-mosses, alluvials, glacial moraines, cones of mountain-torrent detritus, lake-deposits, deltas, marine ooze, calcareous concretions, alteration in rocks by atmospheric agents, the hollowing out of gorges, the backward cutting of waterfalls, the rate of progress or of retreat of glaciers, oscillations in the level of the sea, and so on. We have noted more than forty attempts of this kind, and others must certainly have escaped us.

New Methods of Time-Estimation

During the last few years research into time estimation has made great strides, thanks to the study of certain phenomena of a physical or chemical nature. In some cases these methods have made it possible to establish extremely valuable datings.

The so-called radioactivity method has been applied to the study of rocks. It is based on the fact that the emanations of radioactive bodies, such as radium, uranium, and so on, are transformed first into helium and then into lead. The amount of helium that issues, for example, from a given quantity of uranium during a fixed period has been calculated. Since the rate of disintegration of the uranium atom is, therefore, known, evaluation of the respective proportions of uranium, helium and lead in a mineral whose age it is desired to find gives some idea of the time that has passed since its formation.

This was the method by which the English geologist Holmes[22] estimated the commencement of the Quaternary Era 1,000,000 years, the beginning

[22] Holmes, A., 'An Estimate of the Age of the Earth' (*Geological Mag.*, London, Vol. LXXXIV, 1947).

For this method and everything relating to the chronology of the Quaternary Era in general, see particularly: Zeuner, A., *Dating the Past* (2nd Ed., London, 1951).

of the Tertiary at 60,000,000 years, and that of Primary times at 500,000,000 years.

The same principle is employed in the 'Carbon 14' method, which is, however, limited to the later periods of prehistory. This method is based on the discovery that alongside normal carbon, with an atomic weight of 12, all living organic matter contains various isotopes of this carbon, one of which is radioactive and is therefore known as radio-carbon, or, because its atomic weight is 14, as Carbon 14.[23] After death, Carbon 14 disintegrates progressively at a rate that has been measured and is believed to be constant. The older a bone or an archaeological object is, the less radio-carbon it contains, and it is accepted that by the end of 25,000 years the radio-carbon will have totally disappeared. In the case of any object below this age, the quantity of Carbon 14 present gives a rough idea of its antiquity. In fact, when applied to articles taken from Egyptian tombs, whose age is well established, this method has given exact figures. It may be assumed that it is equally accurate for older material.

The fluorine method is based on quite a different principle. In 1893 the French chemist Carnot[24] showed that the fluorine content of fossil bones increased with their age. Here, he thought, was a means of estimating the age of a bone. No attention was paid to his investigations at the time, but they were renewed quite recently by the English geologist K. P. Oakley,[25] who has confirmed Carnot's basic idea but, at the same time, shown that the fluorine increase varies greatly according to the site, since the chemical composition of the soil and the amount of water it contains play a decisive role in determining the concentration of fluorine. Thus a Pleistocene bone from a deposit that is rich in fluorine will contain far more of this substance than an Eocene bone preserved in a formation in which fluorine is comparatively scanty.

Investigation of the fluorine content therefore gives no results relevant to absolute chronology. Its value is confined to cases in which it is desired to estimate the comparative age, in relation to one another, of objects found in the same stratum, and, in particular, when the problem is to determine whether certain bones are contemporary with the geological formation in which they have been found or were introduced later, either deliberately or by chance. Comparison of their fluorine content with that of other bones in the same level, the age of which is not in doubt, affords conclusive evidence.

[23] Libby, W., Anderson, E., and Arnold, J., 'Age Determination by Radio-Carbon Content' (*Science*, Vol. CIX, p. 227). Arnold, J., and Libby, W., *Radio-Carbon Dates* (Inst. for Nuclear Studies, Chicago, 1950). Johnson, F., 'Radiocarbon Dating' (*Memoirs Soc. for American Archaeology*, Vol. VIII, 1951).

[24] Carnot, A., 'Recherches sur la composition générale et la teneur en fluor des os modernes et des os fossiles des différents âges' (*Ann. Mines*, Paris, Vol. III, 1893).

[25] Oakley, K., 'Fluorine and the Relative Dating of Bones' (*Brit. Ass. for the Advancement of Science*, London, 1948, Vol. IV).

DISCUSSION OF THE RESULTS

Below is a table showing a number of estimates of the duration: (1) of the Quaternary Era; (2) of the Glacial Period; (3) of Post-Glacial times. The figures denote the number of years.

Author	Quaternary Era	Glacial Period	Post-Glacial times
ARCELIN and FERRY, French geologists	10,000	..	4 to 5,000
HOLST, Swedish geologist	30,000	17,000	5 to 6,900
PRESTWICH, English geologist	..	25,000	8 to 10,000
WARREN UPHAM, American geologist	100 to 150,000	20 to 30,000	6 to 10,000
BECKER, American geologist	..	50,000	..
G. DE MORTILLET, French prehistorian	230 to 240,000	100,000	16,000
RUTOT, Belgian geologist and prehistorian	..	140,000	7 to 8,000
CROLL, English astronomer	240,000	160,000	80,000
A. M. HANSEN, Norwegian geologist	..	130 to 190,000	7 to 9,000
J. LUBBOCK, English prehistorian	..	200,000	..
SOLLAS, English geologist	..	400,000	17,000
OSBORN, American palaeontologist	500,000	500,000	25,000
J. GEIKIE, Scottish geologist	620,000 at least	..	..
DANA, American geologist	..	720,000	..
LYELL, English geologist	..	800,000	..
PENCK, German geographer	500,000 to 1,000,000	500,000 to 1,000,000	20,000
L. PILGRIM, German geographer	1,620,000	1,290,000	..
R. S. WOODWARD, GILBERT, RUSSEL, WINCHELL, E. ANDREWS, EMERSON, American geologists	..	..	7 to 10,000
HICKS, American geologist	..	..	15,000
SARAUW, Danish prehistorian	..	..	10 to 25,000
DE GEER, Swedish geologist	..	..	14,000
GOSSE, Swiss prehistorian	..	..	18,280
NUESCH, Swiss prehistorian	..	..	24 to 29,000

Author	Quaternary Era	Glacial Period	Post-Glacial times
FOREL, Swiss prehistorian	..	..	100,000
MILANKOVITCH, Serbian astronomer	..	592,000	21,000
HOLMES, English geologist	1,000,000	..	10,000
ZEUNER, English palaeontologist	590,000	568,000	22,000

The estimates given in the first two columns vary, in round figures, in the ratio of 10,000 to 1,600,000, that is, of 1 to 160. This is an enormous discrepancy. Many of these computations are purely sentimental, the lowest having certainly been influenced by the philosophic or religious views of their authors. But a divergence of this magnitude testifies primarily to the inaccuracy or inadequacy of the methods employed. It is very difficult to choose between them.

The discrepancy of the figures in the third column, relating to the duration of Post-Glacial times, is much less great. Ignoring certain evaluations clearly erroneous—the 80,000 years of the astronomer Croll and the 100,000 years of the geophysicist Forel—we find that the difference is only between 4,000 and 30,000, that is, in the ratio of about 1 to 7. It is still far too great but it shows some improvement. An analysis, into which we cannot enter here, of the processes of calculation which give the lowest estimates, shows that these processes, for example those of Arcelin and Ferry, are marred by error. If, then, we take as the extreme limits the figures 8,000 and 24,000, the ratio of difference is reduced to 1 to 3. Here we approach an agreement sufficiently close to give us confidence. Further, if we note that the majority of the estimates, in spite of the fact that they are based on very different phenomena, fluctuate between 8,000 and 15,000, that is to say, in the ratio of 1 to 2, we are led to place a certain amount of trust in dates which now belong clearly to the same scale of magnitude.

These figures would certainly have been still closer to each other had they really been applied to the same duration of time; but this is not the case, for the meaning of the expression *Post-Glacial times* varies remarkably, according to the authors who use it and the countries in which it is used.

If, in this case, agreement is much less imperfect than in that of the duration of the Glacial Period or of the sum total of Quaternary times, it is, first, because the space of time concerned is much shorter; secondly, because the phenomena that must be studied are much nearer to us, so that their effects are better preserved and more exactly apprehended; and finally, because these phenomena themselves more closely resemble the happenings of modern times, so that the latter afford more equivalent terms for comparison.

Duration of Post-Glacial Times

One of the most ingenious and satisfactory methods is that which enabled the Swede de Geer[26] to measure the rate of retreat of the last great Scandinavian glacier. In proportion as this retreat proceeded, the sea invaded the abandoned tracts of land and deposited there lamellar, or, more accurately, banded, clays (*varved clays*), consisting of alternate thin beds of light and dark clays—the light layers being the sediments laid down in the summer, the dark layers those laid down in winter. One light and one dark bed constitutes a *varve* (a Scandinavian word). A careful count of the number of varves on the successive lines along which the ice retreated, followed by co-ordination of the resulting graphs, yields the elements of a chronology in years. Discussion of the facts arrived at by a study of these varved clays, in America as well as Europe, has enabled de Geer and his pupils to fix the beginning of the decline of the last great glacial phase at about 40,000 years and its end at about 14,000.[27]

According to this, the extreme end of the Glacial Period in France, the departure of the Reindeer, the beginning of the superficial peat-bog formations, and the first evidences of the Mesolithic civilizations, may be estimated at about 12,000 years ago. Consequently, it is permissible to date the end of the Mousterian and the beginning of the Upper Palaeolithic, or Reindeer Age, at about 60,000 years ago.

The round number of these figures—which err on the side of moderation rather than excess—indicates that they are only approximate. They are the only figures we can suggest.

Immense Duration of Quaternary Times

We shall not venture to compute the duration of earlier archaeological or geological epochs, being unfortunately convinced that the estimates put forward up to the present do not rest on any secure foundation; but we hasten to add that everything tends to give the impression that an immense lapse of time separates our age from that of our earliest forefathers.

Let us leave on one side the archaeological aspect of the question, in order to consider only physical and biological facts. Since the end of the Pleistocene times of the geologists, or the Reindeer Age of the archaeologists, that is to say, since about 10,000 years ago, the geological changes undergone by France are inappreciable. This will serve as a starting-point.

The deposits corresponding to the period immediately preceding, that is to the Reindeer Age, are already of remarkable thickness. This is not a matter solely of human contributions, which may have accumulated with great rapidity. We have specially in view those sterile layers due to the activity of

[26] Geer, G. de, 'A Geochronology of the last 12,000 Years' (*Congrès géolog. intern. de Stockholm*, 1910, p. 241).

[27] See Antevs, E., *The Last Glaciation* (New York, 1928, with an important bibliography). Geer, G. de, 'Geology and Geochronology' (*Geograf. Ann. Stockholm*, 1934); *Geochronologia Soerica Principles*, (Stockholm, 1940).

atmospheric agents, which often alternate with the floors of occupation, and correspond to long periods of disuse of the caves and shelters. Thus we can, without fear of error, attribute to this period a duration equal to, if not greater than, that which separates us from it.

Now these deposits of the Reindeer Age, in spite of their relative importance, which impresses us in excavations, in reality play only an insignificant part in the topography of our country. The bones they contain are barely fossilized; nearly all of them belong to animals or men in every way similar to their modern representatives. But when we go back as far as the Mousterian Period, we observe much more important changes. Here everything bears witness to a different topography, brought about by physical forces of which impressive traces are everywhere visible: the demolition of mountain regions, the accumulation of moraine deposits over thousands of square miles, the last stages of sculpturing of the valleys, and the formation of the lower alluvial terraces; enormous deposits of silt over the land surfaces, and of clays containing bones in subterranean caves; variations in the shore-line; orogenic movements; repeated volcanic manifestations, and so on.

These physical phenomena are accompanied by appreciable changes in the fauna, particularly by the disappearance of several species of large mammals, whose bone-remains are more fossilized than those of the Reindeer Age. Man, at least in our region, belongs to a species different from Modern Man (*Homo sapiens*). Who can hope to have any accurate notion of the duration of this period? And yet, can we refuse to accord to it an impressive number of millennia?

We are still, however, very far from the time at which Man's presence in the countries of Europe has been indubitably proved.

This Man, belonging to very old Palaeolithic times, lived in a physical and biological environment altogether different from that of his successor. The topography and even the geography of the Acheulean and Chellean Periods show further changes of very considerable extent and duration. The seas and land-masses had not yet assumed their present configuration; the British Isles were attached to the Continent; Europe and Africa were connected by land-bridges. The sculpturing of our modern valleys, which was particularly the work of the latter part of the Pliocene, had not yet been completed. This was the period of the middle terraces of the Seine, the Somme, the Garonne, etc. Hundreds of craters, now breached and broken, still illumined the Central Massif of France. The geological formations of the period consist of deposits the antiquity of which is still clearly evident in the alteration undergone by their contents.

As different are the scenes revealed by organic nature. Europe was peopled by Asiatic or African mammals, of which many have long been extinct. Others have changed, and their evolution can only have occurred with very great slowness. The human industries of these very remote times show everywhere the same obvious characteristics. The few bone-remains of the makers of the primitive artefacts reveal types very different from those of today. Everything now fades away in the mists of antiquity. The only chronological impression we can gather from these pictures is of an immense duration of time; the vertigo of immeasurable space begins to overwhelm us.

And so, if none of the figures suggested for the duration of Quaternary times and for the antiquity of Chellean Man can satisfy our desire for precision, none can surprise us and still less can any intimidate us.

Thus, in the table on page 30, we have quadrupled the figures given in the earliest editions of this book for the various geological periods. We have thus come to estimate the total duration of the Quaternary era at 500,000 years. The absolute value of this figure is very debatable, but not its order of magnitude.

Even now, we are only at the dawn of Quaternary times. If, pursuing our giddy course, we penetrate into the Tertiary Era in our search for the real beginnings of Mankind, we must needs count no longer by hundreds, but by thousands of millennia!

CHAPTER THREE

LIVING PRIMATES AND
FOSSIL MONKEYS

BEFORE entering into the heart of our subject, we must make a fresh pre-liminary study. We cannot well understand and appreciate the morphological characteristics of our distant ancestors until we have gained some notion of the general zoological bearings of the Primates and reviewed the dis-coveries relating to fossil Monkeys.

LIVING PRIMATES

The term Primates, 'the first' of the mammals, was created by Linnaeus, who also used the designation *Anthropomorphs.*

The Primates include animals of somewhat different appearance, but distinguished from all other mammals by a combination of the following characters: a large brain-box, containing a highly-developed brain; fore-limbs adapted for grasping, and terminating in hands that have typically flat nails; teeth adapted for a mixed diet and primitive in character; two mammary glands on the breast.

CLASSIFICATION OF THE PRIMATES

As this definition applies to Man as well as to all the other Primates, the classification of the group has been the subject of special discussion. Some naturalists, as Isidore Geoffroy Saint-Hilaire and de Quatrefages,[1] wished to set up a separate kingdom for our species, because of the superiority of its intelligence and its 'religiosity'. But in the classification of animals we do not take as a basis their intellectual characteristics. Why change the method when we come to Man? Linnaeus and Lamarck clearly comprehended this; and Darwin observed that much greater differences are to be found in the class of insects, for example between an ant and a parasitic insect, than be-tween Man and Monkeys; and he added with reason: 'If Man had not been his own classifier, he would never have thought of founding a separate order for his own reception.'[2]

[1] Quatrefages, A. de, *L'espèce humaine* (Paris, 1876); *Introduction à l'étude des races humaines* (1887). See also Vialleton, L., *L'origine des êtres vivants* (Paris, 1929).
[2] Darwin, Charles, *The Descent of Man* (London, 1871, Vol. I, p. 191).

Buffon classified Man as *Bimana*, Monkeys as *Quadrumana*; and Cuvier revived these terms.[3] In the genus *Homo*, Linnaeus included Man and the large Monkeys without tails—the Anthropoid Apes; here he had *Homo sapiens*, with his varieties *ferus*, *europaeus*, *asiaticus*, and the rest, but here also he placed *Homo sylvestris*, or Orang, and *Homo troglodytes*, or Chimpanzee.

Cuvier completely separated Man (Bimana) from Monkeys (Quadrumana), and among the latter he distinguished a lower group under the name of *Lemurs*. Today we may still accept the following general classification:[4]

	Bimana	Arms shorter than legs. Very large brain.	*Men* or *Hominians* Very highly developed Primates
Primates		Orbits completely closed; arms longer than legs	*Monkeys* or *Simians* Primates definite and diversified
	Quadru- mana	Orbits incompletely closed; arms shorter than legs	*Lemurs* Primitive Primates still little differentiated

LEMURS

The Lemurs, also called Prosimians, Pseudo Monkeys, or Fox-Faced Monkeys, have neither the vivacity nor the intelligence of the true Monkeys. The face is hairy instead of smooth. The skull is easily distinguished from a Monkey's skull: the occipital foramen is placed behind as in other mammals; the orbits are widely separated, face sideways, and communicate with the temporal fossa; the lachrymal foramen opens in front of the orbits. The cerebral hemispheres of the Lemurs do not completely cover the cerebellum; their structure is relatively simple. The Lemurs again have their lower incisors set in front and projecting forwards; they have long legs and short arms. They are still very primitive Quadrumana and for the most part lead an arboreal, and often nocturnal, existence.

Formerly widely distributed in America and Europe, they are now found only in Africa (*Galagos*), in Indo-Malaysia (*Loris*, *Tarsius*),[5] and above all

[3] For this they have been critized, and not unreasonably, for *anatomically* the lower extremities of monkeys are *feet*, just like the lower extremities of Man. But Cuvier knew this as well as Huxley or Broca. It was therefore rather in a physiological sense that he used the terms *Bimana* and *Quadrumana*. This reservation made, we may continue to use the terms, especially in such a work as this.

[4] For the history of the classification of the Primates, see Topinard, P., *L'Homme dans la Nature* (Paris, 1891). Gregory, W. K., *The Orders of Mammals* (New York, 1910). Simpson, G., 'The Principles of Classification and a Classification of Mammals' (*Bull. Amer. Museum Nat. Hist.*, Vol. XL, 1945).

[5] On the special position of the Tarsius, see p. 78 below.

in Madagascar, where nine-tenths of the species occur, and where the group was formerly represented by strange giant forms, such as *Megaladapis*.

36 A representative of the Lemurs and of each great group of Monkeys

Above, left: A Lemur, the Pied Lemur (*Lemur varius*), after A. Grandidier. Above, right: a Flat-Nosed or New World Monkey, a Marmoset (*Hapale jacchus*). Below, left: a Flat-Nosed or Cebian Monkey from South America (*Cebus capucinus*), after Elliot. Below, right: an African Long-Nosed Monkey (*Cercopithecus brazzai*), from a specimen in the Natural History Museum of France. Centre: an Anthropoid Ape, the Chimpanzee (*Troglodytes niger*), from a specimen in the collections of the same museum.

SIMIANS

The Monkeys or Simians comprise a graduated series ranging from low and insignificant forms, like the Marmosets, to powerful forms and those most akin to Man, the Anthropoid Apes; but they have a certain number of anatomical characters in common. The brain-box is highly developed in relation to the face, which is fore-shortened. The cerebrum, overlapping the cerebellum and covering it, is divided by fissures into lobes; it shows well-developed convolutions. The occipital foramen lies *beneath* the skull. The orbits, directed forwards, lie in front, are closed by a bony septum, and no longer communicate with the temporal fossa; the lachrymal canal opens into the orbits. The teeth are arranged in a continuous series; the lower incisors are upright like their neighbours, not inclined. The fore-limbs are longer than the hind-limbs. The forearm, gifted with the power

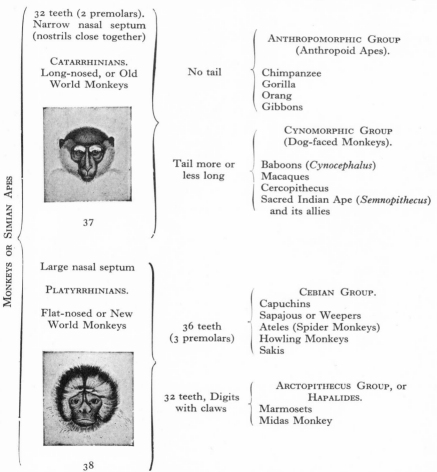

MONKEYS OR SIMIAN APES

CATARRHINIANS.
Long-nosed, or Old World Monkeys

32 teeth (2 premolars).
Narrow nasal septum (nostrils close together)

37

No tail — ANTHROPOMORPHIC GROUP (Anthropoid Apes).
Chimpanzee
Gorilla
Orang
Gibbons

Tail more or less long — CYNOMORPHIC GROUP (Dog-faced Monkeys).
Baboons (*Cynocephalus*)
Macaques
Cercopithecus
Sacred Indian Ape (*Semnopithecus*) and its allies

PLATYRRHINIANS.
Flat-nosed or New World Monkeys

Large nasal septum

38

36 teeth (3 premolars) — CEBIAN GROUP.
Capuchins
Sapajous or Weepers
Ateles (Spider Monkeys)
Howling Monkeys
Sakis

32 teeth, Digits with claws — ARCTOPITHECUS GROUP, or HAPALIDES.
Marmosets
Midas Monkey

of movements both of pronation and supination, has become a perfect instrument for grasping.

Monkeys have expressive faces; their intelligence is superior to that of other mammals. They have strong passions; it has been truly said that they reflect Mankind in its lowest qualities. They inhabit warm or temperate climates, living in trees or among rocks, and feeding on fruit, buds, eggs, and insects.

We may classify the Monkeys as follows:[6]

The ARCTOPITHECIDAE or MARMOSETS (gener *Hapale* and *Midas*) are the smallest of the Monkeys. In certain characteristics they are related to the Lemurs, for their digits are not opposable. They have only 32 teeth, as in the large Monkeys and Man, but they have 3 premolars and 2 molars, in place of 2 molars and 3 molars.

The CEBIANS, like the Marmosets confined to South America, are inferior in organization and intelligence to the Old World Monkeys. Their nostrils are widely separated, their long tails are generally prehensile. The thumb is barely opposable. They have 36 teeth (3 premolars and 3 molars on each side, above and below).

The CATARRHINE or LONG-NOSED MONKEYS of the Old World, with nostrils closer together, have the same dental formula as Man (2 premolars and 3 molars). The CYNOMORPHS or DOG-FACED MONKEYS, of which numerous species are widely distributed in Asia and Africa, are the most common representatives of the Primates in our menageries. Their tails, sometimes rudimentary, as in the Barbary Ape, are never prehensile.

MANLIKE APES (ANTHROPOMORPHS OR ANTHROPOIDS)

The ANTHROPOID or MANLIKE APES (*Anthropomorphs*) are of still greater interest to us as being the higher Monkeys most nearly related to ourselves in their whole organization.[7]

The Gibbons (genus *Hylobates*), of South-Eastern Asia and the Malay Archipelago (Sumatra), are the smallest of the Anthropoids, the largest species, the Siamung, being scarcely 3 feet high. They show certain traces of low degree, suggestive of the tailed Monkeys. Their fore-limbs are very long, but they generally walk erect, and in this, as in certain cranial characters, they resemble Man.

[6] This classification and nomenclature are essentially French. In other countries, the grouping and particularly the terms employed are rather different; and the latter may cause some confusion which it is well to point out. Thus the general group of Monkeys or Simians is sometimes called the *Anthropoidea*, a term long in use in France, concurrently with that of 'Anthropomorphs', to describe the higher monkeys—those most nearly related to ourselves. The Cynomorphic Apes of French authors constitute the *Cercopithecidae* of British authors, and the Anthropomorphic Apes of the former are called *Simiidae* in Britain, a name too closely resembling the expression Simian Apes, used by French writers to describe monkeys as a group.

General works to read or consult regarding the monkeys are: Elliot, D. G., *A Review of the Primates* (New York, 1912) (a large and superb monograph). Sonntag, C., *The Morphology of the Apes and Man* (London, 1924). Weber, M., *Die Säugetiere* (2nd Ed., Jena, 1928). Clark, W. E. le Gros, *Early Forerunners of Man* (London, 1934); *History of the Primates* (London, 1949). Urbain, A., and Rode, P., *Les Singes anthropoïdes* (Paris, 1946). Vallois, H., *Traité de Zoologie* (Vol. XVII, Paris, 1955).

[7] See Hartmann, R., *Les Singes anthropoïdes* (Paris, 1886). Various papers by Owen, Deniker, Selenka and others. Yerkes, R. M., and A. W. *The Great Apes* (New Haven, 1929).

The Orang-Utan (*Pongo pygmaeus*), of Sumatra and Borneo, is much larger and stronger. It is very arboreal in its habits and nests in trees. Its legs are very short; its brain-box is round and high, and bears sagittal and occipital ridges. The males are armed with strong canine teeth.

The Gorillas (genus *Gorilla*) inhabit two different regions of equatorial Africa. There are two sub-species or races. One, less arboreal, frequents the highlands of the east (Belgian Congo); the other lives on the west coast (Gabon and the Cameroons). Largest of the Apes, they are stronger and more robust than Man. Their skull is elongated (dolichocephalic) and, in old males, bears great bony crests, strong supra-orbital ridges and powerful canine teeth. The ears are small.

The Chimpanzees (genus *Troglodytes* or *Pan*), represented by several races or varieties, are also African, inhabiting the equatorial forests of the west. In several respects they resemble Man more closely than do the other Anthropoid Apes. Although the male still possesses stronger canine teeth than the female, sexual dimorphism is nevertheless less marked than in the Gorilla. The skull is also elongated, but it lacks parietal and occipital crests, although the supra-orbital arches are prominent. Such morphological characteristics, together with the playfulness and intelligence of these Apes, add a peculiar interest to the Chimpanzees.

MAN AND HIS GROUP (HOMINIANS OR HOMINIDS)

The HOMINIANS or HOMINIDS comprise one family only, reduced in our day to the single genus *Homo*, a genus the divisions of which have created more disagreement among naturalists than any other in all the class of mammals.

The divergences of the classifications of Modern Man are truly extraordinary: ranging from the monogenistic schemes of Linnaeus, Blumenbach, and Cuvier, with their four or five varieties or races of *Homo sapiens*, and incidentally that of Isidore Geoffroy Saint-Hilaire, with four principal types and twelve secondary races, to modern schemes, such as that of de Quatrefages, with five stems and eighteen branches, themselves dividing into numerous smaller branches; or that of Deniker, who recognizes twenty-nine races and sub-races; to the polygenistic scheme of Sergi, which includes three genera, eleven species and forty-one varieties or sub-species; not to mention the composite scheme of Giuffrida-Ruggeri, etc.[8]

The discussions between 'monogenists' and 'polygenists', resulting in floods of ink, have never reached any settlement of a question which has been described, and with some reason, as 'immaterial'.

Anthropologists have now returned to the ideas of the older naturalists,

[8] Quatrefages, A. de, *Introduction à l'étude des races humaines* (Paris, 1887). Deniker, *Races et peuples de la Terre* (Paris, 2nd Ed., 1926). Sergi, G., *Le Origine umane* (Turin, 1912). Giuffrida-Ruggeri, *L'Uomo attuale* (Milan, Rome, Naples, 1913). Haddon, A. C., *The Races of Man and their Distribution* (Rev. Ed., Cambridge, 1929). Montandon, H., *La race, les races* (Paris, 1933). Eickstedt, E. von, *Rassenkunde und Rassengeschichte der Menschheit* (Stuttgart, 1933). Vallois, H., *Les races humaines* (Paris, 3rd. Ed, 1951).

who divided Modern Man into three main groups: WHITE, YELLOW (including Red-Skins), and BLACK.

According to the monogenists, these three divisions represent only races of the single species *Homo sapiens*. According to the polygenists, they are separate species. (1) *Homo albus* or *Homo caucasicus* (an old and quite inappropriate term), or *Homo indo-europaeus*; (2) *Homo flavus* or *H. mongolicus*; (3) *Homo niger* or *Homo aethiopicus*.

The sub-divisions of these three great groups are usually based much more upon community of language, religion, and morals, than on physical characteristics. They are most often merely ethnographical, a result due to the important part played by migration. Yet even if the hypothesis of the existence of several types, zoologically quite distinct in origin, be admitted, it is clear that innumerable minglings and crossings, repeated during thousands and thousands of years in complex ways, must have markedly reduced the original physical differences, and disguised them under a cloak of more uniform characteristics. This is what makes the task of the physical anthropologist so difficult and unrewarding.[9]

ANATOMICAL DIFFERENCES BETWEEN MAN AND MONKEYS

The anatomical differences separating Man, or the various types of Man, from the highest Monkeys, the Anthropoid Apes, are numerous but of unequal value. These differences we shall have frequent occasion to cite and we must, therefore, now enumerate the most important.[10]

The most significant concerns the great development of the cerebral portion of the skull or brain-box, in which the brain is lodged, and the associated reduction in size of the facial part of the skull (Fig. 39). This relative development of the facial portion, that is to say of the mandibular region, connected with animal functions, and of the cerebral region, set apart for the noble or intellectual functions, is a zoological character of the first importance, as Cuvier long since pointed out: 'Of all the animals, Man has the largest cranium and the smallest face; as animals deviate from these proportions, so they become more stupid or more fierce.'

A second difference, related to the first, is the possession by Man of articulate language. This function implies not only a more highly organized brain, but also certain anatomical arrangements of the tongue and its surroundings which facilitate its working.

Man and the Apes have the same dental formula, but there are differences

[9] Read in this connexion H. Neuville's paper 'L'espèce, la race et le métissage en Anthropologie' (*Archives de l'Institut de Paléontologie humaine*, Mémoire 11, Paris, 1933).

[10] For greater detail, see Huxley, *Man's Place in Nature*. Broca, P., *L'Ordre des Primates* (Paris, 1889). Topinard, P., *L'Homme dans la Nature* (Paris, 1891). Duckworth, W. L. H., *Morphology and Anthropology* (2nd Ed., Vol. I, Cambridge, 1915). Elliot Smith, G., *Essays on the Evolution of Man* (London, 1927). Wood Jones, F., *Man's Place among the Mammals* (London, 1929). Abel, O., *Die Stellung des Menschen im Rahmen der Wirbeltiere* (Jena, 1931). Clark, W. E. Le Gros, *Early Forerunners of Man* (London, 1934). Hooton, E., *Up from the Ape* (New York, 1947).

in the size and shape of the various kinds of teeth. The principal difference relates to the size of the canines, which, highly developed in the Apes, especially in male individuals, are in Man so diminished in size that they

39 Comparative Morphology of the Skull, the Brain, and the Cervical Vertebrae of a Lemur, an Ape, and Modern Man.

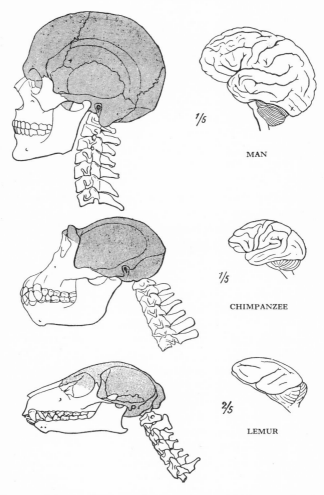

MAN

CHIMPANZEE

LEMUR

In the Pied Lemur (*Lemur varius*), the cerebral portion of the skull (shaded in figure) is small in relation to the facial part. The brain is not large; the cerebrum still lies in front of the cerebellum. The foramen magnum is situated at the hinder portion of the skull; the direction of the vertebral column is obviously in line with the axis of the brain.

In the Ape (Chimpanzee), the cerebral portion of the skull is larger and the facial portion reduced. The brain is larger; the cerebrum has become complicated, and overlaps the cerebellum. The foramen magnum has moved nearer the base of the skull. The vertebral column is more oblique in relation to the axis of the brain; the cervical vertebrae have long spinous processes which stand at right angles to the bodies of the vertebrae.

In modern Man, the cerebral portion of the skull greatly exceeds the facial portion, here reduced to a minimum. The very large cerebrum, highly convoluted, overlaps and extends beyond the cerebellum. The foramen magnum occupies a still more forward position. The vertebral column forms a right angle with the base of the skull; the spinous processes of the cervical vertebrae are inserted obliquely on the vertebral bodies and are directed downwards.

either do not exceed, or exceed only in slight degree, the general level of the other teeth (Fig. 40). This decrease in structures which had formerly served, for example in the Apes, as weapons of offence and defence, must have been effected very gradually, step by step with the attainments of the upright position, of the setting free of the fore-limbs, and of the correlated development of the brain.

The perfectly erect attitude is characteristic of Man alone. The Anthropoid Apes, even the Gibbon, possess it only in an imperfect degree; and this

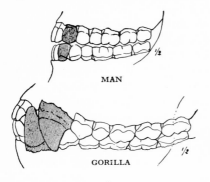

MAN

GORILLA

40 Dentitions, viewed from the side, of a Man and an Ape (Gorilla). One-half natural size. The canines are shaded.

incapacity is accounted for by anatomical differences. In Man, the vertebral column is inserted at the base of the skull, so that, in his normal upright position, the skull is almost naturally balanced on the first vertebrae; and thus the occipital foramen (foramen magnum) lies in a horizontal plane and

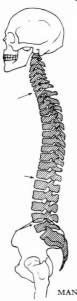

MAN

41 Skull, Vertebral Column, and Pelvis of a Man and a Gorilla.

In the Gorilla, the vertebral column throughout its whole length only shows one single curve, concave in front; its general direction is not vertical. The skull, with heavy face, falls forward, and has to be held back by powerful muscles and ligaments at the nape of the neck. The pelvis is narrow.

In Man, the vertebral column shows several curves, alternately convex and concave in front (the arrows indicate the points where these curves change), in such a way that the whole forms a balanced system on which the head rests naturally in equilibrium, and which extends past the large pelvis in a likewise vertical direction towards the lower limbs.

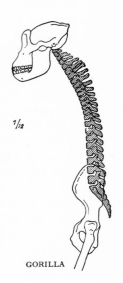

GORILLA

is placed beneath the skull. In the Lemurs, as in almost all four-footed mammals, the axis of the skull and of the vertebral column lie in line with each other, and the occipital foramen, placed almost in a vertical plane, occupies the hinder portion of the skull. In the true Monkeys the occipital foramen has begun to move towards the base of the skull; and in the Anthropoids it approaches, without actually attaining, the human position (Fig. 39).

Certain differences in the vertebral column are also entailed by the more or less erect attitude (Fig. 41). In the Monkeys, whose body is always inclined forward, the column shows only two curves, a dorsal and a sacral, both concave in front. In the unborn or new-born human child, only these two curves occur. At a later stage childish endeavours to stand and walk erect induce a profound modification in the form of the spinal column, which before long shows four curves: a cervical curve, concave behind; a dorsal curve, concave in front; a lumbar curve, concave behind; and a sacral curve, concave in front. As these four curves follow each other alternately, in first one and then the other direction, the general trend of the column is vertical. In this manner, the weight of head and trunk bears principally upon the pelvis, and the direction of the resultant weight plainly falls in line with the general direction of the column, so that equilibrium in an erect posture becomes as easy as possible. Serres made these curves the special attributes of his 'Human Kingdom'.

These modifications in the curves, in their turn, entail modifications in the vertebrae themselves, and particularly of their processes (apophyses), the direction and size of which are determined by muscular action. This is especially evident in the spinous processes of the cervical vertebrae. In consequence of this easy balance in Man which we have just described, the actions of the extensor muscles of the nape of the neck, of the spinal muscles, and of the cervical ligament may be, and indeed are, much less powerful in him than in quadrupeds, whose head and trunk tilt forward. In Man and in the quadrupeds, then, the spinous processes differ both in their development and in their direction (Figs. 39 and 41). And in these characters, Monkeys, and especially the Anthropoid Apes, are intermediate between the exclusively quadruped mammals and Man, the most perfect of the bipeds. Finally, the human races are not all exactly similar to each other, for the lower races, as we shall see later, still preserve certain characteristics of the stage now represented by the Anthropoid Apes.

Further, the form of the pelvis is also correlated with the vertical position and erect gait. In Man, the haunch bones (ilia) are enlarged, widened, and spread out in the form of a bowl or basin, so offering easy support to the abdominal viscera. In Monkeys, the pelvis does not bear all the weight of the intestines, and the much narrower haunch bones are placed almost parallel to the sacrum, thus more closely resembling those of quadrupeds (Fig. 42).

Another difference which Owen, the great English anatomist, considered to be fundamental, is the formation of the foot (Fig. 43). In the Anthropoid Apes, the first toe, widely separated and much shorter than the others, is readily opposable to the latter and plays the part of a thumb. Thus the foot, physiologically speaking, has become a hand (whence the term *Quadrumana*). In Man, the great toe is the largest of the digits and is closely pressed against the others, to which it cannot be opposed. Here we have a true foot, that is to say, an organ for support; and this exclusive adaptation to a particular function is reflected in all the bones of the human foot, for their structures differ from those of the corresponding bones of the hind hand, or shall we say the prehensile foot of Anthropoid Apes.

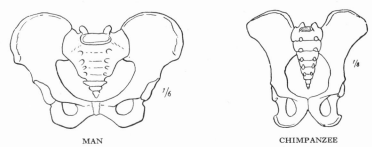

MAN   CHIMPANZEE

42 Comparative structures of the pelvis of Man and of an Ape (Chimpanzee)

In spite of the existence of some transitional grades of structure, observed in certain Monkeys and Man, all these characters are practically so definite that there can be absolutely no confusion between the most highly-developed of living Monkeys and the lowest of living Men.

It must therefore be acknowledged that zoology, the teachings of which we

43 Foot of Man and of a Gorilla

have just summarized, defines with tolerable clearness the boundaries of Man's place in Nature. Can palaeontology supply any supplementary hints regarding the relationships between Monkeys and Man? To answer this question we must first review the discoveries bearing on fossil Monkeys, and this we shall now do briefly, in chronological order.

FOSSIL MONKEYS

THE EOCENE PRIMATES

The precursors of the great group of Primates appeared simultaneously in Europe and North America towards the base of the Eocene, almost at the beginning of the Tertiary Era, when the archaic representatives of other orders of mammals also appeared. But for the most part they were still only generalized forms, difficult to distinguish from closely related groups.

Among the latter were the Eocene Plesiadapidae (*Plesiadapis, Eochiromys*, etc.), small arboreal animals the size of a mouse or a squirrel and belonging simultaneously to the Insectivores, the Rodents and the Primates. The curious *Chiromys* or 'Aye-Aye' of Madagascar is probably the last representative of this ancient family, about which our knowledge is still incomplete.

From the lower Eocene onwards, true Lemurs were also represented in the Old and New Worlds. Certain forms, such as *Pelycodus* and *Notharctus*

44 Skull of a Lemur from the phosphorites at Quercy (*Adapis magnus*). Three-fifths natural size. Palaeontological Gallery of the French National Museum of Natural History

in America and *Protoadapis* in Europe, which were omnivorous in diet and possessed elongated skulls, may be considered primitive forms of modern types.[11]

Lemur remains become abundant in the Mid and Upper Eocene of Europe. The rich phosphorite deposits at Quercy have yielded complete skulls, excellently preserved, of such animals as *Adapis*[12] and *Pronycticebus*. The latter is remarkable for its primitive characteristics. *Adapis* differed from living Lemurs by its strong sagittal ridge and the presence in each jaw of four premolars instead of three (Fig. 44).

The Lemurs seem, therefore, to have been born on a northern Americano-European continent, the former existence of which is revealed by geology.

[11] Osborn, H. F., 'American Eocene Primates' (*Bulletin of the American Museum*, XVI, 1902). Matthew, W. D., (*Ibid.*, XXXIV, 1915). Gregory, W. K., 'On the Structure and Relations of *Notharctus*' (*Memoirs of the American Museum*, New Series, Vol. II, Part II, 1920). Gidley, J. W., 'Paleocene Primates of the Fort Union with discussion of relationships of Eocene Primates' (*Proceed. of the U.S. Nat. Museum*, Vol. LXIII, 1923). For everything relating to the Lemurs and the fossil monkeys, see in particular Abel, O., *Die Stellung des Menschen im Rahmen der Wirbeltiere* (Jena, 1931).

[12] Filhol, H., *Recherches sur les phosphorites du Quercy* (Paris, 1877).

They disappeared from Europe and America with the Upper Eocene or the beginning of Oligocene times. They emigrated to Asia and Africa, and especially to Madagascar, where they have persisted to the present day and have become differentiated and split up into numerous branches, some of which developed into giant specialized forms. These include *Megaladapis*, an animal of large proportions and strikingly bestial aspect with a tiny brain in a skull a foot long, and *Archaeolemur* and *Hadropithecus*, which on the contrary, had short muzzles and a large brain-box and therefore diverged from the normal Lemur type and approached that of the Simians.[13] We are confronted here by a tendency that may also be observed in the other groups of Primates: evolution in the direction of a larger brain.

45 *Tarsius spectrum*, about one-half natural size

In the Eocene formations of Europe and North America, where they accompany the true Lemurs we have just been discussing, there have been found some genera of small animals with reduced faces and very large orbits bearing a clear resemblance to the modern Tarsier of the forests of the Malay Archipelago (Fig. 45). This latter animal has an immense brain in relation to its face, with very large eyes indicative of a nocturnal life. It takes its name from the fact that its tarsus (instep) is greatly elongated, as in all jumping animals. It partially fills the gap between the Lemurs and the true Monkeys, of which it possesses several characteristics, such as orbits completely closed at the back, an occipital foramen situated further forward, and incisor teeth that are not inclined. Thus the single species is sometimes elevated to the status of a sub-order including various fossil forms, which are of considerable importance in relation to the problem of the origin of Man.

The oldest of these forms (Lower Eocene) is *Tetonius* (formerly *Anaptomorphus*) *homunculus*, so named by Cope—who described it as a common

[13] Grandidier, G., 'Recherches sur les Lémuriens disparus' (*Nouvelles Archives du Muséum*, 1905). Lamberton, 'Contribution à la connaissance de la faune subfossile de Madagascar' (*Mémoires de l'Académie malgache*. Section XVII, 1934, and Section XXVII, 1939).

ancestor of the Monkeys and Man—because of its rounded skull and the relatively great volume of its brain (Fig. 46).

Other genera, closely related to the foregoing, have been discovered in the Mid Eocene of America and the Upper Eocene of France. In particular, the Quercy phosphorites have yielded *Necrolemur* and *Pseudoloris*. The latter, according to Teilhard de Chardin, showed all the cranial characters of the Tarsier, from which it differed only by its smaller stature and slightly less reduced face.[14]

Like the true Lemurs, these *Tarsiidae* suddenly disappeared from Europe and North America at the end of Eocene times. The modern Tarsier—a sort of enlarged *Pseudoloris*—now confined to a few islands of the Malay Archipelago, is one of the last vestiges of the Primate fauna that peopled France during the Eocene.

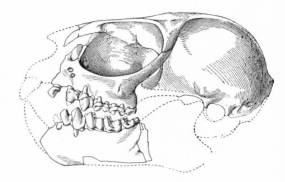

46 Skull of *Tetonius homunculus* from the Lower Eocene of the United States. Enlarged two times. (After Matthew and Granger)

The most ancient forms of the Primates likewise spread from North America to South America. It is probable that, by the loss of a premolar, and the increase of their brain-box at the expense of their face, they became transformed into true Monkeys, the ancestors of the modern Flat-Nosed Monkeys (Platyrrhinians).

In an Oligocene or Miocene deposit in South America, known as the *Santa-Cruzian*, there have actually been found remains of old-time Sapajous, to which the late Argentine palaeontologist, Ameghino, attached the greatest importance, considering them 'as the ancestors of all the Monkeys of the Old and the New Continent', and even of Man. He gave them very expressive names: *Homunculus patagonicus, Anthropops perfectus*, and so on.[15] They are certainly interesting relics; but they are very fragmentary, and quite insufficient to support Ameghino's far-reaching conclusions. For the present they may simply be regarded as ancestral forms of the modern Cebians or Flat-Nosed (Platyrrhinian) Monkeys, a group the evolution and differentiation of which has taken place and is still in process in that very country.

Although fossil Monkeys are absolutely unknown in North America, Ameghino nevertheless announced the existence of higher Monkeys in South America, on account of certain anatomical remains which have been the subject of much discussion. The late palaeontologist has described an

[14] *Annales de Paléontologie*, Vol. X, 1921, p. 3.

[15] Ameghino, F., 'Les formations sédimentaires du Crétacé supérieur et du Tertiaire de Patagonie' (*Anales del Museo nacional de Buenos Aires*, XV, 1906).

atlas vertebra and a femur from Monte Hermoso, which he considers a
Miocene locality, but which the majority of geologists and palaeontologists
who have studied the sedimentary deposits of South America regard as
scarcely even Pliocene. He sought to prove that these bones belonged to a
creature which united his *Homunculus* to the genus *Homo*, and which he
named *Tetraprothomo*, attributing to it a stature of 3 to 4 feet. He was thus
led to conceive a complete new human phylogeny: *Tetraprothomo* was said
to have been followed by *Triprothomo*, this by *Diprothomo*, which was
supposed to have given rise to *Prothomo*, from which in its turn arose the
genus *Homo*. We shall see later that these stages were pure figments of the
imagination.[16]

OLIGOCENE MONKEYS

To return to the Old World. Until recently it was impossible to affirm
that the Catarrhine or Long-Nosed Monkeys were very old in the geological
sense of the word. Dog-Faced Monkeys (Cynomorphs) and Anthropoid
Apes seemed to appear simultaneously
in the Miocene, and the first fossil
Anthropoids were even older than the
known fossils of tailed Monkeys. Such
a state of affairs justified the expect-
ation of important discoveries in the
older deposits. About forty years ago
one such discovery was made.

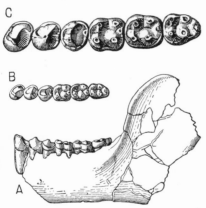

The Eocene and Oligocene deposits
at Fayum in Egypt are famous for
their palaeontological treasures, and
particularly for the remains of primitive
Proboscidians, which form the subject
of important works by Andrews. In
1910 Schlosser announced the discovery of remains of several Primates in
the Oligocene deposits at Fayum, and
soon afterwards he published a detailed
memoir on these curious fossils.[17]

47 Lower jawbone of *Propliopithecus
haeckeli.* (After Schlosser)

A, side view, natural size. B, teeth
seen from above. C, the same teeth
enlarged two times.

Of the three species described, all
of small size, as is usual in archaic forms, two (*Parapithecus* and *Apidium*)
bear some resemblance to the Eocene Lemurs of the United States, while
already constituting primitive forms of Monkeys. They are evidence of an
evolutionary stage from which may be derived, according to Schlosser, all
the higher Primates, Man as well as Apes.

[16] For further details and bibliography, see that part of the last chapter but one of this book
dealing with 'Fossil Man in South America'.
[17] Schlosser, M., 'Beiträge zur Kenntnis der oligozänen Landsäugetiere aus dem Fayum'
(*Beiträge zur Paläontologie und Geologie Oesterreich-Ungarns*, XXIV, 1911). Summary
with figures in *L'Anthropologie*, XXIII, p. 417.

The third species has been given the very suggestive name of *Proplio-pithecus Haeckeli* (Fig. 47). This Monkey is represented by two lower jawbones, and Schlosser considered it to be very closely related to the Gibbons (*Pliopithecus*) from the Mid Miocene deposits at Sansan and other localities. This form may possibly be a descendant from a species of the *Anaptomorphus* group, which had passed perhaps through a Cebian stage, and given rise directly to *Pliopithecus*, from which both the Anthropoids and Man may have been derived.

Certain of Schlosser's views on the phylogeny of Monkeys and of Man have been criticized as being based on too incomplete evidence, and consequently as being very rash. Nevertheless one main fact is brought out in his work: the presence, in a Lower Tertiary, or at any rate an Oligocene deposit, of several generalized forms of true Monkeys, and particularly of one form which might pass for a primitive type of Anthropoid Ape.

MIOCENE MONKEYS:

PROCONSUL

The Miocene deposits of various countries have yielded fairly numerous remains of Monkeys showing very distinct affinities with living forms.

Pliopithecus antiquus (Fig. 48), discovered by Édouard Lartet in 1837 in the Mid Miocene at Sansan (Gers) (see Chap. I) and subsequently found in certain contemporaneous formations in several European countries, was related to the Gibbons,[18] and we have just seen that Schlosser regarded it as a direct descendant of the Egyptian *Propliopithecus*. Between these two, however, there was thought to be interposed a more primitive form that was intermediate in terms of its dentition—*Prohylobates* from the Lower Miocene deposits of Egypt, described twenty years ago by Fourteau.[19]

Limnopithecus, discovered by Hopwood[20] in the Miocene formations of Kenya, also presents characteristics

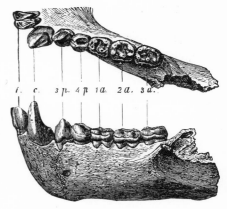

48 Lower jaw of *Pliopithecus antiquus* from Miocene deposits at Sansen, seen in profile and from above. Natural size.

i, incisors; *c*, canines; *3p*, *4p*, premolars; *1a*, *2a*, *3a*, molars. After A. Gaudry. Palaeontological Gallery of the National Natural History Museum of France.

[18] Lartet, É., *Comptes Rendus de l'Académie des Sciences* (January 16 and April 17, 1837).

[19] Fourteau, R., 'Contribution à l'étude des Vertébrés miocènes de l'Égypte *(Ministry of France, Egypt Survey Department, 1920).*

[20] Hopwood, A., 'Miocene Primates from Kenya' (*Journal Linnaean Soc. London, Zool.*, XXXVIII, 1933).

of the archaic Gibbon and, like *Pliopithecus*, is very probably derived from *Propliopithecus*. Certain features of specialization in this Primate nevertheless lead to the supposition that it developed along an independent branch. It would thus appear that two distinct branches, one African, the other European, issued from the Oligocene *Propliopithecus*.

In the same formations as *Limnopithecus*—notably on the island of Rusinga in Lake Victoria Nyanza—first Hopwood and then Leakey brought to light abundant remains of a large Anthropoid which they considered the direct ancestor of the Chimpanzee and therefore called *Proconsul*, after Consul, a chimpanzee at that time in the London Zoo (Fig. 49). But the Miocene form lacks certain characters of specialization that are very typical of modern Anthropoids:[21] the protrusion of the face is less pronounced; the skull-cap has no sagittal crest; the eyebrow arches have not developed into a torus; the lower margin of the symphysis of the chin is not prolonged in a simian plate. Everything goes to show that these Miocene Anthropoids of East Africa were still very close to the ancestral line of the Cynomorphic Apes.

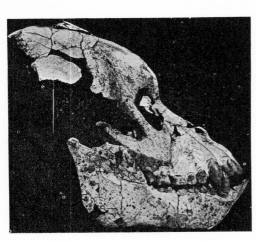

49 Skull of *Proconsul africanus* from the Miocene of Kenya. Half natural size. (After Le Gros Clark and Leakey)

DRYOPITHECUS

A geological horizon in South France, very like that at Sansan, the calcareous sand of Saint-Gaudens, has yielded several remains of large Monkeys. A jawbone was first described in 1856 by Édouard Lartet under the name *Dryopithecus fontani*.[22] This find caused a great sensation, for Édouard Lartet and Albert Gaudry declared that *Dryopithecus* was more closely akin to Man than any other known Monkey.[23] But in 1890, the discovery of a more complete and better preserved lower jawbone (Fig. 50) enabled Gaudry[24] to show that this fossil Monkey was in reality lower in the scale of life than

[21] Le Gros Clark, W. and Leakey, L., 'The Miocene Hominoidea of East Africa' (*British Museum: Fossil Mammals of Africa*, No. 1, London, 1951).

[22] Lartet, É., 'Note sur un grand Singe fossile qui se rattache au groupe des Singes supérieurs' (*Comptes Rendus de l'Acad. des Sciences*, XLII, July 28, 1856).

[23] Gaudry, A., *Les enchaînements du monde animal. Mammifères tertiaires* (Paris, 1878) p. 236.

[24] Gaudry, A., 'Le Dryopithèque' (*Mém. de la Soc. géolog. de France, Paléontologie*, No. 1, Paris, 1890).

the large living Anthropoids. Fragments of even less significance, consisting for the most part merely of isolated teeth, have been found in other countries of Europe (*Anthropodus* in Swabia, *Gryphopithecus* in Hungary), in Africa (Egypt and perhaps Uganda), and—as we shall see—in India. Taken as a whole, they show a much more advanced stage of evolution than *Proconsul* or *Limnopithecus*: in particular, they possess a well-developed simian plate on the lower jaw (Fig. 50).

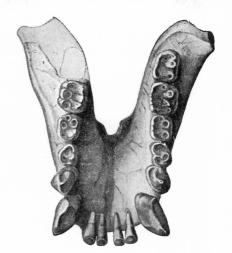

The Upper Miocene at Eppelsheim yielded a femur to which the name *Pliohylobates* (= *Paidopithex*) was given, and which was held to belong to a Monkey allied to the Gibbon, but which should probably be ascribed to *Dryopithecus*.

In addition to the foregoing finds, all of which belong to Anthropoids, there were others involving Monkeys that could, without difficulty, be assigned to the Cynomorphs. Generally speaking, they represent synthetic types. This is true of *Oreopithecus bambolii* from the Upper Miocene for-

50 Lower jawbone of *Dryopithecus fontani* from Saint-Gaudens. Three-quarters natural size. Palaeontological Gallery, French National Museum of Natural History.

mations of Monte Bamboli in Tuscany, which was studied first by Gervais,[25]

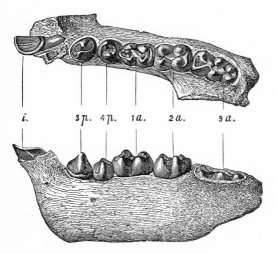

i.   3 *p.*   4 *p.*   1 *a.*   2 *a.*   3 *a.*

51 Lower jawbone of *Oreopithecus bambolii* from the Miocene deposits of Tuscany, seen in profile and from above. Natural size.

i, incisors; 3*p*, 4*p*, premolars; 1*a*, 2*a*, 3*a*, molars. (After A. Gaudry)

and then by Ristori and Schwalbe, and which is said to resemble at one

[25] Gervais, P., *Zoologie et Paléontologie générales* (2nd Series, Paris, 1876) p. 9.

and the same time the Dog-Headed Baboon (*Cynocephalus*), the Long-Tailed Monkeys, and the Anthropoid Apes (Fig. 51).

Mesopithecus pentelici, discovered by Gaudry at Pikermi, Greece, and the

52 Skeleton of *Mesopithecus pentelici*, from the Upper Miocene at Pikermi in Greece. About one-sixth natural size. (After A. Gaudry)

first fossil Monkey of which the whole skeleton has been found (Fig. 52) is intermediate in form between two living types, the Macaque and the Sacred Indian Ape (*Semnopithecus*).[26]

FOSSIL MONKEYS OF THE SIWALIK HILLS

The Siwalik Hills, chains of hills or mountains in Northern India, foothills of the Himalayas, are well known to palaeontologists on account of the rich faunas of fossil vertebrates contained in their layers, the age of which varies from Mid Miocene to Upper Pliocene. These faunas include several species of Monkeys which have been studied by two English palaeontologists, Lydekker and Pilgrim.[27]

Some are Dog-Faced Monkeys (*Cynomorphs*): Sacred Indian Apes (*Semnopithecus*), Short-Tailed Baboons, Macaques and *Cereopithecus*. Others, more interesting in connexion with the present discussion, belong to several genera of Anthropoid Apes (*Simiidae*), and these all lived towards the end of Miocene times.

First of all, there is the European genus *Dryopithecus*, rediscovered by Pilgrim in the Siwalik Hills, where it is represented by three species, one of them a giant of its kind (*D. giganteus*). If to these three species be added the European forms, the genus *Dryopithecus* seems to embrace a group of

[26] Gaudry, A., *Animaux fossiles et géologique de l'Attique* (Paris, 1862).

[27] Lydekker, R., 'Indian Tertiary and Post-Tertiary Vertebrata' (*Palaeontologia Indica*, Series X, Vol. IV, 1886). Pilgrim, G. E. ,'New Siwalik Primates' (*Records Geological Survey of India*, XLV, 1915). *Id.*, 'A *Sivapithecus* Palate and other Primate Fossils from India' (*Palaeontologia Indica*, New Series, Vol. XIV, 1927).

Anthropoid Apes having manifold variations and forming a special branch now extinct. Certain of its smaller branchlets appear to have been fairly closely related to modern Chimpanzees and Gorillas, with, however, certain rather more primitive characters. Others would seem to have been more closely related, judging at least from the characters of their dentition, to the human stock, as Lartet and Gaudry first believed. A similar opinion was expressed by Gregory in America and by Sera in Italy.[28] *Dryopithecus* would seem then to have been an ancestral and synthetic form.

Further there is the genus *Palaeosimia*, which may be considered a direct progenitor or collateral relation of the Orangs (*Simia*).

Finally, there is the genus *Sivapithecus* (Fig. 53), discovered and described by Pilgrim, who did not hesitate in his first memoir to place this new fossil Primate among the Hominians, because of the general shape of its lower jaw and because its back molars looked more human than those of any known Monkey. The characters of this fossil, he declared, compel us to regard it as a direct progenitor of the Hominians—a conclusion whose importance contrasted with the slightness of the evidence on which it was based.

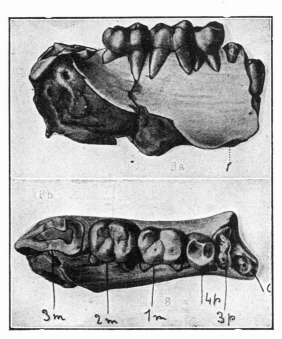

53 Portion of right lower jaw of *Sivapithecus indicus*. Natural size. (After Pilgrim)

Lydekker, who was the first to study the fossil Monkeys of the Siwalik Hills, at once raised doubts as to the value of the new genus; he questioned whether it might not be a form whose upper dentition he had already described, and to which he had given the name *Palaeopithecus*. This comment has been borne out by later discoveries; but since Lydekker's term had been applied earlier to a fossil reptile, it had to give way to Pilgrim's, and the

[28] Gregory, W. K., 'Studies on the Evolution of the Primates' (*Bull. of the Amer. Mus. Nat. Hist.*, XXXV, 1916); *The Origin and Evolution of the Human Dentition* (1921). *Id.* and Hellman, M., 'The Dentition of *Dryopithecus* and the Origin of Man' (*Anthrop. Papers of the Amer. Mus. Nat. Hist.*, XXVIII, 1926). Sera, G. L., 'La testimonia dei fossili Antropomorfi per la questione dell'origine dell'Uomo' (*Atti della Società italiana di Scienze naturali*, LVI, 1917).

genus *Sivapithecus* includes the former *Palaeopithecus*. On the other hand it must not be forgotten that, apart from the presence of a strong canine, the characteristics that truly distinguish Apes from Man occur in the skull and the extremities—that is to say on parts of the skeleton which in the case of the genus *Sivapithecus* are still unknown to us, and in consequence its place in the classification cannot be established with any certainty.[29] Gregory regards it as being allied to *Dryopithecus* and the Orang rather than to Man.

Subsequently, in 1927, Pilgrim described other species of *Sivapithecus* from the definitely Upper Miocene of the Himalayas, but by this time he was far less sure of the affinities of this genus with Man. The discovery of a well-preserved palate (Fig. 56) showed its resemblance to the Chimpanzee.

G. E. Lewis[30] has recently described, under the names of *Ramapithecus*, *Bramapithecus* and *Sugrivapithecus*, fragments of jaw and teeth from the upper strata of the Siwalik Hills. According to the author, these new genera, and especially the first-named, bear a much closer resemblance to the Hominians than any other known Monkey.

These new investigations are exceptionally interesting. They show that during the Miocene period Europe, Asia and Africa were inhabited by numerous Anthropoid Apes with characteristics diverging in several different directions, and perhaps even in a certain degree—as in the case of *Dryopithecus*, *Sivapithecus* and *Ramapithecus*—towards the human type. They have made known to us new types, exhibiting in their jaws and teeth characters representing a new *morphological* transition between the Anthropoids and Man. These are valuable results, to which we shall have occasion to return.

PLIOCENE AND QUATERNARY MONKEYS

In Europe, Pliocene deposits contain various remains of Cynomorphs, but now, even more than in previous ages, we have to deal only with animals closely akin to the genera and even to the species of the present day: Macaques from Montpellier, Tegelen (the Netherlands) and the Val d'Arno (Italy); *Dolicopithecus* from Perpignan, closely related to *Mesopithecus* from Pikermi; and *Semnopithecus* from Montpellier and Italy.

During the Lower Pleistocene Period, Monkeys very near to the modern Macaques lived in various parts of Europe—in England, in Wurtemberg, in the Pyrenees, and in Sardinia. Here the difference is reduced to nothing more important than a difference in the geographical distribution of the species.

On the other hand, no credence should be attached to so-called discoveries of Anthropoid Apes in the Quaternary deposits of Europe. A tooth

[29] For more detail, see the critical analysis of Pilgrim's Memoir in *L'Anthropologie*, Vol. XXVI, 1915, p. 397.

[30] Lewis, G. E., 'Preliminary Notice of New Man-Like Apes from India' (*Amer. Journ. of Science*, XXVII, 1934). Gregory, W. K., Hellman, M. and Lewis, G. E., *Fossil Anthropoids of the Yale-Cambridge India Expedition of 1935* (Carnegie Instit. of Washington, Publication No. 495, 1938).

found in the alluvials at Taubach, which was compared with the teeth of the Chimpanzee, is in reality human, as was already shown by Nehring (see Chap. VI, Fig. 104).

In 1922, several eminent American palaeontologists examined a molar found in Pliocene formations in Nebraska and attributed it to an Anthropoid Ape combining characteristics of the Chimpanzee, *Pithecanthropus* and Man. This *Hesperopithecus*, which was made the type of a family, or even a 'superfamily', was greeted with great scepticism by European palaeontologists. It was not until five years later, in 1927, that the American scientists recognized their error: the famous molar had belonged to a mandible of *Prosthenops*, one of the Suidae akin to the Peccary. The Nebraska Ape-Man became a Pig-Man!

In point of fact, only Asia and Africa—the two continents in which Anthropoid Apes still live—contain representatives of this group from the Pliocene onwards. Apart from the Siwalik Hills, Asia—notably in the Pleistocene deposits of Southern China—has yielded numerous teeth of an Orang that seems very closely allied to the species now living in Indonesia.[31] Some exceptionally large teeth found in the same deposits have been ascribed to a special genus, *Gigantopithecus*, which Weidenreich considered a Human and held to be the ancestor of *Pithecanthropus* (see Chap. V). But by far the most important discoveries were those made in Africa.

AUSTRALOPITHECUS

In 1925, Professor Dart of Johannesburg announced the discovery of a large Primate, *Australopithecus africanus*, which, he said, represented far more fully than the Javan *Pithecanthropus* the eagerly sought-for intermediate form between the Great Apes and Man.[32]

This fossil had been extracted, along with numerous remains of Baboons, from a calcareous tufa quarried at Taungs, a locality eighty miles north of Kimberley, South Africa (Fig. 274), belonging geologically to the Lower Pleistocene Period. It consisted of an incomplete skull, with a natural endocranial cast and a well-preserved face, belonging to a young individual (about 6 years old) having as yet only one permanent molar (Fig. 54).

Dart's statement was received with cautious reserve. The appearance of the head is indeed very similar to that of a chimpanzee or gorilla of the same age: the flattening of the upper part of the face and the nose, the prognathism of the jaws, the absence of a chin, and the large size of the orbits, are distinctly Anthropoid characters. Keith nevertheless laid stress on the great volume of the cranial capacity—500 cubic centimetres—which must have corresponded to a capacity of more than 600 cubic centimetres

[31] Hooijer, D., 'Prehistoric Teeth of Man and of the Orang-Utan from Central Sumatra, with notes on the fossil Orang-Utan from Java and Southern China' (*Zoologische Mededeelingen*, Vol. XXIX, 1948).

[32] Dart, R., '*Australopithecus africanus*: the Man-Ape of South Africa' (*Nature*, February 7, 1925).

in the adult—roughly equal to that of the largest male gorillas. On the other hand, *Australopithecus* exhibits no trace of a supra-orbital ridge. Finally its teeth, the extrication of which was a long and difficult undertaking, showed very human characteristics.[33]

These observations did not seem sufficiently conclusive, however, and most anthropologists took the view that this was a form belonging to the

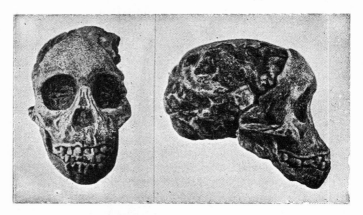

54 Skull of *Australopithecus africanus*, orientated approximately along the auriculo-orbital line. One-third natural size

group of living Anthropoids—a Chimpanzee or perhaps a Gorilla, with some additional 'humanoid' tendencies. New finds were soon to revive the question.

In 1936 Dr. Broom announced the discovery at Sterkfontein, a few miles west of Johannesburg, in the breccia from an old cave, of part of a skull belonging to an Ape that appeared to be very closely allied to the Taungs Ape, which he first named *Australopithecus transvaalensis* and later *Plesianthropus*. This time the skull belonged to an adult individual. Other discoveries followed in rapid succession, some at Sterkfontein, others in the nearby quarry of Kromdraai, where the remains corresponded to a slightly different type—*Paranthropus robustus*. These investigations, which were interrupted during the war, were resumed in 1947, and a third deposit, at Swartkrans, produced yet another form of very great stature—*Paranthropus crassidens*. Finally Dart, exploring the bone breccias at Makapansgat, 120 miles north of Pretoria, in 1947 and 1948, discovered an occipital bone and various other remains, to which he gave the name *Australopithecus prometheus*.

There can be no doubt that, despite these various appellations—which correspond to morphological differences that are almost always of a minor character and some of them probably only individual variations—the aforementioned finds must all be placed in a single zoological group, which may

[33] Keith, A., *New Discoveries relating to the Antiquity of Man* (1931) pp. 37–116. Abel, W., 'Kritische Untersuchungen über *Australopithecus africanus*' (*Morphologisches Jahrbuch*, LXV, 1931).

be given the inclusive name of Australopithecinae. A very considerable amount of material relating to this group has now been accumulated. Of *Plesianthropus* alone, the best represented form, five well preserved skulls have been found and eight in fairly good condition, as well as more than 200 teeth. Fragments of ribs and vertebrae, of the pelvis and of the limb bones have also been recovered. Our knowledge of these fossil Primates of Southern Africa, which were for so long a mystery, has now greatly increased. A certain number of facts may therefore be considered as established.[34]

GENERAL CHARACTERS

Taken as a whole, the head has an apelike appearance (Fig. 55), with a highly developed face that protrudes in a snout and contrasts with the comparatively restricted dimensions of the cranium.

As in all Anthropoids, the cranial vault is low; the forehead is very slanting; the mastoid apophysis is extremely reduced; the retro-mastoid portion of the temporal bone is carried back to the rear surface of the cranium. The pronounced protrusion of the facial mass is altogether reminiscent of the Chimpanzee; but the prognathism is somewhat less marked, particularly in the upper region of the face, where the angle of the orbital orifice is vertical, and not oblique as in Monkeys.

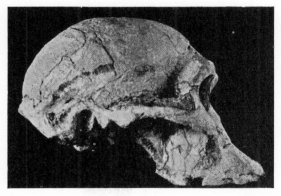

55 Skull of a female *Plesianthropus transvaalensis*. Roughly one-third natural size. (After Broom and Robinson)

In addition to the foregoing characteristics, however, there are a number of others that diverge considerably from those of Anthropoids. The cranial capacity has been calculated in respect of several adults. Leaving out of account figures based on specimens that are too incomplete, it fluctuates between 450 and 600 cubic centimetres, that is between the capacity of the Chimpanzee and the Gorilla. In relation to the general proportions of the body, therefore, the cerebral volume is really high.

The cranium is striking by its very slight development and the complete

[34] The literature on the subject is very copious. The main facts are set out in two important monographs: Broom, R. and Schepers, G., *The South African Fossil Ape-Men: the Australopithecinae* (Pretoria, 1946). Broom, R., Robinson, J. and Schepers, G., *Sterkfontein Ape-Man Plesianthropus* (Pretoria, 1950). The following should also be read: Le Gros Clark, W., 'Observations on the Anatomy of the Fossil *Australopithecinae*' (*Journ. of Anatomy*, Vol. LXXXI, 1947). Dart, R., Several articles on *Australopithecus prometheus*, in *Amer. Journ. of Phys. Anthr.*, Vols. VI and VII, 1948 and 1949.

absence of the supra-orbital ridge or torus, so characteristic of existing African Anthropoids. The temporal lines remain separate from the median line of the calvarium, so that there is no sagittal crest, not even in the male. The occipital ridge is slight and placed very low, recalling the skull formation in primitive human races. Other features, relating to the sutures at the base of the skull and the walls of the orbit, are absolutely identical with those of Man, and like Man the glenoid cavity of the temporal bone is narrow and deep, instead of wide and shallow as in the Anthropoids. An unexpected

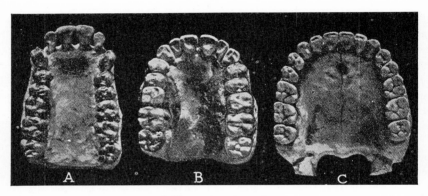

56 Upper dental arcade

A, *Sivapithecus sivalensis;* B, *Plesianthropus transvaalensis;* C, Heidelberg Man reconstructed after the lower jaw. About half natural size. (After W. C. Gregory and M. Hellman)

fact is, finally, the position of the occipital foramen, which is situated distinctly farther forward than in the Anthropoids, while behind it the base of the skull exhibits an almost horizontal segment. An organization of this nature indicates that the head was held far higher in relation to the spinal column than is the case with Apes. It implies a posture approaching the vertical—an observation of the greatest importance.

The lower jaw is thick and massive, generally apelike in shape, with a powerful ramus, and the anterior of the symphysis is receding. But the simian plate is lacking, which recalls the primitive type *Proconsul.*

If the foregoing characters show a mingling of simian and human features, those of the dentition belong mainly to the second category. As long as sixteen years ago, Gregory and Hellman[35] drew attention to the shape of the dental arcade of *Australopithecus,* whose curve is similar to our own, instead of having the U curve of modern Anthropoids (Fig. 56). A study of the teeth shows parallel facts. As in Man, the incisors are small. The canines, though bigger and stronger than ours, barely rise above the level of the incisors; they are very different from the powerful canines of the Great Apes. Instead

[35] Gregory, W. and Hellman, M., 'The Dentition of the Extinct South African Man-Ape *Australopithecus (Plesianthropus) transvaalensis* Broom' (*Ann. Transvaal Museum,* XIX, 1939, p. 303).

of terminating, as among the latter, in a conical point, the first premolars are bicusped as in modern Man. The pattern of the molars and the manner in which they are worn are very reminiscent of our own—indeed the first milk molar is such that, if it had been found in isolation, it would unhesitatingly have been declared human.

A study of the limb-bones is no less interesting. Examination of the fragments discovered by Broom—in particular, the extremities of the humerus and femur and the ankle bone—already revealed manifest differences from modern Anthropoids. Without displaying a categoric resemblance to those of Man, these fragments led to the belief that the limbs of *Australopithecus* were not adapted to the exclusively arboreal life of the Great Apes. This conclusion was disputed. But the finding of important parts of the pelvis reinforced it. Whereas in modern Apes the segment of the iliac bone situated above the hip joint, the ilium, is long and narrow, in *Australopithecus* it forms a broad, spreading plate entirely reminiscent of its shape in Man (Fig. 57). The stance of the lower limbs was therefore the same as our own. Taken in conjunction with the position of the occipital foramen, this leaves no doubt that *Australopithecus* had a roughly upright posture. He may be pictured as a small creature, doubtless about the same size as the Chimpanzee, with an apelike head and

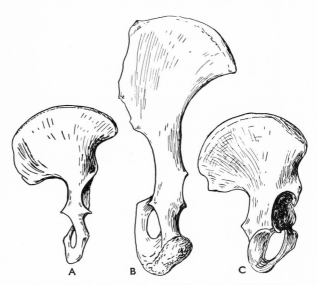

57 Comparison between the right iliac bone of: A, *Plesian-thropus;* B, Chimpanzee; C, young Bushman. One-quarter natural size. (After Broom and Robinson)

powerful jaws, but a less reduced cranium than the Anthropoids and a dentition very like our own. He walked on two legs, and the proportions of his limbs were human rather than simian.

Conclusions

What place are we, then, to assign to these fossil Primates from Southern Africa, and, more especially, what is their exact relationship to Man, with whom they share so many characteristics? Three hypotheses have been advanced: (1) They are true Anthropoids, allied to the Gorilla and Chimpanzee, although possessing certain features curiously reminiscent of Man.

This opinion, which was supported by, amongst others, Abel and Schwartz, was widely held at a time when the Taungs skull was the only one known. (2) At the opposite extreme, Dart, and later Broom and Le Gros Clark, declare categorically that the Australopithecinae are already Hominids, their resemblances to Man being far too numerous to be explained otherwise than by a direct relationship. If they were not our ancestors, they were at least closely related to the first Men, in which case they must be a collateral branch of the Human stock that died out without issue. (3) The majority of palaeontologists subscribe to a theory that is, in a sense, intermediate between the two foregoing. According to this view, the Australopithecinae are a group of Anthropoids in the process of evolving towards humanity, but which never crossed the 'threshold' to this condition and vanished without having become truly human. It cannot be denied that the fundamental human characteristic, that is the great development of the brain, the basis of all our psychological evolution, was never fulfilled in them. Human as they are in their dentition and posture, the Australopithecinae are none the less Apes in terms of their brain.

Dart claimed that the Australopithecinae already knew how to make fire (hence the name *prometheus* which he gave to the Makapansgat fossil), and that they were carnivorous hunters who preyed on small mammals, using as a weapon the humerus of large ungulates.[36] If this were really the case, their humanity would no longer be in dispute. But the arguments advanced by Dart in support of this thesis have failed to convince palaeontologists: no hearth and no definitely fabricated artefact have been found in the beds containing remains of Australopithecinae. For the present, Dart's suggestions cannot be accepted.

Moreover, there is an element of uncertainty in our knowledge that renders the interpretation of all these fossils a particularly delicate matter— our ignorance of their geological age. Basing his opinion on certain analogies in the fauna accompanying them, Broom—at the beginning of his investigations—estimated that *Australopithecus* properly so-called dated from the Upper Pliocene, while *Plesianthropus* and *Paranthropus* were to be assigned to the Mid and Upper Pleistocene. He later shifted *Plesianthropus* back to the Upper Pliocene and ascribed a correspondingly increased age to *Australopithecus*. But for the time being any precise dating is impossible. The Tertiary mammals persisted in Southern Africa much longer than in Europe, and the slight extent of the ancient climatic variations on the African continent make the establishment of an accurate stratigraphy very difficult. It seems, in any case, that the last of the Australopithecinae were contemporary with Man. Far from being our ancestors, these Primates may only have been, in the phrase of Gregory and Hellman, 'Man's less evolved cousins'.

EVOLUTION OF THE PRIMATES

For a long time, the scarcity of evidence relating to the Primates rendered the task of reconstructing their history extremely difficult. It is a fact well

[36] Dart, R., 'The Predatory Implemental Technique of *Australopithecus*' (*Amer. Journ. of Phys. Anthropology*, VII, 1949).

known to every specialist that the bone-remains of tree-dwelling forms are far less likely to be preserved than those of steppe or aquatic animals, and our knowledge of the first Primates has long been inadequate. Even in deposits where bone-remains of mammals abound, the remains of Primates are generally exceedingly rare.

For three years in succession Fihol, on behalf of the French National Museum, carried out extensive excavations in the Miocene bone-layers at Sansan, in the hope of discovering therein skeletons or parts of skeletons of *Pliopithecus* or *Dryopithecus*. He did not discover the smallest fragment. For these reasons the material available to palaeontology was very incomplete and there were large gaps in our knowledge of the Primates.

It must, however, be acknowledged that, since the first edition of this book, various discoveries have cast light on a certain number of obscure points. An order of development appears that conforms almost exactly with the zoological hierarchy. At the commencement of the Tertiary Era, we see the first Primates as small creatures, spread across a northern Americano-European continent, and of so generalized a type that it is sometimes very difficult to distinguish them from certain contemporary small mammals that must be regarded as the starting-point of other orders—that of the Insectivores in particular.

Palaeontology then helps us to group these first types in the world, and to understand their correlative differentiation. It helps us to comprehend, for example, how certain of them were able to surmount the Lemur stage, and to give birth in South America to the Flat-Nosed (Platyrrhine) Monkeys, which have since remained independent and isolated. Palaeontology has discovered at Fayum the remains of several animals with synthetic characters, and so has revealed certain ancestral forms, in several cases of the Long-Nosed (Catarrhine) Monkeys, and in one case of the Anthropoid Apes. Thus it proves the great antiquity of the splitting off of the different ancestral branches.

Much later, after a period of differentiation, the events of which we are only beginning dimly to perceive, we see appearing in the Old World certain Monkeys clearly related to living Monkeys, but still possessing many primitive characters. Cynomorphs and Anthropoids are now absolutely distinct. *Mesopithecus*, *Oreopithecus* and *Dolichopithecus* are among the first representatives of transitional forms leading to the Macaques, the Indian Apes (*Semnopithecus*), and perhaps also to the Dog-Faced Baboon (*Cynocephalus*). Among the Anthropoids, on the other hand, the lines of the Gibbon and of the Chimpanzee are differentiated during the Miocene in the shape of *Limnopithecus* and *Proconsul*. But alongside these, and in the three sections of the Old World, a group of Large Monkeys—*Dryopithecus*, *Ramapithecus*, *Bramapithecus*, and so on—combining characters that are today distributed among several genera of Anthropoids, bear witness to the power of expansion of this group at this period when a warm, humid climate favoured the development of vast forests.

Palaeontology has made known to us the very interesting fact that, in the first of these great fossil Primates, the specialized characters typical of modern Anthropoids are still missing or only moderately developed: the supra-orbital ridge, the sagittal crest on the skull, and the simian plate on the lower jaw are absent or not very marked, and the canine is as yet only slightly longer than the other teeth. Thus, the earliest Anthropoids are closer to Man than their descendants. But it is in the group of Australopithecinae that human characteristics suddenly become so extensive that, in the opinion of some of the most highly qualified palaeontologists, we have to ask ourselves whether these are not already Humans.

It can no longer be asserted, therefore, as was for a long time the case, that palaeontology has not revealed any transitional form, any material proof of a hereditary connexion between the Ape form and the human form. The farther back we go into the geological past, the more indistinct become the morphological differences between the two groups, the more difficult it is to draw a line between Men and Apes, the stronger grows the impression that both groups will finally merge in some common stock. This impression becomes even more definite when, instead of comparing the fossil Anthropoids with modern Man, we compare them with the most primitive Hominids, *Pithecanthropus* and *Sinanthropus*, whom we shall shortly study.

CHAPTER FOUR

THE PROBLEM OF TERTIARY MAN

As soon as the existence of Quaternary Man was definitely proved, the desire was stimulated for evidence of the existence of a Man in still earlier times—of Tertiary Man.

There is much justification for such a research. Most of the genera of living mammals were already present in Pliocene times. Why should it not be the same with Man? On the other hand, archaeologists had been struck by the fact that the oldest known stone industry, the Chellean, not only represented an already evolved form but also appeared at the very outset over a large part of the Old World. This implied the existence of some earlier order of things, and at that period, when the immense duration of Quaternary times had not yet been recognized, it was supposed that this order of things must have belonged to the Tertiary Era.

HISTORICAL REVIEW

The first of the discoveries referred to followed very soon after the victory of Boucher de Perthes. In 1863, Desnoyers, librarian of the French National Museum, announced that he had found in the gravels of Saint-Prest (Eure-et-Loir), regarded as Pliocene, bones of large animals bearing lines or incisions that could only be considered the work of Man.

In 1867, at the International Congress of Prehistoric Archaeology and Anthropology, in Paris, Abbé Bourgeois exhibited flints from the Oligocene deposits at Thenay (Loir-et-Cher). According to him, certain of these flints showed fractures, small pittings, and traces of splitting by fire, while others had been deliberately dressed (Fig. 60, nos. 1 to 3). At the same time, his fellow-worker, Abbé Delaunay, showed some bones, carved in the fashion of those from Saint-Prest, which had been obtained from Miocene shell-beds of marine origin at Pouancé (Maine-et-Loire). Soon after, all the great beds containing mammalian fossils—Oligocene in the Bourbonnais, Miocene in the Orleans district, in the Gers, and at Pikermi in Greece, Pliocene in Siena (Italy)—yielded bones that were alleged to have been deliberately broken, scratched, or incised.

It was soon established, however, that all these so-called traces of human handiwork on bones—both those displayed by Desnoyers and those shown by Abbé Delaunay and his emulators—were the result of purely natural

causes, being due either to physical phenomena such as the dessication of
the bones or the pressure of the soil, or to gnawing by carnivores (Figs.
58 and 59). This is no longer disputed, and the excellent critical study
written more than seventy years ago by G. de Mortillet has lost none of its
value.[1]

In the same year, 1867, Professor Issel of Genoa announced the discovery
of a human skeleton in the Pliocene layers of Savona in Liguria, while Dr.
Collyer described a lower jawbone found twelve years earlier in a Pliocene

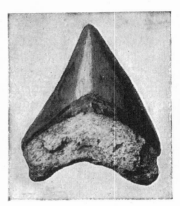

59 (right) Tooth of a large Shark (*Car-
charodon megalodon*) from Miocene shell
deposits in Touraine, probably the
cause of the incisions depicted opposite.
Half natural size. Palaeontological Gallery, French National Museum of
Natural History.

58 (left) Bone of *Halitherium*, a Sirenian
fossil, bearing incisions. From the Miocene shell deposits of the Maine-et-
Loire. Natural size. (After Farge)

quarry in England. In this year, too, the Americans sent word of the discovery of a human skull in their gold-bearing alluvials at Calaveras in
California, which were also regarded as Tertiary.

About the year 1878, the Portuguese geologist Ribeiro recorded certain
dressed flints from a Miocene deposit at Otta, in the neighbourhood of
Lisbon (Figs. 58 and 59); whilst the Cantalian geologist Rames sent to the
International Exhibition a case of flints of the same kind, collected in alluvials
of the Upper Miocene at Puy Courny, near Aurillac (Fig. 60, 5 to 7).

For a decade these discoveries gave rise to many discussions.[2] The
existence, based on certain 'dressed stones', of Tertiary Man or of a Tertiary
forerunner of Man, was ably maintained by de Quatrefages and Gabriel de
Mortillet.

---

[1]   *Le Préhistorique* (1st Ed., 1883) pp. 34ff.

[2]   The literature relating to these discoveries is too extensive to list here. See Mortillet, G.
de, *Le Préhistorique*, and above all Reinach, S., *Antiquités nationales, I, Alluvions et cavernes*. Numerous references will be found on succeeding pages.

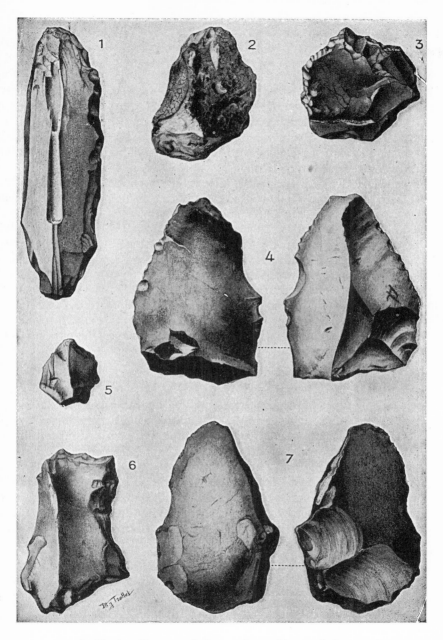

60 Tertiary flints regarded as products of human industry

1, 3, split flints from Thenay; 2, burnt and fractured flints from Thenay (Loir-et-Cher);
4, split flints from Otta (Portugal); 5, 6, 7, flints from Puy Courny (Cantalia). Natural size.

The latter scientist, although he rejected all the other discoveries, became the ardent and zealous supporter of those from Thenay, Otta, and Puy Courny. Since, on the one hand, his ideas on the subject of evolution precluded him from dating the genus *Homo* as far back as the Miocene and Oligocene, and since, on the other hand, he had no doubt as to the deliberate carving on the flints exhibited, G. de Mortillet conceived the existence of a creature intermediate between the Great Apes and Man, and this he first named *Anthropopithecus*, and later *Homosimius*. He even went so far as to found three species corresponding to the three deposits: he proposed to locate at Thenay, *Homosimius bourgeoisi*; at Otta, *H. ribeiroi*; and at Aurillac, *H. ramesi*.[3] This truly childish method of resolving a serious scientific problem aroused lively criticism.

The final result of interminable discussions was definitely antagonistic to the new theory, and the partisans of the belief in the deliberate dressing of Tertiary stones became fewer and fewer. Numerous observations have proved, as we shall see later, that many natural causes can reproduce the characters of crackled flint: changes of water temperature, and meteorological action; the action of hot springs; and, even in our present climate, the prolonged action of atmospheric agents. Laboratory experiments have led to similar findings. There is no need to assume human handiwork in order to explain the flints from Thenay or Otta; and to imagine—as did Gabriel de Mortillet and Abbé Bourgeois—that there existed in the Oligocene an 'Anthropopithecus' who lit a fire in which to crack flints is a fantasy in which no one believes nowadays.[4]

THE EOLITH THEORY

After a lull, the question of Tertiary flints was revived in 1889. The signal for this reawakening was given by the English geologist Prestwich[5] by his publications on the supposed artefacts found at Ightham in England. They dealt with flints showing indistinct traces of working collected from the Pleistocene gravels of the Kentish plateau.

Prestwich enjoyed a considerable reputation, and his example was followed. Before long, stones fashioned after the same manner were being found almost everywhere. English enthusiasts discovered them in other parts of the British Isles, for example in the Norfolk Forest-Bed, and even in the Upper Tertiary of India; while continental workers described them from numerous

[3]   Mortillet, G. de, *Le Préhistorique* (Paris, 1883, p. 105; 3rd Ed., by Gabriel and Adrien de Mortillet, Paris, 1900, p. 96).

[4]   On this subject, see especially: 'Discussion au Congrès de l'Association française à Blois' (*Matériaux*, 1884). Arcelin, A., 'Silex tertiaires' (*Ibid.*, 1885). D'Ault du Mesnil, 'Note sur de nouvelles fouilles faites à Thenay (*Ibid.*, 1885), Mahoudeau, P. H. and Capitan, L., 'La question de l'Homme tertiaire à Thenay' (*Revue de l'École d'Anthrop.*, XI, 1901) Reprints of various publications of the Abbé Bourgeois dealing with Thenay will be found in Houssaye, Dr. F., *L'œuvre de l'abbé Bourgeois* (Paris, 1904).

[5]   Prestwich, J., 'On the Occurrence of Palaeolithic Flint Implements in the Neighbourhood of Ightham' (*Quarterly Journal of the Geolog. Soc. of London*, XLV, 1889).

layers in France, Belgium, and Germany. Among amateur collectors of dressed flints there developed a perfect frenzy for seeing in every broken pebble and jagged edge products of human industry. Thus the question of 'Tertiary times' became again the order of the day, decked in a new name, to wit 'the Eolith theory'. In every country it had warm supporters. Presently a geologist, Rutot, put himself at the head of the new movement by a perfect avalanche of publications.[6]

To the two periods of the stone industry long recognized—the Palaeolithic and the Neolithic—G. de Mortillet had added a more ancient period which he called *Eolithic*, and which was meant to include 'all that related to the Tertiary period'.[7] According to Rutot, who adopted the name invented by G. de Mortillet, but somewhat distorted its original meaning, the Eolithic period furnishes no stone dressed to a *deliberate shape*, but only *natural forms, directly utilized*. We must give the name *eoliths* to these rude and primitive implements, these stones that were simply used. De Mortillet, in his studies on Tertiary flints, had considered the *bulb of percussion* that develops as the result of a sharp blow delivered on a striking-point (Fig. 61) as the criterion of deliberate dressing. Rutot attaches only

61 Splinter of Mousterian flint from the Grotte du Placard, retouched at the point. Three-quarters natural size.

On the inner surface, detached from a mass of flint: p, point where struck; b, percussion bulb. On the outer surface: r, retouching.

secondary importance to this bulb, but ascribes great value to signs of retouching, that is to say the marks left by systematic chipping designed to adapt the piece of flint to a definite end. 'The special appearance', said Rutot, 'that experts rightly name "retouched" is only to be attributed to human and essentially deliberate action, and all eoliths—whether from the Aquitanian (Oligocene) or Mosean (a name given by Rutot to a Quaternary level in Belgium) or from the intermediate stages of Miocene, Pliocene, and

---

[6] The majority have been reviewed in *L'Anthropologie*, VIII to XVIII, *passim*. See particularly Rutot, A., 'Le Préhistorique dans l'Europe centrale. Coup d'œil sur l'état de nos connaissances relatives aux industries de la pierre' (*Congrès d'archaéol. et d'histoire* at Dinant, 1903, Namur, 1904).

[7] *Le Préhistorique*, 1st Ed., p. 18.

Lower Mosean, which exhibit retouching produced by use, must be included among the authentic relics of primitive industries.'[8]

Eoliths, thus regarded, are to be found in huge quantities in Quaternary gravels, along with implements of definite and standard shapes. Rutot goes so far as to describe, from the gravels of the north of France and of Belgium,

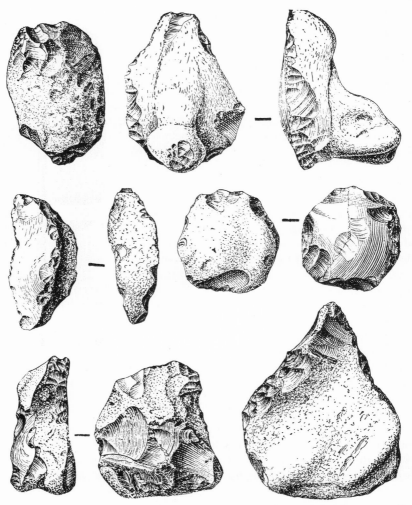

62 Eoliths from the 'Reutelian' of Belgium. The chipped stones figured here, according to Rutot, are considered by him to be hammers, grinders, scrapers and discs. Half natural size.

several 'industries' of this kind—'Reutelian', 'Mafflian', 'Mesvinian', and others (Fig. 62).

But such objects are also to be met with in much more ancient deposits:

[8] *Bull. de la Soc. d'Anthrop. de Bruxelles*, Vol. XX, 1902, p. 66.

chipped stones from the Oligocene at Thenay, from the Miocene at Otta and Puy Courny, flints from the Pliocene in France, Britain, Egypt and India are claimed as eoliths. And here the question becomes much more serious, for the partisans of the new theory believed that a few chipped or fractured stones were enough to prove the existence, in geological times so remote, either of Man or of his immediate forerunners.

DISCUSSIONS OF THE FACTS:

THE OBJECTIONS

After having made numerous converts everywhere, and after a clamorous career that gained it great notoriety, the eolith theory succumbed under the repeated blows of certain geologists and prehistorians. Accurate observations made in every quarter by serious naturalists showed that the play of the physical forces of nature may reproduce eoliths, and that it is impossible to distinguish the so-called human eoliths from eoliths wholly independent of any intelligent or conscious interference. We will briefly survey the main arguments adduced in refutation of the thesis of Rutot and his supporters.

One objection is the very frequency with which the eoliths occur. They have been found in deposits belonging to all ages of the Tertiary, as well as to the Lowest Eocene, as at Clermont (Oise), to the Oligocene, the Miocene and the Pliocene. They have also been found in no smaller numbers in the flint-bearing alluvials of the Quaternary. Their presence in Eocene deposits, which presupposes the existence of a Human or an intelligent Pre-Human at a period when the Primates were only just beginning to be differentiated, is astounding enough. But what is no less surprising is that these 'dressed stones' are everywhere the same. They show no gradations with the passage of time. From the lowest Tertiary to the Quaternary, the eoliths preserve the same rough and defaced aspect. No progress, therefore, could have been made during this immense lapse of time. It is perfectly obvious that such permanent repetition of forms is far more easily explained by the hypothesis of an origin due to natural causes, the effects of which remain always the same, than if we suppose these eoliths to be the work of Man.

Another objection relates to the sites in which eoliths occur. They are only found in flinty regions and never beyond layers naturally containing this mineral, which could not be the case if these stones had been the tools or weapons of Man. In that event they would inevitably have been scattered wherever Man passed or settled. Moreover, while many prehistorians have been impressed by the carefully classified series shown them, in which neatly sorted specimens reproduced the same forms with perfect regularity, creating the impression of deliberate working, these same stones have quite a different significance when studied in their beds.

We then see that the most exacting care in selection has been necessary to obtain these deceptive series; that the stones, said to be deliberately dressed, far from indicating the occurrence at the spot where they were found of the site of a human settlement, of a shelter, or such like, on an ancient surface, really form part of a truly geological formation, usually thrown violently in place, just like thousands of other elements in the same formation; that the specimens, chosen with a preconceived idea, do not differ in any essential characters from their innumerable neighbours in the layer; and that it is easy to find every possible transitional form, ranging from the rudest elements composing the bulk of the gravel, conglomerate or breccia, as the case may be, to those in which traces of fracture and splintering, a little more numerous or a little more definitely grouped, have

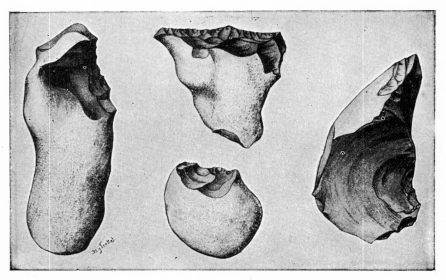

63 Natural eoliths from the base of the Eocene deposits at Clermont (Oise). Two-thirds natural size. (After H. Breuil)

gained for them the honour of being singled out and collected as representative specimens.

Even more important arguments have been furnished by numerous researches showing the major role of natural forces in producing eoliths. Both percussion bulbs and retouching may be produced entirely independently of the human will.[9]

These natural forces are of various kinds. The action of the waves of the sea has been demonstrated by Hardy at Dieppe, by Sollas on the Isle of Wight, and by many others. This fact is all the more interesting because many of the flake beds are clearly of marine origin.

[9] See the general review of this question published by W. C. Pei, 'Le rôle des phénomènes naturels dans l'éclatement et le faconnement des roches dures utilisées par l'Homme préhistorique' (*Revue de Géographie physique et de Géologie dynamique*, IX, 1936).

The action of glaciers, indicated by Penck and H. Breuil, has been studied at length by Mortelmans,[10] who has shown the existence of what may be called 'the glacier dressing', an initial pressure on the pebbles that splits off flakes, on which secondary retouching is then produced by the same mechanism.

Many travellers have reported the effect of changes of temperature. The action of solifluxion has recently been pointed out. Other writers have indicated the part played by pressure and compression due to the weight of the deposits, which are capable of producing, even in the depths of geological layers, results similar to those due to blows, that is to say flakes with percussion bulbs and retouches. H. Breuil's observations on the eoliths of the Lower Eocene in the neighbourhood of Clermont[11] are of particular interest in this respect (Fig. 63). In a large number of cases, flint nodules are found fissured, split and dispersed in small pieces, and these might readily be transformed into eoliths by subsequent resorting, in the course of which they might undergo shocks due to the dynamic forces of streams or of the waves of the sea.[12]

With regard to the play of natural forces, certain experimental facts have been quite conclusive. The most typical are those furnished by the operation of the mixers in cement factories.[13] Flint nodules mingled in the water with chalk and clay are subjected for hours on end, in a round tank, to a rapid rotatory movement in the course of which they are struck violently together. When the machinery stops the flints have assumed the appearance of old river gravels and, as in all ancient flint-bearing alluvials, a certain number of them show retouches presenting all the characters of deliberate dressing (Figs. 64 and 65).

Rostro-Carinate Flints

The observations recorded above ought to have put an end to the eolith theory. They struck it a number of blows from which it never recovered. Nevertheless, the question was resurrected in a different shape in England when, in 1910, Mr. J. Reid Moir of Ipswich announced that he had taken from the bottom layer of a Pliocene marine deposit, called Suffolk Red Crag, flints proving the existence of Man prior to this Pliocene deposit.[14]

[10] Mortelmans, G., 'Une cause d'erreur en préhistoire. La taille glaciaire' (*Bull. Soc. belge Anthr. et Préhistoire*, LVIII, 1947, p. 60.)

[11] Breuil, H., 'Sur la présence d'éolithes à la base de l'Éocène parisien' (*L'Anthropologie*, XXI, 1910).

[12] See among others: Warren, S. H., 'On the Origin of Eolithic Flints by Natural Causes' (*Journal of the Royal Anthropological Institute*, XXXV, 1905); 'A Natural Eolith Factory beneath the Thanet Sand' (*Quart. Journ. Geolog. Soc.*, LXXXVI, 1921). Haward, F. N., 'The Chipping of Flints by Natural Agencies' (*Proceedings of the Prehistoric Society of East Anglia*, I, 1912). Sarasin, P., 'Einige Bemerkungen zur Eolithologie' (*Jahresbericht der Geogr. Ethnogr. Gesellsch. in Zurich*, 1909).

[13] Boule, M., 'L'origine des éolithes' (*L'Anthropologie*, XVI, 1902). Obermaier, H., 'Zur Eolithenfrage' (*A. für Anthropol.*, 1905).

[14] Moir, J. Reid, 'The Flint Implements of Sub-Crag Man' (*Prehistoric Soc. of East Anglia*, I, 1911).

This discovery made a great impression on the mind of the eminent biologist, Sir Ray Lankester, who took an active interest in the matter.[15] Moir and Ray

64 and 65 Eoliths from the cement works at Mantes

Specimens similar to those which Rutot described under the names of hammers, planes, scrapers, retouchers and notched flints. Below in the left-hand corner, flint with plane of fracture and percussion bulb. Natural size.

[15] Lankester, Sir Ray, 'On the Discovery of a Novel Type of Flint Implements' (*Philosophical Transactions*, Series B, Vol. 202, 1912).

Lankester avoided bringing eoliths forward again, that is to say, pebbles simply used and bearing only the marks of this usage. It was now a question of implements of a very definite form, of a type quite as characteristic as, say, the Saint-Acheulean types, but far older—the 'rostro-carinate' or eagle-beak type. The Chellean, Acheulean, and Mousterian flints are essentially flattened, in leaf form. The rostro-carinate type of the Crag is essentially

66 The most perfect example of Keeled Flint (type specimen) from the Crag at Norwich, side view. (After Sir Ray Lankester)

narrowed in a lateral direction (Fig. 66). It is true that they are also associated with scrapers, borers, blades, hammers and picks.

Pursuing his investigations with admirable persistence for thirty years, Moir collected in many places among the Pliocene deposits of the Ipswich region numerous other flints that he considered to have been dressed by the hand of Man. The most important continued to come from the Red Crag, where, at Foxhall—this time in the interior of this formation—he claimed to have discovered a positive 'centre of human occupation', a sort of settlement or workshop where 'the flaking is well defined, accompanied by trimming and retouching', and where, as at Thenay, 'burnt flints are not lacking'.[16]

The views of Moir and Lankester were accepted by prehistorians of standing. They have the advantage over those of their predecessors of relating to deposits belonging to a phase of the Pliocene, which many

[16] Among the very numerous writings of J. Reid Moir, see especially: *Pre-Palaeolithic Man* (Ipswich, 1919). 'Tertiary Man in England' (*Natural History*, No. 6, 1924; critical analysis by M. Boule in *L'Anthropologie*, XXXVI, 1926, p. 332). *The Antiquity of Man in East Anglia* (1927). 'The Age of the Pre-Crag Flint Implements' (*J. of the R. Anthrop. Inst.*, LXV, 1935). See also Breuil, H., 'Les industries pliocènes de la région d'Ipswich' (*Revue Anthropologique*, July-August, 1922, p. 228).

authors now tend to include in the Quaternary—deposits, that is to say, in which the presence of Man is, *a priori*, plausible. But the same arguments that are valid against the eoliths were also advanced against this new theory; Sollas, Haward and H. Warren, among others, vigorously contested it.[17] The fact that the Foxhall level, right inside the marine deposits of the Crag, contains not only flints that may be considered as dressed, but also the same phosphatic nodules and the same remains of old fossil vertebrates as the bottom layer of this Crag, indicates the operation of such physical phenomena as redistribution due to the action of the waves or marine currents. Types similar to these rostro-carinate flints have been found in the mixers used in cement-factories.[18] Finally, according to Barnes,[19] the way these flints are shaped shows features incompatible with human handiwork.

HUMAN BONE-REMAINS

The numerous archaeological discoveries presented up to this point are far from convincing. Though a few may be doubtful, the answer in most cases is categorical: the so-called implements of Tertiary Man are of natural origin, and are not the work of Man. A study of the bone remains attributed to Tertiary Man is equally disappointing, as we shall see. Leaving aside the skull from Calaveras (California) and the so-called Tertiary Men of South America described by Ameghino—which will be discussed later (see Chap. XII)—three discoveries alone remain to be considered: those made at Savona and Castenedolo in Italy, and at Foxhall in England.

The skeleton from Savona, in Liguria, was found in 1852, during the reconstruction of a church, in a shelly clay of marine origin, rich in fossil oysters of Pliocene age; but it was not exhibited by Issel till fifteen years after, at the Paris Congress in 1867. The remains are rather badly preserved, so much so that Issel himself described them under the vague title of 'Anthropoid'.[20] The distinguished professor of Genoa University was convinced of the Pliocene age of the Savona skeleton; nevertheless, he acknowledged that the circumstances of the discovery were not such as to inspire confidence. It must be added that the bones of the skeleton were connected, whereas those of various mammals found in the same stratum were scattered, as is generally the case in marine deposits. No stratigraphic study of the formation was made.

[17] Boule, M., 'La Paléontologie humaine en Angleterre' (*L'Anthropologie*, XXVI, 1915). Haward, F. N., 'The Origin of the "Rostro-Carinate Implements"' (*Proceedings of the Prehistoric Society of East Anglia*, III, 1918/1919). Warren, S. H., 'The Study of Comparative Flaking in 1927' (*Man*, January 1928).

[18] Patte, E., 'Une nouvelle fabrique industrielle d'éolithes reproduisant des types du Pliocène anglais' (*L'Anthropologie*, XXXVI, 1926).

[19] Barnes, A. S., 'Les outils de l'Homme tertiaire en Angleterre. Étude critique' (*L'Anthropologie*, XLVIII, 1938).

[20] Issel, A., 'Résumé des recherches concernant l'ancienneté de l'Homme en Ligurie' (*Congrès Intern. d'Arch. et d'Anthr. préhistorique*, first meeting, Paris, 1867, p. 67). *Ligura preistorica* (Genoa, 1908) p. 140.

The bones from Castenedolo, near Brescia in Italy, belong to several skeletons of men, women and children, and were found on various occasions in a shelly bed of sand and clay, of marine origin and of Pliocene age.   The first discovery was made in 1860, the second in 1880; they were described by Professor Ragazzoni,[21] and immediately aroused a lively discussion. In order to explain the presence of human skeletons in deposits of marine origin, their chief supporter, the anthropologist G. Sergi, was obliged to assume the shipwreck of a whole family. In 1889, the discovery of a new human skeleton was the subject of an official report by Professor Issel, who then observed that the various fossils from this deposit were all impregnated with salt, with the sole exception of the human bones.[22] Despite an attempt to reopen the question made by a pupil of Ragazzoni, Professor Cacciamali, it seems certain that at Castenedolo, as at Savona, we are dealing with more or less recent burials.

The Foxhall jaw does not merit any greater interest. It is the English equivalent of the famous jaw found at Moulin-Quignon in France. It was found in 1855 by workmen in a sand quarry at Foxhall near Ipswich, Suffolk, bought by a chemist and then passed on to an American physician, Dr. Collyer, who described and figured it in 1867.[23] This mandible was considered as originating in the bottom layer of the Red Crag, that is to say as belonging to the Pleistocene. After examination by the best British geologists and palaeontologists of the period, this anatomical specimen, possessing absolutely modern characters, was dismissed as without significance. Today no one knows what has become of it; but thirty years ago Reid Moir[24] sought to attribute it to one of the manufacturers of the eoliths discovered by him in the Suffolk Crag, which we have already discussed. It requires a total lack of critical sense to pay any heed to such a piece of evidence as this.

CONCLUSIONS

This brief study of the arguments put forward in favour of the existence of Tertiary Man produces, in the last analysis, a negative result. Despite the various reasons for believing that Man existed before the Pleistocene, the investigations of anthropologists and the perseverance and skill of archaeologists have failed to provide really convincing proof. What are we to conclude from this? Ought we not to ask ourselves whether the question of Tertiary Man has perhaps been wrongly framed?

It was in the second half of last century, at a time when the science of prehistory was being built in a tremendous wave of enthusiasm, that this

[21] Ragazzoni, G., 'La collina di Castenedolo' (*Commentari di Ateneo di Brescia*, 1880, p. 120).

[22] Issel, A., 'Cenni sulla giacitura dello scheletro umano recentemente scoperto nel Pliocene di Castenedolo' (*Bull. di Paletnologia italiana*, XV, 1889, p. 89).

[23] Collyer, R. H., 'The Fossil Human Jaw from Suffolk' (*Anthropological Review*, V. 1867, p. 221).

[24] Moir, J. Reid, 'Further Discoveries of Humanly Fashioned Flints in and beneath the Red Crag of Suffolk' (*Proc. of the Prehist. Soc. of East Anglia*, 1926).

question presented itself to those who wished to know the true origin of
Man. Geological and palaeontological data on the Quaternary were still
very limited. The most revolutionary scholars did not dare to place this Period
more than a hundred thousand years back; the most ancient Men known at
that time, the Neandertals, in spite of their many primitive features, were
already incontestably human; the oldest industry yet discovered, the Chellean,
was characterized by an implement that had already attained a considerable
degree of perfection. It was recognized that these could not be the first stages
of human evolution, and that the stretch of time ascribed to the Quaternary
was insufficient to contain the whole of this evolution. The assumption that
Man had existed in the Tertiary was inescapable.

We now know that the Quaternary Period was extremely long, and that its
duration far surpassed anything imagined by the boldest prehistorians of
last century. More primitive industries than the Chellean have been discovered, some of them—like those in Africa—belonging to a period so
remote from our own that, a little while ago, the majority of geologists
ascribed it to the Tertiary. We now know the representatives of Humanity
at the beginning of the Quaternary, and these, the Prehominians, are so
apelike in appearance that there was prolonged hesitation as to whether
they were human at all. Astride the end of the Tertiary and the beginning
of the Quaternary, the most highly evolved of the fossil Anthropoids, the
Australopithecinae, had for their part acquired sufficient human characters
to render their zoological position the subject of controversy and to lead some
authors to regard them as the very first Hominids.

It seems, therefore, as though the great turning point in human history,
the moment when Man's very first representatives became differentiated as
such, fell in the period corresponding to the juncture of the Tertiary with the
Quaternary Period, or at most in the very last phases of the Tertiary. Ought
one, under these circumstances, to persist in looking for a Tertiary Man?
Even in the Pliocene, what we shall meet will no longer be—or rather, will
not yet be—true Hominids. They will be the ancestors of the Prehominians,
the ancestors of the Australopithecines—or even these Australopithecines
themselves—all of them forms so apelike that to call them human would be
to give this term an extension that would deprive it of all logical meaning.
There existed at this period 'ancestors of Man', who were very different from
him, and it is they whom we may hope to find. In all probability there was
no such thing as Tertiary Man properly so-called.

But these forerunners, it will be said, may have used some implements,
the first manifestations of the quality of *faber* in which certain philosophers
have wished to see the great distinguishing mark of humanity. This is possible,
even probable, although many prehistorians believe that the Stone Age
was preceded by an Age of Wood, of which naturally no trace remains. But
we have no infallible means of distinguishing natural accidents from the
products of deliberate rudimentary workmanship; and we have just seen that
the last discoveries referred to, convincing as they appear to some observers,

are susceptible of quite a different explanation. Other proofs than those adduced up to the present are needed before we can announce that a vision of the Tertiary 'springtime' of Humanity has really been perceived.

'We must be able to doubt where doubt is needful,' said Pascal.

CHAPTER FIVE

THE PREHOMINIANS
PITHECANTHROPUS AND SINANTHROPUS

IT is not without interest to those concerned with the history of human palaeontology to learn that the discussions nowadays rife as to the zoological place of the Australopithecines arose fifty years ago, on an even larger scale, in connexion with another fossil—*Pithecanthropus*. But whereas the vast majority of authors tend to leave the Australopithecines among the Anthropoids, of which they represent an almost human branch, the opposite conclusion was finally reached in respect of *Pithecanthropus*, and there is no further doubt nowadays that this was a Hominid. It took a long time for this conclusion to impose itself, however.

The discovery of *Pithecanthropus* was one of the most sensational made in the domain of natural science during the course of the 19th century. Regarded as representing the long-sought transition stage from Ape to Man—the 'Ape-Man', *pithecos-anthropos*—it gave rise to prolonged and violent discussions. For almost half a century the question remained undecided. The finding in China of an identical, or at least very closely allied form—*Sinanthropus*—and a few years later of fresh *Pithecanthropi*, finally resolved it. But if *Pithecanthropus* and *Sinanthropus* are now regarded as Hominids, they are none the less exceptional Hominids, extremely primitive in all their characters. They show how close our family still was to the great Anthropoid Apes at the beginning of the Quaternary. They merit the honour of a special chapter in the study of Man's history.

PITHECANTHROPUS

STORY OF THE DISCOVERY

In 1889, Eugène Dubois, a Dutch army doctor, was commissioned by his government to explore the deposits in Java that are of more or less volcanic origin and rich in bone-remains of fossil mammals. These excavations lasted for several years and were most fruitful in results; for besides enormous quantities of bones of various animals, there were found the remains of a large primate—a skull-cap, a femur, and two teeth. In 1894 Dubois published a monograph[1] on his discovery, and its title summarizes its principal conclusion, that this newcomer into the world of fossils represents the 'intermediate form between the Anthropoids and Man', implied by the doctrine of evolution; it is the 'precursor of Man'. The following is the diagnosis which the author gives of the new creature, both as a genus and as a species:

'PITHECANTHROPUS ERECTUS. Skull much larger, absolutely and also relatively to the body mass, than in the Great Apes, but less bulky than in Man; cerebral capacity about two-thirds that of Man. Inclination of the nuchal plane of the occiput much greater than in the Great Apes. Dentition

67 The Island of Java. The shaded square corresponds to the part shown in more detail in Fig. 68

different from that of the latter, although of archaic form. Femur of human dimensions and suited for walking in the upright position.'

Dubois's memoir was read everywhere. Palaeontologists and anthropologists all the world over published their opinions or impressions, so that the list of works relating to *Pithecanthropus* soon became considerable.[2] At the International Zoological Congress held at Leyden in 1896, in spite of divergences of opinion, there was unanimous agreement in recognizing the great interest of the Dutch scientist's discovery.

In 1906, Frau Selenka, the widow of a German zoologist, organized a scientific expedition to Java to prosecute new investigations. The soil round the precise spot at which the remains of *Pithecanthropus* had been exhumed was dug out to a depth of 40 feet, and more than 10,000 cubic yards of earth removed. The expedition was thus enabled to garner important collections of fossil animals, but its principal object was not attained—not the least relic of *Pithecanthropus* could be found. The scientific results of this expedition,

---

[1]   Dubois, E., *Pithecanthropus erectus, eine menschenähnliche Übergangsform aus Java.* In 4to with 2 plates. (Batavia, 1894).

[2]   The most important titles published up to 1923 will be found in earlier editions of this book. Of those published after this date the following should be noted:
Dubois, E., 'On the Principal Characters of the Cranium and the Brain, the Mandible and the Teeth of *Pithecanthropus erectus*' (*Kon. Akad. van Wetenschappen te Amsterdam, Proc.*, XXVII, Nos. 3 and 4, 1924); 'Figures of the Calvarium and Endocranial Cast, a Fragment of the Mandible and the three Teeth of *Pithecanthropus erectus*' (*Ibid.*, XXVII, Nos. 5 and 6, 1924); 'On the Principal Characters of the Femur of *Pithecanthropus erectus*' (*Ibid.*, XXIX, 1926); 'The Distinct Organization of *Pithecanthropus*, of which the femur bears evidence now confirmed from other individuals of the described species' (*Ibid.*, XXXV, 1932); 'New Evidence of the Distinct Organization of *Pithecanthropus*' (*Ibid.*, XXXVII, 1934); Weinert, H., '*Pithecanthropus erectus*' (*Z. für Anatomie und Entwicklungsgeschichte*, LXXXVII, 1928).

recorded in a volume published in 1911,[3] enabled the age of the deposit
to be determined, a question of prime importance that we shall consider in
a moment.

First, however, we must describe a series of discoveries which, in a few
years and at a time when all hope of recovering a new *Pithecanthropus*

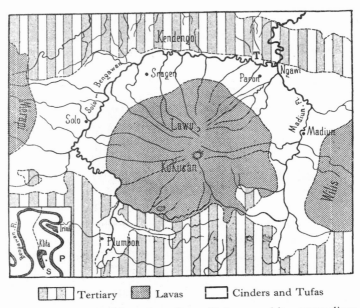

Tertiary   Lavas   Cinders and Tufas

68 Geological Map of the volcano Lawu-Kukusan and its surroundings
Scale, 1:1,250,000. (After Verbeck)

Trinil is 3 miles to the south of Paron, at point T. Inset on left of map, site on scale of
1:1,000,000. P, point where *Pithecanthropus* was found

had been virtually abandoned, furnished fresh specimens of this fossil.[4]
These finds, which were made by the geologist G. H. R. von Koenigswald
on the slope of Sangiran Hill, 40 miles from Trinil (Figs. 68 and 71), comprised: half a lower jawbone, discovered in 1936 (Mandible B) and described
as possibly attributable to *Pithecanthropus*; a skull-cap (*Pithecanthropus II*)
exactly comparable to that found by Dubois, but more complete, extracted
in 1937; a right parietal bone, found the following year, to which were

[3] Selenka, L. and Blanckenhorn, M., *Die Pithecanthropus-Schichten auf Java: geologische
und paläontologische Ergebnisse der Trinil-Expedition, etc.*, in 4to with plates (Leipzig, 1911).

[4] Koenigswald, G. H. R. von, 'Ein Unterkieferfragment des Pithecanthropus aus den
Trinilschichten Mitteljavas' (*Kon. Akademie van Wetenschappen te Amsterdam, Proceedings*,
XL, 1937). 'Ein neuer Pithecanthropusschädel' (Ibid., XLI, 1938); *Neue Pithecanthropus-
Funde, 1936–1938: Ein Beitrag zur Kenntnis der Praehominiden* (Dienst van den Mijnbouw
in Nederlandsch-Indie, Wetenschappelijke Medeedelingen No. 28, Batavia, 1940). For a
general review of all discoveries of *Pithecanthropus* and related forms, see especially von
Koenigswald's autobiographical work *Meeting Prehistoric Man*, trans. M. Bullock (London,
Thames & Hudson, 1956).

attached the contiguous sections of the left parietal and the occipital bones (*Pithecanthropus III*); and finally two pieces, discovered in 1939 (*Pithecanthropus IV*), and corresponding, the first to the rear third of the brain-case, including the base, and the second to the lower part of the upper maxilla with the palate and the alveolar arcades.

STUDY OF THE DEPOSIT

Trinil is a village situated near the town of Ngawi, on the banks of the River Solo, or Bengawan, at the foot of the great volcano Lawu-Kukusan whose terminal cone, still active, rises to a height of 10,738 feet (Figs. 67 to 69). This volcano, like all the volcanoes of Java, rises from a substratum of Tertiary deposits of marine origin. At its base occur layers of sand,

69 The *Pithecanthropus* bed on the bank of the River Solo. The spot of the discovery is indicated by a white cross. (From a photograph in Mme Selenka's work)

cinders, and volcanic lapilli, rearranged by fierce streams of water descending from the volcano, as well as tufas, and clays of more or less fluviatile origin; these are spread over great expanses, sometimes attaining 1,150 feet in thickness, and resting unconformably on more ancient marine formations. The section illustrated (Fig. 70), shown in somewhat diagrammatic fashion as in the Selenka publication, gives the details of the beds forming the bank of the River Solo, at the very spot where the remains of *Pithecanthropus* lay.

These layers contain many fossils of all kinds: plant impressions; shells of molluscs still living in the country; vertebrate bones, of fishes, reptiles, and mammals. Mammals formed a very rich fauna: Elephants, including one or two species of the primitive genus *Stegodon*; Rhinoceros and Tapir, a Hippopotamus with archaic characters; Ruminants antlered and horned;

among them a Pliocene genus, *Leptobos*, still showing relationship to the Antelopes; Carnivores, especially of the Cat tribe; a giant Pangolin; a Monkey (Macaque); and, finally, *Pithecanthropus*. This fauna includes several new genera, and almost all its species are different from existing species. Its affinities with the faunas of India show that, at the period when the Trinil animals lived in Java, this island was united to the Asiatic continent.

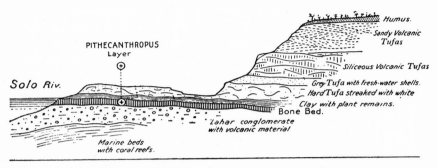

70 Geological section of the *Pithecanthropus* bed

It was in the layer containing lapilli (*bone layer* in section, Fig. 70) that the remains of *Pithecanthropus* were found by Dubois, all at the same level: first, in September 1891, one of the teeth; a month afterwards, the skull-cap, 3 feet distant from the tooth; the following year, in August 1892, the femur 50 feet from the skull; and a little later, a second tooth, 10 feet from the skull.

AGE OF PITHECANTHROPUS

Dubois, founding his conclusions on the similarity between the fossil fauna of Trinil and that of the upper deposits of the Siwalik Hills in India, attributed the *Pithecanthropus* layer to the Upper Pliocene. The underlying marine conglomerate, containing only 53 per cent of existing species of molluscs, he regarded as Miocene. These conclusions were disputed by several geologists of the Selenka expedition, who regarded the marine deposits as Pliocene, and the formations of river sands and lapilli as Quaternary. This was also the opinion of Schuster, who studied the imprints of fossil plants from the same bed. Blanckenhorn, summarizing the findings of his various collaborators, was of the opinion that the *Pithecanthropus* layer might be ascribed to that period of transition which up to then had been termed the *Elephas meridionalis* stage of the Upper Pliocene.[5]

Since then many works on the same subject have been published. Van Es, ascribing to the mammal fauna at Trinil the same age as that at Narbada

[5] Some writers went further. As the fossil plants seem to indicate a somewhat colder, and in particular a moister climate than the present climate of Java, they attributed the formation of the fossil-bearing deposits to a rainy epoch, and endeavoured further to correlate this epoch with the first Glacial Period in Europe. Comparisons of this kind between deposits situated at such distances are exceedingly rash.

in India, holds that the *Pithecanthropus* level dates from the beginning of the Lower Pleistocene.[6] Teilhard de Chardin reaches the same conclusion.[7] Von Koenigswald, after prolonged investigations carried out simultaneously in the regions of Trinil and of Sangiran, has finally shown that after the emergence of Java at the end of the Pliocene, three series of deposits succeeded one another during the Pleistocene in the centre of the island.[8] The most ancient are the Djetis layers with a fauna originating from Southern India, known as the Siva-Malayan fauna; this is the layer in which the second mandible and *Pithecanthropus IV* were found at Sangiran; it is also the layer in which the jaw of so-called *Meganthropus* and the Modjokerto skull, which will be discussed later (Fig. 71), came to light. Above the Djetis beds are

71 Geological section of Sangiran Hill, near the town of Solo, in East Java
(After Father Teilhard de Chardin)

those of Trinil, with a fauna containing numerous animals that came from China, no doubt via a land-bridge that took in Formosa, the Philippines and Borneo; this is the Sino-Malayan fauna. These were the layers from which in addition to the pieces found by Dubois, *Pithecanthropus II* and *III* were recovered. In contrast to the foregoing, the upper or Ngandong layers contain a much more recent fauna. According to von Koenigswald, they belong to the Upper Pleistocene; while the Trinil layers belong to the Mid Pleistocene and the Djetis layers to the Lower Pleistocene.

The chronological divergence between the opinions outlined is more apparent than real. It rests chiefly on differences in the definition of the limits of the Tertiary and Quaternary. The summit of the Upper Pliocene and the base of the Lower Quaternary are obviously the same thing, for the line of separation between those consecutive terms of our geological nomenclature is nothing but a mere mental concept. Von Koenigswald's Lower Pleistocene, the Djetis horizon, seems to correspond to the end of what is called in Europe the Villafranchian, that is to say, the Upper Pliocene. And the important fact is that this horizon, which is certainly older than that of Trinil, also contained *Pithecanthropus*. Hence there is no doubt that the latter existed in Java at the very beginning of the Quaternary. The relatively late date of the classical Trinil layer does not imply that *Pithecanthropus* is of equally recent date: today, as sixty years ago, and leaving aside

---

[6] Es, C. van, *The Age of Pithecanthropus*, in 8to with plates (La Haye, 1931).

[7] Teilhard de Chardin, Father, 'Notes sur la Paléontologie humaine en Asie méridionale' (*L'Anthropologie*, XLVII, 1937, p. 23); 'Deuxièmes notes sur la Paléontologie humaine en Asie méridionale' (*Ibid.*, XLVIII, 1938, p. 449).

[8] Koenigswald, G. H. R. von, *Loc. cit.*, also 'The Discovery of Early Man in Java and Southern China' (*Studies in Physical Anthropology*, No. 1: *Early Man in the Far East*, Detroit, 1949).

the disputed case of the Australopithecines, this fossil may be considered the most ancient known Hominid.

Let us now study the bone-remains of *Pithecanthropus*. In so doing, we shall consider especially the Trinil remains, because of the abundance of works devoted to them. We must mention that to the four pieces already referred to—the skull-cap, two upper molars, and a femur—Dubois added, in 1924, a fragment of lower jaw which he had found thirty-four years earlier at Kedung Brubus,[9] twenty-five miles from Trinil, and which he had at first attributed to a Man, together with a premolar discovered at Trinil in 1898. In 1932 he added four incomplete femurs, originating from the excavations carried out at Trinil in 1900, but only just freed from the gangue that concealed their true nature.

All these remains are perfectly fossilized, as are the bones of the animals that accompany them. Their density is considerable: the intact femur weighs almost double the weight of the femur of a modern Man of the same size.

THE SKULL-CAP

The Trinil skull-cap (Fig. 72) measures 184 millimetres in length and 134 millimetres at its greatest width, which gives a cephalic index of 70, and places the skull in the dolichocephalic group.[10] In spite of its large dimensions, it presents at first sight a simian aspect, due especially to flattening in a vertical direction.

We may estimate the capacity of the whole skull at about 850 cubic centimetres. As, in normal Man, even amongst the primitive races, this capacity very rarely falls below 1000 cubic centimetres, and as in the largest Anthropoid Apes it scarcely ever exceeds 600 cubic centimetres, the volume of the skull of *Pithecanthropus* is intermediate between that of the highest Apes and of the lowest Man. The weight of the brain must have been about 750 grammes.

The bones of the cranial vault are so fused that the sutures can no longer be distinguished. The anterior supra-orbital portion of the frontal bone exhibits a continuous ridge, a kind of rim similar to that which occurs in gibbons and chimpanzees. Behind this rim the forehead is very narrow and receding, more receding than in the Chimpanzee. The frontal bone has a slight keel on the median line, but the skull lacks any trace of the sagittal crest possessed by the largest Anthropoid Apes, the Orang and the Gorilla.

[9]   According to von Koenigswald, the correct spelling is *Kedoeng Broboes.*

[10]   The cephalic index is the relation between the maximum breadth of a skull and its maximum length, multiplied by 100: $\dfrac{\text{breadth} \times 100}{\text{length}}$. Long, or *dolichocephalic*, skulls have the smallest indices (below 75); short, or *brachycephalic*, skulls have the largest indices (over 80); the intermediate category is called *mesocephalic* or *mesaticephalic* (between 75 and 80). In other words, if a skull is termed dolichocephalic this means that its breadth equals *at most* 75 hundredths of its length, while the breadth of a brachycephalic skull equals *at least* 80 hundredths of its length, and so on.

On the contrary, the temporal lines are not very prominent and are widely separated from one another, as in the Gibbons, Chimpanzees, and Man, and this indicates relatively slight temporal muscles and mandibular apparatus.

The nuchal plane, formed by the occipital bone, is more inclined than in

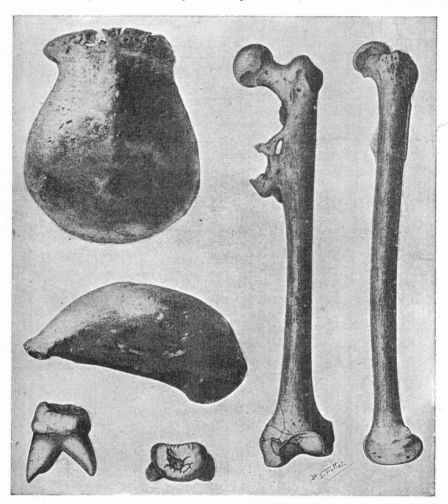

72 The principal bone-remains of *Pithecanthropus*

The skull-cap, seen from above and in profile, about one-third natural size. The femur, front view and profile, about one-fourth natural size. The third upper right true molar, in profile and the crown, natural size. (After Dubois)

the Anthropoid Apes, and less inclined than in Man. Following Dubois, various anatomists, particularly Manouvrier, have rightly laid stress on the presence of the protuberance, here somewhat less but still continuous, which in Apes unites the occipital, temporal, and supra-mastoid crests (*crête inio-mastoïdienne* of Tropinard, or *crête temporo-occipitale* of Manouvrier). This protuberance is always widely interrupted in Man, even in types which appear to us most primitive (Fig. 74).

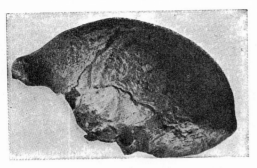

73 The skull-cap of the *Pithecanthropus* found at Sangiran in 1937. About one-third natural size. (After von Koenigswald)

Taken as a whole, these structures are very similar to those of chimpanzees and gibbons. Dubois has said that the skull of *Pithecanthropus* might be compared to a Gibbon skull enlarged to twice its size. Figs. 75 and 76 show that, in its principal characters, the Trinil skull-cap is really intermediate between that of an Ape, like the Chimpanzee, and that of a Man of really low status, such as Neandertal Man.

The skulls found at Sangiran present the same general characters. The best preserved, that known as *Pithe-*

canthropus II (Fig. 73), bears a striking resemblance to Dubois's historic piece; 'they are as alike as two peas', writes von Koenigswald; but it is more complete, for it has retained its temporal bones and the whole occipital shell. The most outstanding fact is the smallness of the encephalic capacity, which reaches only 815 cubic centimetres.[11] This figure might be partly explained by the sex, if—as von Koenigswald maintains—the Sangiran skull is female, while the Trinil cranium is male. Nevertheless, it has the great interest

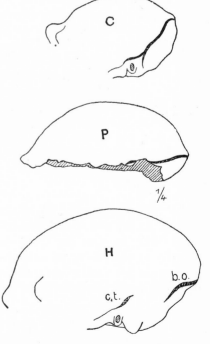

74 Sketch showing by a thick dark line the continuity of the occipito-temporal ridge in the skulls of a Chimpanzee (C) and of *Pithecanthropus* (P). In the skull of a Man as primitive as the type from La Chapelle-aux-Saints (H), the two elements, temporal crest (c.t.) and occipital ridge (b.o.) are already discontinuous.

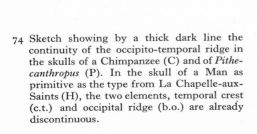

[11]Only 750 cubic centimetres, said von Koenigswald himself in 1938.

of rendering still smaller the gap between *Pithecanthropus* and the great Anthropoid Apes.

Other new observations concern the shape of the articular cavity for the lower maxilla and the situation of the external auditory orifice, both of which are situated as in modern Man. But the mastoid apophysis is reduced almost to nothing, as in the Anthropoids.

The fragments known as *Pithecanthropus IV* deserve special mention. The skull is thicker than those of the other two *Pithecanthropi*. The occipital

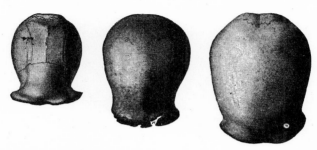

75 Skulls: (1) of Chimpanzee; (2) of *Pithecanthropus;* (3) of Neandertal Man, seen from above and on the same scale (about one-fifth natural size).

ridge is very highly developed. An important fact is that the cranial vault shows a longitudinal torus along the median line, a sort of embryonic version of the sagittal crest we see in Anthropoids. The fragment of upper jaw accompanying the cranium shows that the palate was extremely bulky: its length in the centre is 75 millimetres, whereas the maximum measured in modern Man is only 59; there was marked prognathism (Fig. 79). The cranial capacity has been estimated—very approximately—at 900 cubic centimetres. On account of these characters, Weidenreich considered that these pieces, which came from older levels than the rest, must correspond to a different and special form, which he dubbed *Pithecanthropus robustus*. It would not appear, however, to be more than a racial variation.

THE BRAIN

A cast of the interior of this skull-cap (Fig. 77) enabled Dubois to gain an idea of the brain that had been contained therein.[12] The convolutions, less simple than those of the Gibbons, seem already to be of the human type, an opinion shared by an eminent English specialist, Elliot Smith. But if the centres of sensation are well developed, as in Apes, the association centres are much less developed than in Man. The frontal region, the site of the higher

[12] See also Kappers, A., 'The fissures on the frontal lobes of *Pithecanthropus erectus* Dubois, compared with those of Neanderthal men, *Homo recens* and Chimpanzee' (*Kon. Akad. van Wetenschappen te Amsterdam, Proceedings* XXXII, 1929). Bouman, H., 'The Brain Convolutions of the *Pithecanthropus erectus* of von Königswald' (*Acta nederl. Morphologica*, II. 1939).

faculties, the noblest from the psychical point of view, is particularly reduced
in size. The inferior frontal convolution, double that of a chimpanzee or an

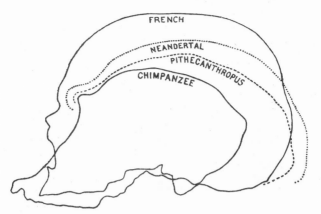

76 Superimposed profiles of the skulls of a Chimpanzee, of *Pithecanthropus*, of Neandertal
Man and of a modern Frenchman. About one-third natural size

orang, is only half that of a European. In his brain, as well as in his skull,
Pithecanthropus may then truly be considered as intermediate between the

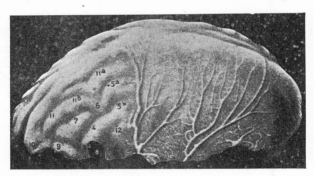

77 Lateral view of the left side of the endocranial cast of the *Pithecanthropus* from Trinil.
About half natural size. (After Ariens Kappers)

Great Apes and Man. Dubois declares that he may have had a rudimentary
articulate language.

THE MANDIBLE AND TEETH

The so-called Kedung Brubus jaw is a fragment of the horizontal ramus,
near the symphysal region, together with the socket of the canine tooth,
the root of the first premolar, and part of the socket of the second. Despite
the mutilated condition of this piece, Dubois did not hesitate to regard it
as 'almost perfectly human', but with a large digastric fossa situated entirely

on the lower margin of the bone: this structure, he says, is 'incompatible with the functioning of the tongue for articulate speech'.

The same characters occur in the half jawbone from Sangiran, a much more complete specimen than the above, because it still possesses four teeth; it is also far more massive.

For a long time the only teeth supposed to belong to *Pithecanthropus* were a first lower premolar and the second and third upper molars described

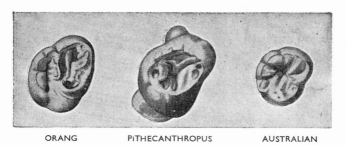

ORANG   PITHECANTHROPUS   AUSTRALIAN

78 Last right upper true molar of an Orang, of *Pithecanthropus* and of an Australian. One and a half times natural size. (After Gregory)

by Dubois. Of the latter, one, almost intact, is from the right side (Figs. 72 and 78); the other, from the left, is much worn and must have belonged to an older individual. These teeth were found separately, at various intervals of time and space. Each is of larger proportions than the corresponding human tooth, even if they be compared with the largest dentitions, such as those of the Australians.

The true molars have strong, very divergent roots, a simian characteristic; on the other hand, their crowns are relatively more developed in a transverse than in a longitudinal direction, and this may be regarded as a human characteristic. In short, these teeth differ both from those of Man and from those of living or fossil Apes (Fig. 78), but their greatest similarities are with those of the Orang and, according to Gregory,[13] of *Dryopithecus*. They are thus more simian than human. Von Koenigswald also does not hesitate to ascribe them to an orang, a diagnosis confirmed by the discovery of other orang teeth in the same level. He believes the premolar to be that of a true man.

Though these three teeth may seem doubtful, this is not the case with those found in position on the mandible (a second premolar with the three corresponding true molars) and the upper jaw (the canine, the two right premolars and the true molars, and the first left true molar) of *Pithecanthropus robustus* from Sangiran. The information they provide is of the greatest possible interest.

[13] Gregory, W. K., 'Studies on the Evolution of the Primates' (*Bull. Amer. Mus. Nat. Hist.*, New York, XXXV, 1916).

The true molars are extremely large and increase in size from the first to the third, a simian feature that does not occur in Humans. The point of the canine rises above the biting surface of the premolars, another simian character only found in Man in the fossil jaw from Wadjak (see Chap. X). No less important is the presence of a diastema or gap between the upper canine and the lateral incisor of 5 millimetres on the right and 6.2 millimetres on the left. In about fifty per cent of cases the diastema is no larger in Anthropoids; this feature, which proves that the lower canine must have been particularly highly developed (see Fig. 40), has never been encountered in the genus *Homo*.

To these characteristics may be added the fact that the upper premolars and true molars are arranged almost in a straight line, so that the form of the palate was more reminiscent of the U-shaped palate of the Anthropoids than of the horseshoe-shaped human palate (see Fig. 56). All these facts provide singularly unambiguous confirmation of those that emerged from a study of the cranium.

THE FEMURS

The left femur described by Dubois in 1894 is complete (Fig. 72). It measures 1 ft. 6 ins. in length: a Man with such a femur must have been 5 ft. 3 ins. to 5 ft. 6 ins. tall. It exhibits in the upper portion, on the level of the lines of bifurcation of the femoral crest (*linea aspera*), a large irregular development of bone (exostosis). This accidental pathological structure has aroused much discussion, the net result of which is to show that it has no bearing on the zoological nature of *Pithecanthropus*.

In its whole structure, this femur is so human that, had it been found alone, there would have been no hesitation in attributing it to a very old representative of our species. After studying it with very special care, Manouvrier found that it exhibited certain simian characters, in particular a convexity of the popliteal surface that is quite exceptional in the human femur. It is remarkable for its almost perfect straightness, a character which the femora of Gibbons and even of Cynomorphic Apes exhibit in the highest degree, but which is also encountered in Man. The very oblique direction of its main part testifies to the fact that the pelvis must have been large, a character correlative with the upright posture.[14] Dubois called particular attention to certain differences in the manner of insertion of the muscles, especially those of the pelvis-trochanterian region and the large adductor. Leaving aside some individual variations, the four femora discovered subsequently present the same general characters as the first. A special direction of the bony trabeculae has been disclosed. Taken as a whole, these characters indicate a more marked aptitude for climbing than Man possesses.

In any case, these femora point to their possessors having the faculty of

[14] Vallois, H., 'Sur quelques caractères du fémur du Pithécanthrope' (*C. R. Acad. des Sciences*, CLXVIII, 1919). Schwalbe, G., 'Studien über das Femur von *Pithecanthropus erectus* Dubois' (*Z. für Morph. und Anthrop.*, XXI, 1919–1921).

standing and walking upright. Hence the qualifying adjective *erectus*, chosen as the specific name for a creature who was *Pithecanthropus*—an Ape-Man— according to his skull.

INTERPRETATION OF THE FACTS

Such are the facts. If we possessed only the skull and the teeth, we should say that we were dealing with beings, if not identical with, at least closely allied to the Anthropoids. If we had only the femora, we should declare we were dealing with Man. Of the two principal characters of the Human Race, its large brain and upright attitude, the latter would seem in this case to have been wholly acquired before the former. Duckworth has pointed out that this is not consistent with the ontogenetic development of Man.[15] But, as we saw in Chapter III, the discovery of the Australopithecines has proved the possibility of dissociation of this nature. The comparative study of fossil Apes and Men also shows that the evolution of various organs was not simultaneous: some of the typically human characters appear earlier and some later, when the first were already fully developed.[16] An upright posture, it seems, was acquired before Man as such existed.

One first and important question was discussed at length from the outset: Did the skull-cap, the teeth, and the first femur, found separately and at more or less considerable intervals of time and distance, belong to the same being? Dubois considered himself justified in asserting that they did, because no remains of large Primates had ever been found in Java, except in this spot at Trinil, and the simultaneous presence of several species appeared very improbable. Further, the various bones were scattered at quite inconsiderable distances from one another. These were certainly good arguments, but they were not conclusive. We have seen that serious reservations had to be made with regard to the teeth; and whatever the presumptions in favour of the femur belonging to the cranium, some doubt remains, and will still remain, until new and more fortunate excavations put us in possession of less imperfect relics found in close association.

All attempts at restoration were undertaken on the assumption that the Trinil remains belonged to one and the same creature. Dubois, Manouvrier, McGregor, Osborn and Weinert published reconstructions of the cranium and even of the whole skull. These attempts, which were based principally on human anatomy, were far too hypothetical, since no data were available for the reconstruction of the base of the skull, the whole face, and all the apparatus of the lower jaw. Painted models of a complete *Pithecanthropus*, such as have actually been made, are pure flights of fancy.

The position is somewhat altered now that the discovery of the Sangiran pieces has greatly increased our knowledge of the Trinil fossil. Although

[15] Duckworth, W. L. H., *Prehistoric Man*, p. 6 (Cambridge, 1912).

[16] See on this subject and other points relating to the evolution of the Hominids, Vallois, H., 'La Paléontologie et l'origine de l'Homme' (*Colloques internationaux du C.N.R.S.*, XXI, *Paléontologie*, Paris, 1950).

the reconstruction made with the aid of these new evidences (Fig. 79) cannot be absolutely guaranteed—since certain parts, such as the ascending ramus of the mandible, and the regions of the nose and cheek, are still unknown—it must at least be pretty near the truth. The half human, half simian appearance of *Pithecanthropus* stands out with particular clarity.

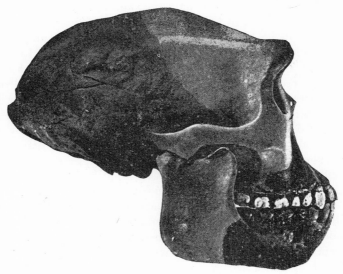

79 Reconstruction of the skull of *Pithecanthropus*. One-third natural size. (After Weidenreich)

Various interpretations have been given of the facts that we have just summarized as briefly but as accurately as possible. Miller, in a review published more than twenty years ago,[17] counted no less than fifteen different opinions at this early period. The views of these various authors may, however, be reduced to three: (1) *Pithecanthropus* is an Ape; (2) he represents a transitional form between the Anthropoids and Man; (3) he is already a Human, or rather a Hominian.[18]

These differences of opinion are at bottom more apparent than real. Those who believe in the simian character of *Pithecanthropus* really look upon it as an Ape superior to all living Apes, while those who believe in its human character regard it as inferior to all known Men, living or fossil. Wherever we place the Trinil fossil, according to its morphological characters in the series between Ape and Man, as at the points: P, P′, P″,

$$\text{APE} \ldots \ldots \text{P} \ldots \ldots \text{P}' \ldots \ldots \text{P}'' \ldots \ldots \text{MAN},$$

the fact remains that in all its characters known to us, this fossil stands in

[17] Miller, G. S., *The Controversy over Human 'Missing Links'* (Smithsonian Report for 1928, Washington, 1929).

[18] We shall merely mention without comment the absolutely unfounded opinion that it was an imbecile or microcephalic human being, and the other equally wild assertion that *Pithecanthropus* was the result of a cross between a Man and an Ape.

an intermediate, or if terminological exactitude be preferred, an interposed, position. This is a positive fact admitted by all competent naturalists.

But it must be distinctly stated, and in this case repeated, that resemblance does not always imply descent. Even if, in the sum of his known characters (poor at the best), *Pithecanthropus* actually forms a structural link between the Great Apes and Man, it does not necessarily follow that he must be regarded as a genealogical link; and this distinction is not, as has been asserted, merely a question of words.

GENEALOGICAL RELATIONSHIPS OF PITHECANTHROPUS

In order to come to a decisive conclusion regarding his true genealogical relationships, we should require to possess the complete skeleton of *Pithecanthropus*. In the present state of our knowledge, we cannot yet state that

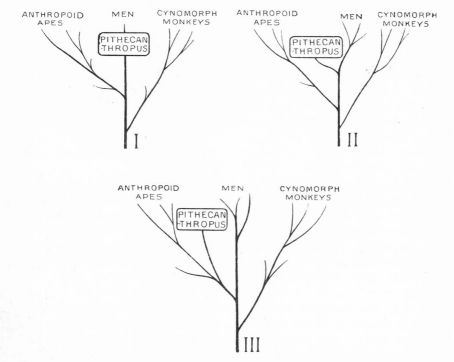

80 Diagrams showing the place of *Pithecanthropus* among the Primates: I, according to Dubois; II, according to other naturalists; III, according to an old hypothesis

there was any direct descent from this fossil to Man, such as the genealogical tree prepared by Dubois in 1894 would indicate (Fig. 80, I).

It is perhaps better to admit that the evolutionary branch to which the famous Javan fossil belongs is different from the human branch. Naturalists have no longer any doubt that we are related to the Apes; but it is of some

interest to try to define this relationship, especially when we meet with a
creature apparently more akin to us than all the others. Dubois rightly
pointed out that if *Pithecanthropus* is, so to speak, only our great-uncle
instead of our grandfather, he is none the less an Ape-Man representing a
stage in human descent. The majority of scientists today adhere to this
view. They consider *Pithecanthropus* to be an extinct lateral twig of the
Hominian branch (Fig. 80, II).

It is possible, however, to interpret these genealogical relationships in
yet another way. Following Dubois, several naturalists have laid stress on
the resemblance between the *Pithecanthropus* remains and the corresponding
portions of a Gibbon's skeleton. In that case, why not assume that *Pithecanthropus* represents a large form, a giant Ape, related to the Gibbon group?
Dubois himself tended strongly towards this view (Fig. 80, III) during the
last years of his life.

A certain number of facts can be adduced in support of this hypothesis.
In all countries, during Pliocene and Quaternary times, there were giant
forms of mammals whose living representatives are now greatly reduced in
size. This is the case—to limit ourselves to the Primates—with *Megaladapis*,
a giant Lemur of the Quaternary in Madagascar, and *Dryopithecus giganteus*,
a fossil Anthropoid of great size from the Siwalik Hills. *Pithecanthropus*,
discovered in the same zoological region as the modern Gibbons, may have
been no more than a particularly large representative of a genus more or less
closely allied to the same group.

THE MODJOKERTO CHILD AND MEGANTHROPUS

The question is, however, less simple than appears at first sight. As long
as only the Trinil fragments were known, they could be regarded as representing one and the same form. The first crania from Sangiran were readily
fitted into this group; but *Pithecanthropus IV* was already sufficiently distinct
to be envisaged as a form of its own. Two finds made in Java, which have
not yet been discussed, show the existence of even more considerable variations: these are the Modjokerto skull and a fragment of jaw called *Meganthropus*.

In 1936 von Koenigswald announced the discovery at Modjokerto, not
far from Surabaya, of the skull of a very young child. This skull, which
was contained in the lacustro-volcanic Djetis strata and is consequently
older than the Trinil *Pithecanthropus*, dates from the bottom layer of the
Quaternary, which renders it a particularly important object of study.[19]
Unfortunately, this very incomplete fragment lacks part of its base and almost

[19] Koenigswald, G. H. R. von, 'Ein fossiler Hominid aus dem Altpleistozän Ostjavas'
(*De Ingenieur in Nederlandsch-Indie*, No. 8, 1936); 'Erste Mitteilung über fossilen Hominiden
aus dem Altpleistozän Ostjavas' (*Kon. Akad. van Wetenschappen te Amsterdam, Proc.*,
XXXIX, 1936). Dubois, E., 'Racial Identity of *Homo Soloensis* Oppenoorth (including *H.
Modojokertensis* von Koenigswald) and *Sinanthropus pekinensis* Davidson Black' (*Ibid.*,
XXXIX, 1936). Grimm, H., 'Untersuchungen über den fossilen Hominidenschädel von
Modjokerto aus Java' (*Anthrop. Anzeiger*, XVII, 1940).

all the face. Basing his conclusion on the thinness of the bones, von Koenigs-wald attributes it to a little girl of four to five years. But Dubois believed that its structure was that of a child of two.

The brain-pan (Fig. 81), which is small and brachycephalic, is relatively high for its length. Its capacity does not seem to be more than 700 cubic centimetres, which would give the figure of approximately 900 c.cm. in the adult. The forehead is more receding than that of a modern child of the same age; there is no trace of an occipital torus, and the supra-orbital arches are beginning to protrude in their lateral sections. But, alongside these primitive

81 The Modjokerto skull, in profile. About two-thirds natural size. (After a photograph of the original by von Koenigswald)

characters, it must be noted that the glenoid fossa is deep, the mastoid apophysis strong, the occipital bone rounded, and the part of the brain-pan occupied by the parietal bone larger than that constituted by the frontal bone. All these characters recall those of modern Man.

Von Koenigswald initially considered this piece as a new species to which he gave the name *Homo modjokertensis*, while Dubois regarded it as a youthful representative of Ngandong Man (see Chap. IX), and Grimm saw in it a 'Neantertaloid form of *Sinanthropus*'. This diversity of opinion is explained by the curious mixture of primitive and recent characters in this fossil. On the other hand, we know how much caution is required in interpreting young subjects, to whom their slight development of the distinctive charac-ters of the adult often gives an appearance recalling less specialized species of the same group.

There seems, in any case, no doubt that this is a juvenile form of *Pithe-canthropus*, and von Koenigswald has now come round to this opinion.

But its geological age indicates that it does not belong to the Trinil *Pithecanthropus* properly so-called. In the Dutch geologist's view, it is related to *Meganthropus*, which we shall discuss.

In 1941 von Koenigswald announced the discovery, still in the Djetis levels, of a fragment of lower jawbone that was incontestably human but possessed far more primitive characters than the known jaws of *Pithecanthropus* and *Sinanthropus*. This jaw was studied at length by Weidenreich.[20] It was distinguished especially by its dimensions, which were greater not only than any known lower jaw of modern or fossil Man, but even of the vast majority of the Anthropoids, with the exception of a few large male gorillas. Thus its circumference at the level of the mental foramen is 131 millimetres, as against 115 mm. in the Gorilla and 80 in *Sinanthropus* and Neandertal Man. The teeth share this gigantism (Fig. 82). In addition, it has certain distinctly primitive characteristics—notably the absence of

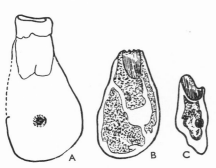

82 Cross-section of the lower jaws of: A, *Meganthropus;*, B Melanesian with hypertrophied jaw; C, European. Natural size. (After Weidenreich)

chin and the receding angle of the fore part of the jaw. But other features, such as the structure of the teeth, prove that this is no Ape, but a Hominid. Von Koenigswald takes the view that it is a special form of *Pithecanthropus*, and gives it the name *Meganthropus palaeojavanicus*.

This unexpected discovery was connected by Weidenreich with mysterious finds made in South China some years earlier. Amongst other substances, the Chinese pharmacopoeia makes use of fossil bones and teeth, and palaeontologists have often reaped a rich harvest from the stock

of Chinese chemists' shops. This was how, between 1934 and 1939, von Koenigswald collected in Hong Kong—mingled with teeth of Orang, Stegodon and Tapir, testifying to a Pleistocene fauna—three extraordinarily large molars that he ascribed to a giant Anthropoid, *Gigantopithecus blackii* (Fig. 83). These teeth are twice the size of the corresponding teeth in a Gorilla and six times those of Man. As far as their worn condition permitted an opinion to be formed, von Koenigswald supposed that their general shape, as well as certain details of their structure, resembled that of the teeth of *Sivapithecus* from the Siwalik Hills, which are huge.

This view was not shared by Weidenreich, who declared that these were not the teeth of Anthropoids, but of a Hominid, claiming that the pattern of the crowns was far more human than simian. The name *Gigantopithecus*, he said, should be changed to *Gigantanthropus*. Taken in conjunction with

[20] Weidenreich, F., 'Giant Early Man from Java aund Soth China' (*Anthrop. Papers of the Amer. Mus. Nat. Hist.*, XL, No. 1, 1945).

the discovery of *Meganthropus*, the new find teaches us that there existed in Java and South China, at the beginning of the Quaternary, giant forms of Man, the earliest representatives of the human race yet known. Going still further, Weidenreich did not hesitate to draw a genealogical tree. *Gigantanthropus*, he claimed, gave rise to *Meganthropus* and no doubt also to *Sinanthropus*, whom we shall study shortly. After emigrating to Java, *Meganthropus*—of which the Modjokerto fossil is a juvenile form—gave rise in its turn to *Pithecanthropus robustus*, which was the ancestor of the

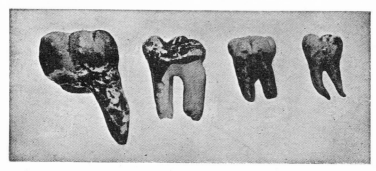

83 Comparison between the teeth (from left to right) of: *Gigantanthropus*, male Gorilla, *Sinanthropus*, modern Man. All these teeth are third molars, except that of *Sinanthropus*, which is a first molar. Nine-tenths natural size. (After Weidenreich)

Trinil *Pithecanthropus*. Finally, the latter gave birth to certain living and fossil races. Man is therefore descended from giant forms with a massive skull, and his evolution was marked by a progressive reduction in stature.[21]

Ingenious as it is, the American anthropologist's thesis presents too many weak points to be taken seriously: in particular, the human origin of the three Hong-Kong molars is far from being proven.[22] But the essential fact is that the Java discoveries show us the multiplicity of types of primitive Hominid on this island during the first period of the Quaternary. *Meganthropus*, *Pithecanthropus robustus*, and *P. trinilensis* represent so many different forms of descending stature, forms whose exact relationship to one another cannot yet be precisely stated, but which manifestly belong to the same group and testify to the unsuspected diversity of the first Hominids.

This diversity is less surprising than it might appear. Study of the fossil Anthropoids has already shown the occurrence in this family, during the Miocene and Pliocene, of an extraordinary flowering of new species, some of which seem to have moved in the direction of the Chimpanzee and the Gorilla, others towards the Gibbon and the Orang, and yet others, with the Australopithecines, towards Man.

[21] Weidenreich, F., *Apes, Giants and Man* (Chicago, 1946).

[22] Hooijer, D., 'Some Notes on the *Gigantopithecus* Question' (*Amer. J. of Phys. Anthropology*, No. 1, VII, 1949).

It is a continuation of this tendency to ramification that we see in the early stages of the Hominids. Whether we adopt Diagram I or Diagram II, *Pithecanthropus* can no longer be regarded as a homogeneous bloc, but as a collection of forms in the process of diversification. One of these forms is perhaps the stock of Mankind, or at least of some section of the human race; others would appear to have been sterile branches in which the tendency to gigantism, as is often the case in vertebrates, was the very cause of their extinction. The evolution of *Pithecanthropus* was, therefore, very complex. In any case, in whatever manner we interpret them, the facts revealed by Dubois's discovery remain of supreme interest to science.

SINANTHROPUS

Although much more recent, the discovery of *Sinanthropus* was no less important that that of *Pithecanthropus*.

In 1921, Drs. Anderson and Zdansky investigated a pocket of bone-remains situated close to the village of Choukoutien, south-west of Peking. There they recovered two molars 'of human type'. A third molar was found in 1927 by Dr. Bohlin and described by Dr. Davidson Black, who boldly created for it a new genus, which he called *Sinanthropus pekinensis*.[23]

During the summer of 1928, a Chinese palaeontologist in charge of the excavations, Dr. W. C. Pei, extracted fragments of crania, two pieces of lower jaws, and numerous isolated teeth, which were immediately published by Dr. Black.[24]

In 1929, Dr. Pei exhumed a well preserved skull-cap resembling that of *Pithecanthropus*.[25] The news created a great stir in the world press.

After the discovery of a second cranium, the Geological Survey of China decided to acquire the site and preserve it for science. Since then it has been systematically explored, thanks to the financial munificence (amounting to about £8,000) of the Rockefeller Foundation of New York.

In 1931, Dr. Pei announced the presence at Choukoutien of hearths denoting the use of fire, and many worked flints. At the same time, Father Teilhard de Chardin and his co-worker Young made a careful study of the stratigraphy and palaeontology of the site.[26]

Continuing his publications, Black described the two skull-caps, an

[23] Black, D., 'On a Lower Molar Hominid Tooth from the Chou Kou Tien Deposit' (*Palaeontologia Sinica*, Series D, Vol. VII, Section 1, 1927).

[24] Black, D., 'Preliminary Note on additional *Sinanthropus* material discovered Chou Kou Tien' (*Bull. of Geol. Soc. of China*, VIII, 1929).

[25] Pei, W. C., 'An account of the discovery of an adult *Sinanthropus* skull in the Chou Kou Tien deposit.' Black, D., 'Preliminary notice of the discovery of an adult *Sinanthropus* skull at Chou Kou Tien' (*Bull. of Geol. Soc. of China*, VIII, 1930).

[26] Teilhard de Chardin and Young, C. C., 'Preliminary Report on the Chou Kou Tien Fossiliferous Deposit' (*Bull. of Geol. Soc. of China*, VIII, 1930).

endocranial cast, a series of lower jaws, and some other pieces of less interest.[27]

These various studies have been lucidly summarized in a volume that includes the final conclusion reached by Black and his collaborators.[28]

The work of research, which was temporarily halted by the death of its principal animator, was resumed under his successor, F. Weidenreich, and continued with the same material resources and the same enthusiasm until 1939. Thanks to these labours, the main problems posed by *Sinanthropus* may now be considered solved.

THE SITE

The village of Choukoutien lies 25 miles south-west of Peking (now called Peiping), at the foot of the hills dominating the plain of Hopei. These hills are formed chiefly of Silurian limestone, fissured, eroded and riddled with

84 Choukoutien Hill and the fossil-bearing deposits. (After Barbour)
Towards the centre, slightly to the right, is visible the great pediculate excavation known as 'Locality I'.

subterranean cavities, which have been laid bare by the quarrying of the limestone and whose fillings are rich in fossil bones of all kinds (Fig. 84).

Investigations have been carried out at several points, that is to say in various fissures or tunnels numbered 1 to 15. The first deposit excavated, known as 'Locality 1', is by far the most important (Fig. 85). It comprises a vast cavern whose roof had collapsed on top of the cave-filling. The materials of the latter today appear on the surface along a distance of a hundred yards, and are about 150 feet thick. They consist essentially of red clays, which are sometimes sandy, containing angular calcareous pebbles, fallen boulders, and, at some points, masses of cinders. The whole formation is generally consolidated, hardened, and sometimes even transformed into a stalagmitic breccia. According to Teilhard, these filling deposits, which

[27] Black, D., 'On an Adolescent Skull of *Sinanthropus pekinensis* in comparison with an adult skull of the same species' (*Palaeontologia Sinica*, Series D, VII, Section 2, 1931); 'On an Endocranial Cast of the Adolescent *Sinanthropus* Skull' (*Proc. Roy. Soc.*, B, Vol. CXII 1933); 'On six Specimens of *Sinanthropus* Mandibulae' (*Palaeont. Sinica*, Series D, Vol. VII, Section 3, 1933).

[28] Black, D., Teilhard de Chardin, Young, C. C. and Pei, W. C., 'Fossil Man in China. The Choukoutien cave deposits with a synopsis of our present knowledge.' (*Memoirs of the Geol. Survey of China*, Series A, No. 11, 1934).

are very similar to those of European caves, may here be divided into three zones or layers: an upper breccia, a sandy formation, and a lower breccia, containing more fossils than the upper breccia.

To begin with, the *Sinanthropus* fragments were found almost exclusively in this 'Locality 1' and at many different levels of its filling. But it is ack-

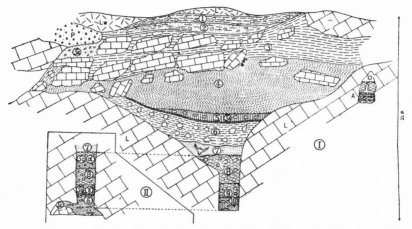

85 Section of 'Locality I' of the Choukoutien deposit. (After Teilhard de Chardin and Young)

1–7, various levels of the main pocket; 8–10 and *a*–δ, level of the vertical offshoot below the main pocket; 5, stalagmite floor; SA–SE, points at which remains of Sinanthropus were found; SE, 'Locus E', from which Skull I was recovered.

nowledged nowadays that the fossil fauna is homogeneous from the summit to the base of the deposits, and that *Sinanthropus* has everywhere the same characteristics. Distinctions between the levels are therefore of little interest.

What age are we to ascribe to this deposit?

The fossil fauna of Choukoutien is very rich, since, according to the accounts of Teilhard and Young, it comprises no less than a hundred species of vertebrates, of which 88 are mammals. Such an abundance of relics might be expected to render the exact dating of the deposits containing them an easy matter. But the enormous distance separating Peking from Europe, whose successions of faunas are well known to us, seriously complicates the problem, since it results in great differences between species. There are, however, certain common forms that serve as landmarks.

The principal elements in the fauna accompanying *Pithecanthropus* are: an Elephant closely allied to our *Elephas antiquus*; two species of Rhinoceros —*Rhinoceros mercki* and *R. tichorinus*; a true Horse; a member of the Cervidae allied to our Megaceros; a Buffalo of extinct species; numerous Carnivores: a Wolf, a Cuon, several species of Bears and Hyaenas closely related to our own, a *Machairodus*, and many Cats. Among the Rodents which were even more abundant, must be mentioned—in addition to more local species—a large Beaver belonging to the European Old Pleistocene, the *Trogontherium*.

Teilhard attributes this fauna to the Lower Pleistocene because, by its composition, it clearly falls between the Upper Pliocene fauna of the same region and the fauna of the Chinese loess contemporary with that of our own loess. A physiographic study of the Choukoutien district corroborates the palaeontological conclusions. Still according to Teilhard, the fossils as a whole, both vegetable and animal, indicate a more temperate and more humid climate than that which obtains at present. It seems, however, as though, by and large, the *Sinanthropus* deposits are more recent than those containing *Pithecanthropus*. This would mean that the Choukoutien fossils are less ancient than those from Java. But it is extremely difficult to establish an accurate chronological correlation.[29]

The osteological material attributed to *Sinanthropus* already comprised a large number of pieces in 1935: three more or less incomplete brain-cases with different fragments of the cranium, a dozen fragments of lower jaws, fifty or so isolated teeth, a collar-bone, two fragments of long bones—one of a humerus, the other of a radius—a semilunar bone, and four ungual phalanges. According to Weidenreich, what this author calls 'the population of Choukoutien' was then represented by the remains of 10 children, 2 adolescents, and 12 adults including men and women. By 1939, according to the same author, this number had risen to 38, of which 15 were children or adolescents.[30]

THE SKULLS

The skulls are all damaged and lack their lower jaw. In the important monograph Weidenreich devoted to them,[31] he counted 14, in 5 of which the neurocranium was virtually complete.

The first to be found, Skull III (it was Skull I in the original nomenclature), came from the deepest section of the deposit, from *Locus E*. It was ascribed by Black to an adolescent and by Weidenreich to a male child of eight or nine years old. Skull II, from *Locus D*, found at a slightly higher level, was described by Black as an adult, while Weidenreich held that it was an adolescent female of fourteen to eighteen.

The three other skulls, discovered in 1936 and belonging respectively to

[29] Movius, Jr., 'H., Early Man and Pleistocene Stratigraphy in Southern and Eastern Asia' (*Papers Peabody Museum of Amer. Archaeology and Ethnology*, XIX, No. 3, 1944).

[30] Weidenreich, F., 'The Sinanthropus Population of Choukoutein. . .with a preliminary report on new discoveries' (*Bull. of Geol. Soc. of China*, XIV, No. 4, 1935); 'The Duration of Life of Fossil Man in China and the Pathological Lesions found in his Skeleton' (*The Chinese Med. J.*, LV, 1939). All this splendid material, of exceptional value for the history of early humanity, has unfortunately disappeared. Seized by the Japanese during military operations in China, the cases containing the remains of *Sinanthropus* have never been recovered.

[31] Weidenreich, F., 'The Skull of *Sinanthropus pekinensis*, a comparative study on a primitive hominid skull' (*Palaeontologia Sinica*, New Series, D. No. 10, Peking, 1943).

an adult man and woman and a 'young adult', came from *Locus L.* They
lay in the same stratum, which was devoid of animal bones or worked stones.
Unlike the earlier finds, they retained parts of the face. Thanks to this body

86 Skull III of *Sinanthropus pekinensis*, see from the side (*norma lateralis*), from above
(*norma verticalis*), from the front (*norma facialis*), from the rear (*norma occipitalis*) and from
below (*norma basilaris*). About one-third natural size. (After the photographs of D. Black)

of material and a few isolated fragments, we now possess—distributed among
several subjects—all the parts of the skull of *Sinanthropus*. It has been possible to make a reasonably accurate reconstruction of this skull (Figs. 91
to 93).

Skull III (Fig. 86) is the one that has been most carefully studied. Seen
from above and from the side it bears a striking resemblance to the skull of

Pithecanthropus, in its dimensions (the same to within a few millimetres), its identical cephalic index, its general shape, its shallowness, its enormous vizor-like supra-orbital ridge, its pronounced post-orbital constriction, its receding forehead, its protuberant occiput, and its occipital torus. The frontal and parietal eminences are more distinct, but this infantile characteristic is of no significance; moreover, it does not occur in Skull II, whose general contour is even more akin to that of the Javan skull (Fig. 87). Another distinctive character it shares with *Pithecanthropus* is the presence of a furrow between the supra-orbital ridge and the beginning of the forehead. This does not seem to have so much significance as has been ascribed to it.

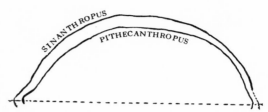

87 Superimposed profiles of the skull-caps of *Pithecanthropus* and *Sinanthropus* (Skull II). About one-third. (Based on the figure by Black)

The bones of the skull-cap are far more massive than is general in Man. Their average thickness of about 10 millimetres may reach 18 millimetres at certain points. This is strange in a child's skull, when the bones of the adolescent or adult Skull II are of normal thickness. It shows primarily that the characteristic of greater or lesser thickness of the cranial bones, sometimes appealed to by anthropologists, cannot be of much importance from a taxonomic point of view.

The lateral portions of the base of the skull, unknown in *Pithecanthropus*, are here preserved, notably the roof of the orbits and the two temporal bones. The central section, that is the periphery of the occipital foramen, has been destroyed in all the examples.

Seen from the occipital or rear view, the skull shows its maximum width near the base, in the temporal region, as in the Apes and *Pithecanthropus*, and not higher up, in the parietal region, as in Men, even of the lowest degree. In respect of this morphological feature, *Sinanthropus* and *Pithecanthropus* are still Apes.

The temporal bones present a curious mixture of characters. The elongated, low and unarched shape of the squamous portion is pithecoid. On the other hand, the glenoid cavity is as deep and narrow as in modern Man. The tympanic bone forming its rear wall is particularly robust. It seems to be made up of two pieces that are incompletely coalesced and still separated at the bottom by a long fissure. Although it was initially considered a special feature, this tympanic fissure seems to be only the persistence of a juvenile characteristic that is found, in more or less accentuated form, in young Neandertals and even in adults of certain existing human races. Moreover, it is lacking in the temporal bones of the other *Sinanthropus* skulls.

The wide auditory meatus opens into a covered vestibule, as in the Great

Apes, under a sort of hood formed by the very marked projection of the zygomatic crest.

Behind the tympanic region, the mastoid apophysis forms a slight projection which, on this side, terminates the occipital torus. Finally, according to Weidenreich, the axis of the auditory meatus and the axis of the petrous pyramid, instead of lying in one straight line, as in Man, form an elbow, as in Apes (Fig. 88).

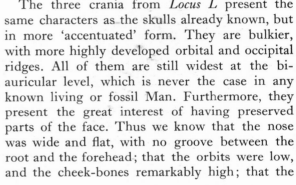

In its totality, the general structure of the *Sinanthropus* skull is still very apelike. The only truly human characteristic is the form of the glenoid fossa, which is evidently connected with the humanoid, if not human, structure of the masticatory apparatus.

The three crania from *Locus L* present the same characters as the skulls already known, but in more 'accentuated' form. They are bulkier, with more highly developed orbital and occipital ridges. All of them are still widest at the bi-auricular level, which is never the case in any known living or fossil Man. Furthermore, they present the great interest of having preserved parts of the face. Thus we know that the nose was wide and flat, with no groove between the root and the forehead; that the orbits were low, and the cheek-bones remarkably high; that the

88 Sketch of the right lower temporal region of a Chimpanzee, of *Sinanthropus* (Skull III) and of a modern Man. The dotted lines indicate the differences of shape and curve of the petrous portions. (After Weidenreich)

upper jawbone, which projected far forward had no canine fossa; that the palate was wide and high.

THE BRAIN

The cerebral capacity of Skull III, estimated by Black at 960 cubic centimetres, was said by Weidenreich to have been no more than 915 c.cm., a figure roughly equal to that of the Trinil *Pithecanthropus*.

The capacities of the skulls from *Locus L* are appreciably higher: 1,015 c.cm. for the woman, 1,030 and 1,225 c.cm. for the men. The last skull, that from *Locus D*, the sex of which could not be established with certainty, had only 1,030 cubic centimetres. Although these figures are very approximate, since the base of the skulls are partially missing, and although they testify to a curious variability, they fall, as may be seen, within the same region as those found for the *Pithecanthropi*. In this respect, as in many others, the Peking fossils and those from Java are closely allied and form a small group situated at about an equal distance from the highest Apes on the one hand, and the archaic type of Neandertal Man on the other.

The excellent endocranial cast of Skull III (Fig. 89) shows a generally chimpanzoid form; but the frontal region, the most favourable for study, seems already to possess human characters. The lateral sulcus is wide open, so that the anterior portion of the *insula* was still exposed; operculization

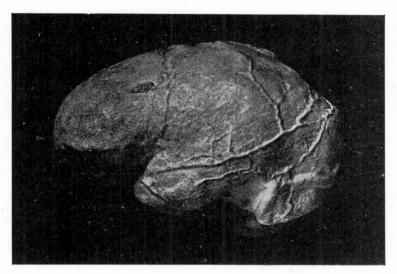

89 Left side of the endocranial cast of *Sinanthropus* (Skull III). Direct photograph. Half scale.

is more advanced, however, especially in the inferior frontal region, where Broca's convolution is already developing. In short, according to Black, *Sinanthropus*, whose hemispheres were slightly unequal, must have been right-handed and in possession of an articulate language.

A Dutch specialist, Kappers,[32] resumed the study of this cast in comparison with similar casts of *Pithecanthropus* and Neandertal Man. His conclusion is that, by virtue of the mode of fissuration of the frontal lobes, the Peking fossil belongs to a human type, but one possessing still more primitive characters than those of *Homo neandertalensis. Pithecanthropus*, he says, is more apelike, 'essentially chimpanzoid'.

More recently, Weidenreich studied two more endocranial casts.[33] A

[32] Kappers, A., 'The Fissuration of the Frontal Lobe of *Sinanthropus pekinensis* Black, compared with the fissuration in Neanderthal men' (*Kon. Akad. van Wetenschappen te Amsterdam, Proceedings*, XXXVI, 1933).

[33] Weidenreich, F., 'Observations on the form and proportions of the endocranial casts of *Sinanthropus pekinensis*, other Hominids and the Great Apes, a comparative study of brain size' (*Palaeontologia Sinica*, Series D, Vol. VII, Section 4, Peking, 1936).

comparison with those of the large Anthropoids and various races of Men makes it possible to trace the manner in which the brain progressively increased in size. From the Chimpanzee to *Sinanthropus* the process is almost regular; from *Sinanthropus* to modern Man it is more marked in the parietal region; the frontal and occipital zones—especially the latter— increase far less. Another characteristic fact mentioned by Weidenreich is the diminutiveness of the temporal lobe in *Sinanthropus*.

The same author also studied the ramification of the middle meningeal artery:[34] from this point of view, *Sinanthropus* more closely resembles the Great Apes, such as the Gorilla, than living or fossil Men. In particular, there is to be observed a poverty of arterial arborization that contrasts with the wealth of arborization in Man. In this respect, again, the Peking fossil is far more primitive than Neandertal Man.

In spite of all these primitive characters, the cerebral volume of *Sinanthropus* is sufficient, in Weidenreich's eyes, to explain 'the relatively highly developed culture' attested by the stone industry of Choukoutien.

THE LOWER JAW AND TEETH

As always in *natural* bone-beds of fossil mammals, lower jawbones are more numerous at Choukoutien than other parts of the skeleton. The known fragments, of varying importance, belong to a dozen individuals of both sexes and all ages. Black tried to reconstruct two mandibles, one of a young individual, the other of an adult. A single glance shows that these restorations are defective: we know now that the half jaw of the 'adult' is made up of two fragments, one really that of an adult, the other of a child. The distinguished Peking palaeontologist concluded from his premature study that the lower jaw of *Sinanthropus* presented 'striking' similarities with that of modern Man. This was going much too far, as could be seen from Black's own work and as emerges from a memoir by Weidenreich.[35]

This new study was carried out on eleven fragments of lower jaw belonging to 6 young individuals and 5 adults. Since none of the pieces was complete, the author was compelled to reconstruct three examples, of a man, a woman (Fig. 90), and a child respectively. The total result was so polymorphous that Weidenreich wondered whether it was really a single species, or at least a single race. It is a fact, however, that this polymorphism is a simian characteristic in singular contrast to the slight sexual dimorphism in human jaws.

Another characteristic, just as important and just as striking, is the receding appearance of the symphyseal region, that is to say the absence of chin. Along with these characteristics and some others no less pithecoid, such as the presence on the lower margin of the bone of imprints of the

[34] 'Weidenreich, F., 'The ramification of the middle meningeal artery in fossil Hominids and its bearing upon phylogenetic Problems' (*Palaeontologia Sinica*, New Series D, Section 3, Peking, 1938).

[35] Weidenreich, F., 'The Mandibles of *Sinanthropus pekinensis*: a comparative study' (*Palaeontologia Sinica*, Series D, Vol. VII, Section 4, Peking, 1936).

digastric muscle, the *Sinanthropus* mandibles present morphological features
—notably the shape of the dental arcade—that move them away from the
Great Apes and bring them closer to the ancient group of the Neandèrtals.
It is impossible here to review in detail all the facts so fully analysed by

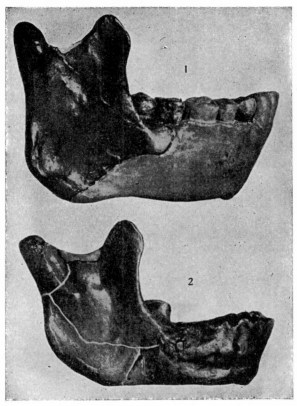

90 Restored lower jaws of *Sinanthropus* seen in profile. 1, a male individual; 2, a female
individual. Two-thirds. (After Weidenreich)

Weidenreich. But we may subscribe to the conclusion, which is certainly
the most important in his memoir, that the *Sinanthropus* mandible presents
'a veritable intermingling of pithecoid and human characters'.[36]

The dentition, too, is less human than was initially supposed. Weidenreich[37] has devoted a painstaking comparative memoir to it. His studies
related to 147 teeth, of which 83 were in their jaws and 64—including a

[36] *Op. cit.*, p. 125. The author goes much further. As the lower jaw of *Sinanthropus* sometimes shows a sort of exostosis in the alveolar region of the lingual surface, and as this *torus
mandibularis* is found in various human races, notable in the Mongoloids, Weidenreich does
not hesitate to consider the Peking fossil the remote but direct ancestor of the Chinese!

[37] Weidenreich, F., 'The Dentition of *Sinanthropus pekinensis:* A comparative odontography
of the Hominids' (*Palaeontologia Sinica*, New Series D, No. 1, Peking, 1937).

large number of milk teeth—in isolation. The total number represented 32 individuals.

The first thing that strikes us in this collection of relics is the high degree of variability, partly connected with sex—the male teeth being larger than the female teeth. This dimorphism, which is slight in Humans, is just as marked here as in living Anthropoids. Generally speaking, all the *Sinanthropus* teeth are bulkier and more robust than those of Man, fossil or recent. Their enamel is thicker, their roots longer.

The backs of the incisors are hollowed out, giving them a shovel shape— a structure found in Apes as well as in certain human races, notably the Mongols. The upper canines are particularly large, both in their roots and in their crowns, which has led to their being described as 'small tusks'. They rise appreciably above the level of the other teeth, as in *Pithecanthropus* and the Apes. But, unlike any of the latter, no diastema separates them from the neighbouring teeth, and it is the same in the lower jaw. The lower canines, on the other hand, look rather like large incisors.

The lower premolars have a very pithecoid structure, with the production of a heel on their distal edge. The back molars are little different in structure from those of living Anthropoids, having retained their basilar ridge (*cingulum*), their more complicated topography with accessory crest and tubercles, and their more wrinkled enamel. They likewise resemble those of *Dryopithecus* and *Australopithecus*. According to Weidenreich, it is easy to distinguish the molars of *Sinanthropus*, which are low and long, from those of the Hominids, which are high and short.

To sum up: By the sum total of their characters, the mandibles and teeth of *Sinanthropus* denote a large Primate that was certainly more closely allied to Man than any known Great Ape, fossil or living, but whose status was not yet frankly human—certainly less human than the Mauer jaw (see Chap. VI), which is probably older than the Peking fossils.

OTHER REMAINS

Apart from the skull fragments just discussed, almost nothing is known about the skeleton of *Sinanthropus*. This is a very curious phenomenon, to which we shall have to return.

The relics that have been described and attributed to the famous fossil[38] are: a semilunar bone, a large fragment of clavicle, two pieces of humerus, and seven femoral diaphyses. Apart from the semilunar bone, all these bones are very badly damaged and lack their epiphyses, a fact that is doubtless attributable to the activities of hyaenas, which have left many traces in the deposit. Four 'ungual phalanges', found by Black in 1929 and associated by him with *Sinanthropus*, really come from the vestigial digits of deer; a fragment of radius, likewise ascribed to *Sinanthropus*, belongs to a macaque.

[38] Weidenreich, F., 'The Extremity Bones of *Sinanthropus pekinensis*' (*Palaeontologia Sinica*, New Series D, No. 5, Peking, 1941).

The clavicle was described and figured by Black, who found that it exactly resembled, both in shape and size, the human collar-bone. The same is true of the semilunar bone, which does not differ in any feature from that of living Men.

Although lacking their articular heads, the femurs reveal interesting details. Though generally human in appearance, they are distinguished from modern femurs, and at the same time from that of *Pithecanthropus*, by a marked antero-posterior flattening that extends along their whole length— even in the popliteal region. The femoral curvature is slight and its summit much closer to the lower extremity of the bone than in modern Man. Another characteristic is the very great thickness of the diaphysal wall, with a correlative narrowness of the medullary canal. As far as may be judged in the absence of the articular heads, it seems as though these femora must have been about 16 inches long, a figure far lower than that of *Pithecanthropus* and one which, in Man, would correspond to a stature of approximately 5 feet. The fragments of humerus are also 'specifically human'; but, as in the femora, the walls are strikingly thick. The deltoid imprint is very strong.

All things considered and taking an objective view free from preconceived ideas, none of these bones differs from those of Man in such a way that they can be said to belong to another being. Are they really to be ascribed to *Sinanthropus*, and is it not surprising that apart from these few fragments nothing has been found corresponding to the remainder of the trunk and the limbs? This is a serious lacuna in our knowledge.

PITHECANTHROPUS AND SINANTHROPUS

While describing the skull-caps of *Sinanthropus*, we indicated their close resemblance to those of *Pithecanthropus*. No one, nowadays, denies this resemblance. In that case, why create a new generic name for the Peking fossil? One of us was among the first, if not the first, to ask this question;[39] nothing we have learnt since has been of a nature to make us retract it. There is no doubt that the two great fossil Primates of Java and Peking, whose geological age is only very slightly different, belong to a single morphological type, and that the differences between the common bony parts have at most a specific, and not a generic, value. No naturalist experienced in the study of fossil mammals could think otherwise.

Black, who had felt justified in forging the term *Sinanthropus* to designate *one* tooth, was naturally concerned to legitimize this creation when he had to describe a skull-cap. While acknowledging the great resemblance of this piece to its Javan counterpart, he stressed the differences and demonstrated them by numerical data. Now, on studying his tables of measurements,[40] it is quite evident that the differences observed between *Pithecanthropus*

[39] Boule, M., 'Le *Sinanthropus*' (*L'Anthropologie*, XXXIX, 1929, p. 455).
[40] 'On an Adolescent Skull. . .', pp. 74 and 92. See also Weidenreich, F., 'Six Lectures on *Sinanthropus pekinensis* and related Problems' (*Bull. of the Geological Society of China*, XIX, 1939).

on the one hand, and the various fragments of *Sinanthropus* on the other, far from possessing generic value, are less than the variations recorded within the very natural specific group of *Homo neandertalensis*. Correctly, therefore, the Choukoutien fossil should be called, until proof to the contrary, *Pithecanthropus pekinensis*. Von Koenigswald's discovery of new *Pithecanthropus* skulls, better preserved than Dubois's historic specimen, removed the last doubts.

This is not as might be thought, a purely formal question. To ignore the prescriptions of nomenclature and the hierarchy of terms employed in taxonomy is a type of indiscipline that may be observed primarily among anthropologists who lack a grounding in the natural sciences. This explains the already considerable number of genera created to designate fossil Men of whose generic, and sometimes even specific, identity with modern Man there can be no doubt.[41]

We must add that Dubois did not admit the identity of his *Pithecanthropus* with *Sinanthropus*. In his view, the first alone really justifies its name of Ape-Man. *Sinanthropus* was already a Hominian belonging to the Neandertal group, or even, he declared in a later work, simply a primitive type of *Homo sapiens*.[42] Dubois based his opinion mainly on the shape of the endocranial casts.

A New Discussion of the Facts

If we accept the close relationship of the two fossil beings we have been studying as proven, we must reconsider the place to be attributed to *Pithecanthropus* and *Sinanthropus* in the hierarchy of the great Primates in the light of the new morphological data furnished by the Peking fossil.

Morphologically, there is not the slightest doubt. *Sinanthropus* confirms and completes the proof that these are creatures with physical characters intermediate between the group of Anthropoid Apes and the group of Hominians. The reader can verify this for himself by comparing the figures of a restored *Sinanthropus* skull (with elements borrowed from at least four individuals), a gorilla's skull, and the skull of a Chinese (Figs. 91 to 93) published by Weidenreich. But if we try to establish phylogenetic relationships the problem becomes far more difficult. It must be acknowledged that the hypothesis of convergence—which, incidentally, was often misunderstood—developed at length in the First French Edition of this book (p. 127), is scarcely tenable today.

The fact is that, in addition to the large cerebral volume, there are in the development of the frontal region of the brain, certain structural features of

[41] See on this subject Vallois, H., 'Nomenclature anthropologique' (*Revue scientifique*, March 1941, p. 181).

[42] Dubois, E., 'The Shape and Size of the Brain in *Sinanthropus* and in *Pithecanthropus*' (*Kon. Akad. van Wetenschappen te Amsterdam, Proceedings* XXXVI, 1933); 'Racial Identity of *Homo solensis* Oppenoorth. . .and *Sinanthropus pekinensis* Davidson Black' (*Ibid.*, XXXIX, 1936).

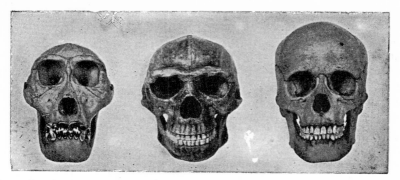

91 Comparison between the reconstructed skulls of a female *Sinanthropus* (centre), a female
Gorilla (left) and a Northern Chinese (right). Full face. One-fifth natural size
(After Weidenreich)

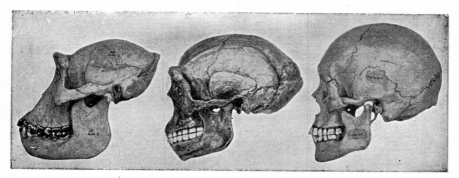

92 Same skulls as Fig. 91, left side. (After Weidenreich)

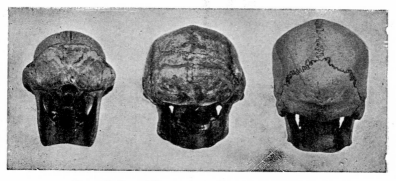

93 Same skulls as Fig. 91, rear view. (After Weidenreich)

the base of the cranium, the lower jaw and the dental system of *Sinanthropus* a collection of concomitant characters which, if they do not yet conform exactly to the human morphological type, are singularly close to it. It would be misleading to continue to speak of convergence: we must now admit a closer and more direct relationship.

A few anthropologists had already proclaimed the human status of *Pithecanthropus*. A greater number, following Black's example, placed *Sinanthropus* among the Hominians, regarding him as the lowest member of the group—lower even than *Homo neandertalensis*, who might have been his direct descendant. According to this view, *Pithecanthropus* and *Sinanthropus* are true ancestors of the genus *Homo*, veritable *Prehominians*.

This conclusion, drawn solely from the study of anatomical factors, is all the more admissible because it accords very well with the general idea we may form of the morphological processes by which the passage from a generalized anthropoid stage to a primitive human stage may or must have taken place.

The discovery, at various levels in the Choukoutien deposit, of the ashes of hearths implying the use of fire and accompanied by a stone and bone industry, confirmed this opinion in the minds of its protagonists and supporters, who did not hesitate to attribute this evidence of truly human activity to *Sinanthropus*.

The products of this industry, on which we cannot dwell here, were first described by Teilhard and Pei,[43] and then studied *in situ* by Abbé Breuil,[44] who confirmed the views of his colleagues. He expresses himself as follows:

'*Sinanthropus* kindled fire and did so frequently, he used bone implements and he worked stone, just as much as the Palaeolithics of the West. In spite of his skull, which so closely resembles that of *Pithecanthropus*, he was not merely a Hominian, but possessed an ingenious mind capable of inventing, and hands that were sufficiently adroit and sufficiently master of their fingers to fashion tools and weapons.'

Teilhard and Pei are less peremptory and put their viewpoint more felicitously:

'All the positive facts so far ascertained', they say, 'tend to give us the conviction that *Sinanthropus* is the Hominid who kindled the fires and dressed the stones in the cave of Choukoutien.'

Obviously, if *Sinanthropus* knew how to make fire, if he knew how to manufacture implements, if he was a *faber*, the question is—by definition—settled in favour of his human status. But are the facts proven? It is permissible to dispute them.

We may note first that, in order to give *Sinanthropus* human status, the

[43] Teilhard de Chardin and Pei, W. C., 'The Lithic Industry of the *Sinanthropus* Deposits in Choukoutien' (*Bull. of the Geol. Soc. of China*, XI, No. 4, 1932). With numerous figures.

[44] Breuil, H., 'Le feu et l'industrie lithique et osseuse à Choukoutien' (*Ibid.*, XI, No. 2, 1931); 'L'état actuel de nos connaissances sur les industries paléolithiques de Choukoutien' (*L'Anthropologie*, XLV, 1935, p. 740).

anatomists lean on the archaeologists and the archaeologists on the anatomists. The two points of view must be dissociated.

The circumstances of the deposit and the unvarying nature of the bone-remains of *Sinanthropus* recall what we find in a purely geological bed of fossil mammals, rather than the manner in which discoveries of human skeletons normally present themselves.

How are we to explain the almost complete absence of long bones and this kind of selection of bony parts all belonging to the skull, in which lower jaws predominate? Weidenreich believed that these selected parts did not come into the cave by natural means, but that they must have been brought there by hunters who chiefly attacked young individuals and chose for preference, as spoils or trophies, heads or parts of heads. In itself, this explanation is thoroughly plausible. But the problem is to name the hunter. To Weidenreich's mind, this was *Sinanthropus* himself, that is to say a cannibal, the first cannibal.

To this hypothesis, other writers preferred the following, which seemed to them more in conformity with our whole body of knowledge: the hunter was a true Man, whose stone industry[45] has been found and who preyed upon *Sinanthropus*.

To this conception the objection will inevitably be raised that, if such a Man, contemporaneous with our Chelleans, had lived at Choukoutien, he would be bound to have left all or part of his skeleton there. But this is not necessarily so. In Western Europe, where heavily filled grottoes and caverns are so numerous and so rich in products of the Palaeolithic human industry, the proportion of deposits that have yielded the skulls or skeletons of the manufacturers of this industry is infinitesimal. We may say that the absence of human bone-remains is the rule and their presence the exception. To give an example: In the Prince's Cave at Grimaldi, which was carefully excavated precisely in the hope of finding skeletons like those of the neighbouring grottoes, not the slightest fragment of human remains was discovered in the 4,000 cubic yards of its filling, which abounded in animal bones and dressed stones. Why should it not be the same at Choukoutien?

We may therefore ask ourselves whether it is not over-bold to consider *Sinanthropus* the monarch of Choukoutien, when he appears in its deposit only in the guise of a mere hunter's prey, on a par with the animals by which he is accompanied.

It is none the less evident that, by the volume of their brains and by what we know of the structure of their skulls, *Sinanthropus* and his brother *Pithecanthropus* fall between the great Anthropoid Apes and Men properly so called in the series of higher Primates. It is certainly permissible nowadays

---

[45] It is important to note that this industry is not primitive, since M. Breuil himself acknowledges that 'many of (its) features are not found in France until the Upper Palaeolithic'. This observation is not calculated to enhance the credibility of the 'typology' from a chronological standpoint. Accompanying a being like *Sinanthropus* one would have expected to find an eolithic industry, and not true gravers and scrapers and other tools 'sometimes of fine workmanship'.

to prefer the hypothesis of genetic relationships to that of resemblances due
to convergence; in other words, to prefer to Scheme III, if not Scheme I,
at least Scheme II, as set out on page 125. This would mean that we are
in the presence of beings greatly superior to all existing Anthropoids and,
by that very fact, resembling the Hominians, at the base of whose line of
evolution they may be placed.

The difficulty here, as in so many other palaeontological problems, is
to know at what moment an intermediate form should leave the category of
ancestors and enter that of descendants. How are the lines of demarcation
to be established? We know that the principal characteristic of the Hominians,
the one that dominates their whole cephalic architecture, is the great development of the brain, the seat of the intellectual faculties. In this respect, the
small new group we are studying is exactly intermediate, since its average
cerebral volume is 1,000 cubic centimetres, 400 cubic centimetres greater
than the maximum volume of the living Anthropoids, which is 600 cubic
centimetres, and smaller by the same amount than the modern human
average, which is 1,400 cubic centimetres.

The most prudent and most convenient, if not the best, solution in the
presence of this equal distance that separates these new biological forms
from the adjacent groups is to create for them a new, and inevitably provisional, designation. The term *Prehominians* (or Prehominids), which has
already been employed, seems to us the best description of the zoological
status of the little group we have been studying.

We have adopted the term Prehominians above all for the following reason.
Recent discoveries in Australia, Java and Africa, which we shall discuss
later,[46] confront us with human skulls possessing primitive characters and
sometimes so akin to the skulls of *Pithecanthropus* and *Sinanthropus* that
they may be considered to represent beings still nearly allied to our Prehominians, but at the same time closely resembling the archaic Neandertal
types, among fossils, and the Australians among living races.

On the ancestral side, the link is much less clear. But, even if we leave aside
the Australopithecines, it is very possible that among the many Tertiary
types of Anthropoid Apes, of which we only know fragments, there will be
found some—like *Dryopithecus*, *Sivapithecus*, *Ramapithecus* and so on—
which, along with prehuman dentitions, presented in their skulls characters
superior to those of living Anthropoids, and notably a higher cephalic
capacity, which would bring them closer to the Prehominians of Java and
Peking. This is a secret that only the future will reveal.

[46] This is particularly true of two groups of fossils which many writers place among the
Prehominians—*Africanthropus* from East Africa and Ngandong Man from Java (see Chaps.
X and XI).

CHAPTER SIX

THE MEN OF THE
LOWER PLEISTOCENE AGE

THE chief geological, palaeontological, and archaeological characteristics of the oldest Pleistocene formations, corresponding very closely to the *Chellean* and *Acheulean* periods of prehistorians, have already been discussed (see page 49). We know that these characteristics indicate a warm climate, rich vegetation, and a fine mammalian fauna—in fact a most favourable environment for human occupation. And, indeed, the presence of Man is disclosed by an industry, admittedly very primitive, which has abundantly scattered its stone artefacts, some of them most carefully wrought, in various lands almost all the world over. It is not implied, however, as we shall see later, that these universally distributed implements are everywhere of the same age.

INDUSTRY OF THE LOWER PLEISTOCENE

Prehistorians have long believed in the extreme simplicity and uniformity of Chellean implements. 'The industry of this period', it has been said, 'is of the simplest, most rudimentary character; it comprised a single stone implement, a flint or fragment of other rock, dressed on both surfaces by hammering, and rendered more or less amygdaloid by means of blows generally of some force. This implement varies much in form, size, finish, and in material; but once known, it is always easily recognized.'[1]

The variations in these 'bifaces' are indeed very considerable, as may be seen from the accompanying drawings (Fig. 94), and as is still better shown by the specimens in the d'Arcy Collection in the Museum at Saint-Germain.

We now know that along with the typical bulky, easily handled, more or less amygdaloid or almond-shaped implement—the classical 'hand-hammer' (*coup de poing*) of G. de Mortillet—the industry of very ancient Palaeolithic Man comprised other, less massive implements, varying in shape though poorly differentiated: a flake industry with retouching more or less localized on one surface only, which survived the industry of heavy implements and gradually changed until it produced all the diversity of the specialized and well-defined instruments of succeeding archaeological periods.

It is important to note that the epithet 'Chellean', in the broad sense, is

[1]   Mortillet, G. de, *Le Préhistorique*, 1st Ed., p. 133.

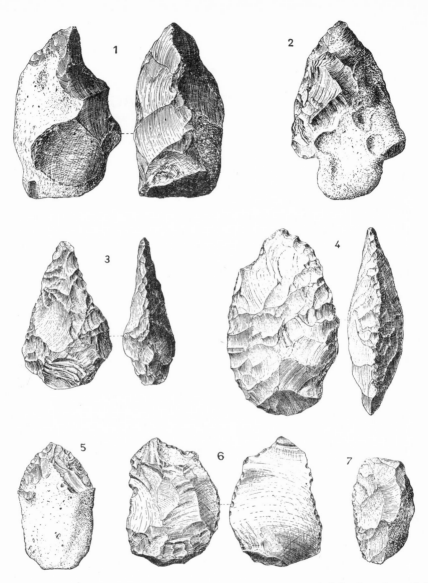

94 The Stone Industry of the Lower Pleistocene (Chellean and Acheulean from Saint-
Acheul, Somme). One-third natural size. (After Commont)

1, Rude implement, with large flakes, of Chellean make; seen full face and in profile.
2, Primitive hand-axe, the base or heel of which, intended for grasping, is formed by part of
the original flint nodule. 3, Amygdaloid of Chellean type, seen full face and in profile; the
cutting edges still present a zig-zag line. 4, Flatter amygdaloid, Acheulean type, seen full
face and in profile; the cutting edges are less sinuous. 5, Flint dressed on one side, and at
the upper extremity retouched into a point. 6, Another flint, dressed on one side only. 7, Flint
dressed in the form of a scraper.

applied in the present state of the science to an epoch of vague but immense duration, lasting perhaps several hundred thousand years. A period of very slow gestation was necessary to lead up to such well defined industrial forms as the splendid biface pieces and certain carefully worked flakes. Prehistoric archaeologists have made meritorious efforts to bring order into this original chaos and trace the probable or possible lines of evolution followed by the work of the first representatives of *Homo faber*.

Their task is relatively easy when it concerns the industry of massive amygdaloids shaped by the repeated chipping off of flakes from a lump of flint. It seems certain, and above all very natural, that the most ancient of these implements are much cruder than the more recent: since they were fashioned by chipping off larger flakes, their cutting edges form a zig-zag (Fig. 94, No. 1). Then dressing becomes more skilled, the product finer; the biface becomes thinner and lighter, and at the same time it assumes a more elegant, more symmetrical shape, often oval or triangular; its cutting edge acquires a straighter line. For archaeologists, a new phase is clearly marked by the Acheulean tool. It must be noted, however, that all possible transitions between the Chellean 'hand-hammer' and the beautiful Acheulean 'almond' occur in the same stratum. These differences in workmanship are then simply due to the skill of the workman, the lengths to which he has carried his work, or the quality of the raw material.

The task is more thankless when it concerns the flake industry. The various aspects of this very primitive stone industry, which the archaeological 'typologists' seek to classify by giving them special names, are of little scientific interest from a general point of view. Their universal distribution in space, and even in time, testifies chiefly to the psychic unity of the first Men and to the common inadequacy of their means of work. We must see in them simply the results of manual operations directed by a spirit of invention still at grips with the difficulties that characterize every beginning; they are inevitably directed towards a few very simple ends—cutting, scraping, piercing.

Thus the oldest human industry could not have started with amygdaloid implements, whose forms are already sophisticated. Flint flakes dressed on one side only, more or less heralding the so-called 'Mousterian' types, are often found entirely on their own in the most ancient archaeological levels containing a warm fauna, such as that at Grimaldi.[2] This category of implements, the simplest, most elementary and most primitive imaginable, must necessarily have preceded, or at least accompanied, that of the thick specimens cut on both sides, first almost shapeless, then more definite but still clumsy, finally thin and elegant like the Acheulean flints. Parallel with this progressive evolution of the amygdaloids, but not separately, ran the development of the flake industries, which have long been known, but

---

[2] Boule, M., *Les Grottes de Grimaldi: Géologie et Paléontologie*, I. (1906). This fact has greatly surprised prehistorians who believe in the chronological stability and infallibility of the various types of Palaeolithic implements.

were also long neglected, and on which eminent archaeologists have recently exercised their typological wisdom. It must merely be said that these flints known as *Tayacian, Clactonian, Chalossian, Languedocian, Levalloisian* and so on, not to mention what certain archaeologists are bold enough to call 'hybrids'—whatever interest they may possess from a strictly typological point of view—cannot be regarded as representing autonomous industrial cycles regularly succeeding one another in time in an order that is always the same: they are, rather, the products of particular techniques, exercised at certain ancient periods on the same stone materials in a raw state. They may be visualized as facies corresponding to transitory needs due to changes in the climate. It would be fruitless to link this that or the other industry to a definite phase of human evolution.

In the course of this very long Lower Palaeolithic period, we may, if we wish, and as an aid to speculation, separate—under the name *Pre-Chellean*—a first phase characterized by a rudimentary, extremely rough, stone industry whose products are often difficult to distinguish from natural eoliths and devoid of true amygdaloids. The origin of this first phase merges with the origin of true Humanity itself. It might be called *Protolithic* or *Eolithic*, if the latter expression had not already been used in a different sense.

The second phase is the true *Chellean*, with clearly defined but still clumsy amygdaloids (Fig. 94, No. 3), accompanied by a flake industry whose products are as numerous as they are undifferentiated (Fig. 94, Nos. 5, 6 and 7). Its origins must lie very far back in the past, certainly prior to the antepenultimate glacial period.

The third and last phase, the Acheulean, which began before the last glaciation but one, spread mainly during the last interglacial period. It passes imperceptibly into the Mid Palaeolithic characterized by a typical industry, the *Mousterian*, which began in France before the extinction or departure of the warm fauna.

The Men of Chelles and Saint-Acheul knew how to kindle fire. Traces of hearths have been observed in the deposits of Téting, between Metz and Saarbruck.[3] They must necessarily have worked wood and utilized it extensively. There is nothing to show that they also worked and used bone, but it is extremely probable.

However that may be, the great quantity of the stone products of these early ages, *which must have extended over an immense period of time*, would lead us to expect many discoveries of contemporary human bones.

REMARKS ON HUMAN BONE DISCOVERIES

In reality, such fossils remained almost unknown till 1908. Certain discoveries in previous years have sometimes been brought forward as belonging to the Chellean period, but we shall see that they are either of uncertain age or belong to a more recent period.

[3] Linckenheld, E., 'Téting, nouvelle station du Paléolithique inférieur' (*Annuaire de la Soc. d'Hist. et d'Archéologie de la Lorraine*, Metz, 1926).

The oldest, the skull-fragment from Cannstadt, near Stuttgart in Wurtemberg, dates back to 1700. The source of this specimen is quite obscure, its antiquity is more than doubtful.[4] It owes its reputation largely to de Quatrefages and Hamy, who selected it as a prototype of their 'early fossil race'.[5]

The second discovery was made, in 1844, amongst the flood-sorted volcanic cinders from the volcano at Denise, near Le Puy, in the district of Haute-Loire. It comprised some portions of skulls and other human bones. The antiquity of these remains has been disputed. In the course of his geological studies in the Velay, one of the present writers devoted much care to the question of their age, or rather of the age of the deposit in which they were found. Having examined the layer several times, he came to the opinion that this deposit dates back to a very remote period of Quaternary times.[6] But perhaps it would be well not to discard the hypothesis of an artificial burial, or, in some cases, of fraud. New investigations, carried out in 1925 by Depéret,[7] did not cast any fresh light on the problem. On this occasion, the study of the bone-remains, begun by Sauvage, was resumed by Dr. Mayet, who, while he attributed great antiquity to them, observed that they possessed all the characteristics of modern Man and noted their slight degree of fossilization.[8]

The year 1863 was marked by the discovery of the famous jaw from Moulin-Quignon, the status of which we have already defined in the chapter, dealing with the historical aspect (p. 23).

The skull from Olmo, discovered near Arezzo in Tuscany, in 1863, was not recorded by Cocchi till 1867. But so much uncertainty surrounds its geological age that it is impossible to place much weight upon it in such a work as this.[9]

With regard to the skeletons from the alluvial soils of Clichy (1868) and of Grenelle (1870), we merely mention the rashness of the anthropologists who attempted to prove their geological antiquity. Such an attempt, made forty years after the discoveries by individuals who had never seen the deposits, cannot be of much value. The most elementary notions of

[4] See Obermaier, H., 'Les restes humains quaternaires dans l'Europe centrale' (*L'Anthropologie*, XVII, 1906, p. 63).

[5] Quatrefages, A. de, and Hamy, E. T., *Crania ethnica*. The history and bibliography of this and the following discoveries will be found in this work.

[6] Boule, M., *Description géologique du Velay* (Paris, 1892) p. 219; *L'âge des derniers volcans de la France* (Paris, 1906) p. 31. See also the recent work by Bout, P., *Les Hommes fossiles de la Denise* (Le Puy, 1948), according to which the deposits containing human remains have been resorted by solifluxion.

[7] Depéret, L., 'Fouilles préhistoriques dans le gisement de l'Homme fossile de la Denise, près Le Puy' (*Comptes Rendus de l'Acad. des Sciences*, February 1, 1926).

[8] Mayet, L., 'Examen anthropologique sommaire des Hommes fossiles de la Denise, près Le Puy-en-Velay' (*Comptes Rendus de l'Acad. des Sc.*, May 17, 1926).

[9] The eminent Italian anthropoligist Sergi believed it to be contemporary with *Elephas antiquus*: 'Su l'Uomo fossile dell'Olmo' (*Rivista di Anthropologia*, XXI, 1916–1917). See also Sera, G. L., 'Esame morfologica del cranio dell'Olmo' (*Archivio per l'Antr. e la Etn.*, XL–XLI, 1931).

caution demanded of human palaeontology that it should base its specula-
tions only on evidences of irreproachable origin. This was not the case with
regard to the skeletons from the Parisian alluvials.[10]

A skull fragment found in 1882 at Bury St. Edmunds, Suffolk, in a mud
which, elsewhere, had yielded Acheulean flints, was considered contemporary
with the latter. But no stratigraphic study of the deposit was ever made,
and the specimen is so badly damaged that it is very difficult to draw any
conclusions from it.[11] Its fluorine content is very low.[11a]

In 1888, portions of the skull and several other parts of a human skeleton
were found in the Pleistocene gravels of Galley Hill, Northfleet, Kent.
These gravels are situated about 100 feet above the level of the Thames and
contain many Palaeolithic flints of different shapes, especially of lanceolate
form. The bones are said to have been discovered at a depth of eight feet
from the surface.

Seven years later, in 1895, they were described by E. T. Newton, the
palaeontologist.[12]   Keith[13] later asserted that the Galley Hill skeleton does
not differ in any important feature from that of a modern Englishman;
but this did not deter him from attributing to it an age of 200,000 years.

Several other anthropologists, in different countries, have magnified the
importance of the Galley Hill discovery; it is said to prove that *Homo sapiens*
there dates back to a very remote period. That is quite possible, but the
proof is insufficient. The fact is that no geologist was present at the discovery of the skeleton, and none examined the layer at the time. When the
bones were presented to the Geological Society of London, two highly
competent scientists, Sir John Evans and Professor Boyd Dawkins, raised
doubts as to their high antiquity and brought forward arguments pointing
strongly to artificial burial. Duckworth[14] later showed that it is exactly like
many comparable specimens from recent burials. Recent investigations by
Oakley,[15] which showed that the fluorine content of the Galley Hill skeleton
was identical with that of modern skeletons from the same region, have
definitely settled the question. The opinion expressed in the first editions
of this book, that the Galley Hill discovery had no more value for human
palaeontology than those which have been made on several occasions in the
Pleistocene alluvials of the Seine, at Grenelle and Clichy, and to which we

[10] Mortillet, G. de, *Le Préhistorique*, 1st Ed., p. 346f.

[11] Keith, A., 'The Bury St. Edmunds Cranial Fragment' (*Journ. of Anat. and Physiol.*,
XLVII, 1913, p. 73). Montagu, M. Ashley, 'Le fragment cranien de Bury St. Edmunds'
(*Bull. et Mém. de la Soc. d'Anthr. de Paris*, 1949, p. 22).

[11] Baden-Powell, P. and Oakley, K. P., 'Report on the Reinvestigation of the Westley
(Bury St. Edmunds) Skull Site' (*Proc. Preh. Soc.*, N.S., XVIII, 1952).

[12] *Quarterly Journal of the Geolog. Society*, 1895.

[13] Keith, A., *Ancient Types of Man* (London, 1911) p. 32. See also *New Discoveries relating
to the Antiquity of Man* (London, 1931) pp. 433–465.

[14] Duckworth, W. L. H., *The Problem of the Galley Hill Skeleton* (Cambridge, 1913).

[15] Oakley, K. and Montagu, M. Ashley, 'A Reconsideration of the Galley Hill Skeleton'
(*Bull. of the British Museum, Natural History, Geology*, I, 1949, p. 27).

in France no longer attach any importance, has now been categorically confirmed.

In 1912, English newspapers contained many references to a similar find brought to notice by Reid Moir, the discoverer of the rostro-carinate flints. It was said that a human skeleton had been found at a depth of $4\frac{1}{2}$ feet in a layer of sand at Ipswich in Suffolk, immediately under glacial clay containing erratics. This skeleton, carefully described by Sir A. Keith, who considered it to be quite a modern type, was said to belong to a period preceding the great glaciation of the region, itself older than the Pleistocene alluvials.[16] After having seen it at the College of Surgeons in London, and after having visited the layer at Ipswich, one of the present authors was obliged to express his opinion as follows: 'The Ipswich skeleton must, as a measure of scientific caution, be entirely dismissed from the series of authentic evidences, such as have an established place and serve as a basis for speculation in the science of human palaeontology.'[17]

Some months later, Reid Moir acknowledged that he had been mistaken. 'I wish to take this opportunity', he said, 'to state that those who opposed my contention as to the great age of these remains were in the right, whilst the views held by me regarding them have been shown to be erroneous.' He later considered, as also did Keith, that the Ipswich skeleton was Aurignacian.[18] But this attribution is not proved any more than the former one.

A further discovery was made in 1925. This was the *London skull*—a fragment of a brain-box found in the very heart of the City, at the corner of Leadenhall and Lime Street, while the foundations were being dug under 'Lloyds'. It lay about 38 feet below the level of the street in a layer of blue-clay, the result of the reshuffling of the Eocene clay called 'London clay', which is covered over with a river gravel belonging to the lower terrace of the Thames and containing bone-remains of Mammoth and *Rhinoceros tichorinus*, that is to say elements of a cold fauna.

The 'London skull', also called 'Lloyd's skull' or the 'Lady of Lloyds', actually comprises only the occiput, most of the right parietal and a small portion of the left parietal bones of a woman of about fifty. It was first described by Elliot Smith,[19] who, while he attributed it to an Aurignacian *Homo sapiens*, found that it showed similarities to female skulls of the Neandertal type. His study was taken up again, in most minute detail, by Keith.[20] Starting from certain ideas of his own concerning the evolution of the

[16] Moir, J. Reid, 'The Occurrence of a Human Skeleton in a Glacial Deposit at Ipswich' (*Proc. of the Prehist. Soc. of E. Anglia*, I, 1912, p. 194). Keith, A., 'Description of the Ipswich Skeleton' (*Ibid.*, p. 202); *The Antiquity of Man* (London, 1915).

[17] Boule, M., 'La paléontologie humaine en Angleterre' (*L'Anthropologie*, XXVI, 1915, p. 38).

[18] Moir, J. Reid, *The Antiquity of Man in East Anglia* (Cambridge, 1927) p. 130. Keith, A., *The Antiquity of Man* (2nd Ed., 1925) Vol. 1 p. 300.

[19] *Nature*, November 7, 1925, and *British Medical Journal*, November 7, 1925.

[20] Keith, Sir Arthur, *New Discoveries relating to the Antiquity of Man* (London, 1931) pp. 433–467.

Hominians, Keith believed that the situation would be improved if the London skull were more ancient, and did not hesitate to date it from the beginning of the Pleistocene, which is inadmissible from a palaeontological viewpoint and conflicts with the stratigraphic section of the deposit which he gives. To his mind, there is nothing Neandertaloid about the London skull, *Homo londonensis*. He considered that its anatomical characters were those of modern Man, but that its closest affinities were with 'Piltdown Man', which is discussed below.

More recently, the London skull was studied by Friedrichs.[21] After criticizing the theories of his English colleagues, whom he considered to have been mistaken in their judgment of this anatomical specimen, he showed that its structure was similar to that of the Cro-Magnon type. In his view, there was nothing Neandertaloid about it, nor did it resemble 'Piltdown Man'. The chief lesson to be drawn from this total divergence of opinion is that one cannot be too cautious in the interpretation of such incomplete anduncertainly dated relics as the London skull.

'PILTDOWN MAN'

As a pendant to the foregoing discoveries mention must be made of the famous Piltdown fragments, both by reason of the long discussion of which they were the subject, the special role certain anthropologists assigned to

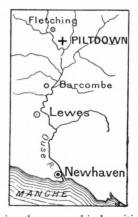

95 Sketch showing the geographical position of Piltdown

them in the palaeontological history of Man, and the interest of the experiments that finally proved them the products of a fraud.

In a field near Piltdown, Sussex (Fig. 95), there is a small quarry where the countrymen of the district obtained stones for repairing the roads. One day in 1912 a local amateur geologist, Charles Dawson, presented to Dr. A. Smith Woodward, the eminent palaeontologist of the British Museum,

[21] Friedrichs, H. F., 'Die morphologische Einreihung des 1925 in London City gefunden paläolithischen Schädels' (*Zeitschr. f. Anat. und Entwicklungsgeschichte*, XLVIII, 1932).

two very ferruginous-looking fragments of human skull, one of which, he said, had been accidentally discovered in the quarry by workmen, while the second had been found *in situ* by himself. Since this quarry was considered to belong to a very ancient Quaternary formation, these human remains automatically assumed considerable interest. Systematic investigations were immediately undertaken and brought to light fresh cranial fragments along with half a lower jaw. Beside these remains, Dawson claimed to have collected the bones of fossil animals and a few worked flints. All this material was exhibited before the Geological Society of London on December 18, 1912.[22]

The skull, of which Smith Woodward had attempted a reconstruction, seemed at a preliminary estimate to have a capacity of only 1,070 cubic centimetres; the fragment of jaw had a very simian appearance; and, according to Elliot Smith, the intracranial cast revealed the most simian brain so far known in the human family. Smith Woodward therefore believed that it was a very primitive form representing the dawn of humanity, and gave to the remains the highly expressive name of *Eoanthropus dawsoni*.

These early communications were followed by discussions bearing on the age of the bed, the reconstruction of the skull, and on the attribution to one and the same being of a brain-box that was completely human and a mandible that was completely simian. Other discoveries seemed, however, to confirm those already made. These new finds, made in 1913, consisted of two nasal bones, a fragment of a 'turbinate bone', and an isolated canine, which were ascribed to the same individual as the earlier pieces; the whole of this collection of fragments constituted what came to be known as Piltdown I. Finally, in 1915, a fragment of the frontal bone, a fragment of the occiput, and another molar, were found by Dawson some distance away from the first batch, but not announced until after his death in 1917; Smith Woodward considered them to belong to another individual—Piltdown II.[23]

After this short historical preface, let us examine the facts, considering first those which bear on the geological age of so-called *Eoanthropus dawsoni*, and thereafter those which relate to the fossil itself.

GEOLOGICAL AGE OF THE LAYER

The Piltdown gravels cover a plateau, 100–130 feet high, about 80 feet above the river Ouse; and at Piltdown their depth varies from 1 foot to 5 feet. They rest on the Wealden sandstone at the base of the Cretaceous formation. The gravels are composed of Weald pebbles, dark brown and ferruginous, mixed with angular flints and fragments of quartzite, all of

[22] Dawson, C., and Woodward, A. S., 'On the Discovery of a Palaeolithic Skull and Mandible. . .at Piltdown. . .with an Appendix by Elliot Smith' (*Quarterly Journal of the Geol. Soc. of London*, LXIX, 1913). 'Supplementary Note. . .' (*Ibid.*, 1914). Woodward, A. S., *A Guide to Fossil Remains of Man in the British Museum* (London, 3rd Ed., 1922).

[23] Woodward, A. S., 'Fourth Note on the Piltdown Gravel, with evidence of a second skull of *Eoanthropus Dawsoni*' (*Quart. Journ. of the Geolog. Soc. of London*, LXXIII, 1917).

which are embedded in a sand markedly stratified in places and strongly cemented together by iron oxides, conditions particularly noticeable towards the base of the formation, where the palaeontological discoveries were made (Fig. 96).

The gravels are the remains of an alluvial formation which formerly spread over vast areas, before the last sculpturing of the valley of the Ouse took place, excavating it to a depth of 80 feet. This topographical and stratigraphical arrangement seems to us to be similar to that which occurs in the

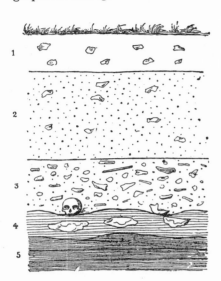

96 Section of the Piltdown Bed

1, Superficial soil, 1 foot. 2, Pale yellow clayey sand, containing, in its flood-sorted condition, certain constituents from the underlying bed; a palaeolithic implement was taken from the middle of this layer, the depth of which is about 2 ft. 5 in. 3, Dark brown ferruginous gravel, with subangular flints and pieces of tabular iron ore. Bed of 'Eoanthropus' and water-worn Pliocene fossils, Eoliths and a dressed flint. The surface of the bottom layer shows depressions. Depth about 1 ft. 5 in. 4, Bed of sand and clay, a sort of mud formed at the expense of the underlying beds and containing large blocks of flint. 5, Strata of the Tunbridge Wells Sands (Wealden) *in situ.*
(After Dawson)

valleys of Northern France, where the middle terraces, generally situated from 80 to 100 feet above the river channel, have been ascribed to the Lower Pleistocene, characterized by the fauna containing *Elephas antiquus.* This was also the opinion of the English geologist, Clement Reid, who compared the Piltdown gravels to the ancient Palaeolithic gravels of the Thames valley, both having been formed subsequent to the great Glacial Period of the British Isles.

Palaeontology expresses no very definite opinion on the subject. The mammal remains collected in the gravels have been attributed to two faunas of different ages. On the one hand, fragments of the teeth of a mastodon, of *Stegodon*, and of a rhinoceros, can only be of Pliocene age; but as they are much worn by transporting agencies, we may suppose that they originally came from a more ancient deposit. The teeth of a hippopotamus may have belonged equally well to Quaternary or to Pliocene times. The other remains, fragments of the antlers of red deer, beaver's teeth, and the molar of a horse, would appear to be less impregnated with mineral matter and less water-worn. They may be regarded as Pleistocene and really contemporary with the gravel.

There remains the archaeological aspect. The flaked flints said to have been found in the Piltdown gravel are of two kinds. A large number of very water-worn and weathered fragments may be looked upon as eoliths, and, like the water-worn teeth of the proboscidians, as originating from an older geological formation.

Some other fragments are distinctly worked, and their sharp edges are almost as well preserved as when they were made. They have been dressed or flaked on one surface only, and their general form is in no way remarkable. In spite of the absence of hand hammers, Dawson regarded them as of Chellean age.

Subsequently, the same author announced the discovery in the same gravels of a detached splinter of a bone of a proboscidian, which measures no less than 1 foot 3 inches in length and 3 inches in breadth. Of the artificial character of this object, which is rounded at one end, and pointed at the other, there was no doubt in the minds of Dawson and Smith Woodward, who regarded it as 'an implement'.[24] But this opinion was far from being universally accepted.

To sum up, stratigraphy led to the Piltdown gravels being dated from a very remote period of the Pleistocene. The palaeontological data were less clearly in favour of this supposition, because a more ancient fauna seemed to have become mingled with the normal fauna of the stratum. The archaeological evidences, while not categorical, did not seem to be in marked contradiction to the foregoing data.

DESCRIPTION OF THE BONES:

THE SKULL

The skull known as Piltdown I is represented by four pieces made up of nine fragments. The largest of these pieces are part of the right parietal, a left temporal, and a portion of the occiput. The bones are normal, with no trace of disease; they have been in no way deformed by their mineralization. Their thickness is remarkable—10 to 12 millimetres on the parietal and frontal bones (as against 5 to 8 mm. in modern Man)—and so also is the depth of the impressions of the meningeal vessels on the inside of the skull. Apart from this peculiarity, detailed examination of each of the bones hardly reveals any characteristics that are not perfectly human, and even more akin to those of modern *Homo sapiens* than to those of other fossil Men such as *Homo neandertalensis*.

As there is preserved in the left frontal region a portion of the external or malar tuberosity (Fig. 97), it can be definitely ascertained that the supraorbital ridges were not more developed than in modern Man. This conclusion was confirmed in 1915 by the discovery of a second piece of frontal bone attributed to Piltdown II.

[24] Dawson, C., and Woodward, A. S., 'On an Implement from Piltdown' (*Quarterly Journal of the Geolog. Soc. of London*, LXXI, 1915).

On the parietal bones, the curved temporal lines are very high; and the squamous suture is as arched as in a modern skull. The very pronounced

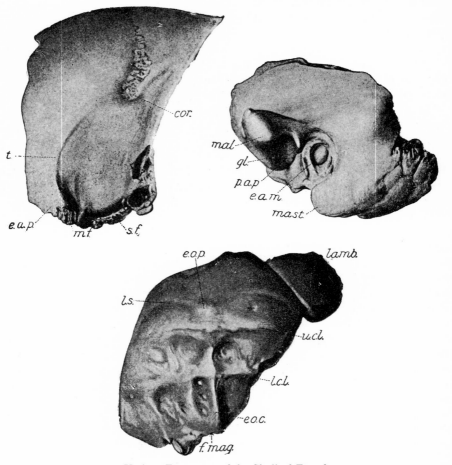

97 Various Fragments of the Skull of *Eoanthropus*

Above, to the left; left frontal bone, seen from the outer surface; *cor.*, coronal suture; *e.a.p.*, external angular process; *m.f.*, facette for malar; *s.f.*, facette for the sphenoid; *t.*, temporal ridge. Above, to the right; left temporal bone, external surface; *e.a.m.*, external auditory meatus [blocked by a pebble]; *gl.*, glenoid fossa; *p.a.p.* post-articular apophysis; *mal.*, process for malar; *mast.*, mastoid process. Below; occipital bone, external surface; *e.o.c.*, external occipital crest; *e.o.p.*, external occipital protuberance; *f. mag.*, occipital foramen (*foramen magnum*); *lamb.*, portion of lamboid suture; *l.s.*, linea suprema; *u.c.l.*, upper curved line; *l.c.l.*, lower curved line. All the figures are two-thirds natural size. (After Smith Woodward).

parietal bosses are situated almost in the middle of the parietal and a large flat area extends behind these bosses.

The left temporal bone, which is well preserved (Fig. 97), is similar in all its details to that of modern races: the glenoid cavity is as deep; the tympanic bone is reduced; the mastoid process is large. Certain somewhat special characteristics have been noted in the bone, but they do not seem to be of any fundamental significance. The external occipital protuberance is placed, as is the case in modern Man, below the plane separating the cerebral hemispheres from the cerebellum, instead of above it as in Mousterian Man. It is not thus in the portion of the occipital found in 1915, where the external occipital protuberance lies above the lateral sinuses. But this may also be observed in modern Man. The nasal bones, in an excellent state of preservation, are relatively small and broad. They are very human in character.

Many attempts have been made to reconstruct the skull, a task rendered particularly difficult by the absence of any point of contact between the pieces belonging to the right and left sides or between these and the occiput, which explains the divergence in the results due to different authors. After his 1913 reconstruction, Dr. Smith Woodward made a second (Figs. 100 to 102), which gave a mesocephalic, almost brachycephalic, skull with a cephalic index of 78 and a slightly flattened vault. The cranial capacity, according to this new reconstruction, was no longer 1,070 but 1,300 cubic centimetres, in other words comparable to the average capacity of many primitive races of today. On the other hand Sir Arthur Keith, the skilful anatomist of the Royal College of Surgeons, considered that neither of these reconstructions was satisfactory. Initially, he declared the cranial capacity to be 1,500 cubic centimetres, a figure which he later revised to 1,410 cubic centimetres.[25] This would make the skull entirely similar to that of a modern Man, of an 'ordinary Londoner'.

As a whole, and in spite of certain peculiarities of a primitive type and of the extraordinary thickness of bone, the skull possesses in high degree the structure of a human skull. The individual to whom it belonged, far from representing a different genus, can at the most be regarded only as the representative of a primitive race of *Homo sapiens*.

THE JAW AND TEETH

But we have still to consider the jaw; and here the story of the Piltdown discovery becomes truly extraordinary.

The lower jaw, contrary to all the indications of the cranium, was very simian! It showed the same degree of mineralization as the skull, with which it appeared to correspond fairly well in point of size. The condyle was missing, as well as the upper portion of the front half of the horizontal ramus, but in the remaining portion the two anterior true molars were in place (Fig. 98).

The ascending ramus was broad; the mandibular notch was not very deep, and the condyle must have been short. The mark of attachment of the temporal muscle was large. The mylo-hyoid groove was situated below the dental canal, instead of originating from it, as in Man. There was no mylo-hyoid ridge (internal oblique line).

[25] Keith, A., 'Ape-Man or Modern Man?' (*Illustrated London News*, August 16 and 23, 1913), etc. See especially his book *The Antiquity of Man* (2nd Ed., 1925, Vol. II, pp. 537–602).

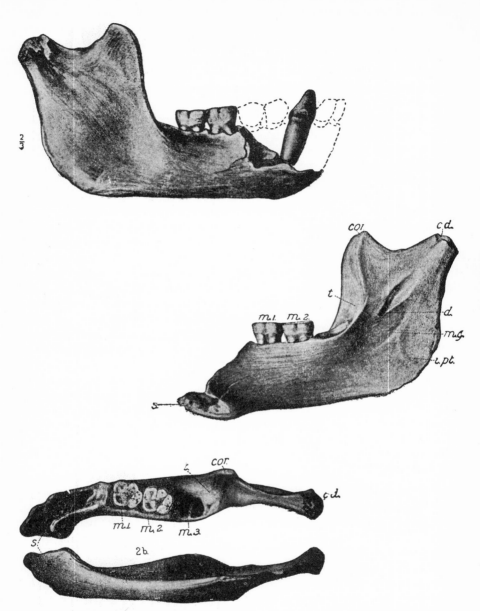

98 Lower Jaw from Piltdown. Two-thirds natural size. (After Smith Woodward)

Top, Jaw seen from outer surface. The canine tooth has been drawn here as belonging to this jaw. It is now considered to be an upper canine. Centre, Jaw seen from inner surface; *cd.*, neck of condyle; *cor.*, coronoid process; *t.*, area of insertion of temporal muscle; *d.*, inferior dental foramen; *m.g.*, mylo-hyoid groove; *i.pt.*, area of insertion of internal pterygoid muscle; *s.*, incurved bony flange of symphysis; *m.1*, *m.2*, first and second true molars. Bottom, Jaw seen from above and below; *m.3*, socket of third true molar; other symbols as above.

The lower symphyseal margin was not thickened and rounded as in Man; it formed a kind of thin plate, projecting inwards, as in the Apes and particularly in the Chimpanzee (the simian shelf). The reconstruction of this region could not but suggest a very receding symphysis, with complete absence of chin.

A single glance at Fig. 99 will suffice to show, on the one hand, the close

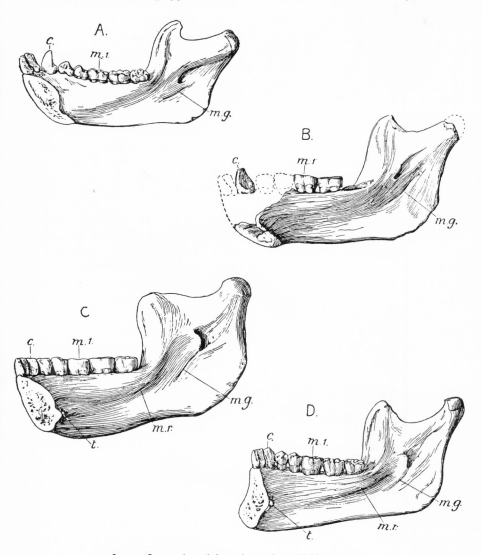

99 Lower Jaws, viewed from inner face. Half natural size

A, Chimpanzee; B, *Eoanthropus;* C, Mauer (Heidelberg) Man; D, Modern Man. *c.*, canine tooth; *m.*1, first true molar; *t.*, genial tubercle; *m.g.*, mylo-hyoid groove; *m.r.*, mylo-hyoid ridge (internal oblique line). (After Smith Woodward)

resemblance of the Piltdown mandible to that of a chimpanzee, and on the other hand, the great difference which separates these two from a second small series comprising the Mauer jaw and that of modern Man.

The canine tooth found in 1913 also differed from a human canine in its much larger dimensions, in the more raised, more conical, and more compressed form of its crown, and in the way in which it had worn, for this implied the existence, in the opposing jaw, of a similar tooth and possibly of a corresponding space or diastema.

At first Smith Woodward regarded this canine as belonging to the mandible, and described its resemblance to the canine teeth of apes, and to the lower milk canine of a human being. Gregory and Miller thought that the tooth was in reality an upper left canine, very similar to that of a female chimpanzee.

The first and second true molars, preserved in position in the jaw, were relatively long and narrow. Their neck was well marked, the roots were not attached. The crowns had five well-developed cusps, arranged as in certain Anthropoids, where the fifth cusp is more important and projects more markedly at the back edge of the tooth than in man. These molars were clearly much more simian than human, and wholly resemble those of the Chimpanzee or Orang Utan.

In its general build as well as in the details of its structure, then, the Piltdown mandible exactly reproduces an ape's jaw, or, to be precise, the jaw of a chimpanzee or orang. Had this jawbone been found alone in the Piltdown gravels, along with the remains of Pliocene mammals, it would have been taken as a clear testimony to the existence in England in Pliocene times of an Anthropoid Ape.

Palaeontologists were, therefore, confronted by the problem of a small collection of bone-fragments, which present the paradoxical association of an essentially human skull with an essentially simian jaw. It was this juxtaposition of facts that came to be known as the riddle of Piltdown.

INTERPRETATION OF THE FACTS

The very great age attributed to all these fragments rendered this riddle particularly irritating. Naturally, many authors strove to solve it. By 1952 the literature relating to it comprised no less than 250 articles, notes or memoirs.[26] On the whole, opinions were divided into two major categories.

The *unicist* view, defended from the outset by Smith Woodward, accepted as a fact that the cranium and the mandible belonged to the same individual. According to this view it was impossible to suppose that in two different deposits, Piltdown I and Piltdown II, human and simian remains, which were, moreover, complementary, lay side by side in Lower Pleistocene

[26] Only fifteen years after the Piltdown discovery, in a very complete general review or the controversy surrounding it, G. Miller listed no fewer than twenty points of disagreement between the principal authors: Miller, G. S., 'The Controversy over Human "Missing Links"' (*Smithsonian Report for* 1928, Washington, 1929).

strata. The only logical explanation was that the fragments belonged to a primitive form of Hominid in whom the evolution of the jaw had not followed that of the cranium and the brain. This interpretation led to reconstructions in which the facial mass, in being adapted to the mandible, assumed an aspect that was curiously out of harmony with the cranium (Figs. 100–102). Smith Woodward, as we have seen, proposed two successive reconstructions. Sir Arthur Woodward, also a firm supporter of the unicist view, proposed two others.[27] The German anatomist Weinert,[28] after studying the original fragments in London, likewise reached the conviction that the jaw and the bones of the cranium came from the same individual. He concluded that the cranium was of the *Homo sapiens* type but with certain primitive characters—while the jaw could easily be adapted to the cranium: in spite of certain incontestably simian characters it was definitely human.

From the very beginning, however, Professor Waterston had expressed doubts. He found difficulty in believing that the skull and the jaw could have belonged to the same being, and drew attention to the fact that the glenoid fossa of the temporal was not formed to fit the jaw of an ape. 'It is just as possible,' he said, 'to attribute this jaw to the skull, as it would be to articulate a chimpanzee's foot with the bones of an essentially human thigh and leg.'[29] This opinion, which may be called the *dualist* view, gained the adherence of other naturalists. The American mammalogist Miller[30] endeavoured to show, with a great wealth of evidence, that the jaw was that of a Pleistocene species of Chimpanzee, and named it *Pan vetus*. Similar reservations were advanced the same year by one of the present writers.[31] The same view was adopted by Gregory,[32] in New York, and by Ramström,[33] in Sweden. In Italy, Frassetto[34] declared that the jaw was definitely simian but that it bore a closer resemblance to that of the Orang than of the Chimpanzee. After a new and detailed study of the Piltdown fragments, Friedrichs,[35] a pupil of Weidenreich, added his voice to the dualists: the jaw could not possibly belong to the skull. Like Frassetto, he held that it resembled the

[27] Keith, A., 'A Resurvey of the Anatomical Features of the Piltdown Skull, with some observations on the recently discovered Swanscombe Skull' (*J. of Anatomy*, LXIII, 1938/39).

[28] Weinert, H., 'Das Problem des *Eoanthropus* von Piltdown' (*Z. für Morph. und Anthrop.*, XXXII, 1933).

[29] Waterston, D., 'The Piltdown Mandible' (*Nature*, November 13, 1913).

[30] Miller, G. S., 'The Jaw of Piltdown Man' (*Smithsonian Miscellaneous Collections*, LXV, No. 12, 1915); 'The Piltdown Jaw' (*Amer. J. of Phys. Anthrop.*, I, 1918). These two memoirs contain a long critical bibliography.

[31] Boule, M., 'La paléontologie humaine en Angleterre' (*L'Anthropologie*, XXVI, 1915).

[32] Gregory, W. K., 'Studies on Evolution of the Primates' (*Bull. Amer. Mus. Nat. Hist.*, XXXV, 9116, p. 316).

[33] Ramström, M., 'Der Piltdown-Fund' (*Bull. of Geol. Inst. of Upsala*, XVI, 1919).

[34] Frassetto, F., 'New Views on the "Dawn Man" of Piltdown, Sussex' (*Man*, XXVII, 1927).

[35] Friedrichs, H., 'Schädel und Unterkiefer von Piltdown *Eoanthropus Dawsoni* Woodward in neuer Untersuchung' (*Zstchr. für Anat. und Entwicklungsgeschichte*, XCVIII, 1932).

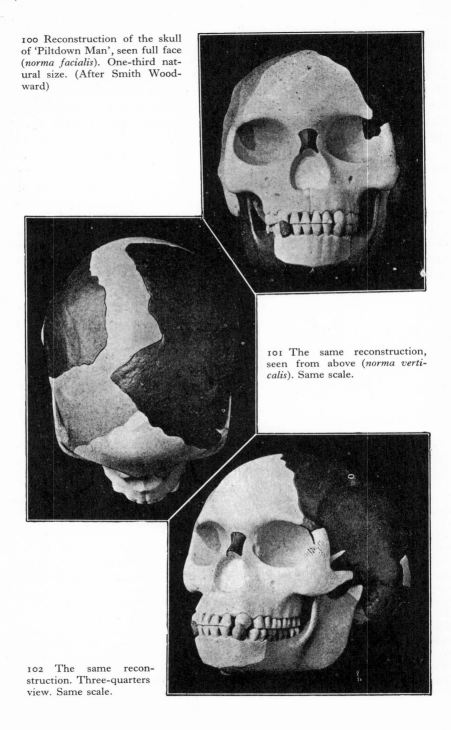

100 Reconstruction of the skull of 'Piltdown Man', seen full face (*norma facialis*). One-third natural size. (After Smith Woodward)

101 The same reconstruction, seen from above (*norma verticalis*). Same scale.

102 The same reconstruction. Three-quarters view. Same scale.

Orang rather than the Chimpanzee, and ascribed it to a new genus of Anthropoid Ape which he named *Boreopithecus*. He considered that the skull possessed all the characteristics of any modern English skull.

Finally, it must be added that most of the supporters of the dualist theory, contrary to the unicists, held that the Piltdown fragments were not of the same age. The jaw alone was ancient: it belonged to a Pleistocene ape. The skull was that of a modern man, and its presence in the stratum was inexplicable. As may be seen, this theory, like the first one, left many unexplained mysteries.

'PILTDOWN MAN' A HOAX

All these discussions were eventually proved pointless when Messrs. Weiner, Le Gros Clark and Oakley[36] declared in two sensational communications to the Geological Society that the so-called fossil Man of Piltdown was a fraud. Basing their opinion on detailed experimental research carried out with the aid of qualified experts, the authors had accumulated an impressive body of evidences.

(a) The first related to the artificial coloration of the fragments. All the Piltdown remains are of reddish-brown colour in keeping with the ferruginous nature of the deposit. This colour, which is due to an iron salt, had afforded, at first glance, a perfect guarantee of their authenticity. Now, chemical analysis has shown that this coloration is limited to the surface of the bones; it disappears as one comes to the deeper parts. This is astonishing in itself, but graver still is the fact that in the canine tooth the layer of red is only a thin film under which the ivory is identical with that of modern teeth. Analysis of this film showed that it does not contain any iron: it is a paint, which an expert from the National Gallery identified as being very probably Van Dyck brown.

When Dawson found the first Piltdown fragments he treated them with a solution of potassium bichromate, to strengthen them, he said. Smith Woodward considered this procedure worthless and did not follow it on the fragments he himself found *in situ* in 1912. It is therefore curious to note that the mandible discovered at the same time by Dawson, in the presence of Smith Woodward, contains bichromate. As no statement has ever been made that it was treated after discovery, for which there would in any case no longer have been any justification, the only explanation is that the fragment had been 'prepared' before its discovery—no doubt at the same time as the rest of the remains. Although recovered later still, the fragments of Piltdown II also contain bichromate.

---

[36] Weiner, J. S., Le Gros Clark, W. E. and Oakley, K. P., 'The Solution of the Piltdown Problem' (*Bull. of the British Museum, Geology*, II, No. 3, 1953); 'Further Contributions to the Solution of the Piltdown Problem' (*Ibid.*, II, No. 6, 1955). Read also the interesting volume in which J. S. Weiner, the first to suspect the fraud, describes the conditions in which the hoax was perpetrated and the psychological atmosphere that surrounded it: Weiner, J. S., *The Piltdown Forgery* (London, 1955).

(b) A second series of arguments concerns the dental abrasion. The manner in which the Piltdown teeth are worn down has always astonished investigators. The molars are of the simian type; yet the masticating surfaces are worn flat like human teeth. Messrs. Weiner, Le Gros Clark and Oakley have established that this wear has been produced artificially: the molar found in isolation bears scratches identical with those caused by the action of an abrasive; on the molars still in position the worn surface has a clearly defined margin, whereas it would normally slope gradually down into the two lateral faces of the tooth; finally, the plane of wear in the two teeth is not parallel, but at a slightly oblique angle to one another, which would be inexplicable if the abrasion had been produced by natural means.

At the level of the canine, the simian appearance of which has always been recognized, the worn surface occupies a position on the lingual side of the tooth that differs from anything met with in either Man or Apes. Here, too, examination with a binocular microscope shows parallel scratches such as would have been produced by an abrasive. On the other hand, the extremity of the root of this canine is not formed, indicating that it is not an adult tooth. Notwithstanding this, the tooth is so worn that the pulp has been opened—an extraordinary thing in a young tooth. Even more abnormal is the fact, revealed by radiography, that the pulp has not reacted by the production of secondary dentine, as always happens in such cases.

(c) The results of chemical analysis are no less conclusive. When they determined the fluorine content of the jaw and teeth, using a more exact technique than those previously employed on the same bones by one of their number, the authors obtained values absolutely incompatible with any degree of antiquity. These values were confirmed by the percentage of organic substances, especially of nitrogen, which recent research by Cook and Heizer (1947) has shown to diminish at an approximately uniform rate during the initial period of fossilization. The figures obtained for the first cranium and the frontal bones of Piltdown II alone indicate a certain antiquity, but this does not seem to go even as far back as the Upper Pleistocene.

	%F	%N
Upper Pleistocene:		
Animal bones	$\geqslant$ 0.1	0.7
Animal teeth	$\geqslant$ 0.1	0.2
Piltdown, skull fragments:		
Piltdown I	0.1	1.4
Piltdown II, frontal	0.1	1.1
Piltdown II, occipital	0.03	0.6
Jaw and teeth:		
Jaw	< 0.03	3.9
Molar in the jaw	< 0.04	4.3
Isolated canine	< 0.03	5.1
Molar of Piltdown II	< 0.01	4.2

Finally, X-ray examination of the skull showed that a new substance, sulphate of lime (gypsum), had partially replaced the normal phosphate of lime. Such a transformation was all the more astounding because a chemical study of the underground water and soil at Piltdown had indicated that it could not have taken place in the deposit. It was due to an unexpected fact: when the skull was, as we have heard, artificially coloured with sulphate of iron, this sulphate secondarily penetrated the bone and brought about the formation of sulphate of lime.

(d) The last group of proofs relates to the bones of large mammals and stone implements found at Piltdown. They, too, have been artificially dyed, but a study of the radioactivity of the bones revealed an amazing fact. Recent research has established that fossil bones lying in a deposit where the water of interstitial circulation contains traces of uranium gradually become laden with this substance. Since uranium is radioactive, the amount can be measured by instruments designed for this purpose without the necessity of destroying part of the bone, as has to be done in testing the fluorine content. The absorption of uranium varies greatly with the deposit, being more rapid in gravel and sand, for example, than in limestone or clay, but generally speaking it increases with the geological age. It therefore provides a method which, parallel with testing the fluorine content, reveals— if not the absolute age of a fragment—at least its relative age as compared with other fragments in the same deposit.

This method was applied to the fragments of Elephant molars found at Piltdown and attributed to *Elephas planifrons*, a species whose very presence in Great Britain seemed surprising. Now, the radioactivity of these teeth proved greater not only than all the Pleistocene fossils found in Great Britain, but even than all the Tertiary fossils discovered in this country! It likewise surpassed those of fossil elephant teeth from any other country, with one exception: a specimen in the collection of the British Museum that came from Ichkeul, in Tunisia, and whose uranium and fluorine content are both virtually the same as in the Piltdown fragment; and it so happened that this, too, was an *Elephas planifrons*! This was a disturbing coincidence. In strange contradiction of the foregoing result, a hippopotamus tooth found at Piltdown, which was also artificially dyed, presented scarcely a trace of radioactivity and contained very little fluorine. This double fact would make it appear recent. But it contained almost no organic matter, which would suggest a certain degree of antiquity. This contradiction has been explained by the authors according to a new theory: In limestone caves the deposition of fluorine and uranium is extremely slow, whereas the disappearance of organic matter proceeds at the normal rate. The fact that the tooth was dyed indicated that it, too, had been introduced secondarily into Piltdown; chemical analysis proved that it must have come from a cave. Now, it is only in Sicily and Malta that remains of hippopotami are found in Quaternary cave-deposits. The Piltdown hippopotamus must, therefore, have come from one of these islands. . . .

68   FOSSIL MEN

The conclusions to which all these investigations lead are, therefore, very clear. The Piltdown deposit is a fake in every respect: human, or so-called human, remains, the bones of large mammals, stone implements—all these finds were placed in the ground secondarily after having undergone artificial preparation. The jaw, in which the electronic microscope reveals the presence of collagenous fibres, is a recent bone belonging to a modern anthropoid ape; various investigations lead Messrs. Weiner and Le Gros Clark to believe that it is the jaw of a young orang. The isolated molar of Piltdown II probably also belongs to it. Although the skull, to which the Piltdown II frontal bone doubtless belongs, may be fairly old, its age cannot be very great, since its fluorine content is less than that of Würmain bone-remains from the same district; while its nitrogen content is comparable with that of Neolithic skeletons found in Kent. At most, it might date from the Upper Palaeolithic age, but the authors consider it as being a sub-fossil and probably of Neolithic date. The Piltdown II occipital is even less ancient. As for the so-called 'turbinate bone', microscopic examination has shown that there is nothing 'turbinate' about its structure and that it is probably non-human in origin.

Thus, thanks to combined investigations utilizing the most modern procedures, the riddle of Piltdown has been solved after forty-two years, and Piltdown Man must be regarded as having been definitely erased from the list of human fossils.

*   *   *

The palaeontological evidences we shall now consider were found under very different circumstances from those we have just been discussing These are authentic discoveries, made in the course of the last half century in formations belonging to various levels of the Lower Pleistocene. In spite of their small number, which is in striking contrast to the relative wealth of the deposits that have yielded remains of Prehominians, they furnish extremely valuable data which cast fresh light on the primitive forms of Man.

For a long time, following G. de Mortillet, the great majority of pre-historians, because of the dearth of human fossil remains from the Lower Pleistocene deposits, considered that the Neandertal type was characteristic of the Chellean period. This was an *a priori* opinion, for Neandertal Man is essentially Mousterian, and there was no justification for crediting him with greater antiquity than this. The discovery, in 1908, of a Chellean human jaw at Mauer, near Heidelberg, finally provided the first evidence, to which, shortly afterwards, there were added fresh specimens brought to light in Germany, near Weimar.

New discoveries made later in Germany, Britain and France raised an important problem, for while some of them may be considered as representing more or less distant forerunners of Neandertal Man of the Mid Pleistocene, others introduced us to quite a different type, a great deal closer to modern Man. Provisionally at least, and leaving aside Heidelberg Man, whose antiquity is far greater than that of any of the others, we may distinguish two essential groups: the first is manifestly connected with the Neandertalians of the following period, and we shall call it the *Preneandertalian* group; the second, although at least as ancient as the first, seems to have no connexion with Neandertal Man but to be linked with *Homo sapiens*, who succeeded the Neandertalians in the Upper Palaeolithic period: this may be called the *Presapiens* group. We shall consider the two groups in turn.

We shall exclude from this study various bone-remains found outside Europe and also regarded as belonging to the Lower Pleistocene period. The most important of these are: Rabat Man from North Africa; Kanam and Kanjera Man and so-called *Africanthropus* from East Africa; the Men of Mount Carmel and Kafzeh in Palestine; and Ngandong Man from Java. It will be best to postpone examination of these specimens until later chapters devoted to the fossil Men of these various parts of the world.

THE MAUER JAW
(Homo Heidelbergensis)

At the end of 1908 Otto Schoetensack, of Heidelberg University, published a memoir entitled, 'The lower jaw of *Homo heidelbergensis*, taken from the sands at Mauer, near Heidelberg.'[37]

The Site

The village of Mauer is situated 6 miles south-east of Heidelberg on the Elzenz, a tributary of the Neckar (Fig. 103). The bed-rock in this region

103 Geographical position of Mauer, near Heidelberg

is of Triassic formation, overlaid in places by a covering of Pleistocene deposits, and particularly of river sands representing the ancient bed of the Neckar. On October 21, 1907, in one of the pits worked in these sands, the 'Sandgrube Grafenrain', a lower jaw was found 80 feet below the surface of the soil.

[37] Schoetensack, O., *Der Unterkiefer des* Homo Heidelbergensis *aus den Sanden von Mauer bei Heidelberg* (Leipzig, 1908). See also Weinert, H., 'Dem Unterkiefer von Mauer, zur 30 jährigen Wiederkehr seiner Entdeckung' (*Z. für Morph. und Anthrop.*, XXXVII, 1937).

The accompanying photograph and geological section of the face of the
sand-pit were made by Schoetensack (Fig. 104). The lower part of this
section is formed by the 'Mauer sands' the base of which contains gravels
with beds of rounded pebbles, and the upper portion of which, separated
from the lower by a bed of clay, consists of fine sand. The upper part of
the section is formed by silt or loess, subdivided into a lower or ancient

104 Photograph and Geological Section of the Grafenrain Quarry at Mauer
+ indicates the spot where the human jaw was found, 80 ft. below the surface of the soil.
(After Schoetensack)

level, of a brown and sandy character, and an upper and more recent level
containing small calcareous concretions.

The Mauer sands, very rich in fossils, contain shells of both land and
fresh-water molluscs, which, taken as a whole, indicate a climate more
continental than at present. Of thirty-five species, eight have emigrated to
the East.

The mammalian fauna comprises the Ancient Elephant (*Elephas antiquus*),
the Etruscan Rhinoceros, a Horse which may be a transitional form between
the Pliocene Horse (*Equus stenonis*) and the present-day *Equus caballus*,
a Wild Boar, Red Deer, Roe Deer, an Elk, a Bison, two Bears resembling
the Pliocene *Ursus etruscus*, a Dog, a Sabre-Toothed Tiger, Lion, Wild
Cat and Beaver. This fauna is most closely related to that of the lowest
Pleistocene of France, such as we find in the oldest gravels of the valleys

of the Somme (Abbeville) and of the Seine (Chelles), in the deepest deposits
and settlements of the Grotte du Prince at Grimaldi, and in a few archaic
formations in the caves of the Pyrenees. It even exhibits the same zoological
gradations as these—a Horse akin to *Equus stenonis*, a small Bear nearly
related to *Ursus etruscus*, and so on.

It has been suggested that the Mauer sands date from the Pliocene, but
this is straining the facts of the case. The fauna of these sands hardly differs
at all from that of various other European deposits, such as those at Süssen-
born and Mosbach in Germany, in the Norfolk Forest-Bed in England, at
Solilhac and Saint-Prest in France, all of which lie on the borderland between
Pliocene and Pleistocene. Yet the closest resemblances are with our 'Chellean'
fauna, a possibility which it is all the more important to keep in view because
there is no proof that the relics of the most ancient animals of the Mauer
sands were not derived from deposits of greater age.

AGE OF THE JAW

As the topographical and stratigraphical conditions of the Mauer river
formation confirm this interpretation, there is every reason to believe that
the ancient owner of the human jaw extracted from the gravels was a representative of the oldest workers of Palaeolithic stones. There can be no doubt
that the jaw was found in the place ascribed to it, and that it is of the same
age as the gravels, an age indicated by the animal bone remains amongst
which it was lying and with which it agrees in its state of fossilization.

The Mauer discovery is of the utmost importance, since it brings us into
touch with one of the rare relics of the most ancient human race known to
us. Accordingly, it deserves to be studied in some detail.

ITS CHARACTERS

The Mauer jaw is almost complete and is well preserved. At the very first
glance it impresses one by its great size, its massive and extraordinarily
powerful appearance, by the great breadth of its ascending rami, and by the
complete absence of chin (Figs. 105 and 106). These are simian features,
or shall we say, marks of the beast.

On the other hand, the dentition is altogether human; the canines are small,
and the other molars possess dimensions and characters frequently found
in modern Man. Therefore Schoetensack placed his fossil in the genus
Homo, naming it *Homo heidelbergensis*, whilst Bonarelli[38] invented a new
generic name for it: *Palaeoanthropus*.

Let us examine its morphology more closely.

The ascending rami are extraordinarily broad and low. They measure
60 mm. in breadth (in place of an average of 37 mm. in modern Man), and
their height is 66 mm.; so that, seen in profile, they are almost square in
form. The mandibular notch (on the upper surface of the ramus) is not

[38] *Rivista italiana di Paleontologia*, 1909.

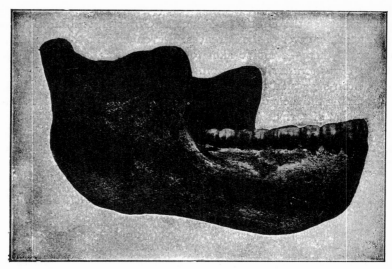

105 Heidelberg (Mauer) Jaw, seen in profile but at a slight angle. Three-fourths natural size.
(After Schoetensack)

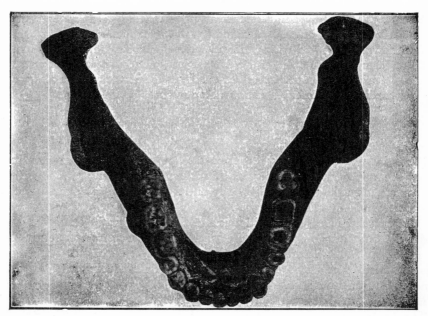

106 Heidelberg (Mauer) Jaw, seen from above. One-third natural size. (After Schoetensack)

deep; the coronoid process is blunt, rounded, and at a lower level than
the condyle; the latter possesses a large articular surface. Among Anthropoids, the Gibbon most closely resembles our fossil in these three characters.

The angle of the jaw has the truncated appearance noticeable in Anthropoids, particularly in the Orang, as well as in *Homo neandertalensis*, whose remains we shall examine later.

The horizontal rami are high and massive. They attain a thickness of 23 mm. at the level of the last molar; at the level of the mental foramen they are still 18 mm. thick, while in modern Man they rarely exceed 14 mm.

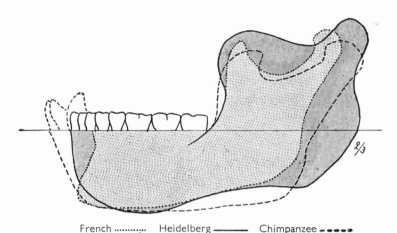

French .... Heidelberg ———— Chimpanzee ▬▬▬▬

107 Superimposed Profiles of the Heidelberg Jaw, of a Chimpanzee's Jaw, and of a modern Human Jaw (French). Two-thirds natural size

The lower edge is concave, as in the case of many Cynomorphic Apes, and contrary to the case in Anthropomorphic Apes and Man. On the interior surface, the oblique ridge is faint, indicating weak mylo-hyoid muscles.

Fig. 107 represents the Heidelberg jaw superimposed on the jaws of a

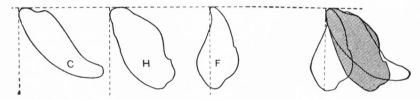

108 Vertical sections of various Lower Jaws at the symphysis. Two-thirds natural size. C, Chimpanzee; H, Heidelberg Man; F, Frenchman. To the right, the three profiles superimposed, that of Heidelberg being shaded

Chimpanzee and a modern Man (French), clearly revealing and summarizing the differences exhibited by these three specimens as seen in profile.

The symphysis is very thick (17 mm.), its external surface has a convex and receding curve, resembling that of the Apes and quite different from that of modern Man (Fig. 108). There is really no trace here of a chin. Now the chin is essentially a characteristic of the human race.

Seen full face, the region of the symphysis has, at its lower edge, a strongly marked chin pit (mental fossa); this structure occurs also in the Gibbons, and, to a less degree, in certain human jaws, either fossil or recent, as in the case of the Australians.

In modern Man the lower part of the front of the jaw-bone terminates in a definite edge, and the imprints of the insertions of the digastric muscles

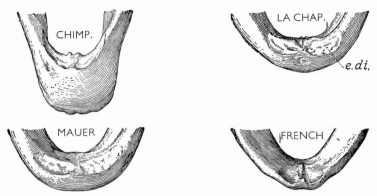

109 Inner lower edge and digastric impressions of various jaws. About half natural size.

e.di., impressions of digastric muscles

are apparent on the other side of this edge, that is, on its inner surface. But in the Mauer jaw the edge is replaced by a flattened area, a facet bearing the two digastric muscle impressions, which are here shorter than in the Chimpanzee, although longer than in modern Man. In this respect Neandertal Man stands intermediate between Heidelberg Man and modern Man (Fig. 109).

The region of the symphysis further shows certain peculiarities on its inner surface. It slopes strongly from the front backwards, as does the outer or chin surface. Moreover, it is not uniformly developed: the part near the lower third, the genial region, instead of projecting as in Man, contains, as in the Anthropoid Apes, a hollow which takes the place of the upper genial tubercles for the insertion of the muscles of the tongue. (Fig. 110).

In the characters of its symphysis, therefore, as Fig. 108 shows, the Mauer jaw is more akin to that of the large Apes than to that of modern Man. We shall see later that in this respect the jaw of Neandertal Man (*Homo neandertalensis*) takes a place exactly between that of Heidelberg Man (*Homo heidelbergensis*) and of recent Man (*Homo sapiens*).

The structure of the anterior part of the Mauer jaw shows that the space left for the tongue was greatly constricted, less so than in Anthropoid Apes, but more so than in modern Man and even than in other fossil Men known to us. The play of the tongue in articulate language must in consequence have been singularly restricted. It would even seem, to borrow an expression which Gaudry thought might be justifiably applied to *Dryopithecus*, that,

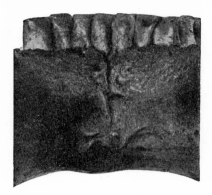

110 Inner surface of the body of the Mauer Lower Jaw, genial region. Photograph from a cast. Natural size

from an anatomical standpoint, we have here the embodiment of a kind of 'intermediate stage between speaking Man and the howling beasts'.

DENTITION

The dentition, as we have said, is definitely human, both in its entirety and in the details of its characters.

The alveolar borders, defining the dental curve, have a parabolic shape instead of the U-form of the Great Apes.

The teeth are well preserved, slightly worn on the left side; the molars on the right side have been partially broken in disengaging the relics from its matrix. The dental series is regular, continuous, without any interval (diastema) between the teeth.

The incisors are normal: their roots are slightly arched, following the curve of the region of the symphysis. Unlike *Pithecanthropus* and *Sinanthropus*, the canine is not more developed than in modern Man, even of the civilized races; its crown does not perceptibly rise above the level of the neighbouring crowns. This fact is very important, for it bears on a human adaptation which is thus shown to date from a very remote period. Even at the primitive stage represented by this simian jaw, the canines were no longer used as defensive weapons.

The premolars also are quite normal. The true molars are almost as broad as long, whilst in apes they are generally longer than broad. Compared with those of civilized Man, their dimensions are considerable, and may be compared with those of many modern savages, such as the Australians (Fig. 111). On the other hand, they appear weak in comparison with the strength of the jaw which bears them.

The second true molar is the largest, as is the rule in Man, but is likewise the case in apes. The last molar, or wisdom tooth, had not been cramped in its development, for the alveolar border is prolonged backward sufficiently far to accommodate a supplementary molar.

Minute study of the crowns of the true molars proves of interest, and the smallest details are important enough to be taken into consideration, for while Man and the large Apes have molars which are much alike they differ from those of other Monkeys.[39]

In the Anthropoid Apes (Fig. 111), the crown of the large lower molars

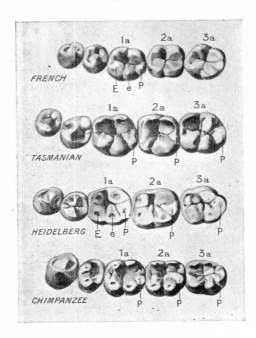

111 Comparative morphology of the Lower Molars of a Chimpanzee, of Heidelberg Man, of a Tasmanian and of a modern Frenchman. Natural size.

1a, 2a, 3a, first, second and third true molars; E, e, external cusps; p, posterior cusps, highly developed in the true molars of the Chimpanzee and Heidelberg Man, less developed in the Tasmanian, and only present in the first molar of the Frenchman.

is always formed of five well-developed cusps or tubercles. In civilized Man, the fifth cusp (Fig. 111, p) is reduced or even completely lost, save in the case of the first true molar, which is the largest and where it is always present. In certain savage races, such as the Australians, in several types of fossil Men, and in the Heidelberg Man, this fifth cusp persists more or less in all the true molars; but instead of projecting in the form of a heel, as in the Apes, it has already become reduced in size and is wedged in between the two neighbouring cusps, as in the first true molar of men of the white races.

All the teeth in the Mauer jaw have large pulp cavities. In the lower races at the present day these cavities are also larger than in Europeans. Here is illustrated the persistence of an infantile character which represents a primitive stage in the dentition of the large primates.

[39] On this subject, see A. Gaudry's brilliant notes, 'Sur la similitude des dents de l'Homme et de quelques animaux' (L'Anthropologie, XII, 1901); 'Contribution à l'Histoire des Hommes fossiles' (Ibid., XIV, 1903). See also Gregory, W. K., 'The Dentition of Dryopithecus and the Origin of Man' (Papers Amer. Museum Nat. Hist., XXVIII, 1926).

CONCLUSIONS

Such are the principal morphological characters of the valuable Mauer fossil. According to Schoetensack, this ancient jaw represents a very primitive form, for certain of its characters are found in the lower Monkeys and even in the Lemurs (great breadth of ascending rami, shallow mandibular notch). Thus it would seem to have retained some aspects of a stage through which the common ancestors of the Anthropoid Apes and Man must have passed. However that may be, it is certain that, in this very remarkable anatomical specimen, in this ancient relic of one of our oldest ancestors, there is a skilfully proportioned mixture of human and simian characters.

Duckworth considered that the jaw discovered by Schoetensack might have belonged to *Pithecanthropus*—an unnecessary hypothesis which the comparison we are now able to make with the teeth and lower jaw of *Pithecanthropus* and *Sinanthropus* in no way supports. We may go so far as to say, however, that the lower jaw of the Mauer fossil, like the brain-box of the Javan fossil, actually represents an almost ideal intermediate stage between the Apes and Man.

Others have wished to go further, and to deduce from this valuable but too isolated relic more than it can signify. Reconstructions of the skull and even the portrait of *Homo heidelbergensis* have been published. Such attempts may serve as pleasant pastimes for men of science; but they should not be allowed to pass beyond the study walls.

On the other hand comparisons between the Mauer fossil and similar fragments of other human fossils are justifiable. While reserving this examination for the following Chapter, we may say here and now, that between the lower jaw of *Homo heidelbergensis* and that of *Homo neandertalensis*, his successor in Western Europe, there are certain similarities favouring the hypothesis of a fairly close relationship.

THE PRENEANDERTALIANS

THE TAUBACH TEETH

In 1908 the discovery at Ehringsdorf, near Weimar in Germany, of human remains embedded in deposits incontestably belonging to the Lower Pleistocene, as it has been defined here, disclosed the existence at this period of a type, if not identical with, at least very similar to the Neandertal Man of the succeeding period. The finding, in the same conditions, between 1929 and 1933, of other fossil remains at Saccopastore, near Rome, and at Steinheim in Germany, confirmed the existence of this human type. We shall examine these various pieces, but first we must say a few words about a discovery made more than eighty years ago, the significance of which was for long unrecognized.

The village of Taubach, in the neighbourhood of Weimar, is situated on a terrace of the Ilm, the river gravels of which are surmounted by calcareous tufa, sandy or of a close nature. For many years there had been collected in these tufas, along with bones of large animals belonging to the warm fauna of ancient Pleistocene times, dressed flints, and bones, broken, burnt, and possibly utilized as tools. The deposit, with its traces of hearths, seemed to correspond to a station and place of encampment of a tribe contemporary with *Elephas antiquus*.

As early as 1871, the proprietor of the deposit presented anthropologists with a human skull which he said he had found in the fossil bed, but which was identified by Virchow as Neolithic. In 1892, a naturalist, Dr. Weiss, himself extracted from the deposit containing remains of the warm fauna a tooth, which was sent to Nehring of Berlin, along with another tooth, whose source, although less definite, nevertheless appeared to be the same. The first is a lower milk molar; the second a permanent lower molar, the first on the left side.

As a result of comparative study, Nehring[40] considered them to be human teeth, at the same time pointing out that they differed from the latter in their greater size, and in certain other simian characters. The true molar in

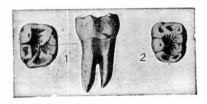

112 1, Tooth from Taubach (first lower left true molar), seen from the crown and in profile (inner side); 2, first lower left true molar of a Chimpanzee. Natural size. (After Nehring)

particular is remarkable, on account of its length, the arrangement of the cusps of the crown, and its much corrugated enamel, all characters which give it a resemblance to the tooth of a chimpanzee (Fig. 112).

Speaking of this tooth, Duckworth[41] said later: 'It is difficult to decide if it is a human tooth, or the tooth of a pithecoid precursor of Man.' The American zoologists, Miller and Gregory,[42] did not hesitate to ascribe it to a species of fossil Chimpanzee. But Virchow[43] finally showed that the characteristics of this tooth are exactly the same as those of the corresponding tooth belonging to the Ehringsdorf jaw. Its human appearance is incontestable.

THE EHRINGSDORF FOSSILS

Ehringsdorf is another locality situated between Taubach and Weimar, where Quaternary formations, identical with those at Taubach and worked

[40] Nehring, A., 'Über fossile Menschenzähne aus dem Diluvium von Taubach' (*Naturwissenschaftliche Wochenschrift*, August 4, 1895).

[41] *Prehistoric Man*, p. 23.

[42] *Studies on the Evolution of the Primates*, loc. cit., p. 313.

[43] Virchow, H., 'Der Taubacher Zahn des prähistorischen Museums der Universität Jena' (*Prähist. Zeitschr.*, IX, 1917, p. 1).

in several quarries, are surmounted by a deposit of loess and by a tufa of overlying travertine containing a cold fauna.[44]

A human lower jaw was first found, on May 8, 1914, in the lower tufa, 40 feet below the soil. Schwalbe, the German anatomist who described it, called it the 'Weimar jaw'.[45]

Two years later, in 1916, a few bones of the skeleton of a child aged about ten years—in particular a lower jaw and some isolated teeth—were collected at the same level. These new relics were studied by Hans Virchow.[46] According to this anthropologist the lower travertine here contains, along with dressed flints consisting of points and scrapers of a Mousterian type, bones

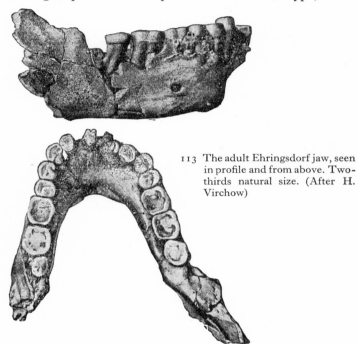

113 The adult Ehringsdorf jaw, seen in profile and from above. Two-thirds natural size. (After H. Virchow)

of Merck's Rhinoceros, of the Brown Bear, a Horse, the Red Deer, and Elk, shells of molluscs and imprints of plants, all denoting a climate similar to that of Thuringia at the present day. In all probability this material dates from the end of the last interglacial period.

Much mutilated and lacking the ascending ramus on the left side, the first jaw, which belonged to an adult individual, retains only a small part of the right ramus. Almost all the teeth are in position (Fig. 113).

[44] On the Ehringsdorf deposit, see Vaufrey, R., 'Les progrès de la Paléontologie humaine en Allemagne' (L'Anthropologie, XLI, 1931).
[45] 'Über einen bei Ehringsdorf in der Nähe von Weimar gefundenen Unterkiefer des Homo primigenius' (Anatomischer Anzeiger, XLVII, 1914).
[46] Virchow, Hans, Die menschlichen Skeletreste aus dem Kämpfe'schen Bruch im Travertin von Ehringsdorf bei Weimar (Jena, 1920).

The absence of chin is striking, the more so since it is accompanied by a very marked alveolar prognathism. It follows that the inner region of the symphysis slopes strongly from the front backwards, and so is very noticeable when the jaw, lying in a horizontal plane, is observed from above. The chin region appears to be deprived of tubercles for the genio-glossal and genio-hyoid muscles, nor is there any mylo-hyoid ridge on the inner surface of the horizontal branches. The foramina on the chin are long and situated directly below the first true molars (almost as in *Homo neandertalensis*). Schwalbe lays stress on the narrowness of the mandibular arch, but he sup-

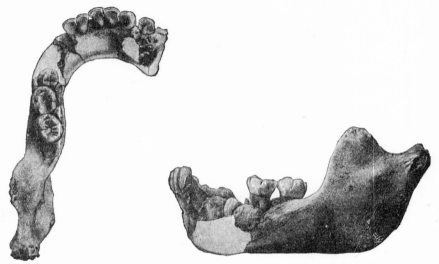

114 The child's jaw from Ehringsdorf, seen in profile and from above. Two-thirds natural size. (After H. Virchow)

poses that the specimen may have undergone some post-mortem deformation, which is confirmed by H. Virchow; according to the latter, a correction made to the arrangement of the teeth also reduces the alveolar prognathism.

The teeth are much worn; and as the premolars are less so than the canines, we must suppose that the crowns of the latter extended beyond the level of the crowns of the premolars. There is no interval (diastema) between the canine and the first premolar. A remarkable and rather unexpected fact is the diminutiveness of the last true molar; which seems to prove that the tendency of this tooth to disappear is much older than has been supposed.

The child's jaw described by H. Virchow (Fig. 114) is of the same type, except that certain characters are less pronounced. The alveolar arch is relatively larger, the dental prognathism less marked. It is remarkable for the same absence of chin, the same thickness of the lower border, the same horizontal arrangement of the digastric muscle insertions (see p. 174). In this case, one of the ascending rami, in good preservation, resembles the ascending rami of jaws of Neandertal Man. The teeth are intact; the canine does not rise above the level of the neighbouring teeth; in all their structural details the molars are essentially human, and the last true molar is not reduced in size.

In the opinion of Virchow, as of Schwalbe, the Ehringsdorf jaws belonged to the Neandertal human type, with certain more primitive characteristics.

The third discovery at Ehringsdorf was made, in September 1925, in the lower travertine of the Fischer quarry containing *Elephas antiquus*,

115   The Ehringsdorf Skull, left side view. One-third natural size. (After Weidenreich)

Rhinoceros mercki, and so on. This time it consisted of a brain-box broken into several fragments. After being freed from their gangue at Weimar Museum, they were reassembled on the basis of a reconstruction made by Dr. Weidenreich. A comprehensive study was published by this anatomist in collaboration with a geologist, F. Wiegers, and an archaeologist, E. Schuster.[47]

The poor state of preservation of the bones, together with the difficulty of extracting them undamaged from a very hard gangue, made it impossible to achieve an exact reconstitution of this brain-box without face or lower jaw. The bones composing it—the frontal and temporal bones and the occiput—which were all more or less broken and lacked the margins of contact with their neighbours, had to remain isolated (Fig. 116). Their artificial assemblage, however carefully executed, therefore permits only an approximative study, and may easily lead to errors of interpretation.

Marks of blows in the frontal region are said to denote the practice of cannibalism. Weidenreich believed that the skull belonged to a woman aged about twenty years. Keith, who studied it in his turn,[48] ascribed it to a young man of eighteen years.

The resemblance of the Ehringsdorf skull to the skull of *Homo neander-*

[47] Weidenreich, F., Wiegers, F. and Schuster, E., *Der Schädelfund von Weimar-Ehringsdorf* (Jena, 1928).

[48] Keith, A., *New Discoveries relating to the Antiquity of Man* (London, 1931) pp. 315–338.

talensis, which will be discussed in the following chapter, is evident at first glance: the same general shape, dolichocephalic (cephalic index = 74), the same supra-orbital arches developed into a powerful torus, the same structure of the occipital region, the same characters of the temporal bones with their small mastoid apophyses, and so on. But there are some differences, the most

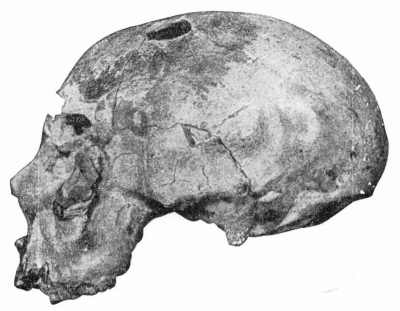

116 Saccopastore Skull No. I, left side view. One-third natural size. (After S. Sergi)

manifest of which is the shape of the forehead, which is less receding and thus reminiscent of the forehead of modern Man.

To Weidenreich's mind, Ehringsdorf Man represents a transitional form between Neandertal Man and modern types. In Keith's opinion it is, rather, a variety, a race, a special branch of *Homo neandertalensis*. The uncertainties left by the reconstruction make it difficult to reach more definite conclusions.

SACCOPASTORE

In May 1929, Duke Mario Grazioli showed Professor Sergio Sergi a human skull that had just been found in the Saccopastore quarry, two miles north-east of Rome, on the left bank of the Aniene, a small tributary of the Tiber.[49] It lay 20 feet down in a bed of sand and gravel corresponding to the oldest section of the lowest terrace of the river. In the same terrace and at roughly the same point, but at a depth of only 10 feet, a second skull was found in

[49] Sergi, S., 'La scoperta di un cranio del tipo di Neandertal presso Roma' (*Rivista di Antropologia*, XXVIII, Rome, 1929).

1935 by H. Breuil and A. C. Blanc.[50] The deposits in which these skulls were embedded also contained bones of large animals, notably ancient elephant and rhinoceros. They bore witness to a warm period corresponding to the last interglacial phase. At the same level as the second skull Blanc found, in 1936, a few Mousterian implements.

A detailed study of these two skulls was carried out by S. Sergi.[51] The first, which was well preserved, but lacking the lower jaw, must have belonged to a young woman. The second, that of an adult man, consisted of little more than the face and the major portion of the base. Both present the main features of *Homo neandertalensis* of the succeeding period (Fig. 116): very strong supra-orbital arches, receding forehead, flattened vault, very long 'snout-like' face with canine fossae reduced in size or lacking altogether, and very highly developed orbital openings. But these characteristics are accompanied by others of quite a different nature. The cranial capacity is only 1,200 cubic centimetres in the female skull, and something like 1,280 to 1,300 in the male skull; these figures fall far below those obtained for the Neandertalians properly so called. The cranial vault is even lower than in the latter; the face is more developed in relation to the cranium, and the cheek-bone is particularly massive. These various features must be regarded as primitive. But others, on the contrary, are curiously reminiscent of modern Man: the occipital foramen is situated just as far forward as in modern Man, which, Sergi points out, implies a perfectly upright posture; at the level of the base of the skull, the angle formed by the base part of the occiput (Fig. 142) is identical with that formed in modern Man, whereas this angle is very open in Neandertal Man, as in the Apes. The occiput is rounded, instead of elongated as in the classical Neandertalians. The vault of the palate is remarkably undeveloped, and the alveolar arches have a horseshoe shape that recalls modern Man and differs from the type with parallel branches which occurs in true Neandertal Man. As in the Ehringsdorf jaw, the wisdom tooth is already very much reduced in size.

This mixture of primitive and highly evolved characters sets a disquieting problem. Sergi takes the view that Saccopastore Man represents the initial type of Neandertal Man, a type which had not yet attained the degree of specialization it was to achieve later and which, furthermore, presents such polymorphism that we find in it, as it were in a prophetic state, features that were later to disappear in the Neandertalian branch properly so called, while they developed in modern Man.

THE STEINHEIM SKULL

At Steinheim on the Murr, a tributary of the Neckar, 20 miles north of Stuttgart in Wurtemberg, there are gravel-pits containing abundant

---

[50] Sergi, S., 'Le crâne néandertalien de Saccopastore, Rome' (*L'Anthropologie*, XLI, 1931).

[51] Sergi, S., 'Craniometria e craniografia del primo Paleantropo di Saccopastore' (*Ricerche di Morfologia*, XX–XXI, 1944, p. 1); 'Il cranio del secondo Paleantropo di Saccopastore (*Palaeontographia Italica*, XLII, Mem. I, No. 2, 1948).

bone-remains of fossil mammals that have been studied by F. Berckhemer, Curator at the Stuttgart Natural History Museum. It was the source, in particular, of one of the finest known skulls of *Elephas antiquus*.

In 1933, a human skull was found in one of these quarries. The section in Figure 117 clearly shows the stratigraphic position of the human fossil. The Pleistocene formations here comprise, beneath a covering of loess varying in depth from 5 to 6½ feet, an initial layer of gravel of varying thickness containing a cold fauna (including abundant remains of mammoths)

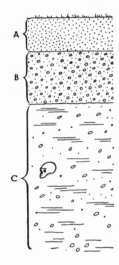

117 Geological section of Steinheim. (After H. Obermeier)

A, loess; B, gravels with abundant remains of mammoth; C, interglacial gravels with beds of sand and marl.

and resting on a thicker layer of gravel mixed with beds of sand and containing many relics of the so-called warm fauna—Ancient Elephant, Merck's Rhinoceros, a Buffalo resembling Arni's, and so on. In the deepest part of this layer, the cold fauna reappears. We are therefore dealing with two glacial formations and the interglacial deposits separating them. It is very probable that the whole formation corresponds to the two last glaciations and the intermediate period (Riss-Würm Interglacial). Berckhemer, however, wonders whether the mass of gravel does not belong to the penultimate glaciation: the intercalated layer with a warm fauna would then be only an intermediate stage in this glaciation.

The human skull came from the interglacial gravel, where it lay 23 feet beneath the surface of the soil. Its lower jaw is wanting, as well as part of the left side of the face and the area surrounding the foramen magnum. It is preserved in the Stuttgart Natural History Museum and was the subject first of a brief note by Berckhemer,[52] and then of a longer work by Weinert.[53]

[52] Berckhemer, F., 'Notiz über den Fund eines Urmenschenschädels in den Schottern von Steinheim' ((*Anthropologischer Anzeiger*, X, 1933). See also 'Vorweisung des Steinheimer Schädels im Original' (*Deutsche Gesellschaft für Rassenkunde*, IX, 1938).

[53] Weinert, H., 'Der Urmenschenschädel von Steinheim' (*Z. für Morphol. und Anthrop.*, XXXV, 1936).

As may be seen by Figure 118, this skull—which is relatively small, with a capacity estimated at 1,070 cubic centimetres, is dolichocephalic in shape (cephalic index 72), and seems to have belonged to a young woman—presents a Neandertaloid appearance by virtue of its enormous supra-orbital

118 The Steinheim Skull, seen in profile and full face. About one-third natural size
(After Weinert)

ridges, the great breadth of its nose, and the reduced size of its mastoid apophysis. The cranial vault is lower and flatter than in any of the known Neandertalians. But other characters move the Steinheim fossil away from *Homo neandertalensis* and bring it closer to modern Man: a lower degree of facial prognathism and the presence of canine fossae, that is to say no 'snout'; an occipital region that describes a rounded curve and shows no trace of a *chignon* nor of a transverse torus; well developed squamous portion of the temporal bone limited by a convex border; and a noteworthy reduction in the size of the wisdom tooth.

In this skull, therefore, Neandertal characters, equally or even more pronounced than in the typical specimens of this group, exist side by side with completely modern characters. Weinert sought to explain this by suggesting that the skull, being that of a woman, had preserved juvenile characteristics. But the true female Neandertalian skulls we know—the La Quina skull, for example—have the same general characters as the male skulls. In Berckhemer's opinion, the Steinheimer fossil represents a branch both more ancient and more primitive than the Neandertal branch, and nevertheless closer to the branch of modern Man. This hypothesis agrees in general outline with that proposed by Sergi for Saccopastore Man.

THE PRESAPIENS

Swanscombe

In 1935 an English prehistorian, A. T. Marston,[54] announced the discovery of a human occipital bone at a depth of 26 feet in the Pleistocene gravels of the Thames, at Swanscombe, Kent. The following year he uncovered at the same depth and 23 feet from the original spot a left parietal bone that exactly fitted the occipital. These finds, which were immediately compared to the Piltdown discoveries, were of such interest that a committee of geologists, archaeologists and anthropologists was formed to report on the Swanscombe skull. Their report appeared in 1938.[55]

The geologists were agreed as to the authenticity and antiquity of the bone remains. The gravels in which they were found, and which correspond to the Barnfield Pit, belong to the so-called 100-foot terrace of the Thames, which contains a warm fauna with *Elephas antiquus* and *Rhinoceros mercki* generally associated with the penultimate interglacial period. This fauna is accompanied by a well characterized Acheulean industry. A test of the fluorine content recently carried out by Oakley and Hoskins[56] confirmed the great age of the human skull.

This skull, which was studied by Morant and Le Gros Clark, must have belonged to a woman of about twenty (Fig. 119). The two bones, in excellent condition, appear at first sight very similar to those of modern Man and very different from those of Neandertal Man. In particular, two very typical characteristics of the latter—the elongation of the occipital into a 'chignon' and the presence on this bone of a relatively marked torus—are totally lacking in the Swanscombe skull.

[54] Marston, A. T., *Nature*, August 1, 1936, and *Journ. of the Royal Anthrop. Inst.*, LXVII, 1937.

[55] 'Report on the Swanscombe Skull' (*Journ. of the Royal Anthrop. Inst.*, LXVIII, 1938, p. 17). To the two preceding discoveries must be added that of the right parietal bone unearthed by Mr. and Mrs. B. Wymer and Mr. A. Gibson in 1955.

[56] *Loc. cit.*, 1949, p. 44.

In his report, Morant insists on the 'recent' character of the two bones, stating that their general shape is virtually identical with that of modern English female skulls. According to the numerous measurements made by this author the dimensions are approximately the same. The orientation of the foramen magnum, the position of the parietal, and the shape of the cranial curves are practically identical. The supposed capacity—1,325 cubic

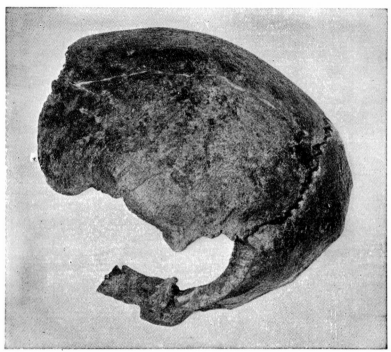

119 Parietal and occipital bone from Swanscombe, profile view. About five-ninths natural size. (After G. Morant)

centimetres—is absolutely normal for a female skull. The endocranial cast is of the *Homo sapiens* type. There are, however, certain distinctive features including the very great thickness of the bones and the exceptional width of the squamous part of the occipital bone.

Incomplete as it is, these facts are sufficient to prove that the Swanscombe skull does not belong to *Homo neandertalensis*. Morant thought it might come from a type comparable to Steinheim Man, in which the occipital is also rounded, but the Swanscombe skull is far bulkier and other characteristics are not in accord. After prolonged and detailed study, A. Keith declared that Swanscombe Man was a descendant of Piltdown Man, already farther evolved in the direction of Homo sapiens.[57] This hypothesis is without

[57] 'A Resurvey of the anatomical features of the Piltdown Skull, with some observations on the recently discovered Swanscombe Skull' (*Journ. of Anatomy*, LXIII, 1938/1939).

interest, since we now know that Piltdown Man is not a fossil. The points of resemblance between Swanscombe Man and modern Man are none the less manifest.

We should perhaps associate with the same type as the Swanscombe skull an occipital bone found in 1938 in one of the caves at Quinzano, near Verona, Italy, and described ten years later by Battaglia.[58] This occipital, which is limited to a severely damaged squamous portion and is as thick as that from Swanscombe, presents roughly the same curve. But the conditions under which this fragment was found are not completely satisfactory. Its antiquity cannot be positively stated. Fortunately the situation is quite different as regards a final discovery which we shall now discuss.

THE FONTÉCHEVADE MEN

At Fontéchevade (Charente) there is a small cave in which earlier excavations brought to light deposits belonging to the Upper and Middle Palaeolithic periods. A thick layer beneath these seemed to be the floor of the cave.

Examining this layer, Mlle G. Henri-Martin realized that it was only a thick bed of stalagmite, and that it surmounted 20 to 30 feet of deeper formations. In the upper layers of these formations she discovered, on August 16, 1947, a fossil human skull-cap; a little while earlier she had discovered, at the same level and a short distance away, a small fragment of another skull.[59]

The stratum containing human bone remains also contained a very crude industry of the type known as Tayacian, which passed imperceptibly towards the base to even more primitive implements of the type called Clactonian. These are special forms belonging to the Lower Palaeolithic, characterized by the manner in which they are dressed. The fauna comprised, among other animals, Merck's Rhinoceros, the Fallow Deer and the Greek Tortoise—a warm-temperate fauna which must, in all probability, be attributed to the last interglacial. Archaeology and palaeontology therefore agree in assigning Fontéchevade Man to this period, and the undisturbed condition of the layer of stalagmite covering the deposits guarantees the absolute authenticity of these finds. The age of the bone-remains was confirmed by the fluorine test.[60]

The skull-cap (Fig. 120) comprises the major part of the parietals with the upper two-thirds of the frontal bone.[61] Similar to modern Man in shape and size, its thickness is greater than that of most of the Neandertalians

[58] Battaglia, R., 'Ossa occipitale umano rinvenuto nel giacimento pleistocenico di Quinzano nel Comune di Verona' (Palaeontographia Italica, XLII, No. 2, 1948).

[59] Henri-Martin, G., 'L'Homme fossile tayacien de la grotte de Fontéchevade' (C. R. Acad. Sc., CCXXV, 1947, p. 266).

[60] Oakley, K., Hoskins, R. and Henri-Martin, G., 'Application du test de la fluorine aux crânes de Fontéchevade, Charente' (L'Anthropologie, LV, 1951, p. 239).

[61] Vallois, H. V., 'The Fontéchevade Fossil Men' (Amer. J. of Phys. Anthrop., VII, 1949, p. 339).

but comparable to that of the Swanscombe skull. Seen from above, it has a pentagonal outline with no trace of the post-orbital contraction characteristic of Neandertal Man. Its maximum width—154 millimetres—is close to that of the Swanscombe skull. As in the latter, and those of the majority of Neandertalians, the maximum width of the occipital is considerable, very much greater than in modern Man. A reconstruction of the

120 The Fontéchevade Skull, seen from above. Half natural size

missing parts shows that the index of the skull must have been mesocephalic, like that from Swanscombe. The capacity may be tentatively assessed at about 1,450 cubic centimetres, which corresponds to a well developed brain.

In Neandertal Man the parietal is often longer at the bottom than at the top. This feature, which is absent in *Homo sapiens* as well as in Swanscombe Man, is also lacking here, where the upper margin of the bone measures 125 millimetres, while the lower margin can scarcely have exceeded 100. The curve of the parietal bone along the median line indicates a certain platycephaly. The parietal bosses, which are largely noticeable, correspond to the middle part of the bone, instead of being shifted down and to the rear as in Neandertal Man. The bevel of the lower margin where it met the temporal bone is much more oblique than in modern Man, where the angle is almost vertical. This obliqueness is absent in other fossil Men.

The existing part of the frontal bone measures 70 millimetres along the median line. Much more curved than in Neandertal skulls, it reveals on its section surface the extremity of the right frontal sinus. Even at this level there is no sign of the supra-orbital ridge typical of *Homo neandertalensis*. A reconstruction of the front part of the skull, taking account of the position of the sinus, shows that the forehead was vertical and that there was no visor (Fig. 121). This important finding is corroborated by a study of the

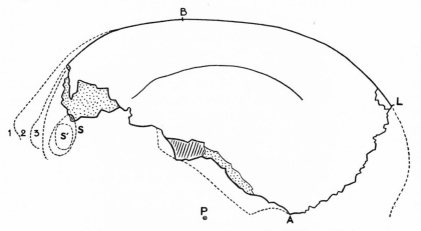

121 The Fontéchevade Skull, seen in profile. Half natural size

1, 2, 3, profiles of the foreheads of the Man from La Chapelle-aux-Saints, Cro-Magnon Man and 'Piltdown Man' No. II; *s*, supposed contour of the frontal sinus of Fontéchevade Man; *s'*, contour of the frontal sinus of 'Piltdown Man' No. II

second fragment from Fontéchevade, which is the lower part of the forehead of another individual. There is no trace of a ridge, and the glabella itself is barely visible. The forehead of the Fontéchevade Men was therefore shaped like that of modern Man and quite differently from that of Neandertal Man.

CONCLUSIONS

Such are the results of European discoveries relating to the oldest fossil Men. Their paucity is in striking contrast to the wealth and the vast dispersion of archaeological evidences regarding this very ancient period of humanity. It is also in contrast to its duration, since the Lower Pleistocene embraces at least four-fifths of the whole Quaternary Age. It must not be forgotten, however, that forty years ago we possessed no authentic relics of a Man belonging to this epoch. Today we have several skulls and several jaws and can form an initial idea of these very ancient human types.

First, we have found that they are very far from being the same age. The Mauer jaw, which is by far the oldest, goes back to a very old Chellean period. It is undoubtedly anterior to the Mindel glaciation and more or less coeval with *Sinanthropus*. It is the oldest human relic found in Europe. It is separated by a very long interval of time, during which we know absolutely nothing about the history of our species, from Swanscombe Man, who was contemporary with an Acheulean industry and corresponds to the penultimate interglacial epoch. All the other finds fall within the last interglacial epoch, and the Men of Weimar and of Saccopastore were doubtless only slightly earlier than the last glacial phase.

It was thought for a time that all these specimens belonged to one and the same morphological type, whose general characteristics placed it mid-way between the Prehominians of the beginning of the Pleistocene and Neandertal Man from the Mid Pleistocene. Nowadays this conception is untenable.

Despite their small number, these few relics confront us with an extremely important fact: the coexistence, at least during the second half of the Lower Pleistocene, of two very different morphological types, one descended from *Homo neandertalensis* of the Mid Palaeolithic, the other apparently descended from *Homo sapiens* of the Upper Palaeolithic. This coexistence, which was long a matter of discussion, must now be considered certain. Anthropological and stratigraphical evidences have furnished final proof of it.

The study of certain representatives of the first group, to which we have given the name *Preneandertalians*, has shown us first that, if the latter are more primitive than Neandertal Man in the sum total of their characters, they differ from him in certain features which bring them closer to *Homo sapiens*. This fact would be inexplicable if Neandertal Man, as was long thought and as certain anthropologists still think today, was an intermediate form between Humanity's most archaic representatives and modern Man. But we shall see in the next chapter that, in the family tree of mankind, Neandertal Man is no more the tip of a branch. It is a lateral branch that attained a very marked degree of specialization and then disappeared. It was not Neandertal Man who gave birth to *Homo sapiens*. Hence it is not surprising that the specialized characteristics we may observe in him are absent or at least still very undeveloped in his predecessors, who, in consequence, are less far removed than he from the non-Neandertalian branches of humanity.

The Preneandertalians of Steinheim and Saccopastore therefore give us an idea of what Neandertal Man's ancestors may have been like. Archaic features, such as the extreme development of the supra-orbital arches, existed side by side with features like the rounded shape of the occipital bone and the pronounced curvature of the base of the skull, which disappeared in their successors, while it continues to exist in the lineage of *Homo sapiens*.

The study of the *Presapiens* is particularly important, since the question of the very existence of this group, which only took scientific shape with the Piltdown 'discovery' and aroused bitter controversy for more than thirty years, has only recently been resolved by the discovery—under conditions that eliminate any possibility of doubt—of the Fontéchevade Men. The term Presapiens, which has been used to describe this group for lack of a better

one, indicates its incontestable morphological relations with *Homo sapiens*.
The general shape of the cranium and the presence of an upright forehead
devoid of supra-orbital visor constitute, in this respect, characteristics of
the first order that mark a radical difference from Neandertal Man and his
predecessors. The little we know about this type shows us that it was not,
however, identical with modern Man, that it presented at least a certain
number of special features: very great thickness of the skull, enlargement of
the occipital, and perhaps a certain platycephaly. At present, we are ignorant
of the characters either of the face or of the lower jaw.

It will be understood that, under these circumstances, we cannot yet say
to what extent the term Presapiens, which is morphologically valid, indicates
that there was in addition real continuity from the evolutionary point of
view.[62] Between the Presapiens we have just been studying, and who date
from the Lower Pleistocene, and the first *Homo sapiens* whom we shall see
appearing at the beginning of the Upper Pleistocene, there stretches the
enormous duration of time corresponding to the Mid Pleistocene. Now,
during the whole of this period, at least in Europe, we only meet Neandertal
Man. Until the evidences are more numerous, until we know more about
what happened during this epoch in the regions bordering our continent,
it is more prudent to abstain from premature hypotheses; we must reserve
judgment.

The essential fact, in any case, is that we know that in Europe, from
the first phases of Quaternary times, and even leaving aside the Prehominians,
Men properly so-called were already diversified. Our evolution was, therefore,
much more complex than used to be supposed. It did not follow a single line,
but at least two, and no doubt more. The future certainly holds for us
curious and thrilling discoveries relative to the history of these various
branches.

[62] Vallois, H. V., 'L'origine de *l'Homo sapiens*' (*C. R. Acad. Sciences*, Vol. CCXXVIII,
March 14, 1949).

CHAPTER SEVEN

NEANDERTAL MAN
(HOMO NEANDERTALENSIS)

IF the poverty of human fossil remains in the Lower Pleistocene or *Chellean* period is marked, there is a striking contrast in the wealth of human fossils in the Mid Pleistocene, which almost corresponds to the *Mousterian* period of archaeologists.

CHARACTERS OF THE MOUSTERIAN

We already know that this period differs greatly from the preceding one in its geological, palaeontological, and archaeological characters. It corresponds to the last glacial invasion, to a period of great floods and deposition of alluvium, of the formation of the greatest accumulation of superficial muds and natural cave deposits.

The Mousterian flora and fauna of Central and Southern Europe differ both from the Chellean flora and fauna, and from the flora and fauna of the present day, and indicate a much moister and colder climate. The large extinct species of mammals, the Mammoth, the Woolly (Tichorine) Rhinoceros, etc., were covered with a thick coat of hair; the majority of the species still living at the present day, such as the Reindeer, Musk-Ox, Glutton, Ibex, Chamois, Blue Fox and Marmot now only inhabit northern countries or the highest mountains. Wild equidae and bovidae were abundant everywhere and formed the prey of great beasts, such as bears, hyaenas and cave lions.

From the archaeological point of view there are also changes, revealing great progress which seems to have been achieved by stages. This is clearly shown by the study of particularly rich French deposits—such as those of Le Moustier, La Ferrassie (Dordogne) and La Quina (Charente)—by archaeologists like Peyrony and H. Martin.

Amygdaloid flints persist, especially at the beginning, but they are smaller and finer (Fig. 122, 1, 2, 3). The flake industry in particular, which has remained up to this point extremely rudimentary, evolves in variety and precision and yields a whole series of weapons and tools, of which the predominating types are points and scrapers dressed and retouched on one face only. There are also disks and balls, generally of limestone, which were

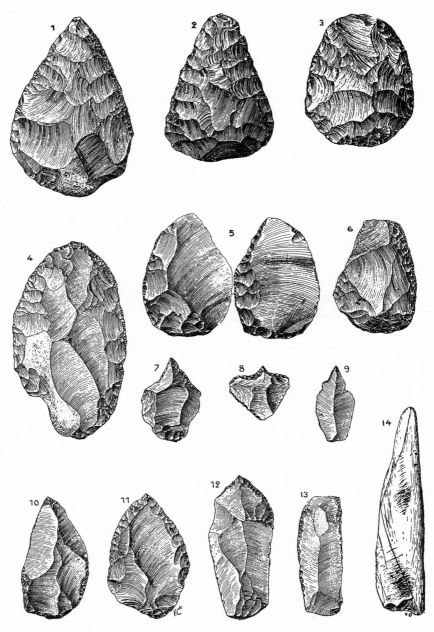

122 Mousterian industry from the North of France. One-third natural size. (After Commont)

  1, 2, 3, amygdaloid flints carefully dressed on both faces; 4, 5, 6, scrapers; 7, 8, 9 piercers; 10, 11, 12, points; 13, flake, retouched as a knife; 14, fragment of bone with striations, probably used as a compressor.

probably used as throwing stones. The stone implements also include cleavers, knives, concave scrapers, borers and saws answering various purposes relating to the working of wood. The bone industry, which seems to be limited in France to the utilization of bones in their natural state, shows signs of greater development in certain regions of Central Europe that are poor in flint, where it is represented by objects deliberately shaped, repeated, and polished by use. The most striking of these deposits is the one in the Petershöhle, near Nuremberg, in Franconia.[1]

Here we have to deal with conditions of environment totally different from, and, in certain respects, much more severe than those of the Chellean period. Man, obliged to protect himself against the rigours of the climate, had to modify his habitat. He sought refuge in caves, and there he lived, died, and left the bones which we exhume today with such excited curiosity.

HISTORICAL SUMMARY

Moreover, the discoveries of human fossils attributed to the Mousterian period are very numerous, numbering, indeed, about fifty, and dating from the year 1700 to our own day.

Many must be set aside or ignored, either because of the poor state of preservation of the remains obtained, or more particularly because of uncertainty regarding the age and even the identity of their beds. In the historical summary which we think it useful to insert here, we shall limit ourselves to discoveries the geological age of which justifies discussion and which have yielded bone-remains sufficiently well preserved to permit of serious study.

The oldest is that at Cannstadt, and this has already been described (see p. 151).

Next in chronological order comes the Lahr find, of 1823, which was given to Cuvier (see p. 11). In spite of Hamy's[2] attempt to vindicate this discovery, neither the conditions of the deposit nor the morphological characters of the bones themselves justify us in regarding them as authentic fossil remains.

The situation is different when we come to a child's skull (Fig. 154) found in 1828 by Schmerling in a low level of the Engis cave (province of Liège) with a Mousterian fauna and industry. Ch. Fraipont showed the great age and interest of this specimen, which represents the earliest discovery relating to what was to be called thirty-six years later, 'Neandertal Man'.[3]

---

[1] Cf. Vaufrey, R., 'Les progrès de la Paléontologie humaine en Allemagne' (*L'Anthropologie*, XLI, p. 638, with fig.).

[2] Hamy, E. T., 'Nouveaux matériaux pour servir à l'étude de la paléontologie humaine' (*Congrès intern. d'Anthrop.*, Paris, 1889, p. 423).

[3] Fraipont, C., *loc. cit.*, see Note on p. 12.

NEANDERTAL

In 1856, a skull-cap and some long bones were dug up by workmen in the small Feldhofer grotto, situated between Düsseldorf and Elberfeld in Rhenish Prussia, in the valley known as Neandertal,[4] through which flows the River Düssel. This is the famous discovery of *Neandertal Man*, whose remains were rescued by Fuhlrott and described by Schaaffhausen.[5]

The greatly depressed skull-cap with its large superciliary arches (Fig. 123) keenly interested the foremost naturalists of last century. Some, along with Schaaffhausen and Huxley, saw in it the representative of a primitive human race, preserving simian characteristics; others, including the German Virchow, leaned to the view that it was rather a pathological specimen or the skull of an imbecile. For long its high antiquity was suspected, since there was no irrefutable argument in its favour. The extraordinary morphology

123 Neandertal Skull-Cap, seen full face and in profile. One-third natural size.
Photograph from a cast

of the skull-cap could not be successfully appealed to, for this was an isolated case. But we shall see how later discoveries have destroyed this isolation, and have justified us in affirming that the clay whence the Neandertal bones were taken, indeed dates, like the majority of analogous formations, from the Mid Pleistocene.

The next find was a fragment of human lower jaw discovered in 1859 in the Grotte des Fées, near Arcy-sur-Cure (Yonne). But the assignment of this piece to the Mousterian is far less certain than was originally claimed, and a study of its morphological characteristics shows that it differs greatly from other remains belonging to this period.[6] It is safest to leave it out of account.

[4] The word is often written 'Neanderthal', the old German form; but this spelling was long ago replaced by 'Neandertal' in Germany and there is no reason for retaining it in other countries. (Dr. Kenneth Oakley prefers the old form—Publisher.)

[5] The very voluminous bibliography is now of historical interest only. It is to be found in: Quatrefages and Hamy, *Crania ethnica*; Reinach, S., *Description raisonnée du musée de Saint-Germain;* Obermaier, 'Les restes humains quaternaires dans l'Europe centrale' (*L'Anthropologie*, XVII, 1906). Among later works on the morphology of the skull, we must mention especially Schwalbe, G., 'Der Neanderthalschädel' (*Bonner Jahrbücher*, Vol. 106, 1901).

[6] Puccioni, N., 'La mandibola di Arcy-sur-Cure appartiene al tipo di Neanderthal?' (*Arch. per l'Antr. e l'Etnol.*, XLII, 1912).

GIBRALTAR

In 1864, at a meeting of the British Association, an English geologist, Busk, exhibited a human skull obtained in the year 1848 from the bone-breccia of an excavation known as Forbes's Quarry at Gibraltar. Busk compared this skull to that from Neandertal; de Quatrefages and Hamy attributed it to their *Cannstadt race*; and then this palaeontological specimen, remarkable for its receding forehead, its great orbital arches and enormous face (Fig. 124), seemed to have been forgotten. The more recent researches of

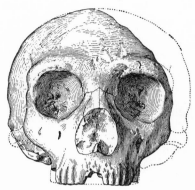

124 Gibraltar Skull, seen full face. Diagraph drawing from a cast. One-third natural size.

Sollas, Sera, Keith and others, however, once more brought it to notice.[7]

The high antiquity of the Gibraltar skull cannot be doubted. It is contemporary with the fauna of the breccia and deep deposits of the caves described by Busk,[8] and this represents a southern facies of the Mid Pleistocene fauna. The human skull and the animal bones are in the same state of fossilization.

The antiquity of the Gibraltar skull has been clearly confirmed by a much more recent discovery. In 1926 an old rock-shelter not far from the site of the former Forbes's Quarry, facing the Devil's Tower, yielded to its explorer, Miss Garrod, in a stratum containing Mousterian implements, the scattered fragments of a skull belonging to a child of about five: a left frontal and parietal bone and, 13 feet away, a temporal bone, a fragment of upper jaw and a damaged lower jaw. We shall return later to this juvenile Neandertalian skull, which has been reconstructed and anatomically studied by Buxton.[9]

[7]   Sollas, W. J., 'On the Cranial and Facial Characters of the Neanderthal Race' (*Philosophical Transactions*, B, CXCIX, 1907). Sera, G. L., 'Di alcuni caratteri. . .nel cranio di Gibraltar' (*Soc. romana di Antrop.*, XV, 1909); 'Nuove osservazioni. . .' (*Arch. per l'Antrop.*, XXXIX, 1909). Keith, A., *Ancient Types of Man* (London, 1911) p. 121.

[8]   Busk, G., 'On the Ancient or Quaternary Fauna of Gibraltar' (*Transact. of Zoolog. Soc. of London*, X, 1879).

[9]   Garrod, Miss D., Buxton, L. H. D., Smith, E. G. and Bate, D., 'Excavation of a Mousterian Rock-Shelter at Devil's Tower, Gibraltar' (*Journ. of the Roy. Anthrop. Inst.*, LVIII, 1928).

LA NAULETTE

The year 1866 was marked by the discovery of the lower jaw from La
Naulette, almost as famous as the Neandertal skull-cap itself (Fig. 125).
Found by a distinguished Belgian geologist, Dupont, in an undisturbed
layer in the Trou de la Naulette, near Dinant, and accurately dated by
animal remains of Mid Pleistocene age which accompanied it,[10] its morphological peculiarities, its strength, its absence of chin, and its large molar alveoli
made a great impression upon anatomists.[11]

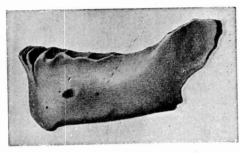

125 Lower jaw from La Naulette. Three-
     fourths natural size.
     (After de Quatrefages and Hamy)

To Hamy belongs the credit of foreseeing, if not of proving, that, on the
one hand, skulls with receding foreheads and heavy superciliary arches, and,
on the other hand, strong jaws without chin, known at that period, must
have belonged to the same type, that is to say, to the same race. Dr Topinard[12] later took up again, in detail, the study of this jaw from La Naulette.

Some doubt overhangs the geological age of the skull-cap obtained in
1872 from the ancient alluvials at Brüx in Bohemia. Scientists are agreed
in regarding this specimen as Neandertaloid, but its poor state of preservation has rendered it of little use as evidence.

The discoveries made, in 1881 in the Schipka cave in Moravia, in 1883 in
the Marcilly clay (Eure), and in 1884 in a clay pocket in the chalk at Bury
St. Edmunds in Suffolk, consist of mere fragments of jaws or of skulls in a
state of preservation barely sufficient to warrant their classification as of
Neandertal type.

It is equally impossible to date the skull obtained towards the close of
1883 from the loess at Podbaba, near Prague. This piece, which has now been
destroyed, seems at most to have been only Neandertaloid.[13]

THE SPY DISCOVERY

The year 1886 is remarkable for the very important discovery made by

[10] Dupont, É., 'Étude sur les fouilles scientifiques. . .dans les cavernes de la Lesse' (*Bull.
de l'Acad. roy. de Belgique*, XXII, 1866).
[11] Pruner-Bey, 'Sur la mâchoire humaine de La Naulette' (*Bull. de la Soc. d'Anthrop. de
Paris*, 1866). Hamy, E. T., *Précis de Paléontologie humaine*, p. 232.
[12] Topinard, D., 'Les caractères simiens de la mâchoire de La Naulette' (*Revue d'Anthrop.*,
1886, p. 385).
[13] Matiegka, J., 'Le crâne de Podbaba' (*Anthropologie*, II, Prague, 1924).

Marcel de Puydt and Max Lohest, in the Spy cave in the province of Namur in Belgium. Here the requirements of scientific precision are all fully met. The stratigraphy of the layer was definitely ascertained by a geologist; the fauna accompanying the human remains was that of Mid Pleistocene times— the Mammoth (*Elephas primigenius*), the Woolly Rhinoceros (*R. tichorhinus*), etc.—and the dressed flints were Mousterian in form.

The human bones (Fig. 126) are numerous and relatively well preserved: two brain-boxes, some portions of the face, two lower jaws, and a large

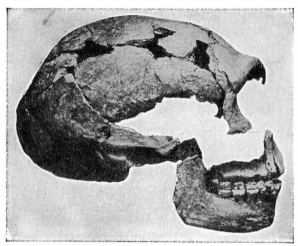

126 Spy Skull (No. I), seen in profile. About one-third natural size. (After Fraipont)

number of long bones, more or less perfect, comprise the remains of three skeletons. These valuable relics have been studied by Fraipont and Lohest,[14] whose fine monograph has added much to our knowledge of the human type known as Neandertal. Till 1909 the Spy skeletons were justly regarded as the most complete and the most important of Early Palaeolithic remains.

In 1889, Hamy[15] examined certain human remains discovered by Piette in the Gourdan Cave, some of these being Magdalenian and others Mousterian. The latter comprised a fragment of lower jaw and a portion of face (upper maxillary and malar). Hamy associated them with corresponding parts of the Gibraltar and Spy skulls, but this attribution is extremely dubious.

In the same year, H. Filhol described a lower jaw taken from the Malarnaud cave, near Montseron in Ariège. It was embedded in a mud containing bones of the Cave Bear and Mammoth, that is to say, in an environment

[14] Fraipont, J. and Lohest, M., 'Recherches ethnographiques sur des ossements humains découverts dans les depôts d'une grotte quaternaire à Spy' (*Archives de Biologie*, VII, 1886; Ghent, 1887).

[15] *Congrès intern. d'Anthrop.*, Paris, 1889, p. 413.

and at a level corresponding to those of the La Naulette jaw, the anatomical characters of which are repeated in the Malarnaud specimen[16] (Fig. 127).

A portion of skull, obtained in 1892 in a brick-field at Bréchamps (Eure-et-Loir), was considered by Manouvrier to exhibit certain Neandertaloid

127 Lower jaw from Malarnaud (Ariège), seen in profile. Three-fourths natural size (After Filhol)

characteristics. The conditions of deposit were not subjected to any examination, and the skull was not seen in place at the level occupied by the Mousterian flints of the brick-fields.

A human jaw, found in 1895 at Isturitz (Basses-Pyrénées), in a neighbourhood rich in bone-remains of the Cave Bear and Rhinoceros, should, according to M. Breuil, be compared to that from Malarnaud.[17]

About the same time, in the caves of Estelas in Ariège, at Aubert in Arièrge, and at Sallèles-Carbardès in Aude, there were found, by F. Regnault and L. Roule, two lower jaws of children and a frontal bone with well-developed orbital arches. These have been assigned to Mid Pleistocene times, but without any definite proof.

KRAPINA

The discovery at Krapina in Croatia, is of greater import. In 1899, a professor in the University of Zagreb, Gorjanovic-Kramberger, described a Palaeolithic shelter where, in an undisturbed Pleistocene layer (Fig. 128), he collected portions of from ten to twelve skulls, fourteen pieces of lower jaws, one hundred and forty-four isolated teeth, as well as numerous fragments of vertebrae, ribs, and long bones. Many of these bones, found in hearths, are calcined. They have formed the subject of a long and painstaking monograph.[18]

The true age of the deposit has often been misinterpreted. An attempt

[16] Filhol, H., 'Note sur une mâchoire humaine trouvée dans la caverne de Malarnaud. . .' (*Bull. de la Soc. philomathique de Paris*, 1889). Boule, M., 'La caverne de Malarnaud' (*Ibid.*).

[17] Breuil, H., 'Les plus anciennes races humaines connues' (*Revue des sciences philosophiques et théologiques*, 1909).

[18] Gorjanovic-Kramberger, K., *Der diluviale Mensch von Krapina in Kroatien* (Wiesbaden, 1906).

has been made to regard it as very ancient, on the strength of the presence of *Rhinoceros mercki* in the fauna the remains of which accompany the human bones, and this in spite of the fact that, in respect of its other members, this fauna contains nothing to distinguish it from the typical Mid Pleistocene fauna. Now, in France, *Rhinoceros mercki* persisted much longer than the Ancient Elephant (*Elephas antiquus*) and the Hippopotamus, with which it is associated in the fauna of the Lower Pleistocene. None of the really characteristic members of this fauna are to be met with at Krapina.

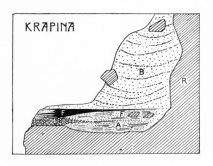

128 Section of the Krapina bed.
  (After Gorjanovic-Kramberger)

  R, rock, forming shelter; A, alluvial deposit of the Krapina, the bed being now 80 feet lower; F, hearths, bed where human remains were mainly found; B, products of disintegration of the Miocene sandstone forming the shelter, towards the topmost layers of which are still to be found bones of the Cave Bear.

From the palaeontological point of view, therefore, this deposit cannot date further back than Mid Pleistocene times. And on this point the archaeological evidence agrees with the palaeontological evidence: the dressed stones belong to the recognized Mousterian types.

In 1906, Rzehak described a fragment of jaw found in a layer 'containing glacial fauna', in the grotto of Ochos in Moravia. This fragment is too incomplete to enable us to be certain of its Neandertaloid character, but it seems to have possessed a chin. According to Bayer it only dates from the Upper Palaeolithic.

It will be sufficient simply to mention the discovery by M. Favraud of three fragments of human jaws in a Mousterian environment at Petit-Puy-Moyen in Charente. The jaws are strong, and have a receding chin and large teeth.

We come now to a series of recent discoveries of such interest that they must be described at somewhat greater length.

La Chapelle-aux-Saints

The first is that of the skeleton from La-Chapelle-aux-Saints.[19] Near the village of that name, in the Corrèze district, there is a small cave (Fig. 129), the excavation of which was undertaken by three priests MM. the Abbés A. Bouyssonie, J. Bouyssonie, and Bardon, already well known for their researches in prehistoric archaeology. On August 3, 1908, they discovered

[19] Boule, M., 'L'Homme fossile de La Chapelle-aux-Saints' (*Comptes rendus de l'Acad. des Sciences*, December 14, 1908) Bouyssonie, A. and J., and Bardon, L., 'Découverte d'un squelette humain moustérien. . .' (*Ibid.*, December 21, 1908).

in it a quantity of human bones, and these they sent to one of the present writers at the Paris Museum, and, with the utmost generosity, were good enough to hand over to him.

This fortunate discovery provided the most complete and best preserved

129 The hill, showing entrance to the cave at La Chapelle-aux-Saints. The entrance to the cave is almost in the centre of the picture

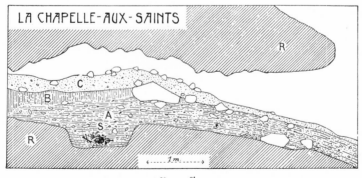

1M : 3·28'

130 Longitudinal section of the cave at La Chapelle-aux-Saints
(After A. and J. Bouyssonie and L. Bardon)
R, rock in which the cave is hollowed out; A, archaeological layer; B, clay; C, shifting sandy clay; S, human skeleton

Mousterian human fossil known up to that time. It was found in unexceptionable topographical and stratigraphical conditions. The age of the skeleton was established as clearly as possible, and the conditions of its burial, beneath a thin coat of débris in the cave where it was found, accounted for its quite unusual state of preservation.

The section here shown, from a drawing by MM. Bouyssonie and Bardon, clearly shows the arrangement of the layers (Fig. 130).

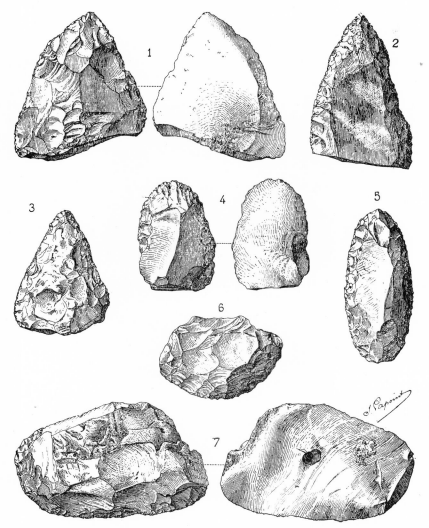

131 Some dressed flints from the Mousterian layer of the cave at La Chapelle-aux-Saints. Three-fourths natural size

On the floor of the cave extended an unbroken layer, 1 foot to 1 foot 4 inches, containing archaeological relics; it was covered by superficial deposits of much more recent appearance.

The animal remains collected in this archaeological layer belong to numerous species, the most characteristic of which are the Woolly Rhinoceros (*R. tichorhinus*), Reindeer (*Rangifer ratandus*), Ibex (*Capra ibex*), Extinct Bison (*Bison priscus*), Cave Hyaena (*Hyaena spelaea*), and Marmot (*Arctomys marmotta*).

The layer was very rich in dressed flints, comprising in the main the two well-known Mousterian types, points and scrapers (Fig. 131). Not the smallest object of bone showing real indications of workmanship was observed.

According to MM. Bouyssonie and Bardon, the man whose skeleton they found had been deliberately buried. He lay at the bottom of a trench, hollowed out of the marly soil of the grotto, at a depth of about 1 foot.[20]

The parts of the skeleton which one of us was able to reassemble are the

132 The skull from La Chapelle-aux-Saints in its bed. (Photograph by Bouyssonie and Bardon)

skull (cranium and lower jaw), twenty-one vertebrae and fragments of vertebrae, about twenty ribs or portions of ribs, a collar-bone (clavicle) two almost complete upper arm bones (humeri), two incomplete radii, two cubital bones (ilia), two incomplete femora, two knee-caps, portions of two tibiae, an astragalus, a calcaneum or heel-bone, five right metatarsals, two fragments of left metatarsals, and one phalanx.

LE MOUSTIER

In January 1909, a dealer in antiquities, of Swiss nationality, who had only too long exploited, for German profit, the deposits in the Dordogne district, that is to say, the most ancient and the most valuable archives in France,

[20] Bouyssonie, A. and J., and Bardon, L., 'La station moustérienne de la "Bouffia" Bonneval, à La Chapelle-aux-Saints' (*L'Anthropologie*, XXIV, 1913).

revealed the circumstances under which he had discovered and exhumed a human skeleton at Le Moustier.[21]

The exhumation took place on August 10, 1908, in the presence of a tribunal of scientists from beyond the Rhine—Klaatsch, H. Virchow, von den Steinen, Hahne, Wüst, and others—and in the absence of any French scientist. Even so the scientific value of this relic is markedly diminished by the poverty of significant stratigraphical or palaeontological data, and especially by the deplorable manner in which it was extricated and restored.[22]

Four successive reconstructions of the skull have been made. The first, by Klaatsch, a professor of anatomy, is a positive caricature (Fig. 133).

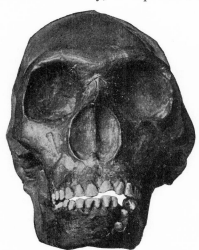

133 Skull from Le Moustier, seen full face, as reconstructed by the German anatomist Klaatsch. Photographed from a cast. One-third natural size

The second by the same author and the third by Krause being manifestly inadequate, a fourth was attempted by Weinert in 1925;[23] according to another German anatomist, H. Taeger,[24] this latter is still very imperfect. The monetary value of the skeleton from Le Moustier was, on the other hand, thought outstanding by the 'Museum für Völkerkunde' in Berlin, which paid Hauser, the dealer, the fabulous price of 125,000 gold francs!

The Le Moustier skeleton is that of a young man of about fifteen years. Klaatsch wanted to make of it the type of a new race. Weinert has clearly

[21] Hauser, O., 'Découverte d'un squelette du type de Néandertal. . .' (L'Homme préhistorique, January 1909), followed by Klaatsch, H., 'Preuves que l'Homme mousteriensis Hauseri appartient au type de Néandertal.'

[22] On this subject, see Virchow, H., 'Skelet von Le Moustier' (Anatomischer Anzeiger, LXXXVIII, 1939). Summary in L'Anthropologie, XLIX, 1940, p. 776. This skeleton was completely destroyed during the last war.

[23] Weinert, H., Der Schädel des eiszeitlichen Menschen von Le Moustier in neuer Zusammensetzung (Berlin, 1925).

[24] Zeitschr. für Morphol. und Anthrop., XXVIII, 1930, p. 312.

demonstrated that, despite certain juvenile characteristics, the skull is completely Neandertalian.

LA FERRASSIE

At La Ferrassie, near Bugue in the Dordogne (Fig. 134), there is a rock shelter containing many superimposed settlements, rich in Palaeolithic

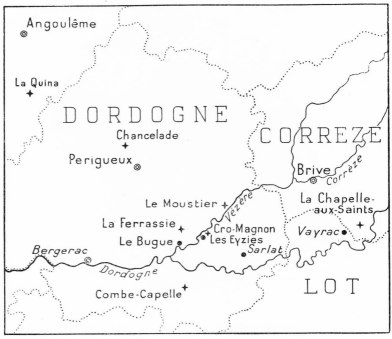

134 Principal Palaeolithic beds in the Dordogne region which have yielded human remains.

dressed artefacts, which were explored for ten years by Capitan and Peyrony. On September 17, 1909, Peyrony saw some human bones projecting from the soil. At the invitation of the two prehistorians, several persons repaired to La Ferrassie to be present at and collaborate in the extrication of the skeleton —Cartailhac, Breuil, Bouyssonie, and one of the present authors. They ascertained: (1) that the stratigraphical level is clearly the same as that at La Chapelle-aux-Saints, at the base of a layer containing Mousterian relics, and resting, according to Capital and Peyrony, on an Acheulean layer; (2) that the skeleton belonged to an individual of the Neandertal type; (3) that the bones of this fossil Man had retained their anatomical relationships and that they lay in the very midst of undisturbed layers, without any observable trace of burial.

In 1910, Peyrony obtained from the same layer a second skeleton, which lay not far from the first, and indicated a slighter individual of smaller stature, very probably a woman. Finally, in 1912, he collected some portions of the skeletons of four children.[25] This series, which is of outstanding value, was generously presented to the French National Museum of Natural History by Capitan and Peyrony. The clearing of the skeletons, their preparation, and the reconstruction of a skull (Fig. 135), almost as complete as that from La

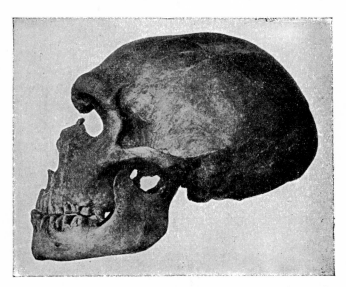

135 Skull of male skeleton from La Ferrassie, seen in profile. One-third natural size. Palaeontological Gallery, French National Museum of Natural History

Chapelle-aux-Saints, were carried out in the laboratory of one of the present authors. Reference will frequently be made to them in the course of this chapter.

La Quina

It was also a long-continued exploration which led to the fortunate discovery made by Dr. Henri Martin in 1911, at La Quina in Charente (Fig. 134). After several years of slow and most careful excavation, he found a human skeleton in an environment which was clearly Mousterian. The well-preserved portions of the head (Fig. 136) possess the characters of the corresponding portions of the Neandertal skull-cap and the lower jaw from La Chapelle-aux-Saints.[26]

[25] Capitan, Dr, and Peyrony, D., 'Deux squelettes humains au milieu de foyers de l'époque moustérienne' (*Revue de l'École d'Anthrop.*, December, 1909); 'Station préhistorique de La Ferrassie' (*Revue anthropologique*, January 1912). See also Peyrony, D., (*Préhistoire*, III, 1934).

[26] Martin, H., 'Sur un squelette humain de l'époque moustérienne trouvé en Charente' (*Comptes rendus de l'Acad. des Sc.*, October 16, 1911); 'L'Homme fossile de La Quina' (*Archives de Morphologie générale et expérimentale*, No. 15, 1923).

A few years later Dr Martin discovered in the same bed a fine skull of a child aged about 8 years, and a large number of fragments belonging to 19 other individuals.[27]

In 1911, likewise, in a cave in the bay of Saint-Brelade to the south-west of the Island of Jersey,[28] some human molar teeth were collected along

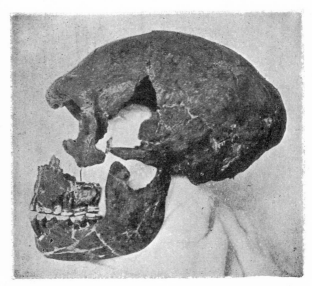

136 Skull from La Quina, seen in profile. One-third natural size
(Photographed by Henri Martin)

with bones of the Woolly Rhinoceros (*R. tichorhinus*) and the Reindeer, and also with Mousterian dressed flints.

Hillebrand has mentioned bones of children taken from the Cave of Balla, near Repashuta in Hungary; but their stratigraphical position has not been definitely established.

In 1915, Pacheco and Obermaier described a lower jaw found, in 1887, in a Pleistocene calcareous tufa at Bañolas in Catalonia. They classified it as of the Neandertal type.[29]

Another damaged lower jaw, together with some bones of the trunk and limbs, was found in 1932 in Hungary.[30]

[27] Martin, H., *L'enfant fossile de La Quina* (Angoulême, 1926).

[28] Marett, R., 'Pleistocene Man in Jersey' (*Archeologia*, LXII, 1911). Keith, A. and Knowles, F., 'A Description of Teeth of Palaeolithic Man from Jersey' (*Journ. of Anat. and Physiol.*, XLVI, 1911).

[29] Pacheco, E. Hernandez and Obermaier, H., 'La mandibula neandertaloide de Bañolas' (*Comisión de Investigaciónes paleontologicas y prehistoricas*, No. 6, Madrid, 1915).

[30] Szabo, J., 'L'Homme moustérien de la grotte Mussolini, Hongrie' (*Bull. et Mém. de la Soc. d'Anthrop de Paris*, 1935).

RUSSIA

Certain recent discoveries have the double interest of enlarging the area
of distribution of the ancient Neandertal human type and of revealing some
of its variations.

The first in chronological order were made in Russia. In 1924 Bontch-
Osmolovsky, while excavating the rock-shelter of Kiik-Koba, near Kipchak,
18 miles east of Simferopol in the Crimea, exhumed human bone-remains
from a stratum containing a Mammoth fauna and a Mousterian industry.[31]
These bones belonged to two skeletons, one an adult's and the other a child's,
buried in a pit and both lacking their skull and lower jaw. Examination of
some bones from the lower limb of the adult, which one of the present
writers was able to carry out in Paris with the author of the discovery,
convinced him that it was a true Neandertalian.[32]

Gremiatzky[33] is certainly wrong in taking the same view of a skull-cap,
a fragment of lower jaw and a few other fragments found, during the digging
of a canal, at Pyatigorsk (Northern Caucasus) in a loess deposit in the Podkumok valley attributed to the last great glacial phase. All the evidence
points to their being of recent origin.[34]

In spite of their Neandertaloid appearance, it seems also that certain
skull fragments found in 1925 at Oundory, on the right bank of the Lower
Volga, in an alluvial deposit containing Mammoth, and described by
Pavlov,[35] who compares them with the skulls from Combe-Capelle, Cannstadt, Galley Hill, etc., cannot date further back than the Upper Palaeolithic.
Of much more serious significance is the discovery by A. Okladnikoff, in
1938–1939, in the little cave of Teshik-Tash in Uzbekistan of the skeleton
of a child of eight to nine years, contemporaneous with a Mousterian industry.
Despite its youth, there seems no doubt about its Neandertal characteristics.[36]

PALESTINE

Then came the fine discoveries made in Palestine.

First there was the 'Galilee skull' found in 1925 by a young English

[31] L'Anthropologie, XXXV, 1925, p. 403. Bontch-Osmolovsky, 'Le Paléolithique de Crimée'
(Bull. de la Commission pour l'étude du Quaternaire,, No. 1, 1929); Paleolit Kryma (Academia
Naouk, Moscow, 1941). In the latter work the author classes the industry with the Tayacian.
[32] L'Anthropologie, XXXVI, 1926, p. 604.
[33] Gremiatzky, M. A., 'The Podkumok Skull-Cap and its Peculiarities' (Russian Journ. of
Anthrop., XII, 1922); 'The Mandible and Teeth of the Podkumok Man' (Ibid., Supplement,
XIV, 1926). These two publications are in Russian.
[34] Jegorov, N. M., 'Zur Frage über das Alter des sogenannten Podkumok Mann') Anthrop.
Anzeiger, X, 1933).
[35] Pavlov, A. P., 'L'Homme fossile de l'âge du Mammouth à l'Est de la Russie et les Hommes
fossiles de l'Europe occidentale' (Russian Journ. of Anthrop., Supplement, XIV, 1925).
In Russian with summary in French.
[36] Debetz, G., 'Sur les particularités anthropologiques du squelette humain de la grotte de
Techik-Tach' (Acad. of Sc. of the U.S.S.R., Uzbekistan Section, Ser. I, Part I, 1940).

archaeologist, Turville-Petre,[37] in the cave of El Zuttiyeh (or 'Robbers' Cave') to the north-west of the Sea of Galilee (Lake Tiberias). This skull lay in an archaeological level containing numerous Mousterian amygdaloid flints, disks, points and scrapers. The four fragments recovered—frontal, malar and the two wings of the sphenoid—were assembled and joined together by Keith, who was charged with the task of studying them (Fig.

137 Skull from Galilee, seen full face. Half natural size. Photograph of a cast

137). The eminent English archaeologist reached the conclusion that, although it belonged to the Neandertal type, the 'Galilee skull' exhibited certain characteristics of modern Man.[38]

In 1931 an American prehistorian, McCown, working under the direction of Miss Garrod, found in a cave on Mount Carmel, called Mugharet es-Shkül, near Athlit, a Mousterian breccia from which he extracted the remains of a skeleton of a very young child (two and a half years). During the following years, 1932 and 1933, the es-Shkül cave proved to be a positive 'cemetery'. Its Mousterian levels yielded their fortunate explorer the bone-remains of fifteen or so individuals of various ages, among them six almost complete skeletons. Another skeleton and a lower jaw were obtained from the nearby cave of Et Tabun.

This important material was the subject of a particularly detailed study by McCown and Keith.[39] Their conclusions will be exposed at length further

[37] Turville-Petre, F., 'Researches in Prehistoric Galilee' (Publication of the *British School of Archaeology in Jerusalem*, London, 1927).

[38] Keith, A., in the preceding memoir. See also *New Discoveries relating to the Antiquity of Man* (London, 1931) pp. 173–198.

[39] McCown, T. and Keith, A., *The Stone Age of Mount Carmel, II. The Fossil Human Remains from the Levalloiso-Mousterian* (Oxford, 1939).

on (see Chap. X). It will be enough to say that the skulls, which were wide and lofty, with a rounded occiput and a lower jaw that sometimes possessed a chin, were appreciably different from our Western type of Neandertal. The authors therefore made of them a separate species, in which they included the Galilee skull: *Palaeoanthropus palestinus*.

Finally, in the course of excavations carried out under the patronage of the Institut de Paléontologie Humaine in a cave of the Djebel Kafzeh, very close to Nazareth, R. Neuville and his fellow-worker, M. Stekélis, exhumed several skeletons the preparation and study of which is at present being carried out in the laboratories of the Institut de Paléontologie Humaine. The best preserved of the skulls present characters noted by Keith in those from es Shkül. We shall return to this point later, for it is an important phenomenon.

THE MOST RECENT DISCOVERIES

In February 1939 A. C. Blanc discovered in a small cave on Monte Circeo, an isolated massif in the Pontine Plain, sixty miles south of Rome, a skull[40] placed on the ground and deliberately covered with stalagmite, accompanied by bone-remains of Quaternary animals and a Mousterian industry. An isolated lower jaw was found some distance away. The cave had been invaded by the sea, which had formed a small beach during the last interglacial epoch, and occupied by Man during Mid Pleistocene times. It had been blocked by a landslide which rendered it inaccessible for more than 50,000 years. A summary study of this skull was made by S. Sergi.[41] Its resemblance to the skull from La Chapelle-aux-Saints is striking (Fig. 138).

Again on Monte Circeo, and in the vicinity of the same cave, a second lower jaw, also of distinctly Neandertalian type, was found in 1950 in a very hard breccia.

Other discoveries have been made in France. In 1949 M. Cammas discovered at Montmaurin (Haute-Garonne), in a cavity attached to a group of caves long known for their abundance of fossil Quaternary mammals, a lower jaw in excellent preservation and of thoroughly primitive appearance.[42] No implements accompanied this bone, but an archaic Mousterian industry is found in neighbouring formations, and the fauna resembles, in certain characteristics, those of interglacial periods.

The same year, a portion of skull-cap and some teeth were found in the Mousterian deposit at La Chaise (Charente);[43] while in 1951 L. Coulonges

[40] Blanc, A. C., 'L'Homme fossile du Mont Circé' (*L'Anthropologie*, XLIX, 1939).

[41] Sergi, S., 'Il cranio neandertaliano del Monte Circeo' (*Rendiconti della R. Acc. dei Lincei*, XXIX, 6a, Rome, 1939).

[42] 'Découvertes récentes dans les grottes de Montmaurin, Haute-Garonne' (*L'Anthropologie*, LIV, 1950, p. 262).

[43] David, P. and Bordes, F., 'Découverte d'une calotte cranienne fragmentaire et de dents humaines dans un niveau moustérien ancien de La Chaise, Charente' (*C. R. Acad. Sciences*, Vol. CCXXX, February 20, 1950).

announced the discovery, in an indisputable stratigraphic position, of part of a Mousterian upper jaw at Sauveterre-la-Lémance (Lot-et-Garonne); and A. Leroi-Gourhan brought to light an upper and lower jaw in place in a Mousterian environment at Arcy-sur-Cure (Yonne), in the Hyaena Cave.

138 Skull from Monte Circeo. Half natural size. (Photograph by A. C. Blanc)

Outside France, we must note that an endocranial cast from a Quaternary travertine at Gànovic, near Poprad in Slovakia, has recently been considered by Vlček[44] as belonging to Neandertal Man, of whom it does indeed exhibit the general characteristics.

SUMMARY

Of this series of discoveries, having credentials sufficiently reliable to allow of their being allocated to Mid-Pleistocene times, about half consist only of mere fragments. The remainder have yielded bone-remains in such condition as to render them suitable for thorough morphological study—Neandertal, Gibraltar, Spy, Krapina, La Chapelle-aux-Saints, La Ferrassie, La Quina and Palestine. So that today our knowledge of the Neandertal type of human fossil has been gained from well preserved, easily studied specimens, numbering at least some twenty individuals.

What, then, of the ideas of Pruner-Bey, Gratiolet, Virchow, Hartmann, and others, regarding the exceptional, quite abberrant or pathological nature of the skulls of the Neandertal type? It is hardly necessary to point out that they are now only of historic interest. The opposition of German

[44] Vlcek, E., 'Le moulage en travertin du crâne néandertalien de Ganovce, en Slovaquie' (*Zpràvy Anthropologické spolecnosti*, III, 1950, p. 3).

scientists, who have since bought the Mousterian skeleton for its weight in gold, was still at its height in 1892, when the 'Neandertal Race' was looked upon as 'imaginary', as a 'creation of fancy', and was 'laid to rest' by Virchow, von Hölder, Haas, Kolmann, and others.[45]

Today, then, we are in possession of a comprehensive collection of materials, relating to the same homogeneous human type, which differs greatly from all living types, and is osteologically better known than many of them. This human type, which exhibits many characters of inferiority, must be known (for reasons we shall consider later) by the name of *Homo neandertalensis*. We shall give here a brief but as complete a description as possible of it, taking as a basis the most complete and best known skeletons, that from La Chapelle-aux-Saints, on which a detailed monograph has been published,[46] and those from La Ferrassie.

DESCRIPTION OF THE SKULL

The skull of the man from La Chapelle-aux-Saints looks strange even to the eyes of an observer only slightly acquainted with anatomy (Fig. 139).

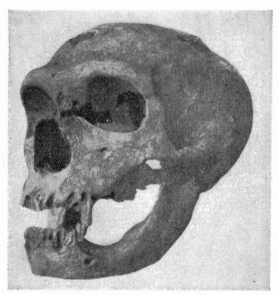

139 The skull from La Chapelle-aux-Saints, three-quarters view. About one-third natural size. Anthropological Gallery of the Musée de l'Homme

[45] The late J. Fraipont published at this time an eloquent paper in vindication entitled, 'La race imaginaire de Cannstatt ou de Néandertal' (*Bull. de la Soc. d'Anthrop. de Bruxelles*, XIV, 1895).

[46] Boule, M., 'L'Homme fossile de La Chapelle-aux-Saints' (*Annales de Paléontologie*, 1911–13). Numerous bibliographical references will be found there to works already published on the morphology of *Homo neandertalensis* or useful for consultation in studying it, but these we cannot repeat in this volume.

First its great size strikes us, especially regarded in relation to the small stature of the individual to whom it belonged, and who, as we shall see later, was less than 5 feet in height. Next we are impressed by its bestial appearance or rather by the general effect of its simian characters. The brain-box, elongated in form, is much depressed; the orbital arches are enormous; the forehead is very receding; the occipital region very projecting and much depressed; the face is long and projects forwards; the orbits are enormous; the nose, separated from the forehead by a deep depression, is short and very broad; owing to the prolongation of the malar bones, the upper jaw forms a kind of muzzle; the lower jaw is strong and thick; the chin rudimentary.

GENERAL MORPHOLOGY OF THE SKULL

Beginning with the general morphology of the skull, we find at first glance that the face is highly developed in comparison with the brain-box and here, as we have seen (p. 73) lies a zoological character of the highest importance. It may be strikingly depicted in diagrammatic form by superimposing the profiles of the skulls of this fossil, of a chimpanzee, and of a modern Frenchman upon a common base line closely following the boundary between the facial and the cerebral portions, after having, it must be clearly understood, made the three basi-axial lines of the same length, Na-Ba, and reproduced the skulls in due proportion (Fig. 140). In the chimpanzee, the facial region is almost as great as the cerebral region. In the Frenchman, on the contrary, the face is much reduced, and the brain-box greatly developed. Between these two extremes lies the skull from La Chapelle-aux-Saints. While it is more akin to that of its congener, modern Man, in regard to the face, in regard to the brain-box it is almost intermediate between Man and the chimpanzee.

No less striking is Fig. 141, in which are shown, superimposed, the profiles of the skulls of our fossil Man and of the famous American palaeontologist, Cope. They are almost equal in cranial capacity, but we see how great is the difference between the size of the face in one of the most intelligent of men and in our savage of Quaternary times.

In the relative development of its facial and cerebral regions, the skull from La Chapelle-aux-Saints differs widely from the skulls of living Men even of the lower races, yet to a certain degree it reduces the morphological gulf separating the latter from the Anthropoid Apes. The broad lines of the architecture of the skull are no less different.

All mammalian skulls are composed of the same parts, but the relative development and correlated arrangement of these component parts vary according to the nature of the skulls. The essential portion, constituting the keystone of the cranial edifice, is the base of the skull, formed, from behind forwards, by the basi-occipital, the basi-sphenoid, and the pre-sphenoid. Around this *basicranial axis*, as Huxley named it, the principal modifications of the brain-box occur, under the influence of the development of the various parts of the brain. This axis itself is straight in the majority of mammals, but it becomes bent, curved, and more or less broken, as we consider ascend-

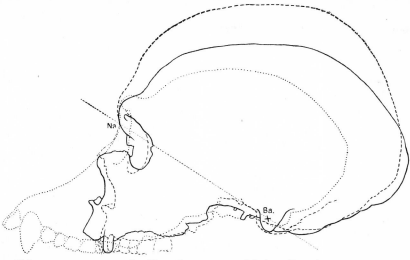

Chimpanzee........   La Chapelle————   Modern Frenchman— — — —

140 Profiles of the Skulls of a Chimpanzee, of the Man from La Chapelle-aux-Saints, and of a Modern Frenchman, superimposed along the basio-nasal line, which has been made the same length in each. Ba, Basion; Na, Nasion

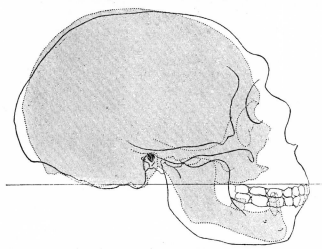

141 Superimposed profiles of the skull of the famous American naturalist Cope (shaded) and of the Fossil Man from La Chapelle-aux-Saints (unbroken line). One-third natural size.

ing types of skull from the lower Monkeys and Anthropoid Apes to Man.[47]
    On these facts we have constructed geometrical diagrams of median

[47] Huxley, T., *Evidence as to Man's Place in Nature* (London, 1863). Topinard, P., 'La transformation du crâne animal en crâne humain' (*L'Anthropologie*, II, 1891).

longitudinal sections of the skulls of a Chimpanzee, a European and the Man
from La Chapelle-aux-Saints (Fig. 142). They clearly show the intermediate

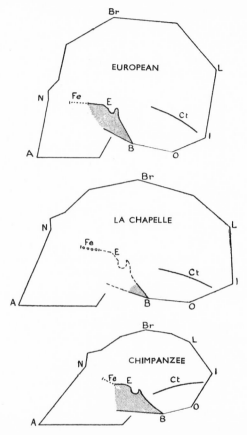

142 Geometrical Diagrams of the Skulls of a Chimpanzee, of the Fossil Man from La
   Chapelle-aux-Saints, and of a Modern Frenchman. About one-fourth natural size

A, prosthion or incisive alveolar point; N, nasion (root of nose); Br, bregma (point of
contact of the frontal and two parietal bones); L, lambda (point of contact of the two parietals
and of the occipital); I, inion (base of the external occipital protuberance); O, opisthion
(posterior margin of the foramen magnum); E, ephippion (anterior margin of the *sella
turcica*); Fe, ethmoidal fossa; Ct, upper level of cerebellum

position of the last. The same result follows from a study of the relations
of the various *planes* and *lines of orientation* used by anthropologists.

THE REGIONS OF THE SKULL

After this general view, we proceed to the examination of morphological
details. Seen from above (*norma verticalis*), all the skulls of Neandertal Man
appear remarkably uniform (Fig. 143). All are dolichocephalic; their cephalic

index,[48] ranging from seventy to seventy-six, corresponds well with the average human index as it occurs in an archaic type. The skulls are much more enlarged behind than in front, where the frontal bone recedes greatly above the great swelling ridges of the orbital arches.

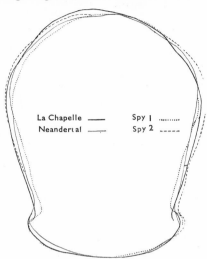

La Chapelle _____   Spy I ....
Neandertal _____   Spy 2 _ _ _ _ _

143 Superimposed profiles of different skull-caps of the Neandertal type.
One-third natural size

An interesting comparison of the fossil skull with that of a modern Chimpanzee and of a modern Man, photographed in the same position, is shown in Fig. 144.

In the lateral aspect of the skull (*norma lateralis*) the chief characters of

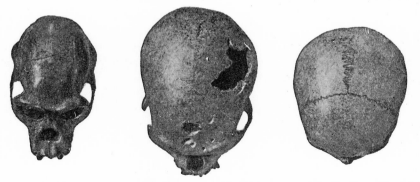

144 Photographs showing a comparison of the upper aspect of the skulls of a Chimpanzee, of the Fossil Man from La Chapelle-aux-Saints and of a modern Frenchman

the cerebral region are displayed. We can here observe the importance of the face, the overhanging projection of the supra-orbital ridges, the very

[48] For definition of this term, see footnote p. 116.

receding profile of the forehead, the general flattening of the vault, the form of the occipital region like a flattened protuberance, and so on.

The general flattening of the skull (*platycephalis*) is a character of the greatest importance in which, at first glance, the whole series of our Mousterian skulls[49] differ widely from modern skulls and resemble those of the Anthropoid Apes without sagittal crests, like the Gibbons and the Chimpanzees, even to such a degree as to warrant their inclusion in this group (Fig. 145).

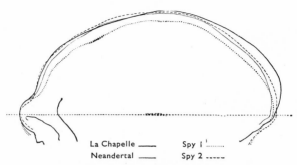

La Chapelle —— Spy 1 ....
Neandertal —— Spy 2 -----

145 Superimposed lateral Profiles of different Skulls of the Neandertal type, oriented on the glabello-iniac line. One-third natural size

In its receding forehead, one might almost say its absence of forehead, the Neandertal type still occupies the lowest rung of the human ladder and strikingly resembles the Anthropoid Apes, as shown by the various methods invented by anthropologists for measuring the development of the forehead.

The parietal bosses are projecting and situated far back. The temporal lines are not more marked than in modern Man.

The line of suture of the temporal and parietal bones is not much arched; it is known that while this line is rather straighter in apes and new-born children, it is more or less arched in the various human races, where, in the case of higher types, it finally forms a well-rounded curve. The zygomatic apophyses are massive, more inclined forward than in modern Man; the post-glenoid apophyses, relics of an ancestral condition, are more developed. The supra-mastoid crest is also very projecting. The mastoid apophyses are extremely small. The resemblance of the petrous portion, with its great extent, its disposition as a large, oblique surface, forming with the neighbouring parietal and occipital surfaces a single plane which inclines inwards and backwards, is much more akin to the same region in the skull of the Chimpanzee than to that of modern human skulls.

The occipital region has a somewhat strange profile. Huxley already described it thus: 'To the eye of an anatomist, the posterior portion of the Neandertal skull is even more remarkable than the front portion.' The

[49] By *our* Mousterian skulls, we mean those of Western and Southern Europe. We shall see later that those of Palestine are very different.

complete specimens from La Chapelle and La Ferrassie are admirably fitted for the study of this region, which forms a sort of chignon, very prominent but much compressed in a vertical direction.

The posterior surface of the skull (*norma occipitalis*) does not show the

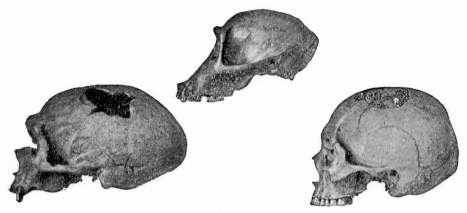

146 Photographs comparing the lateral aspects of the skulls of a Chimpanzee, of the Fossil Man from La Chapelle-aux-Saints and of a modern Frenchman

usual pentagonal form, but has an almost circular contour, which is in keeping with the general platycephalia (Fig. 147). A marked transverse ridge, arched in shape, the *torus occipitalis transversus*, divides the upper from the lower part of the skull. The ridge is much more developed in apes, where it connects the temporal and the supra-mastoidean crests, forming together with

147 Photographs comparing the occipital aspects of the skulls of a Chimpanzee, of the Fossil Man from La Chapelle-aux-Saints and of a modern Frenchman

them one continuous ridge. This uninterrupted protuberance is present, as we have said, in *Pithecanthropus*, but in lesser degree. In Neandertal Man, no junction takes place between the occipital protuberance and the temporal crest (Fig. 74, p. 118).

There is no external occipital protuberance. In its place we find, on the transverse ridge, a sort of cup or cupule, which is present on every one of

the known examples. The central point of the cup does not correspond
with the division between the cerebral hemispheres and the cerebellum;
it is situated higher up. The cerebellar protuberances are much reduced.

The whole surface of this region is very uneven; the projections and depressions representing the muscle-imprints are sharply defined, and this
denotes an exceptional development of the muscles of the nape of the neck,
in keeping with the enormous size of the head.[50]

The lower surface (*norma basilaris*) of the skull of Neandertal Man reveals
a whole series of important characters, although, even in the best examples,
its state of preservation leaves much to be desired, because of the fragile
nature of the bones of which it is composed (Fig. 148).

148 Photographs comparing the lower surface of the skulls of a Chimpanzee, of the Fossil
Man from La Chapelle-aux-Saints and of a modern Frenchman

The foramen magnum is placed in a relatively backward position. Though
still widely removed from the Apes in respect of this character, the Man from
La Chapelle nevertheless resembles them rather more than does modern
Man. The direction of the plane of the foramen magnum is likewise intermediate.

Seen from below, the temporal bones are remarkable for their general
flatness, that is to say, for the slightness of their prominences and hollows.
This appearance differs from that of the temporal bones of modern Man,
and resembles that found in apes, where, however, it occurs in accentuated
degree. We have already pointed out the slimness of the mastoid apophyses,
hardly more developed than those of orangs and gorillas. In front of the
mastoid·region, the tympanic resembles that of the large Apes. The glenoid
cavities, wide and shallow, recall to a certain degree those of the Chimpanzee,
which are almost flat at the bottom.

The maxillaries stand out as a continuation of the zygomatic arches, and

[50] Vallois, H., 'La sustentation de la tête et le ligament cervical postérieur chez l'Homme
et les Anthropoïdes' (*L'Anthropologie*, XXXVI, 1926).

accentuate the muzzle-like form of the face (Fig. 149). The palate is remarkable for its large surface, which in the Man from La Chapelle-aux-Saints is

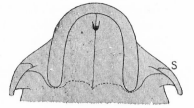 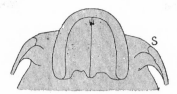

149 Front portions of skulls from La Chapelle-aux-Saints (on the left) and of a modern Frenchman (on the right), seen from below to show the difference in the profiles of the region of the upper jaw and cheeks. One-third natural size. S, maxillary suture

about 2,700 square millimetres, whereas it is only about 1,670 square millimetres in the skull of a normal Frenchman.

THE FACE

There remains to be examined the anterior surface of the skull (*norma facialis*), which corresponds to the face in the living subject (Fig. 150).

150 Photographs contrasting the faces of the skulls of a Chimpanzee, of the Man from La Chapelle-aux-Saints and of a modern Frenchman

From the La Chapelle specimen we obtained our first accurate and complete knowledge of the physiognomy of Neandertal Man.

In its dimensions, the face exceeds the largest known human faces. If it does not appear very high in relation to its breadth, this is due to the flattening of the brain-box and consequent reduction of the forehead (Fig. 151).

An immense development of the orbital arches characterizes all known skulls of Neandertal Man. They unite in a projecting unbroken ridge, absolutely resembling the bony visor of the skulls of chimpanzees, of gorillas, and also of *Pithecanthropus* (see p. 119).

Opinion is undecided as to the physiological part played by these protuberances. The fact that they are more developed in males lead to their
being looked upon as a character favouring sexual selection. Turner suggested that perhaps they heightened an appearance of ferocity which was
of some value in the struggle for life. In the opinion of many anatomists
their development is directly correlated with that of the jaws and the appara-

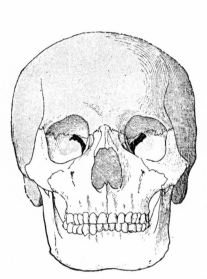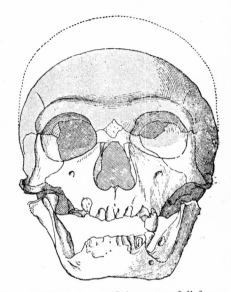

151 Skulls of a Frenchman and of the Man from La Chapelle-aux-Saints, seen full face,
in order to show the difference of the relative development of cerebral and facial portions.
One-third natural size

The dotted line indicates the supposed outline of the cranial vault had it been of the same
proportions as in the French specimen

tus concerned in mastication. For our part, we regard them as a means of
protection of the organs of sight, acquired under the influence of particular
environments. Whereas, in apes and modern Man, they are absent in young
individuals, in young Neandertalians they developed at an early age.

The orbits present a strange appearance owing to the projection of the
superciliary ridges, which, by extending the roof of the orbits, form over
them a kind of awning. They are widely separated from each other, and are
rounded in form. Their size is relatively very great, half as great again as in
modern Man of the same brain capacity.

The base of the nose marked by the point of junction (nasion), with
the fronto-nasal sutures, is situated in a deep depression, as in native
Australians. This arrangement is the opposite of that found in apes, even
in the apes with strong orbital ridges. The nose was very large (Platyrrhinian), as in the majority of modern men of the black races. The nasal bones,
preserved in the Gibraltar skull, are essentially human and fundamentally

different from those of monkeys. In other characters also, such as the development of the nasal apophysis of the maxillary and the area of the nostrils, the nose of Neandertal Man, far from resembling that of anthropoid apes, differs from it much more than does that of living Man. This fossil Man, which in so many of his characters approaches the Apes more than any other Man, is nevertheless so widely divergent from them as regards his nasal region, that instead of being simian in this respect, he might rather be looked upon as *ultra-human* (Fig. 152).

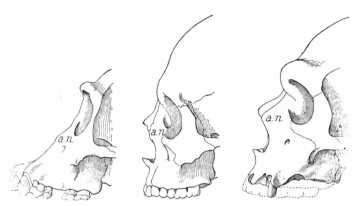

152 Facial profiles of skulls of a Chimpanzee, of a Frenchman and of the Man from La Chapelle-aux-Saints. One-third natural size

a.n. nasal apophysis of the maxillary

The arrangement of the malar or jugular bones indicates flat or receding cheeks.

The maxillaries are strong and massive, and project prominently forwards. Their anterior surface, instead of being concave and exhibiting *canine fossae*, as in the case of all modern Men without exception, is almost flat. This flat surface exactly continues the plane of the external surface of the malar bones, and so gives rise to the muzzle-like appearance which we have already described (Fig. 149), and which is one of the most characteristic traits of our Mousterian Man. It has the effect of adding greatly to the bestial appearance of the face of this Man. We do not think, however, that we can regard these structures as simian, for, although the Chimpanzee has no canine fossae, they are very deep in the Gorilla and Orang.

The sub-nasal or incisive area is very large. It continues the general direction of the profile of the face without projecting forwards. There is no alveolar prognathism.

CHILDREN'S SKULLS

The discovery at La Quina of a well-preserved child's skull (see p. 208) justifies the statement that the majority of the very special facial characters of Neandertal Man which we have described (p. 221), seem to be present in Neandertal individuals even from youth (Fig. 153). According to H. Martin[51] the skull of the child from La Quina, aged about eight years, presents

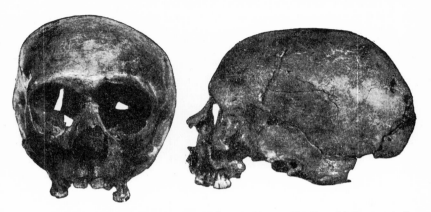

153 Skull of the La Quina Child, seen full face and in profile. One-third natural size (Photo by M. H. Martin)

an ovoid shape and a cephalic index of 77 (sub-dolichocephalic), whilst modern children are generally brachycephalic. The general outline is depressed. It has a receding forehead, without frontal bosses; the orbital arches

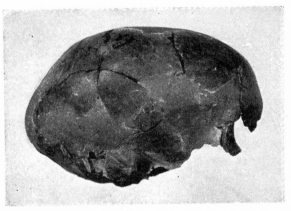

154 Child's skull from Engis, seen in profile. One-third natural size. (After Ch. Fraipont)

are already continuous and projecting. The occipital region is beginning to protrude in chignon-like form. The mastoid apophyses are rudimentary, almost negligible. The face is Neandertal in type, both on account of its

[51] Martin, H., 'Un crâne d'enfant néanderthalien du gisement de La Quina' (*L'Anthropologie*, XXXI, 1921, p. 331); *Recherches sur l'évolution du Moustérien dans le gisement de La Quina (Charente)*. Vol. IV: *L'Enfant fossile de La Quina* (Angoulême, 1926).

muzzle-like appearance due to the absence of canine fossae, as well as on account of its immense rounded orbits and broad nose.

The position is more or less the same as regards the skull and lower jaw of a younger child (five years) found more recently at Gibraltar. Its cephalic index, however, is higher, which gives the brain-box a more modern look, while the lower jaw is very primitive in appearance.[52]

In his memoir on the Mousterian child's skull found nearly a century ago, by Schmerling, in the Engis Cave, Ch. Fraipont[53] has stressed the numerous Neandertalian features of this historic specimen (Fig. 154). Moreover, the tympanic bone here presents a bifid structure entirely comparable with that of the young *Sinanthropus* from Peking (see p. 135).

All these facts show that the cranial morphology of *Homo neandertalensis* is a very ancient morphology, dating from a very distant past, and that it is really specific in character.

THE LOWER JAW

At the present day the lower jaw of Neandertal Man is known from a large number of fragments all possessing the same family likeness. These jaws are massive and very strong, and their size corresponds to that of the skulls.

They have no chin, or only a rudimentary and receding one, a fact first observed in the jaw from La Naulette, the discovery of which caused a great sensation. Regarding it, Broca expressed the following opinion: 'I have no hesitation in saying that the jaw from La Naulette is the first evidence to provide the Darwinists with an anatomical argument. It is the first link in the chain which, according to them, ought to lead from Man to monkeys.'[54]

Assuredly we are dealing with a most remarkable character, of the significance of which, from the point of view of its morphological rank in the Primate group, there does not seem to be any question. Anatomists regard the projection of the chin as an essentially human characteristic. Now, as regards the retreating character of chin, the jaws of Neandertal Man are exactly interposed between the jaws of anthropoid apes and those of groups of modern human beings; and this is so even if we chose for comparison the races lowest in type in this respect. One of the most receding, if not the most receding chin in the Anthropological Gallery of the French National Museum of Natural History, is that of the famous Hottentot Venus. Yet its symphyseal angle (the angle formed by the anterior and inferior margins of the jaw) does not exceed 94°, whereas in the Man from La Chapelle-aux-Saints it reaches 104°. It must be added that certain fossil jaws exhibit a chin in process of formation, such as that of the skeleton from La Ferrassie, in

[52] Buxton, L. H. D., *loc. cit.* (See note on p. 197). For further details consult *L'Anthropologie*, XXXVIII, 1928, p. 571.

[53] Fraipont, Ch., 'Les Hommes fossiles d'Engis' (*Archives de l'Institut de Paléont. humaine*, Memoir 16, 1936).

[54] In Topinard, P., 'Les caractères simiens de la mâchoire de La Naulette', *loc. cit.*

which there is really an indication of a chin triangle (Fig. 155). While the Heidelberg Man (Mauer jaw) from the Lower Pleistocene, possessed a jaw just as much lacking in chin as that of the Apes, a study of various fossil jaws of Mid Pleistocene origin from various districts in France shows the

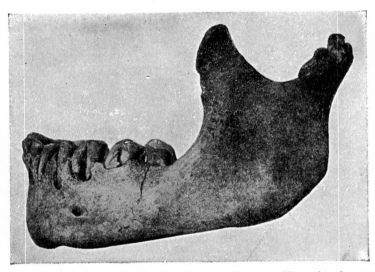

155   Lower jaw, seen in profile, of the Man from La Ferrassie. Three-fourths natural size. Anthropological Gallery of the Musée de l'Homme, Paris

gradual formation of a chin, the special attribute of *Homo sapiens*.[55] This is shown in the series of diagrams in Fig. 156.

The inner or buccal surface of the symphyseal region, or area of the chin, inclines in general direction from front to back; that is, the hinder as well as the anterior surface of the chin recedes, so that when we place a lower jaw of Neandertal Man on a table and look at it from above, we see, not the anterior surface of the body of the bone, but the posterior surface, whereas in the case of the jaw of modern Man we see exactly the reverse.

The morphology of this inner surface shows certain interesting peculiarities (Fig. 157). We find here, but rather less developed, the genial fossa which we observed in the Mauer jaw, and which is still deeper in apes. But there are well-developed upper and lower genial apophyses, just as in modern Men. To the right and left of the lower genial apophysis there may be observed two rounded, elliptical or depressed tubercles, situated transversely, and united to the mylohyoid or oblique internal lines, which are very marked.

[55] Important researches have been made with regard to the development and significance of the chin by the anatomists Mies, Walkhoff, Toldt and others. Bibliographical references will be found in the monograph *L'Homme de La Chapelle-aux Saints*. See also Bolk, L., 'Die Entstehung des Menschenkinnes' (*Verh. Kon. Akad. Wetenschappen*, Section 2, XXIII, 1925) and Weidenreich, F., 'Das Menschenkinn und seine Entstehung' (*Ergebn. Anat. und Entwicklungsgesch.*, XXXI, 1934).

These protuberances (*b.t.*) separate the sublingual fossa (*f.l.*) from the impressions of the digastric muscles (*e.di*), and may be taken as simian characters. But, on the whole, this arrangement of the genial area is quite human, although a little different from the usual arrangement.

The development of the genial apophyses appears to have no connexion with the development of articulate language, contrary to what has been believed and taught only too long. All that can be said of Neandertal Man in this respect is that he had marked projections for the insertions of the genio-glossal and genio-hyoid muscles, whose functions are specially related to the movements of mastication and of swallowing, which are as necessary in animals as in Man.

The lower part of the body of the jaw in the symphyseal region is arranged in two facets, bearing impressions of the insertion of the digastric muscles. Thus we find here the arrangement already noted in the Mauer jaw, but in this case the impressions are shorter and differ less from those on the jaw of modern Man, where a true edge is developed, and where the marks of the attachment of the digastric muscles, smaller in size, are situated on the inner surface of the bone. So there exists a series of intermediate morphological stages which are brought out clearly in Fig. 158.

The vertical branches are very wide, somewhat narrower, indeed, than in the Mauer Man, but wider than in modern Man. On the inner surface the rugosities for the insertion of the interior pterygoid muscle are very marked. The angle of the jaw, that is to say, the junction of the lower margin of the horizontal branch and of the posterior margin of the vertical branch, is as if it had been truncated and replaced by an oblique line corresponding to the whole area of attachment of the internal pterygoid muscle. This arrangement occurs in the majority of the Anthropoid Apes, particularly the Gorilla.

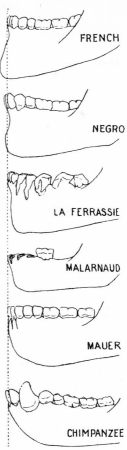

156 Profiles of various types of Lower Jaws showing a gradual series from chinless forms (Chimpanzee and Mauer Jaw) to forms with very pronounced chin (Frenchman), passing through intermediate forms (Malarnaud and La Ferrassie). Two-fifths natural size.

The region of the angle is very thin, and at the same time deviates greatly from the vertical. But the deviation takes place inside the angle, as in the majority of human jaws; and this inversion is another indication of the great power of the pterygoid muscles. It really seems that the muscles of mastication, intended for the lateral movements of the jaw, were relatively more developed than the elevator or biting muscles (the masseter and temporalis muscles).

The coronoid apophyses are low, broad and blunt; the sigmoid notch,

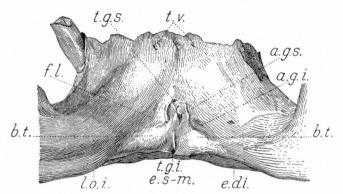

157 Posterior surface of the body of the jaw of the Man from La Chapelle-aux-Saints. Natural size

t.v., openings for blood vessels; *t.g.s.*, upper genial foramen; *a.g.s.*, upper genial apophysis; *a.g.i.*, lower genial apophysis; *t.g.i.*, lower genial foramen; *l.o.i.*, internal oblique line; *b.t.*, transverse prominence; *f.l.*, sublingual fossa; *e.d.i.*, impression of digastric muscle; *e.s.m.*, submental notch.

shallow. The proportions of the condyles are really simian; their structure merely forms the counterpart to that of the large and shallow glenoid fossae: they confirm what we have just said with regard to the strength of the whole

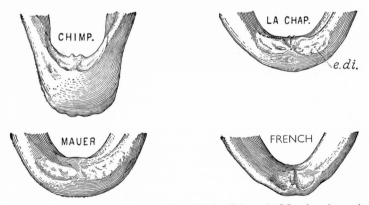

158 Lower edge of the Jaw and impressions of the Digastric Muscles, in various Jaws. About one-half natural size

e.di., impressions of digastric muscles

masticatory apparatus and of the relatively greater development of the chewing muscles than of the biting muscles.

DENTITION

Human dentitions preserve a much greater similarity amongst themselves than do human skulls. It would seem that the general characters of these dentitions must be very ancient, and that the human branch must have acquired them, so to speak, from its origin; or rather that they are associated with the very origin of this branch. And this is in accord, not only with what palaeontology teaches regarding other groups of mammals, but also with the Mauer discovery; for it revealed a dental morphology which, though quite human in character, was associated with a jaw differing greatly from other known human jaws.

The dentition of Neandertal Man is also definitely human. Several of the somewhat special secondary characters which it possesses are of a primitive nature, but they can have no specific value.

The dental arches are very wide. The upper curve (Fig. 159) corresponds

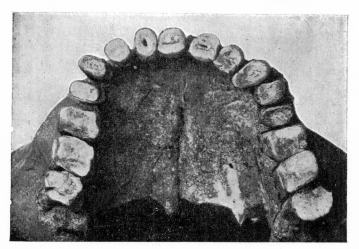

159 Palate and upper dentition of the skull of a man from La Ferrassie. Natural size. Anthropological Gallery of the Musée de l'Homme, Paris

almost exactly to the architectural form known as a semicircular or Romanesque arch. On the arched portion are placed the incisors, canines, and premolars; the relatively short pillars of the arch are formed by the series of the three molars. This is rather different in plan from the parabolic, hyperbolic, or elliptical forms found in the majority of human jaws; it is indeed rather the U-form of the Anthropoid Apes, but in this case the vertical branches of the U are shorter and diverge slightly, thus showing an approach towards a parabolic form.

The form of the lower arch (Fig. 160) is more akin to that of the upper arch than is usual in modern Man. It follows that the two arches stand to each other in a somewhat different relationship from what is the rule in modern Man, especially in civilized races, where the upper teeth overlap the lower, particularly in front and in the region of the incisors. Here when the jaws were closed, the upper and lower incisors met exactly, as in

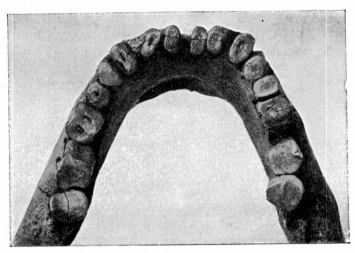

160 Lower jaw and dentition, seen from above, of the skull of a man from La Ferrassie. Natural size. Anthropological Gallery of the Musée de l'Homme, Paris

the case of modern Australians; or sometimes even the upper incisors were slightly behind the lower incisors, suggesting a little the condition in the bull-dog (see Fig. 135, p. 207).

The study of the worn surfaces of complete sets of teeth, such as that of the skull from La Ferrassie (Figs. 159, 160), shows that mastication must have beeen performed partly by a forward movement of the lower jaw against the upper jaw—a movement which furthered the great surface development and slight depth of the glenoid cavities, as well as the barely projecting form of the temporal condyles. This structure indicates also great freedom in the lateral movement of the jaws, an indication confirmed by the strength of the pterygoid muscles; all of which, in short, points to a dentition more employed for chewing than for biting, and implies a vegetarian rather than a carnivorous diet.

The teeth are strong, like the jaws which bear them (Fig. 161). They form a continuous series without intervals or diastemas, and all the crowns are at the same level. The canines do not project beyond the neighbouring teeth, and are in no way simian. The alveolar border, however, extends beyond the last molar in both upper and lower jaws; so that not only were the wisdom teeth not cramped in their development, as in the jaws of civilized races, but there even remained space beyond them sufficient to accommodate a supplementary molar.

An English anatomist, Keith, regarded as a distinguishing characteristic of the teeth of Neandertal Man a special development of the roots and of the pulp cavity. His observations were made mainly on isolated teeth recovered from a cave in Jersey (see p. 208). The teeth found in position in the skull from La Ferrassie do not exhibit the features recorded by Keith, which are also lacking from the Ehringsdorf jaws. On the other hand, they have been noted in several modern Men. They cannot, therefore, be considered a distinctive characteristic of the Neandertalians.

The teeth of Neandertal Man became very rapidly worn, because of the coarseness of the food, mingled with earth, which they had to grind; so

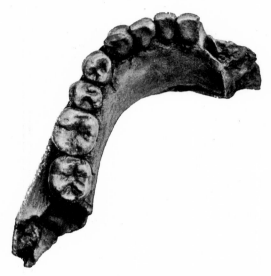

161 Portion of a lower jaw from Krapina, remarkable for the size and good preservation of the teeth. Natural size. (From a cast by Gorjanovic-Kramberger)

that study of the crowns can only be carried out in specimens of young individuals. Some specimens from Krapina are particularly helpful in this respect (Fig. 161).

No important characteristic distinguishes the incisors, the canines, or the premolars from the corresponding teeth in modern Man. The true molars were almost equally developed. They present the primitive human form so well described by Albert Gaudry (see p. 175). The upper molars had all four cusps well developed. All the lower molars had five cusps, as in the jaw of Heidelberg Man and in the jaws of certain modern savage races, known for this reason as megadontic.

To sum up, the dentition of Neandertal Man does not differ in any important character from that of the Men of today; but, as was to be expected, the points of resemblance are with savage, and not with civilized races. This similarity in character extends even to their pathology. The jaws of the Man from La Chapelle-aux-Saints bear numerous signs of diseases, which must have caused serious suffering to their owner, due to inflammation of the gums (simple pyorrhoea) or to pathological growths on the socket-rims of the teeth (general pyorrhoea). But in not a single specimen have we observed a trace of caries.

THE TRUNK AND LIMBS

Until recent years, the study of other parts of the skeleton was somewhat neglected. The skeletons from La Chapelle-aux-Saints and La Ferrassie, which were almost complete and well-preserved, have enabled the study to be taken up afresh and completed.

In general these skeletons, composed of relatively short thick bones, with large articular heads and powerful muscle attachments, give evidence of great strength. They have retained a large number of simian vestiges.

THE VERTEBRAL COLUMN

The vertebral column was short and massive. The first vertebrae are much more like those of a chimpanzee than those of a man (Fig. 162). Their

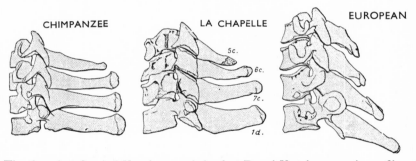

162 The three last Cervical Vertebrae, and the first Dorsal Vertebra, seen in profile, of a Chimpanzee, of the fossil Man from La Chapelle-aux-Saints, and of a European One-half natural size

spinous processes are long, lying at right angles to the axis of the vertebral column, instead of inclining backwards, and they are not bifurcated at the end. The articular apophyses are remarkable for the slight obliquity of their facets. These peculiarities seem to indicate in the cervical region of the vertibral column either a complete absence of curves, or a slight curve, in a direction opposite to that in modern Man, prolonging the dorsal curve, as occurs in anthropoid apes, such as the Chimpanzee. If the reader bears in mind what has been said regarding the differences of the curves of the vertebral column in the Primate series (see p. 74), he will appreciate the interest of these observations.

The vertebrae of the other regions are not so well preserved. It would seem as if the lumbar curve were less pronounced than in the majority of modern men. The portions of the sacrum which we possess point to narrow sacral vertebrae, slightly arched, and deeply set between the iliac bones. These are simian characters.

The ribs are extraordinarily strong, denoting a broad thorax with very powerful intercostal muscles.

THE GIRDLES AND LIMBS

The clavicles are long, slender, and much arched, like those of the Chimpanzee. The shoulderblades (scapulae) show, at their anterior or axillary margin, a special formation which we have not found in the skeleton of any modern Man.[56]

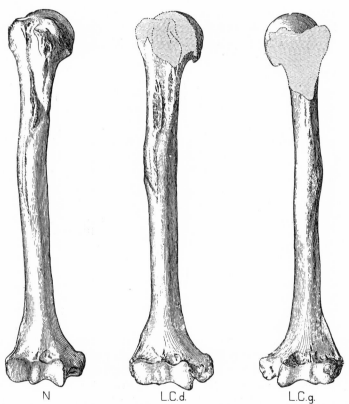

N   L.C.d.   L.C.g.

163 Humeri seen full face. N., from Neandertal; L.C.d., L.C.g., right and left humeri from La Chapelle-aux-Saints. One-third natural size

The upper-arm bones (humeri), which are short, strong, and possess large articular heads, do not differ in any essential character from the humeri of modern Man. The right humerus is always a little stronger than the left: Mousterian Man was already right-handed (Fig. 163). Such

[56] See Vallois, H., 'L'omoplate humaine, étude anatomique et anthropologique' (*Bull. et Mém. de la Soc. d'Anthrop. de Paris*, 1931 and 1946).

observations are not surprising, as the forelimb provides one of the chief characteristics of the genus *Homo*, acquired at an early stage in the evolution of our most distant ancestors.

The bones of the forearm are equally strong. All the known specimens of radius, instead of being almost straight as in modern Man, show a very pronounced curve. Hence the interosseous spaces for the muscles of the forearm were greater. The bicipital tuberosity is situated a little lower than in modern Man, and lies on the prolongation of the inner crest of the bone, instead of being diverted to the anterior surface. These are altogether simian traits, reproduced in the radius of anthropoid apes (Fig. 164). But we

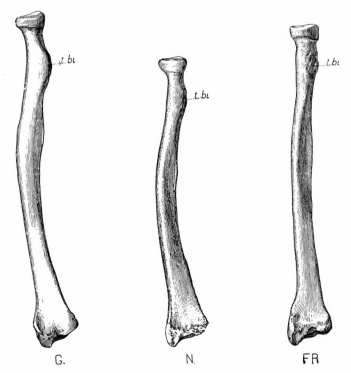

G.   N.   FR

164 Radii seen from inner surface. G, Gorilla; N, Neandertal Man; FR, Frenchman. One-third natural size. *t.bi.*, bicipital tuberosity

must hasten to add that the lower end of the bone and the surface of the carpal articulations, corresponding to the region of the wrist, are very human.

The ulna also shows certain peculiarities. But contrary to the case of the radius, it does not exhibit so much resemblance to the Anthropoid Apes as to the lower Apes; that is to say, we consider that Neandertal Man has retained in his ulnar bones, as in the majority of the other bones of his skeleton, some relics of a primitive state far distant from the point at which the various branches of the larger Primates split off.

When extended, the upper arm and forearm lay almost in line with each other, whilst in our case the forearm forms an angle with the upper arm scarcely ever exceeding 170°. On the other hand, the strong development of the olecranon process of the ulna must have impeded the full extension of the forearm, as in the lower Monkeys, whereas in the anthropoid species complete extension is as easy as possible.

The hand is already very human in character (Fig. 165). The carpal, however, is relatively small, as in the Great Apes. The metacarpals are large and

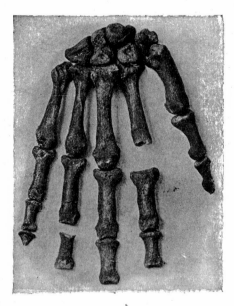

165 Right hand of the skeleton of a woman from La Ferrassie. Half natural size. Anthropological Gallery of the Musée de l'Homme, Paris

thick, that of the thumb being relatively shorter than is the rule in modern Man. The articulations of the metacarpals permitted of easy movement. All the fingers are comparatively short.

According to F. Sarasin,[57] this hand exhibits a curious mixture of primitive and advanced characteristics.

We already know that the pelvis of Man differs from that of all other Primates, because of its arrangement in correlation with the upright position and erect gait (see pp. 73, 74). We possess only portions of the pelvis of Neandertal Man, but these portions are sufficient to allow a complete reconstruction to be made and to enable us to ascertain the persistence of certain vestiges of simian structure—great length in relation to breadth, flattened haunch (iliac) bones, much reduced sciatic spine, more pronounced ischial tuberosity, etc.

[57] Sarasin, F., 'Die Variationen im Bau des Handskeletts verschiedener Menschenformen' (*Ztschr. für Morphol. und Anthrop.*, XXX, 1931).

A priori, the osteology of the lower limbs must of necessity be interesting, since it is so closely correlated with the more or less upright carriage of the body.

The femora have massive shafts and large heads, and are much bent

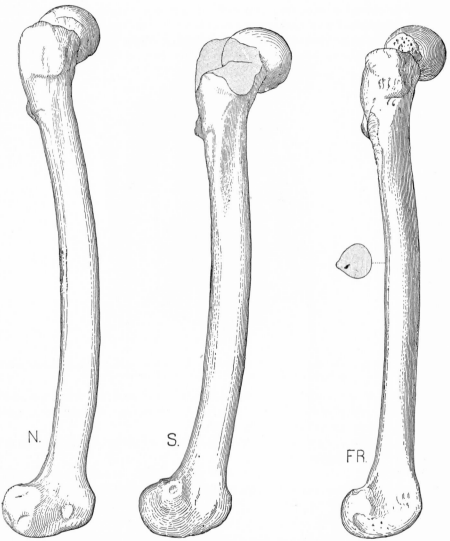

166 Femora seen in profile, exterior surface. N, of Neandertal Man; S, of Spy Man; FR, of a Frenchman. One-third natural size

(Fig. 166). They thus resemble the femora of gorillas and chimpanzees, whereas modern Man has almost straight femora, like the Orangs and

Gibbons. In the cylindrical form of their shafts they differ from the femora of anthropoid types and resemble those of macaques, dog-faced monkeys, etc. There is often a *third trochanter* and *sub-trochanteric fossa*, osteological peculiarities related, it is said, to the development of the gluteal muscles and to muscular activity adapted to movements in mountainous country. Certain frictional surfaces seem to indicate that the owners of these femora habitually adopted a squatting position.

The tibiae were short but very strong (Fig. 167). The upper head is bent back, that is to say, curved towards the rear, which causes the plane

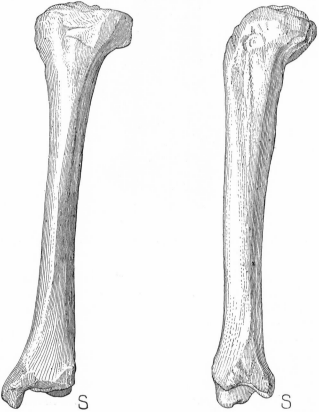

S   S

167 Tibia of Spy skeleton, seen full face and in profile, external surface. One-third natural size.

of articulation with the femur to slope downwards and backwards. In this character, first described by Dr. Collignon and further observed by Fraipont and Manouvrier,[58] the tibia of Neandertal Man resembles that of the Apes; only rarely is it present, even in much less pronounced form,

[58] Collignon, Dr, 'Description des ossements fossiles humains trouvés à Bollviller' (*Revue d'Anthrop.* 1880). Fraipont and Lohest, in their memoir on Spy, *loc. cit.* Manouvrier, L., 'Étude sur la rétroversion de la tête du tibia' (*Mém. de la Soc. d'Anthrop.* 2nd Series, Vol. IV, 1893).

in Man today. Presently we shall discuss the interpretation of this fact. At the same time, the general slope of the articular plane, from without inwards, is much more pronounced, as in the Gorilla. The lower head of the tibia bears one or two supplementary facets corresponding with analogous facets on the astragalus (Fig. 168), such as may be met with in certain native types and many Apes which habitually adopt a squatting position.

168 Lower extremity of the tibia and the astragalus of a woman's skeleton from La Ferrassie. Two-thirds natural size. *f.a.*, supplementary facets

The fibula is strong. The arrangement of the articular facets shows that this bone played then a much more important part in the functions of the lower limb than it does today. To a much greater degree it must have shared in supporting the weight of the body.

Up to a few years ago, only some isolated and more or less fragmentary bones of the foot of Neandertal Man were available for study. The discoveries of Capitan and Peyrony at La Ferrassie have put us in possession of skeletal remains of three almost complete feet (Fig. 169). These remains are of exceptional interest, the foot being one of the most distinctive characteristics of the genus *Homo*.

The tarsal bones are particularly instructive, because their characters and variations depend on physiological conditions relatively easy to determine.

The astragalus or ankle-bone is short, high and broad. The head is much bent, denoting that the great toe was widely separated from its neighbours. The articular surface for the scaphoid points to a much depressed instep. The malleolar facets for the tibia and fibula show a development comparable to that observed in apes (Fig. 170). In its extent, the facet for the fibula recalls that of anthropoid types.

These arrangements and some others, into the details of which we need not enter here, teach us that the foot must have rested chiefly on its outside

169 Photograph of right foot of the female skeleton from La Ferrassie, still partially in its matrix. Half natural size

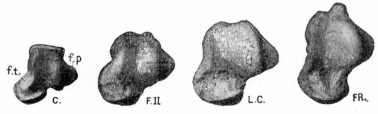

170 Photograph of the astragalus or ankle-bone seen from the upper surface. Half natural size. C., of a Chimpanzee; F.II, of the female skeleton from La Ferrassie; L.C., of the Man from La Chapelle-aux-Saints; FR., of a Modern Frenchman; *f.t.*, tibial facet; *f.p.*, fibular facet.

edge; and we understand how, in order thus to support the weight of the body, the fibula required to be of stronger structure. To sum up, the astragalus of our fossil Man is the astragalus of a walking mammal, which, however, has retained many relics of a former climbing state. The example

from the smaller skeleton of La Ferrassie is very remarkable for the prominence of these vestigial simian characters, now effaced in the white races,
but found in a transitory form in the newly born, a fact which confirms their
phylogenetic significance.

The heel-bone (calcaneum), no less robust, likewise recalls in its structure
the heel-bone of the newly born European child. It is remarkable for the
extraordinary development of the small apophysis (Fig. 171), a development

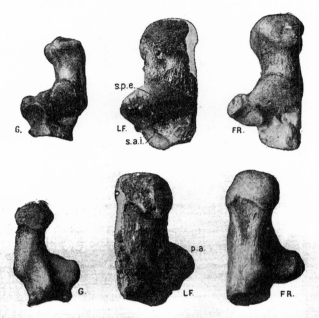

171 Photographs of the heel-bone (calcaneum) seen from above (upper row) and seen from
below (lower row). Half natural size

G., Gorilla; L.F., Man from La Ferrassie; FR., Frenchman; *p.a.*, small apophysis; *s.a.i.*,
anterior inner surface; *s.p.e.*, posterior outer surface

comparable to that present in the Great Apes, especially the Chimpanzee
and Gorilla. This kind of support, this *sustentaculum tali*, must have borne
a large proportion of the weight of the body by way of the astragalus and
tibia.

Another peculiarity of the heel-bone relates to what is termed its torsion.
In apes, whose feet rest on the ground, mainly on the outer edge, the axis
of the posterior surface of the heel-bone is much inclined from within
outwards. In men of the civilized races, whose feet rest equally upon the
whole sole surface, this axis oscillates on an almost vertical plane, the torsion
being rather from without inwards. In our fossil Men, as also in modern
Veddahs, the torsion is intermediate (Fig. 172).

The other bones of the tarsus and metatarsus do not exhibit any important peculiarity. But when their various components are brought together and articulated, we find a considerable separation of the first toe, a separation which the deviation in the neck of the astragalus had led us to expect. This arrangement has been described in the Negritos and Veddahs, whose prehensile feet readily lend themselves to the action of climbing. The forms of the articulate facets of the majority of the bones also point to greater mobility of the other toes.

The lower limb of Neandertal Man was, then, not altogether like that of modern Man. Yet it differed much less in possessing new characters than in

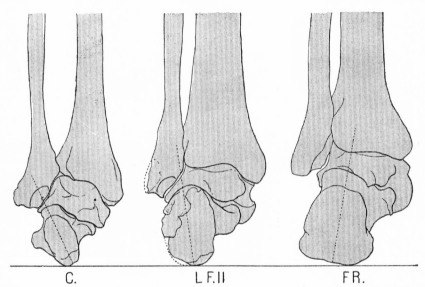

C.   L F. II   F R.

172 Hind view of part of the left leg and foot. C., of a Chimpanzee; LF. II, of the female skeleton from La Ferrassie; FR., of a Frenchman. Half-natural size

The dotted lines represent the axis of the hind face of the heelbone

presenting the conjunction of certain morphological characters which, indeed, were already known, but were scattered amongst several living races still leading a life of savagery. The majority of these characters could be readily described as simian or pithecoid, but here we must use these terms in the widest sense. For it is not even with the Anthropoid Apes that the points of resemblance are most pronounced, but rather with the lower Monkeys. This fact welds more closely those links of relationship which unite Man, not in this case to the anthropoids, but to a more generalized type of Ape—a quadruped and a climber.

ATTITUDE AND PROPORTIONS OF THE BODY

However this point of view may be regarded, and it will be necessary to return to the matter again, the differences between the skeleton of Neandertal

Man and that of modern Man are such that they necessarily imply certain differences in the general bearing and attitude of the body. The great development of the face, the backward position of the *foramen magnum* which must have caused the body to incline forward, the slighter curve of the cervical vertebrae, all testify to this fact. With regard to the lower limb, it is clear that if the formation of the pelvis and the great development of the gluteal muscles indicate that a biped attitude had already been attained,

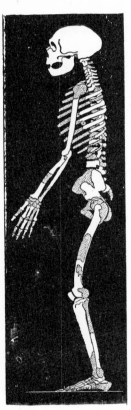

the anatomical characters of femur and tibia, seen in profile in the upright position, show that the leg and thigh, when extended, could not have been in a precisely straight line with each other; that the femur must have sloped downwards and forwards, and that the tibia, sloping in a contrary direction, must have formed behind a wide angle with the femur. So that, without being mechanically impossible, the total extension of the knee could not have been normal, and the habitual attitude must have been one of semi-flexion (Fig. 173).

The fibula, stronger in character, had a most important part to play as a support. The general appearance of the articulations of the foot indicates a greater degree of mobility and freedom. The foot, still only slightly arched, must have rested on the ground on its outer edge, and must have assumed naturally an in-toed position; the wide separation of the great toe shows that it may have played the part of a prehensile organ.

In general, the ordinary, normal carriage of Neandertal Man must then have differed in some degree from our own. This fossil Man often exhibits an infantile morphology, that is to say, a morphology the most striking and surprising traits of which are found in either the newly born or unborn infant of Europeans. It has long since been noted

173 Reconstruction of the fossil Man from La Chapelle-aux-Saints, side view. About one-fifteenth natural size.

that the child is not born with the faculty of walking upright: he first of all tries to walk 'on all fours', quite in the manner of a quadruped ape, and when he learns to walk in the biped position he places his foot on the ground on its outer edge. The squatting position, habitual to fossil Man and savage peoples, is likewise an ancestral survival. Here we have a case of individual evolution recalling and repeating the evolution of the race. Neandertal Man represents a stage in this evolution certainly already far removed from the starting point, a stage closely resembling the modern state of Man, but still quite distinct from it.

Now that we have studied separately each component part of the skeleton of Neandertal Man, let us try to imagine, as precisely as possible, the general appearance of his whole body.

For long anthropologists have sought to determine the stature of a being by means of the size of the long bones. The formulae used to this end are not altogether beyond criticism, especially in their application to fossil Man. While quite appreciating the results attained through these formulae, we have made use of a different and more direct method. Having drawn, in profile and life-size, each part or each bone of the skeleton of the Man fom La Chapelle-aux-Saints, we cut out these drawings and fixed them upon a panel, one by one, according to their anatomical relationships and as exactly as possible. We thus obtained a kind of working-plan of the skeleton in orthogonal projection and of natural size (Fig. 173). The total height of this drawing, that is to say the height of the skeleton, is 1.52 metres (4 ft. 11.8 ins.). As we must add 20 millimetres to obtain the height of the living subject, this must have been from 1.54 to 1.55 metres (5 ft. 1 ins.). The skeletons from La Ferrassie give somewhat different figures: the male skeleton, 1.60 metres (5 ft. 3 ins.); the female, barely 1.45 metres (4 ft. 9 ins.). We may therefore look upon the figure 1.55 metres (5 ft. 1 in.) as an approximate average.

The stature of Neandertal Man was thus much lower than the average stature of modern Man—1.65 metres (5 ft. 4.96 ins.) according to Topinard. From Deniker's tables[59] we can compare in this respect the men of the Neandertal type with the following ethnographic groups: the Bushmen, among African races; the Veddahs, Samoyeds, Dyaks, Japanese, and the Annamese of Cochin-China, among Asiatic peoples; the Caribs of the three Guianas and Venezuela; the Labrador Eskimoes; the Fuegians in America; the Lapps, among Europeans.

We know that the genus *Homo* clearly differs from the whole group of the Anthropoid Apes with respect to the relative proportions of the upper and lower limbs. In our fossil specimens, these proportions are quite human, but the forearm is very short in relation to the upper arm, and the leg is extremely short in relation to the thigh, more so than in any living race.

RECONSTRUCTIONS

The reconstruction of the whole skeleton of the Man from La Chapelle-aux-Saints, carried out according to the method we have just described, is reproduced in Fig. 173. The general aspect here shown may be described as follows: a large head upon a short and massive trunk; short, thickset and very strong limbs; a peculiar attitude, due to the somewhat different curve of the vertebral column and to the slightly bent lower limbs.

Can we go still further and restore the plastic form? Can we present a portrait of Neandertal Man as he was in life? The artist is at full liberty to attempt to produce works of imagination, original in character and striking in appearance; but men of science—and of conscience—know too well the

[59] Deniker, J., *Les Races et les Peuples de la Terre* (2nd Ed., Paris, 1926) p. 699.

difficulties of such attempts to regard them as anything but pastimes and recreations. Certain accredited experts have published portraits in the flesh, not only of Neandertal Man, whose skeleton is now sufficiently well known, but also of Heidelberg Man, of whom we have only the lower jaw; and of *Pithecanthropus*, of whom we only possess a fragment of skull and two or three teeth. At the best, such productions might find a place in works aiming at extreme popularity, but they singularly mar the books, estimable in other respects, into which they have been introduced.

174 Reconstruction of the muscles of the head and neck of the Neandertal Man from La Chappelle-aux-Saints. About one-fourth natural size.

In only one attempt did we feel justified in indulging, and it was as follows: we put into the hands of a young sculptor, M. Joanny-Durand, an enthusiast in anatomical studies, a cast of the skull of the Man from La Chappelle-aux-Saints. We requested him to model, in plasticine, the most important muscles, and to superimpose them one by one on this plaster cast, proceeding from the deep to the superficial layers, and carefully marking their points of insertion, the strength of which helps us to judge to a certain extent the power of the muscles attached to them. The bust obtained, shown of course without skin, is represented in Fig. 174. Far from emphasizing in his work a simian or bestial tendency, an easy thing to have done, the artist has clung as far as possible to the human feeling.[60] Apart from the shape of the ears and of the extremity of the nose, for which we have no data, our reconstruction cannot differ greatly from the real appearance of the skinless head of our fossil Man. We leave the reader to study this physiognomy, to distinguish in it the basal structure of the skull, to compare it with the face of modern Man, and to enquire how the expression of this countenance might be modified by a covering of skin and hair, to say nothing of the more or less dramatic play of muscles represented here in a state of rest.

[60] This replied in advance to the criticisms levelled against this reconstruction by Professor E. Loth of Warsaw, who has himself published an interesting study on the musculature of Neanderta! Man (*Ztschr. für Rassenkunde*, VII, 1938).

THE BRAIN

The osteological studies we have just summarized have shown us very satisfactorily the physical attributes and various aspects of the physical life of Neandertal Man. We shall now attempt to imagine his psychic attributes, his mental life. First of all we may appeal to archaeological evidence. All the Mousterian handiwork known to us is very primitive and rude in character, and does not argue in favour of the superiority of the brain which conceived and created it. A second kind of evidence is furnished by the study of the brain itself, so far as it can be carried out under the conditions which we shall presently describe, when we have said a few words regarding the cranial capacity, that is to say, the volume of the brain.

BRAIN CAPACITY

Several anthropologists, including some of the most distinguished, such as Schaaffhausen, Huxley, Virchow, and Schwalbe, attempted to calculate the capacity of the Neandertal skull, assuming that it was complete. The resultant figures varied from 1,100–1,300 cubic centimetres, very much lower than that of the average human being.

Measurements of the complete skull from La Chapelle-aux-Saints, obtained either by the use of orthodox formulae or by direct cubic measurements, lead to a very different result. The capacity of this skull may be fixed at about 1,600 cubic centimetres.

The relative size of this figure may well astonish those who regard cranial capacity as a zoological and anthropological character of the first importance, directly related to the development of the intellectual faculties. Our fossil Man shows many signs of morphological inferiority, which somewhat lessen the gulf separating the human group from its nearest relatives, the Anthropoid Apes, and yet he clearly belongs to the human series. He even occupies one of the highest stages in it, as the following table shows:

Anthropoid apes (maximum)	621 c.c.
Pithecanthropus and Sinanthropus (estimated)	855 ,,
Andamans (average of men)	1,300 ,,
Australians (average of men)	1,340 ,,
African negroes (average of men)	1,477 ,,
Parisians (average of men)	1,550 ,,
Auvergnese (average of men)	1,585 ,,

This result is all the more surprising in that it differs so greatly from the estimates suggested for the Neandertal skull. Now, the dimensions of the skull-cap of the latter are so near those of the skull from La Chapelle-aux-Saints that the result obtained by direct cubing of the latter must cast the most serious doubt upon the earlier estimations, as we shall verify.

However that may be, the Man from La Chapelle had a brain as large as that of the most civilized of modern races. But it must be remembered that we are dealing with the absolute value of this capacity. We must ask if the relative value is of the same order, and to discover this we must try to estimate the latter by taking into account the size of the head.

Now it is easy to calculate, according to formulae in current usage, what would be the capacity of a normal skull, the horizontal diameters of which would equal those of the skull from La Chapelle-aux-Saints, and whose vertical diameter would be in the same relation to the former as in a modern skull. We thus obtain a figure exceeding 2,000 cubic centimetres. Certain German skulls almost fulfil these conditions, such as that of Bismarck, whose cranial capacity was estimated at 1,965 cubic centimetres.

We have seen (p. 215, Fig. 140) that by superimposing the profiles of the skulls of a chimpanzee, of the Man from La Chapelle-aux-Saints, and of a white man, and taking care to make the axes of the three skulls uniform in length, a figure is obtained plainly showing the differences between the *relative* capacities of the brain-box.

Thus there disappears, or is greatly lessened, the paradox seemingly indicated by the magnitude of the absolute volume of the La Chapelle skull, when due account is taken of the numerous signs of its structural inferiority. In reality, other things being equal, the brain is relatively rather less than the brains of modern large-headed men.

Further, it would appear that the examples of Neandertal Man from La Chapelle-aux-Saints and La Ferrassie were individuals who were specially outstanding in this particular. We now possess casts of the brain-cavity of other examples, notably specimens from Neandertal, Gibraltar, and La Quina; and comparative measurements of these casts have enabled us to determine their capacities, which are compared in the following table with those given by various authors for certain other Neandertalians.[61]

Neandertal	1,408 c.c.
Monte Circeo	1,550 ,,
Le Moustier	1,564 ,, (?)
La Chapelle-aux-Saints	1,600 ,,
La Ferrassie	1,641 ,,
Saccopastore No. 1 (female skull)	1,200 ,,
Gibraltar (female skull)	1,300 ,,
La Quina (female skull)	1,367 ,,

The Men from La Chapelle and La Ferrassie therefore possess a distinctly higher brain capacity than the others in this small series. We are justified in supposing that they approach the maximum figure, while the Saccopastore skull perhaps represents the minimum of the same type. The difference between the maximum and the minimum is by no means abnormal. Apart from the fact that there regularly exists a difference of 150 cubic

[61] For the Neandertalians of Palestine, see Chap. X below.

centimetres between the capacity of men and of women in modern human races, variations of 300 to 400 cubic centimetres are frequently observed within each of these races, savage or civilized.

The average brain capacity of Neandertal Man is therefore about 1,540 c.c. in the men, very much the same as that of the so-called 'superior' living races, but only 1,290 c.c. in the women—a particularly high sexual variation.

What do these figures signify? Do they give us the measure of the intellectual or psychic faculties of our fossil Men? Nothing could be more uncertain.

We know, of course, that the brain capacity may vary enormously in a series of recent men selected for their eminence, from 1,294 c.c. (Gambetta), or 1,485 c.c. (the anthropologist Broca) to 1,830 c.c. (Cuvier) and perhaps even 2,012 (Turgeniev), that is to say in the relation of 1 to $1\frac{1}{2}$. Considered by itself, then, this capacity cannot be taken as a criterion of the intellectual standard of a human being. There is an old saying: 'A small chronometer is better than a big alarm clock', and large heads are not always the best heads. As *Homo neandertalensis* belongs to a type different from modern types, it would appear that one of his characteristics was the great size of his head rather than the volume of his brain, whatever may have been the *quality* of the latter.

Further it must be enquired whether the organizaticn, or more simply, the divisions of the brain substance do not also show certain differences. In some measure the study of the cast of the endocranial surface will answer this question.

STUDY OF THE BRAIN

We cannot by means of such evidence claim to be able to penetrate all the secrets of the structure of the brain of any being. The results of such studies as can be carried out on casts of the cranial cavity may be likened to our idea of the form of a statue the covering of which we have been forbidden to raise, the covering being represented in the present case by the meninges which in the living body separate the brain substance from the bony surface of the brain cavity. Nevertheless, such casts, when made with the necessary skill and accuracy, enable us, in comparing them with similar casts made from skulls of apes or modern Men, to arrive at some interesting conclusions. We now possess casts of the brain cavities of six individuals of Neandertal Man: that from Neandertal itself, from Gibraltar, from La Chapelle-aux-Saints, from La Quina, from Le Moustier, and from La Ferrassie. Their general characters are remarkably uniform. The following description applies specially to the cast of the La Chapelle skull, which is the most complete and the most skilfully executed.[62]

[62] For further details see Boule, M. and Anthony, R., 'L'encéphale de l'Homme fossile de La Chapelle-aux-Saints' (*L'Anthropologie*, XXII, 1911). See also Kappers, A., 'Further Communication on the Fissures of the Frontal Lobes in Neanderthal Men' (*Kon. Akad. van Wetenschappen te Amsterdam, Proceedings* XXXII, 1929).

The brain, the general form of which is reproduced in this cast, is, like the skull, long, broad and flattened. It presents a somewhat marked asymmetry; the left hemisphere of the brain was slightly more developed than the right, and this is in accord with the observation made on the inequality of the right and left upper arm-bones (humeri).

One of the most remarkable characters of the cerebrum, as the cast shows, is the simplicity and coarse appearance of the convolutions. Casts of the brain cavity of modern Men generally show traces not only of more numerous but of much more complicated convolutions. In respect of this character the brain of Neandertal Man more resembles the brains of the great anthropoid apes or of microcephalic man.

The Sylvian fissure, which, in the brains of mammals, separates the frontal from the temporal lobe (Fig. 175 and 176), is shown here gaping in front, a disposition which seems to indicate a certain degree of exposure of the striated body called the *island of Reil*. This arrangement is seen in modern Man in the course of embryonic development; in the adult, the Sylvian fissure is closed by the encroaching of the cerebral matter on all sides.

A study of the lobes of the brain reveals some important facts, first of all with regard to their relative development.

Today we agree in admitting that the lobes, within the orthodox limits ascribed to them by anatomists, are far from corresponding exactly to physiological regions. It is interesting all the same to measure, not the volumes of these lobes, which would be impossible in the present case, but simply their external surfaces in relation to the total external surface of the cerebral hemisphere, and especially to compare the results of these measurements with those furnished by similar casts of anthropoid apes and modern Man.

We have thus obtained certain numerical data, discussion of which cannot be entered into here, but the significance of which may be summarized in the statement that the relative development of the lobes in our fossil Man was not found in modern Man. The difference is especially marked in the frontal lobe. In anthropoid apes the outer surface of this lobe forms about 32 per cent. of the total surface of the corresponding cerebral hemisphere. In modern Man the proportion averages about 43 per cent. In the man from La Chapelle-aux-Saints it is about 36 per cent. and the same figure has been obtained for the woman from La Quina. From the point of view of the relative development of his frontal lobe, which is depressed and slants backwards, fossil Man may thus be ranked between the Anthropoid Apes and modern Man, and even nearer to the former than to the latter.

The frontal convolutions are fairly well marked, at least towards their lower portions. The third frontal convolution, which is very clear, had a large cap,[63] but it was much simpler than in modern Man. It is noteworthy that it seemed to have had no *base*, that is to say, no supplementary fold

[63] The *cap* is the part of the frontal lobe between the two anterior branches of the Sylvian fissure named the pre-Sylvian branches (*Spa* and *Spp* in Fig. 179).

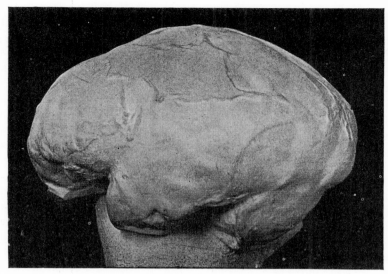

175 Photograph of intracranial cast of the fossil Man from La Chapelle-aux-Saints. Left side.

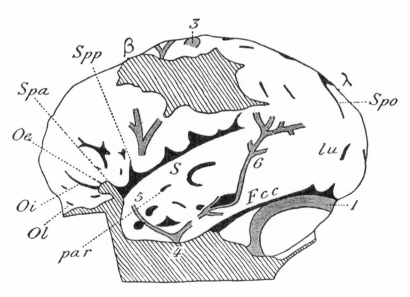

176 Topography of Surface of Left Side of Brain. Half natural size

β, bregma; λ, lambda; 1, lateral sinus; 3, Breschet's sinus; 4, 5, 6, medial meningeal vessels; *Fcc*, cerebro-cerebellar fissure; *S*, fissure of Sylvius, along which are the parietal fissures of **Broca**; *Spa*, anterior pre-Sylvian branch; *Spp*, posterior pre-Sylvian branch; *Spo*, parieto-occipital fissure; *Ol*, olefactory groove; *Oi*, internal orbital groove; *Oe*, external orbital groove; *par*, parallel groove; *lu, sulcus lunatus*

attaching the cap to the ascending frontal convolution, or that, if sucn a fold was present, it was much reduced in size. In consequence of the weak development of the frontal lobe, the cap of the third convolution seems, as in the Anthropoids, to occupy a much more forward position. These are primitive and simian characters, for an English anatomist, Cunningham, has affirmed that the great development of the third frontal convolution is more characteristic of apes than of men.

There is nothing of importance to describe relating to the temporal and parietal lobes. The occipital lobes, which are relatively highly developed, exceed and overhang the cerebellum much more than is the case in modern Man. In the sum of their characters, and in particular because of the presence of a well-marked *sulcus lunatus* or 'Ape fissure', they greatly resemble those of the Anthropoid Apes.

The cerebellum is remarkable for the slight projection of the lateral cerebellar lobes, separated by a large fissure, at the bottom of which the median lobe, or *vermis*, must have been exposed as in the Apes. In the anterior region, the cerebellum was, on the contrary, relatively more developed and more projecting than in Man, here again resembling that of the Apes.

The medulla oblongata must have been disposed in a much more oblique direction from front to back than in modern Man, but less oblique than in the Apes, even the Anthropoids. This character agrees with what we have learnt from a study of the skeleton, particularly from the direction of the cervical portion of the vertebral column.

FUNCTIONAL SIGNIFICANCE OF THE BRAIN

The anatomical facts here revealed enable us to some extent to obtain an idea of the brain functions of Neandertal Man.

If the great volume of the brain argues in favour of the intelligence of this Man, the coarse appearance and general simplicity of the design of the convolutions indicate, on the contrary, rudimentary intellectual faculties. The relative development of the different parts of the grey matter testify to this fact.

Flechsig has shown that the different regions of the cortex of the brain may be divided, from a physiological point of view, into two groups. The one comprises the sensory-motor regions, correlated with the different peripheral organs of sensibility and movement; the others comprise the 'zones of association', where sensations are condensed or diffused, and movement is regulated. Such would be the 'intellectual centres and the true organs of thought'.

In the lowest orders of mammals, the centres of association are almost lacking. In the Apes their importance is already considerable, and their development almost equals that of the sensory-motor centres. In Man, in whom intelligence reaches its highest point, they have come to occupy two-thirds of the cortex.

On the external surface of the human brain, three principal centres of association, wedged in between four sensory-motor zones, have been approximately mapped out. Comparing these facts and those derived from the study of the lobes of the brain of Neandertal Man, we find that the visual zone (occipital lobe) was relatively more developed, and that the first centre of association was very ill provided for, since this centre corresponds to the anterior region of the frontal lobe, here specially reduced.

Now, if there is one assured fact in the physiology of the brain, it is that the anterior portions of the frontal lobes are indispensable to the intellectual life. Lesions in these parts affect neither sensibility nor powers of movement, but they give rise to intellectual disturbances; bilateral atrophy of the frontal lobes always causes dementia or defective control known as gatism.

'In the development of the cerebral hemispheres throughout the geological periods', Dr Houzé[64] writes, 'it is the frontal lobe, the seat of the most complicated associations and of the most perfectly adapted mental combinations, which has increased in size. In Man, it has acquired such pre-eminence that it has done away with the necessity of adaptations for defence (*Homo nudus et inermis*). The frontal lobe has become the most formidable weapon for attack and defence.'

It is probable therefore, that Neandertal Man must have possessed only a rudimentary psychic nature, superior certainly to that of the Anthropoid Apes, but markedly inferior to that of any modern race whatever. He had doubtless only the most rudimentary articulate language. On the whole, the brain of this fossil Man is already a human brain because of the amount of its cerebral matter; but this matter does not yet show the superior organization which characterizes modern Man.

CONCLUSIONS

The long description the reader has just perused may be summed up in a concise form which may serve as a diagnosis of the Neandertal type of fossil Man.

DIAGNOSIS OF THE NEANDERTAL TYPE

Body of short stature, but very massive. Head very large, with facial region much developed in comparison with cerebral region. Cephalic index medium. Skull much flattened; orbital arches enormous, forming a continuous ridge; forehead very receding; occiput protuberant and compressed in a vertical direction.

Face long and projecting, with flat and receding malar bones, upper jaws lacking canine fossae and forming a kind of muzzle. Orbits very large and round. Nose prominent and very large. Sub-nasal space extensive.

Lower jaw strong and chinless, with large ascending rami, and truncated in the region of the angle.

[64] Houzé, Dr, 'Les étapes du lobe frontal' (*Institut Solvay, Sociologie*, 1910).

Dentition massive, structure of back molars retaining certain primitive characters.

Vertebral column and limb bones showing numerous simian characters and indicating a less perfect bipedal or upright carriage than in modern Man. Legs very short.

Brain capacity averaging about 1,450 cubic centimetres. Brain formation presenting numerous primitive characters, especially in the relatively great reduction of the frontal lobes and the general pattern of the convolutions.

It is important to note that the physical characters of the Neandertal type are quite in agreement with what archaeology teaches us as to his bodily capacity, his psychology, and his habits. As we have already pointed out, there is hardly a more rudimentary or degraded form of industry than that of our Mousterian Man. His use of one simple material only, stone (apart probably from wood and bone), the uniformity, simplicity, and rudeness of his stone implements, and the probable absence of all traces of any preoccupation of an aesthetic or of a moral kind, are quite in agreement with the brutish appearance of this energetic and clumsy body, of the heavy-jawed skull, which itself still declares the predominance of functions of a purely vegetative or bestial kind over the functions of mind.

COMPARISON WITH MODERN TYPES

A comparative study of the morphology of various living human groups confirms the idea that we are here concerned with an altogether special type, very different not only from the so-called superior races, but also from the Eskimoes, the Fuegians, the Bushmen, the Pygmies, African or Asiatic, the Veddas, the Polynesians, the Melanesians, and even from the Australians, with whom attempts at comparison have often been made.[65]

The skeleton of the last-mentioned racial type is as dissimilar as possible from that of Neandertal Man (Figs. 177 and 178). It can no longer be asserted that the Australians are descended from our Mousterians; indeed, the idea of this relationship would probably not have occurred to the mind of the early observers, if, in place of having only a mere skull-cap, they had had the opportunity of examining a complete skull with its facial portion. All that can be admitted in this respect is that the Australian group of Men, certainly one of the least developed groups of modern mankind, is less far removed than other races from the primitive forms, and that, in consequence, it ought to have certain characteristics in common with the Neandertal type.

HIS PLACE IN THE HUMAN SERIES

Neandertal Man thus represents a new type in the human family. Ought he to form a separate genus, or ought he to take a place in the genus *Homo*?

It was claimed, even at the time when we were acquainted with only a

---

[65] These comparisons are detailed in the Monograph, *loc. cit.*

portion of his skull, that the fossil Man of Neandertal differed generically from modern Man. Later, Sergi created the genus *Palaeoanthropus* for this type, Bonarelli suggested the name *Protanthropus*, and Ameghino, regarding

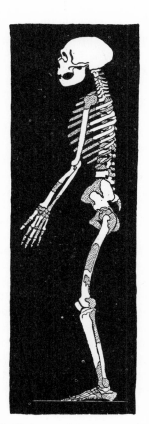
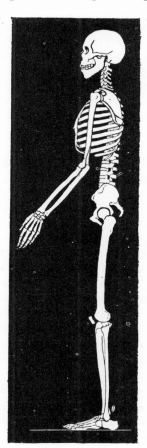

177 (left) Skeleton of fossil Man from La Chapelle-aux-Saints, reconstructed, side view. About one-fifteenth natural size

178 (right) Skeleton, side view, of an Australian. About one-fifteenth natural size

Neandertal Man as the ancestor or forerunner of the genus *Homo*, called him *Prothomo*.[66]

In our opinion, the Hominian of the Neandertal type is certainly a *Homo*. After all, we are discussing a creature who greatly resembles us, and so the opinion we have expressed is that generally adopted, even by naturalists

[66] For further information on these appellations, consult Bonarelli, G., 'Sylloge synonymica *Hominidarum fossilium. . .*' (*Ultima Miscellanea*, I, 1944 and II, 1946), and Kaelin, J., 'Zur Systematik und Nomenklatur der fossilen Hominiden' (*Bull. Schweizerischen Ges. für Anthr. und Ethnol.*, XXI, 1944/45).

who are inclined to multiply genera. It would probably be a different matter if we were dealing with a Feline, a Ruminant, or a Monkey!

It has still to be decided whether this fossil Man represents a distinct species, or race, or simply a variety of Man or of modern Men. The majority of anthropologists generally speak of the *Neandertal Race*, but numerous specific names have also been created. One of them is of old standing, *Homo neandertalensis*; others are more recent, *Homo primigenius*, *Homo europaeus*, *Homo krapinensis*, *Homo mousteriensis*, *Homo antiquus*, etc.

If we argue from the polygenistic point of view, it is at once clear that the Neandertal type represents a new species, easily distinguished from all others. If, on the contrary, we believe in the specific unity of modern Man, this conclusion is not so evident; it may be deduced, however, from the following considerations.

A first point is that the fossil type differs much more from all the types existing today than these types differ amongst themselves. Between the extremes of the series of modern skulls we can discover all the transitional forms, but this series is clearly separated from the group of fossil skulls by a kind of hiatus, corresponding to a real morphological break.

Morant,[67] after studying Neandertalian skulls according to the laborious biometrical methods, has arrived at virtually the same conclusions. The sum total of modern human races form a 'continuous and homogeneous bloc', to which the Neandertal type of Mousterian Man is completely opposed. There is a 'very distinct break' between the two groups.

A second point is that the osteological differences between our fossil Man and the mass of existing Men are much more important than the differences appealed to by mammalogists as a basis for separating the various species of mammalian genera. From this point of view, the Neandertal type clearly represents a species different from *Homo sapiens* taken collectively, existing or fossil, because it presents a certain number of constant characters which are not met with, normally and in association, in any human race or species existing at the present day. The majority of these distinctive characteristics have a morphological value, and consequently a classificatory value, greater than the value of the characters made use of in mammalogy for classifying forms of the same genus. Each of them would be almost sufficient in itself to justify a specific distinction, were it a question of a mammal not belonging to the genus *Homo*.

We may consider the matter from yet a third point of view. Palaeontologists, compelled to study beings simultaneously in space and time, cannot have exactly the same conception of a species as zoologists who study them only in regard to space. Finding it impossible to designate by different names all the fine degrees of evolutionary development which are revealed by the never-ending modifications of forms of life, and which they trace out throughout the ages, palaeontologists claim that new names should

[67] Morant, G. M., 'Studies of Palaeolithic Man. II: A Biometric Study of Neanderthaloid Skulls and their relationships to modern racial types' (*Annals of Eugenics*, II, 1927).

be reserved for those changes which mark a step, or, if we may be allowed the expression, a new rung in the evolutionary scale of these forms, or a quite distinct ring amongst the links of their chain.

Now the human fossil type which we have been studying corresponds ideally to the conception held by transformist palaeontologists regarding species. No one can doubt that this type represents a degree in the human scale lower, morphologically speaking, than all the stages of modern humanity, and that it marks a step very distinctly separated from the step above it. The long series of primitive or simian traits, which are imprinted on each constituent part of the skeleton, can only be interpreted as the marks of a more backward evolutionary stage than that reached by modern Mankind, and the difference is such that, according to the principles laid down, it fully justifies the distinction of a specific title.

What name should be applied to this species? A name much in use is that of *Homo primigenius*, which apparently we owe to Wilser.[68] It should be rejected. It has, to begin with, the very serious drawback of making an affirmation or suggestion which is certainly erroneous; for the Neandertal type cannot be regarded as the absolutely primitive form of the genus *Homo*. It recalls a similar egregious confusion which has led to the application of the absurd name *Elephas primigenius* to the Mammoth, the last and most specialized of the Elephants.

It ought to be abandoned for yet another reason. The rules established by the International Congress of Zoology lay down that the proper name of a species shall be that which is first applied to it. Now, as early as 1864, an English scientist, King,[69] created the expression *Homo neandertalensis* for the skull-cap and other fossil bone-remains discovered at Neandertal, and these remain the type specimens of the new species. In justice, then, this is the name which should be adopted. The terms *Homo antiquus*, *Homo incipiens*, *Homo europaeus*, *Homo spyensis*, *Homo mousteriensis*, *Homo krapinensis*, *Homo breladensis*, proposed by various authors, ought to be regarded as synonyms.

An Archaic and Extinct Species

That *Homo neandertalensis* is a species with archaic characteristics is clearly evident from its general morphology. The numerous simian traits which it has retained are so many relics, still strongly in evidence, of an ancestral state.

Alongside these characteristics, however, are others that are undoubtedly not primitive, but rather the consequences of special physiological adaptations or else the result of that tendency to specialization which marks the evolution of many groups of Primates. The discrimination is often very difficult; but even if many of them may be regarded as simply the outcome

[68] Wilser, 'Menschenrassen und Weltgeschichte' (*Naturw. Wochenschr.*, XIII, 1, 1898).
[69] King, 'The Reputed Fossil Man of the Neanderthal, (*Quart. Journ. of Science*, 1864, p. 6).

of convergence, there can be no doubt that the majority appear at an early age and consequently have a real genealogical value.

There is every reason to believe that *Homo neandertalensis* is a species even more archaic than the geological age of the remains in our possession would indicate.

The discoveries at Ehringsdorf, Saccopastore and Steinheim have taught us that Neandertal Man was already in existence at a geological epoch anterior to most of our Mousterian deposits. This explains such facts as the increase in cerebral capacity, which is very low in Steinheim Man, higher in the Neandertalians of Saccopastore and Gibraltar, and reaches its maximum among Mousterians in the Men of La Chapelle-aux-Saints, La Ferrassie and Monte Circeo. In the course of time, a progressive differentiation must have taken place within the group, which did not acquire its final type until the height of the last Ice Age.

On the other hand, we have seen that Men of a different physical structure, the probable ancestors of the various races of *Homo sapiens*, had existed in Europe since the Lower Pleistocene alongside the precursors of the Neandertalians. Cro-Magnon Man, who seems suddenly to have replaced Neandertal Man in France, appears to us like the descendant of this primitive stock, which was particularly well endowed and whose evolution in a progressive direction was more regular and sustained. By contrast with this line, that of the Neandertals represents the product of a different branch, now withered, a belated form, a survival of ancestral prototypes.

What do we know of these ancestral forms?

Unfortunately, there are very few of the more ancient types with which comparison can be made. Apart from *Pithecanthropus* and *Sinanthropus*, whose evolution may have been confined to the Far East, the only European fossil than can be placed on the line leading to the Preneandertalians is the Mauer jaw.

The lower jaws of *Homo neandertalensis* resemble the lower jaw from Mauer in their general form, strength, and dimensions, so much so that if the Mauer jaw is articulated with the La Chapelle skull, the general aspect of the whole skull is but little altered. It is true that certain differences do exist, but the points of resemblance are so great that they lead us to believe in a close, if not direct, relationship between the ancient owners of these jaws. As the Neandertal type can only be a survival, in some respects further evolved, of a still more primitive type, it is very possible that the Mauer jaw, from a much more remote geological period, may have belonged to a more primitive representative of this type, which would have been slowly modified in consequence of changes of environment and climate or rather by a slow process of selection acting upon mutations tending in one and the same direction.

Neandertal Man, whose origins are, in any case, extremely ancient, became extinct without leaving any posterity. This species is fossil in a double sense: because it dates from a geological period prior to the present day, and because we are aware of no descendants from the Upper Pleistocene onwards. In the Mousterian period it represented a belated type existing side by side with the direct ancestors of *Homo sapiens*; its relation to the latter was similar to that which exists at the present day between the races we call inferior and the superior races. Perhaps one might go so far as to say that it was a degenerate species.

In the Mousterian period this survival must have come to an end, for the Neandertal race seems to disappear abruptly. The Aurignacians and the Madgalenians, who succeeded it in Europe, differ from it in their much higher organization, and we do not think that, in Europe at any rate, true transitional forms have been found either in the Upper Palaeolithic,·or in the Neolithic, or in the present period. The position may perhaps be different in other countries, as the curious structure of the Palestine Mousterians might suggest. This question will be considered later.

Did there take place a simple substitution, or a migration, or even an extermination? We do not know. We have seen that it is impossible, among the modern ethnographic groups, to point to any single one which could be considered a descendant of the Neandertal people.

The foregoing opinion is not, however, shared by all anthropologists. Some of them, such as Stolyhwo,[70] Hrdlička,[71] Weidenreich,[72] and Weinert,[73] have attempted to demonstrate, by arguments of very unequal value, that Neandertal Man is not a particular species of the genus *Homo*, but simply a race which has been gradually transformed into modern types, the direct ancestors of living Men. They consider this transition to be exemplified in certain human skulls from the Upper Palaeolithic in France and Central Europe—such as those from Combe-Capelle, Brno (Brünn), Brüx and Predmost—because these skulls present certain Neandertaloid characteristics.

But such skulls obtained from prehistoric, historic, or modern burials in Europe have long been known. Numerous anthropologists have described and figured such specimens; there is today no important collection which does not contain at least one specimen of this kind. Now the most 'Neandertaloid' of these skulls possesses only a very small number of the characters of the Neandertal type, usually only a marked projection of the orbital ridges and a somewhat receding forehead. The face is always very different, the chin always well defined. In fact, all these 'Neandertaloid' skulls are only pseudo-Neandertal types, that is to say, are really *Homo sapiens*, remarkable

[70] Stolyhwo, K., '*Homo primigenius* appartient-il à une espèce distincte de *l'Homo sapiens?*' (*L'Anthropologie*, XIX, 1908); 'Les Prénéanderthaloïdes et les Postnéanderthaloïdes et leurs rapports avec la race de Néanderthal' (*Etnolog: Bull. of the Ljubljana Museum of Ethnography*, X, 1937).

[71] Hrdlička, H., 'The Neanderthal Phase of Man' (*J. of the R. Anthropological Institute*, LVII, 1927).

[72] Weidenreich, F., 'Der Schädel von Weimar-Ehringsdorf' (*Verh. Ges. Phys. Anthrop.*, II, 1927); 'The "Neanderthal Man" and the Ancestors of "Homo sapiens"' (*American Anthropologist*, XLV, 1943).

[73] Weinert, H., *Der Schädel des eiszeitlichen Menschen von Le Moustier* (Berlin, 1925); *Entstehung der Menschenrassen* (2nd Ed., Stuttgart, 1941).

on account of the fortuitous presence of certain morphological traits normally greatly developed in Neandertal Man.

The appearance or reappearance, in sporadic fashion, of these characters is generally looked upon as atavistic. But this is not to say that *Homo sapiens* is descended in direct line from *Homo neandertalensis*. It may be admitted that the characters in question are really primitive, that they formed part of a common inheritance from the remote ancestors of these two species. In *Homo neandertalensis* they have been preserved at a stage much nearer to their origin; in the more highly developed *Homo sapiens* they no longer reappear except by accident.

Finally, we cannot affirm that an infusion of Neandertaloid blood, by way of hybridization, never entered into other human groups belonging to the branch, or to one of the branches, of *Homo sapiens*. But this infusion could only have been casual and had no great influence, as no modern human type can be considered as a direct descendant, even with modifications, of the Neandertal type.

CHAPTER EIGHT

THE MEN OF THE REINDEER AGE

WE know that from the geological and palaeontological points of view it is difficult to make a sharp distinction between the Upper Pleistocene and the Mid Pleistocene (see p. 54). The Upper Pleistocene corresponds to the latter part of the last Ice Age, including the ultimate phase of the final retreat of the glaciers; for which reason, as we have stated, it is sometimes known as the 'Post-Glacial' period. This expression, accurate enough when applied to southern regions, is far less so in relation to other zones, for the retreat of the ice, which was slow and irregular, took place in stages, more tardily in the heart of the mountains than in the plains, in Scandinavian countries than in those of Central and Western Europe.

The duration of the Upper Pleistocene was relatively short. In fact, the formations laid down through the action of physical forces during this epoch are very thin in comparison with those of the preceding age; now it is human debris that predominates, and we know that this can accumulate with great rapidity. It is to the Upper Pleistocene that the most superficial alluvial deposits belong, either inside or outside the grottoes and caverns. The final relief of a topography to which modern, or Holocene, times have made only minor modifications also dates, in Europe, from this Period.

The fauna is still that of the last Ice Age, sometimes augmented by minor species which afford the palaeontologist a greater wealth of forms and greater variety between different strata. Since the retreat of the glaciers was accompanied by changes in the climate, the first areas to be uncovered were initially occupied by a fauna analogous to that of modern tundras; then, as the climate became drier, by a fauna resembling that of the steppes (see p. 55). After this, and little by little, these bare tracts of land were covered by an arborescent vegetation that harboured a 'forest fauna', which soon became, through the northward migration of the cold elements, the wild fauna of the present day.

By contrast, the distinction between the Upper and the Mid Pleistocene is relatively clear and simple, at least in France, when looked at from the anthropological standpoint.

THE REINDEER AGE

From the prehistoric archaeologist's point of view, the Upper Pleistocene corresponds to the *Upper Palaeolithic*, the artefacts of which are very different from those of the Lower Palaeolithic; it is also the period of the Reindeer or *Reindeer Age*. This latter term expresses an ethnographical rather than a palaeontological fact, for the bones of the Reindeer are already numerous in Mousterian deposits. It means, first, that this animal has now become very abundant; it denotes particularly the age when the Reindeer played a great part in the life of Man, for whom it provided food, clothing, and the raw materials for a large proportion of his industry.

Weapons and implements are more abundant, much more varied, and more perfect than in the Mousterian period. Thus archaeologists, with more data at hand, have long sought to establish definite divisions of the Reindeer Age, based upon the different methods of employing this material. We already know that they now distinguish three successive stages: the *Aurignacian*, the *Solutrean* and the *Magdalenian*, which was followed by the *Mesolithic*, a transition stage bordering on the *Neolithic* period, that is to say, on the *recent* times of geologists.

179 The village and Museum of Les Eyzies

In spite of the differences which serve as a basis for these divisions, the Reindeer Age presents a combination of characters which give it great unity, and which denote considerable progress beyond the Mousterian world. So there exists a striking contrast between Men of the old and the new Palaeolithic periods.

Discoveries of human skeletons now bring us in touch with really superior types. The majority have a more graceful body, a finer head, and a large straight forehead. In the caves in which they lived, they have left so many evidences of their manual skill, of the resources of their inventive genius, of their artistic and religious preoccupations, and of their powers of thought, that they truly merit the great name of *Homo sapiens*.

Each one of these types has, indeed, its own particular physiognomy, but the peculiarities are only of the degree exhibited in the various races of the present day, and in general appearance the types of the Reindeer Age do not differ more from modern Men than these differ among themselves. We have reached a point after which the physical evolution of Mankind may be considered as finished; the problem of human origins loses its zoological character and becomes purely anthropological and ethnographical.

Nothing could be more engrossing than the study of these Men of the

Reindeer Age, of the relics they have left us, and of the manners and customs which these relics reveal or lead us to surmise. Archaeological deposits due to them are distributed throughout most of Europe, as well as being present in Asia and Africa. But it is in France, notably in the south-west and the districts bordering on the Pyrenees, that they are most abundant and varied. The pleasant little town of Les Eyzies, on the banks of the Vézère in Dordogne (Fig. 134), is the centre of a picturesque district where Reindeer Age deposits, in caves or rock-shelters, are numbered by hundreds, a fact which has led to its being called 'the prehistoric capital of France'. A national museum organized by one of the most active of French prehistorians, D. Peyrony, has been established at Les Eyzies in a very old château sheltered by the overhanging crags of majestic limestone rocks (Fig. 179).

The study of the Upper Palaeolithic has furnished material for many works and memoirs of the greatest interest, but a summary of these cannot find a place in the present volume, written, as it is, chiefly from the anthropological point of view. The essential facts must, however, be mentioned.[1]

PRODUCTS OF INDUSTRY

The Men of the Reindeer Age lived by preference in caves or rock-shelters. They were mainly devoted to hunting and fishing. They had widespread commercial relations. Their dressed stones are neither so heavy nor so uniform as those of the preceding periods. Their weapons, intended to be hafted, are fine, graceful, sometimes beautifully worked with a most skilful technique (Figs. 180–182). Their tools are no less slender, very varied in form, and adapted to manifold purposes: knives, scrapers, piercers, gravers, saws, etc., new types of which were constantly being developed. Dressed flints are found by hundreds and thousands, mixed with kitchen debris, in their ancient settlements in caves and rock-shelters.

Thus the stone industry of the Reindeer Age is essentially an industry of long, narrow flakes, that is to say an *industry of blades*, retouched in every conceivable fashion, for the working of bone and wood.

Stone is no longer the only raw material used. Our industrious cave-dwellers knew how to work in varied fashion the ivory of Mammoth tusks, the antlers of the Reindeer, and the bones of all kinds of animals. From these they made daggers, the tips of javelins and arrows for the chase, harpoons for fishing, spear-throwers, and so on. They also made utensils for domestic use: spatulae, smoothing implements for preparing the skins of animals,

[1] The very considerable bibliography is chiefly in French. It is to be found, in part, in Reinach, S., *Antiquités nationales, I. Époque des cavernes* and Déchelette, *Manuel d'archéologie préhistorique*, I. Consult also Mortillet, G. and A. de, *Le Préhistorique* and *Musée préhistorique* and Cartailhac, É., *La France préhistorique*. Among more modern elementary works we may name Peyrony, D., *Éléments de Préhistoire* (1934); Goury, H., *Origine et évolution de l'Homme* (1948); Alimen, H., *Atlas de Préhistoire* (1950). In particular, the collections of *Matériaux* and *L'Anthropologie* should be consulted. See below some remarks concerning the art of the Reindeer Age.

needles pierced with an eye to sew their garments of fur and so forth.

From such archaeological materials, archaeologists are enabled to establish their divisions.[2]

SUBDIVISIONS

In many deposits, the lower layers of the Upper Palaeolithic, or *Aurignacian*, are difficult to distinguish from the Mousterian by their industry, in which there still persist ancient Palaeolithic forms, even amygdaloid flints. But new forms begin to appear. Elongated flakes become more frequent and are carefully retouched on their edges, which are often notched. There are gravers of a special form known as 'arched' (*busqué*), and thick massive scrapers known as 'keeled' scrapers. Bone is now made use of to a great extent. Many shafts are to be found ornamented with striae, or 'hunting tallies', as well as flattened darts, often with split base, and various kinds of rude pins (Fig. 180).

The *Solutrean*, which succeeds the Aurignacian in some localities, is marked by extremely able and careful work in stone. The characteristic types are narrow points known as 'willow leaves', larger points called 'laurel leaves', and tanged or shouldered points. These weapons are manufactured with much art, by means of skilled retouches, long and regular, which often cover both surfaces of the flints (Fig. 181). These are beautiful objects, precursors of the wonderful flints, lance-heads, arrow-heads, and daggers of the Scandinavian, Portuguese, and Egyptian Neolithic culture. The bone industry was further enriched by new forms of javelins with a pyramidal base and varied objects in ivory; the first needles with an eye appeared.

During the *Magdalenian* period, stone implements, far from attaining perfection, comprise countless flints generally small in size, and often hardly retouched at all, but varying greatly in form: flakes, scrapers, various gravers, piercers, saws, etc. Sometimes the same flint is adapted for different purposes; at one end it is a scraper, at the other a graver or piercer. The bone industry, on the other hand, is exceedingly diversified; javelins are numerous and varied, often decorated with designs; needles are abundant and also harpoons, which, to begin with, consist of simple notched bone sticks, and develop into barbed instruments, first with a single row, then with two rows of barbs (Fig. 182). Reference must also be made to the abundance of pierced staves of reindeer horn, known as *bâtons de commandement* or sceptres.

Each of these divisions in the Upper Palaeolithic has been subdivided in its turn into several levels: at least three for the Aurignacian, three for the Solutrean and up to six for the Magdalenian. This subdivision bears witness to the analytical capacities of the archaeologists, whom no typological subtlety escapes; but we must be careful not to accept the over-simplified view of the prehistorians who are inclined to see in this sequence, established in France by means of data collated from numerous beds, the steady evolution

[2] See in particular Breuil, H., 'Les subdivisions du Paléolithique supérieur et leur signification' (*Congrès intern. de Genève*, 1912; 2nd Ed., 1937).

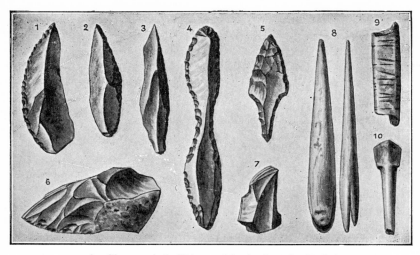

180 Characteristic Objects of the Aurignacian Period

1, 2, Flint points with arched and retouched back, type known as 'Châtelperron'; 3, flake of flint for cutting, formed by retouching, 'La Gravette' type; 4, notched flake retouched along whole profile; 5, shaped flints retouched with a tang or tongue; 6, keeled scraper; 7, graver of arched type (busqué); 8, bone point of a dart, split at base; 9 and 10, bone objects. (After H. Breuil)

181 Solutrean flints, carefully dressed in shapes of laurel leaves and willow leaves, shouldered points and double piercers. Half natural size. From Grotte du Placard in Charente. Palaeontological Gallery, French National Museum of Natural History

of Upper Palaeolithic industry. It was long ago demonstrated[3] that these
subdivisions cannot have the general significance which has often been
attributed to them. Today this is scarcely contested any longer. More effi-
ciently conducted investigations, extended to countries far from France,
have shown that the Aurignacian, to which the major deposits everywhere
correspond, is really the fundamental element of the Upper Palaeolithic,

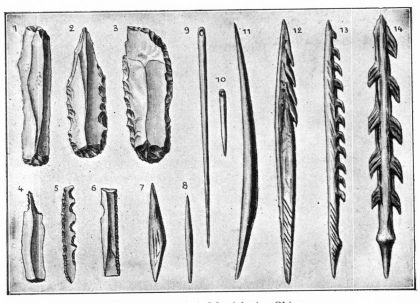

182 Characteristic Magdalenian Objects

1, Flint flake, ending in double scraper; 2, flake dressed as straight graver at upper end, and
as scraper at lower end; 3, scraper and graver of 'parrot-beak' type; 4, small flint combining
piercer and scraper; flake of which one end has been trimmed by fine retouching, while its
other edge bears a series of regular notches; 6, small flake trimmed for cutting; 7, javelin point
with bevelled base; 8, bone piercer; 9 and 10, bone needles with eyes; 11, bone javelin point,
bevelled and curved; 12, harpoon of reindeer antler, with barbs not prominent (primitive
type); 13, harpoon with only one row of barbs; 14, harpoon with double row of barbs.

extremely widely distributed (Europe, Asia, Africa). The other terms represent only local or regional modifications, varying in importance, of an essential common property, or else elements introduced from outside. The
Solutrean and Magdalenian periods are, therefore, only more or less localized
(and magnificent) episodes in the long history of the Reindeer Age. Hence the
Aurignacian is a single unit of considerable extent that merges with the
Upper Palaeolithic period as a whole; and its various successive or collateral
elements, though possessing distinctive features, are all linked by one general
and unique characteristic of the first importance—the practice and development of the plastic arts—not to mention the comparative racial unity. All

[3] *L'Anthropologie*, Vol. XVIII, 1907, p. 650.

this can be explained by somewhat extensive movements of populations.

The future of the science here depends principally on the establishment of this racial palaeography, which is certainly far more complicated than we can at present imagine.

THE FIRST ARTISTS

The men of the Reindeer Age had also a taste for personal adornment; they used the teeth of wild animals killed in the chase (Fig. 197, p. 274), shells, pierced stones, etc., from which they made trophies, necklaces, bracelets and amulets. Endowed with a sincere and deep feeling for nature, and great sensibility to beauty, they were true artists, *the first artists*, existing thousands of years before the Chaldeans, the Egyptians or the Aegeans.

It is in France, and by Frenchmen, that most of the wonderful evidences of this blossoming of the plastic arts have been discovered. Next to the names of Édouard Lartet and Vibraye, that of Piette will always remain associated with the history of Quaternary art. After the death of Piette, the famous discoveries or publications of Cartailhac, Capitan, Peyrony, Lalanne, Breuil, Bouyssonie, Saint-Périer, etc. have enriched prehistoric archaeology with a mass of relics of the greatest interest, still insufficiently known to the artistic world or to the enlightened public.[4]

183 Portrait of Édouard Piette

All these productions, varying greatly in value, from indecipherable scrawls to true works of art, show that the Men of the Reindeer Age must have had ample leisure, like all populations engaged almost entirely in hunting. During this leisure, they practised every kind of art work, bent on reproducing likenesses of the creatures living around them, either by sculpture, by engraving, or by painting.

[4] The most important works are: Lartet, É. and Christy, H., *Reliquiae aquitanicae*, 1865–1875. Girod, P. and Massénat, É., *Les stations de l'âge du Renne dans les vallées de la Vézère et de la Corrèze*, 1888–1900. Piette, É., *L'art pendant l'âge du Renne*, 1907. The series of large monographs published by the Institut de Paléontologie humaine, under the general title *Peintures et gravures murales des Cavernes paléolithiques*, by Cartailhac, É., Capitan, L., Breuil, H., Peyrony, D., and others. See also the works by Cabré, Pacheco and Obermaier on the art of the Spanish caves published by the *Comisión de Investigaciones palaeontologicas y prehistóricas* of Madrid. And the memoirs of H. Martin, D. Peyrony and R. de Saint-Périer in the *Archives de l'Institut de Paléontologie humaine*. S. Reinach has produced a very useful *Répertoire de l'art quaternaire*, with bibliography of publications that appeared up to 1913.

Among works of a more general character, attention must be drawn to: Luquet, G. H., *L'art et la religion des Hommes fossiles* (Paris, 1926). Saint-Périer, R., *L'art préhistorique* (Paris, 1932).

The ivory of mammoth tusks and soft stone served them as the raw material for sculpture; they knew also how to model in clay. They engraved on any kind of bone, on reindeer antlers, on rounded pebbles from the river

184 Reindeer carved in ivory, from Bruniquel, now in the British Museum
About half natural size. (After H. Breuil)

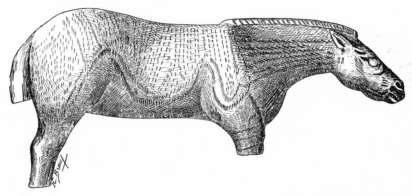

185 Statuette of a horse in ivory. Grotte de Lourdes. About four-thirds natural size
(After Piette. Drawing by H. Breuil)

186 Head of a horse, carved in reindeer antler, from the cave at Mas d'Azil in Ariège
Piette Collection, in the Musée de Saint-Germain

nearby. Often these objects may be likened to regular leaves of a sketchbook, whereon drawings of all kinds are grouped, mingled, or superimposed.

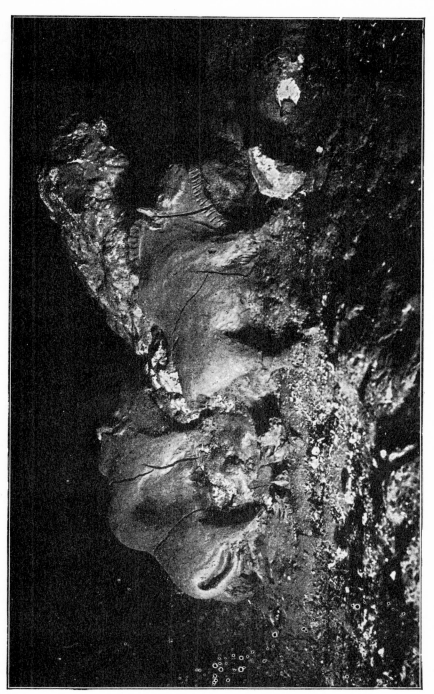

187 Clay bisons in the Tuc d'Audoubert Cave, Ariège. About one-ninth natural size. (Photographed by M. Max Bégouen)

But coexistent with this movable art, there was also a mural art. Our cave-dwellers sculptured, engraved and painted large figures on the walls of dim caverns. The saucers and polychrome ochres of these primitive painters

188 Heads of chamois and badger (?) engraved on a piece of reindeer antler from the Cave of Gourdan. About five-sixths natural size. Piette Collection in the Musée de Saint-Germain. (After Piette)

have been discovered, as well as the primitive lamps which gave them light.

A great many of these productions bear strong evidence of a real aesthetic sense, a masterly realism, skilled technique, and great strength of execution.

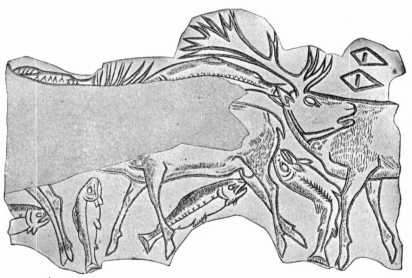

189 Red deer and salmon engraved round antler of a stag from the Lorthet Cave in the Hautes-Pyrénées. Piette Collection in the Musée de Saint-Germain. Reduced by about one-fourth and represented on the flat. (After Piette)

Notice above to the right two lozenges divided by a small vertical line in the centre, perhaps representing the signature of the artist

They are frequently masterpieces full of life and movement, representations of mammoths with long hair and bent tusks, rhinoceroses of massive form, horses of spirited bearing, bristly boars, crowds of ruminants of elegant build, bears with bulging heads, felines with supple body and so on. The frieze of horses carved life-size on the rocky wall of the Laussel Cave in the Dordogne, the bisons modelled in clay at Tuc d'Audoubert in Ariège,

190 Reindeer engraved on stone from the Limeuil Cave in the Dordogne. Two-thirds natural size. (Photograph kindly lent by MM. Bouyssonie and Capitan)

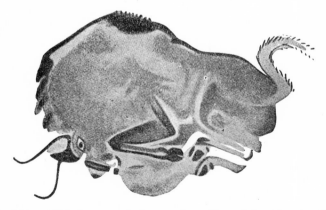

191 'Leaping' bison. Polychrome painting on the ceiling of the Altamira Cave in Spain. Length of animal 5 feet. (After Cartailhac and Breuil)

that of horses and bovines in the cave beside the Roc in Charente, the polychrome paintings in the Altamira Cave in Spain, and the wonderful frescoes in the Lascaux cave—the 'Sistine Chapel' of prehistory—are only a few extraordinarily striking evidences of the intellectual superiority and

192 Polychrome hind, with small black bison, from the Altamira Cave. Length of the hind 7 ft. 2 in. (After Cartailhac and Breuil)

193 Red and black deer painted on a rock at Calapata, near Cretas, in Lower Aragon, Spain. (After Breuil and Cabré Aguila)

masterly skill of these very ancient artists. We have here grouped together some masterpieces of different kinds; they will give an idea of the perfection of Palaeolithic art (Figs. 184–194).

It is above all an animal art. But its productions include purely decorative patterns made up of various combinations of straight and curved lines.

194 Horse and pseudo-bovine from the frieze sculptured on stone in the workshop by the Roc, Charente. Length of block 5 ft. 3 in. (After H. Martin)

It also attempted—but with much less success—to reproduce human forms. This is a point we shall examine later.

The miracle of Palaeolithic art is all the more extraordinary because it occurred amidst unpromising natural surroundings. In some respects the material existence of these cave-dwellers was very miserable: they knew nothing even of pottery. Brave in contact with cave bears and lions, they were, nevertheless, peaceful and gentle in character; they possessed a sense of mystery, for their decorated caves seem to have served as sanctuaries, where they must have devoted themselves to practising the arts of magic;[5]

[5] Following the lead of Salomon Reinach, many prehistorians believe that the art of the Reindeer Age was by no means disinterested; that it had especially a practical purpose related to their magical practices. We do not entirely share this view.

The truthfulness of the drawings, the purity of the lines, the grace of the attitudes, cannot be accounted for simply by the practices of magic. Poor designs, childish drawings, and simple compositions, such as those of present-day natives, would have sufficed for that. It is impossible that such figures, drawn with so great a feeling for form, and really extraordinary certainty and delicacy in the manner of engraving, were not accomplished by the artist except for love's sake; he could not have attained to such heights of perfection or to such mastery except by disinterested study. No one, having sufficiently practised the art of drawing and having devoted some time to the study of Palaeolithic masterpieces, could think otherwise. The hypothetical suggestion of the practices of magic may satisfy scholars, but we do not think that it would be wholly accepted by artists. We do not hesitate to confess that we believe in the theory of art for art's sake, without at the same time refusing to allow a certain influence due to the practice of magic. But, in point of fact, diagrammatic and stereotyped art, better suited to this purpose, is more recent than true Palaeolithic art, which, to begin with, is realistic only. In its real, and much earlier beginnings, art is probably only a special manifestation of the general spirit of imitation, already highly developed in the Apes.

they engaged in religious practices, for their sculptures testify to funeral rites and to a true worship of the dead. We may therefore be proud of the spiritual and moral qualities of these distant ancestors of ours. We shall see that in their physical characters, also, they were as closely related to modern Mankind.

HISTORICAL SURVEY

Discoveries of human bone-remains attributed to the Reindeer Age are numbered in hundreds. Unfortunately, most of them were accompanied by inexact observations leading to errors of attribution, or consist of evidence of no value for scientific study.[6] The list of accurately dated finds that furnished material really worthy of serious study is a great deal shorter.

To an English scientist falls the credit of having exhumed and placed in a museum the first human skeleton of the Reindeer Age. This skeleton, with bones coloured red, the famous *Red Lady of Paviland*, was excavated in the Paviland Cave in Wales by Buckland in 1823, and was placed in the Oxford Museum, where for long it remained forgotten. In the meantime, Professor Sollas[7] has told us that the 'Red Lady' is probably a man, whose skull-less skeleton dates from the Aurignacian period and exhibits the characters of the race known as Cro-Magnon, as de Quatrefages and Hamy thought.

The skull discovered in 1833 by Schmerling, in the cave at Engis in Belgium, which was examined by the best anthropologists of last century, was long attributed to Neolithic times. We now know through Fraipont that it is Aurignacian.

It may be that among the skeletons discovered in 1852, in the famous cave at Aurignac in the Haute-Garonne, there were human remains contemporary with the settlements of the Reindeer Age, as Édouard Lartet believed. But this we have now no means of ascertaining.

The famous settlement at Solutré, in the Saône-et-Loire, discovered in 1866, has yielded investigators a great number of human bone-remains. Unfortunately, in this case, we have to deal with burials dating from different periods, and it is not easy to separate Quaternary bone-remains from more recent skeletons. De Quatrefages and Hamy estimated at about fifteen the number of human skulls at Solutré which might have been contemporary with the Mammoth and Reindeer, but only six of these are fit for detailed examination.[8] Their morphology is not very homogeneous, and while they certainly show some characters of Cro-Magnon type, they differ so much as to lead us, at the present day, more than ever to regard their age with certain reservations. The Solutrean deposits required new and more methodical investigation.

This investigation was carried out from 1922 to 1924, on quite a large

[6]   A list of the deposits with complete bibliography is to be found in Quenstedt, W. and A., *Hominidae fossiles*, Part 74 of the invaluable *Fossilium Catalogus* (The Hague, 1936).

[7]   Sollas, W. J., 'Paviland Cave' (*J. of the Roy. Anthrop. Inst.*, XLIII, 1913).

[8]   For bibliography of former discoveries, see *Crania ethnica* by these two scientists.

scale, by C. Depéret, F. Arcelin and L. Mayet. The stratigraphy of the bed was clearly established and three adult skeletons accompanied by three skeletons of children were recovered from deliberate burials, dug in the Aurignacian stratum. They seem to have been contemporary with this stratum, although some doubt still exists on this point. Only a brief description has been published.[9]

The following discoveries are of greater importance.

CRO-MAGNON, LAUGERIE, DURUTHY

Cro-Magnon is a locality in the Commune of Tayac, near Eyzies in the Dordogne. In 1868, during the construction of the railway from Périgueux to Agen, workmen found under a sheltering rock the remains of five human skeletons, placed upon floors of occupation containing numerous bone-remains of animals, dressed flints, and great quantities of sea-shells. Informed in time, an experienced geologist, Louis Lartet, son of Édouard Lartet, went to Eyzies to continue the excavations and to devote himself to the scientific investigation of the bed.[10]

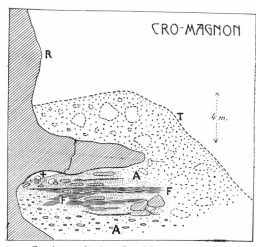

The human bones were grouped at the back of the shelter, in conditions suggestive of burial. Indeed, beside them there were collected numerous shells pierced with a suspension hole, and other objects prepared for making up ornaments. The skeletons,

195 Section of the Cro-Magnon Rock-shelter. (After L. Lartet) R, Cliffs of Cretaceous chalk forming shelter. T, former talus; A, Cave deposits; F, Floors of occupation of Reindeer Age; + Bone-remains of the old man.

studied first by Broca and Pruner-Bey, and later by de Quatrefages and Hamy, were considered by the latter anthropologists as prototypes of a new fossil race—the *race of Cro-Magnon*.[11]

No doubt could be cast on the antiquity of this bed, which was definitely established by L. Lartet, for even a casual inspection of the section reveals the fact that the deposit of human bone-remains was necessarily prior to the formation of the enormous mass of fallen débris, covering, and so to speak sealing up, the prehistoric shelter (Fig. 195). Nevertheless, its age was

[9] Arcelin, F. and Mayet, L., 'Solutré, les fouilles de 1907, 1922 and 1923' (*Revue anthropologique*, XXXIV, 1924).
[10] Lartet, L., 'Une sépulture des troglodytes du Périgord' (*Bull. de la Soc. d'Anthrop. de Paris*, III, 1868; *Annales des Sciences naturelles*, 5th Series, Vol. X; *Matériaux*, 1869).
[11] *Crania ethnica*, 1882, pp. 45–82.

hotly disputed by G. de Mortillet, who all along refused to believe that fossil Men could have practised the veneration of the dead. Almost all the prehistorians rallied to his opinion, in spite of the protestations of a few scientists of the first rank, such as de Quatrefages and Hamy, and in spite also of a whole series of other discoveries testifying in the same sense.

Thus in 1872, an archaeologist from Brive, named Massénat, carrying out excavations at Laugerie-Basse, on the farther bank of the Vézère opposite Cro-Magnon, discovered in the depths of a great archaeological deposit of

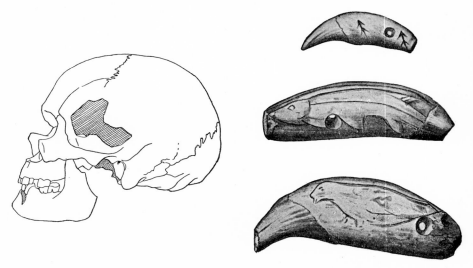

196 (left) Profile of skull from Laugerie-Basse. One-quarter natural size. (After Hamy)

197 (right) Bear's teeth decorated with engravings (arrowheads, a fish and a seal) and pierced by a hole for suspension. From the Duruthy Cave near Sordes (Landes). (After Louis Lartet)

the Reindeer Age a human skeleton, accompanied by sea-shells. Cartailhac, summoned by Massénat, agreed that the man had been crushed by the falling of the rock under which he lay,[12] a conclusion that cannot be accepted without reservations. Since no question of burial arose, the Palaeolithic age of the skeleton was not questioned. The bone-remains, which were in poor preservation, were examined by Hamy, who attributed them to the Cro-Magnon race (Fig. 196).

Some months afterwards, Louis Lartet and Chaplain-Duparc, exploring the Duruthy rock-shelter at Sorde in the Landes, found at the bottom of the deposit, in Palaeolithic surroundings, a human skeleton, the elements of which were scattered and crushed, and were accompanied by ornaments.[13]

On this occasion no shells were present, but about forty canine teeth of

[12] Massénat, É., Lalande, P. and Cartailhac, É., 'Un squelette humain de l'âge du Renne à Laugerie-Basse' (*Matériaux*, VII, 1872). Hamy, E. T., 'Description d'un squelette humain fossile de Laugerie-Basse' (*Bull. de la Soc. d'Anthrop. de Paris*, 1874).

[13] Lartet, L., and Chaplain-Duparc, 'Une sépulture des anciens troglodytes des Pyrénées' (*Matériaux*, IX, 1874).

bears and three canines of lions were found, almost all pierced with a hole for suspension, ornamented with engravings (Fig. 197), and 'divided into two groups lying at unequal distances from the skull, as if one had formed a necklace and the other a girdle'. In spite of their poor state of preservation, Hamy was able to prove the resemblance of the human bones to those from Cro-Magnon.

THE GRIMALDI CAVES

From the same year, 1872, date the first discoveries of fossil Men in the caves which are variously known as the Mentone, Baoussé Roussé, or Grimaldi Caves.[14]

These caves were nine in number, but one has been completely destroyed.

198 The Red Rocks, or *Baoussé Roussé*, at Grimaldi, near Mentone. General view of the Caves.

Except the *Prince's Cave*, they are relatively shallow, and lie wide open towards the blue sea, in the midst of a charming landscape (Fig. 198). So they have been frequently visited at all times, and, before 1872, numbers

[14] The *Baoussé Roussé*, or *Red Rocks*, are indeed in the neighbourhood of Mentone, but they lie in Italy, in the territory of the Commune of Grimaldi, so that the most accurate name for the natural excavations into which the rocks have been hollowed is the *Grimaldi Caves*.

of archaeologists carried out there excavations of a superficial kind. At this period, É. Rivière, living at Mentone, undertook more thorough investigations. His observations and results were rendered easier by the work executed in the construction of the road from Marseilles to Genoa, which, skirting the foot of the cliffs, cut into the talus of debris and pierced the Red Rocks by a tunnel.

On March 26, 1872, Rivière discovered a human skeleton in the cave known as the *Cavillon Cave*, below a stalagmite floor. This is the famous 'Mentone Man' (Fig. 199). In the following year, three new skeletons were dug up in the cave known as the Cave of *Baousso da Torre*. In 1874 and 1875, Rivière extracted two skeletons of children from Cave No. 1, since called on this account the *Grotte des Enfants* (Fig. 200).

All these human spoils were found in conditions resembling those already observed in the Dordogne. Here as there, the skeletons were accompanied by a whole series of objects, particularly by a quantity of shells which had been used for purposes of decoration or of dress. It is to Rivière's credit that he understood and affirmed that these were Palaeolithic burials. His opinion was contested by the majority of prehistorians, headed by Gabriel de Mortillet. Later discoveries, which we shall presently discuss, have proved that Rivière was not mistaken.[15]

199 The 'Mentone Man', found by É. Rivière. Anthropological Gallery of the Musée de l'Homme, Paris.

CHANCELADE

In 1888 two archaeologists from Périgueux, Féaux and Hardy, excavated a rock shelter at Raymonden, a commune in Chancelade, near Périgueux, and found a human skeleton under the lower Magdalenian floors of occupation, that is to say, in the upper stages of the Reindeer Age. The doubled-up, unnatural posture of the skeleton pointed to deliberate burial. As at Mentone, the corpse must have been sprinkled with red ochre. The skeleton, exhumed with great care, was examined by Dr. Testut,[16] who established it as the type specimen of a new race called the *Chancelade race*. It is now in the Museum at Périgueux.

[15] Rivière, É., *De l'Antiquité de l'Homme dans les Alpes-Maritimes* (Paris, 1887).

[16] Testut, L., 'Recherches anthropologiques sur le squelette quaternaire de Chancelade (*Bull. de la Soc. d'Anthrop. de Lyon*, VIII, 1889).

MORAVIA: BRNO, PREDMOST

In the very heart of Central Europe, Moravia has furnished a whole series of important Palaeolithic beds. The most interesting of them are ancient settlements in the open air, now buried beneath layers of mud or loess. The old inhabitants of this region were 'mammoth hunters', as is proved by the enormous quantities of bone-remains belonging to this archaic Proboscidian which the excavations have brought to light. Sites of this kind are numerous. The most important are those at Brno (or Brünn), the capital of Moravia; at Predmost, near Prerav, on the railway line from Vienna; and at Vestonice, in Southern Moravia.

The Quaternary silts on which the town of Brno is situated have yielded several human skeletons. One of them, found in 1891, had been richly decked with Tusk Shell (*Dentalium*) pendants, while some of the bones still preserved traces of deep red coloration.[17] It was accompanied by a tiny human figure of ivory that was broken in pieces. The skull, reduced to the brain-box, is dolichocephalic with marked superciliary ridges; certain anthropologists refer it to the Cro-Magnon type; others regard it as distinct from that type, as we shall see later.

In 1927 another, more complete, skeleton, also coloured with ochre, was obtained by Absolon from an Aurignacian level. This skeleton has been described by Matiegka.[18]

The Predmost bed possesses an important Palaeolithic settlement enclosed in a covering of gravels and clays surrounding the 'Hradisko' rock. Excavations carried out from time to time since 1878 by Wankel, Maska, and Kriz have revealed a cold-climate Pleistocene fauna, so rich that the Mammoth is represented by remains of more than a thousand individuals. In addition, this settlement had yielded a collection of flint implements comprising more than 30,000 specimens, a whole series of products of an industry in ivory, bone and reindeer horn, and works of art, in particular a curious statuette of ivory representing a mammoth.

Some human remains were also found at different times.[19] In 1894 Maska discovered a large burial containing forty complete skeletons, as well as the remains of six other individuals.[20] The bodies, which were in a squatting position and pressed close together, were protected by a sort of stone rampart. The skeleton of a child bore a necklace formed of forty small oval beads of ivory. This burial is prior to the main archaeological layer, which belonged to the Aurignacian period. This osteological material was studied by Dr. Matiegka, who described its characteristics in two sober, detailed

---

[17] Makowsky, A., *Der Mensch der Diluvialzeit Mährens* (Brünn, 1899).

[18] Matiegka, J., 'The Skull of the Fossil Man Brno III and the Cast of its Interior' (*Anthropologie*, Prague, VII, 1929).

[19] Maska, K., *Der diluviale Mensch in Mähren* (1886). Kriz, M., *Beiträge zur Kenntnis der Quartärzeit in Mähren* (1903).

[20] *L'Anthropologie*, XII, 1901, p. 147. This inestimable series, preserved in Brno Museum was completely destroyed during the fighting in 1945.

and well illustrated memoirs.[21] We shall make use of them shortly when we take up, in our turn, the long discussion of which these Predmost Men have been the object; their affinities are, above all, with the great Cro-Magnon race.

Vestonice (or Dolni Vestonice) is another 'Mammoth cemetery', investigation of which has been carried on since 1924 by Mr. Absolon, Curator of Brno Museum. Although so far poor in human bone-remains, this vast Aurignacian settlement has proved rich in objects of art, figurines and statuettes, amongst which is a bone or ivory 'Venus' that recalls the statuettes of the French Aurignacian period.

LES HOTEAUX

The chronological order of the discoveries brings us back to France. In the Ain, at the mill of Les Hoteaux, near the village of Rossillon, there is a cave containing floors of occupation dating from the Reindeer Age. In 1894, Tournier and Guillon[22] brought to light a burial in the most ancient of these settlements. The bones of the skeleton were covered with red ochre. The articles accompanying the burial consisted of a red deer's tooth, pierced with a hole for suspension, dressed flints, and a *bâton de commandement* of Magdalenian age. The skeleton is that of a youth of sixteen to eighteen years of age. The publication of these facts revived the discussions between the partisans and opponents of the theory of Palaeolithic burials. Agreement could only be reached after further and conclusive discoveries; and such were soon forthcoming.

THE GRIMALDI CAVES: FURTHER EXPLORATIONS

The exploration of the Grimaldi and Mentone caves did not cease with the labours of Rivière. Different archaeologists undertook investigations, particularly in the fifth cave, known as *Barma Grande*. In 1884, one of them, Julien, found there a human skeleton of which the skull is now in Mentone Museum. This Barma Grande Cave seems to have been the richest and most interesting of the Grimaldi group. Its proprietor, Abbo, the owner of the quarry, partially destroyed it by exploiting it as a quarry for building stone. His work of excavation, unfortunately lacking in any scientific method, produced several human skeletons, which were examined by Dr. Verneau.[23]

These finds of Abbo in the Barma Grande afforded material for fresh discussion, which would probably have continued to this day but for an intervention as generous as it was enlightened.

The late Prince Albert I of Monaco, whose noble spirit of scientific

[21] Matiegka, J., 'L'Homme fossile de Predmosti, en Moravie' (In Czech, but with a long résumé in French. *Czech Acad. of Arts and Sciences*, 2nd Cl., *Anthropologica*, Prague, 1934 and 1938).

[22] Tournier, Abbé, and Guillon, C., *Les hommes préhistoriques dans l'Ain* (Bourg, 1895).

[23] Verneau, R., 'Nouvelle découverte de squelettes préhistoriques aux Baoussé Roussé, près de Menton' (*L'Anthropologie*, III, 1892).

enquiry was so many-sided, had already taken a great interest in the Grimaldi caves. From 1883 onwards he had himself worked with great method in the Barma Grande Cave. In 1895, anxious at least to advance, if not to decide, the solution of the important problems arising out of the Baoussé Roussé investigations, the Prince gave orders for the carrying out of a systematic exploration. The excavations, conducted with rare skill and patience by M. the Canon de Villeneuve assisted by M. Lorenzi, were first of all directed to the large cave known as the Prince's Cave, then almost untouched. They produced interesting results from the geological and palaeontological points of view, thanks to which we now possess accurate information regarding the succession of events in Quaternary times in this part of the Côte d'Azur. Innumerable fossil bones of animals were recovered from about 4,000 cubic yards of the deposits of this cave; but not a single human relic was met with. Herein lay disappointment; for everyone had counted on the Prince's Cave to decide definitely the ages of the various skeletons of fossil Men discovered in the neighbouring caves, concerning which there had been so much dispute.

The Prince then decided to transfer his enterprise to other points. The Grotte des Enfants (Fig. 200) had only been imperfectly excavated. Rivière's work had stopped at a depth of 9 feet, whilst below this level cave-deposits, nearly 26 feet deep, still remained untouched. Here the investigations met with the greatest success from the anthropological point of view, for in the cave four human skeletons were discovered at three different levels. Since, at the same time, many bone-remains of animals were collected and the stratigraphy of the cave could be accurately determined, the geological age of the skeletons was readily and indisputably established. The Prince having confided to one of the present writers the task of collaborating in this work, his geological and palaeontological observations were able to furnish a firm chronological basis for his friends, MM. Cartailhac and Verneau, to whom was assigned the archaeological and anthropological study of the layers.[24]

The main result of these observations was that all the human skeletons were really Pleistocene and dated from the earliest part of the Reindeer Age. Contrary to what was previously asserted, the Reindeer formed part of the Pleistocene fauna of the Côte d'Azur; its bones were discovered in association with those of its usual companions of the cold-climate fauna (notably the Glutton and the Arctic Fox), superimposed, here as elsewhere, upon the more ancient warm-climate fauna.

The new skeletons exhumed from the Grotte des Enfants had been the objects of true burial, the articles deposited with them resembling those accompanying the skeletons previously discovered—perforated shells, objects of decoration, bones coloured red, and so on. Dr. Verneau recognized the fact that the two skeletons from the lowest level represented a special

[24] *Les Grottes de Grimaldi* (Baoussé Roussé): *Historique et description*, by L. de Villeneuve. *Géologie et Paléontologie*, by M. Boule. *Anthropologie*, by R. Verneau. *Archeologie*, by É. Cartailhac (2 Vols., Monaco, 1906-19).

race, which he called the *Grimaldi Race*. The skeletons from the upper layers, like those discovered by Rivière, Julien, and Abbo, entirely agree with the Cro-Magnon type. These precious relics, along with all the results of the

200 View of the Grotte des Enfants in the Baoussé Roussé

Prince of Monaco's excavations, have been collected and are now exhibited to the public in the Anthropological Museum of Monaco.

More Recent Discoveries

In 1909, Hauser, the dealer in antiques, found a skeleton ornamented with

sea-shells in a bed at Combe-Capelle, near Mont Ferrand, in the Dordogne, at the bottom of Aurignacian layers. This skeleton was acquired by the Berlin Museum for which Hauser acted in the capacity of agent. An attempt has been made to establish it as the type specimen of a particular species under the name *Homo aurignacensis*, and the German anthropologist Klaatsch propounded the most extravagant hypothesis with regard to it.[25] As a matter

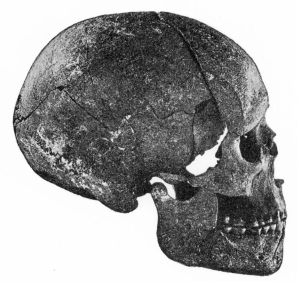

201 Skull from Combe-Capelle. (After Klaatsch)

of fact, as we shall see later, it also is nothing more than a variety of the Cro-Magnon Race (Fig. 201).

In 1912, Capitan and Peyrony exhumed at Cap-Blanc, near Laussel (Dordogne), the skeleton of a man of about twenty-five lying beneath a Magdalenian stratum.[26] This skeleton was acquired in 1927 by the Field Museum of Chicago. It has been described by von Bonin.[27]

In 1914, the German physiologist Verworn published an account of the discovery of a double burial, the skeletons of a man and a woman, in a settlement of the Reindeer Age at Obercassel, near Bonn. These skeletons, accompanied by some bones engraved in the Magdalenian manner, had been coloured red. While showing characteristics of both the Cro-Magnon and Chancelade races, they also exhibit certain Neandertaloid features.[28]

[25] Klaatsch, H. and Hauser, O., 'Homo Aurignacencis Hauseri' (*Praehistorische Zeitschrift*, I, 1910). Klaatsch, H., 'Die Aurignac-Rasse und ihre Stellung im Stammbaum der Menscheit' (*Zeitschrift für Ethnologie*, 1910).

[26] Peyrony, D., *Éléments de Préhistoire* (Ussel, 1914) p. 87.

[27] Bonin, G. von, 'The Magdalenian Skeleton from Cap-Blanc in the Field Museum of Natural History' (*University of Illinois Bulletin*, XXXII, No. 34, 1935).

[28] Verworn, M., Bonnet, R. and Steinmann, G., *Der diluviale Menschenfund von Obercassel bei Bonn* (Wiesbaden, 1919).

The cave in the Valley of the Roc (Charente), from which H. Martin disengaged a fine sculptured frieze belonging to the Solutrean era (Fig. 194), contained a burial that was brought to light in 1923 and whose three skeletons, probably dating from the Magdalenian period, displayed certain Mongoloid characters which gave them an affinity with Chancelade Man.[29]

We may mention here certain finds made in England from 1924 to 1928. First there is the famous 'London skull'. We have said that this specimen, very incomplete and considered by some to be of Chellean date, seems very likely to be Aurignacian (see p. 153). Then there are various human remains extracted from Gough's Cavern, near Cheddar Gorge, in the Mendip Hills, in Somerset, and described by Parry; five skulls from Aveline's Hole in the same region; and some new specimens from Kent's Cavern, near Torquay, Devon. The age of most of these discoveries is poorly established. Keith considered the majority as Mesolithic, but without adequate grounds.[30] The situation is the same with regard to skulls and bone-remains taken from Kilgreany Cave, County Waterford, Ireland.

In 1931, G. Riek obtained some human remains, including two skull-caps, from a Palaeolithic level of the Vogelherd Cave, near Stetten-on-the-Lon, in Wurtemberg, a cavern also noteworthy for the curious relief sculptures of animals found there. One of these skull-caps is perhaps post-Palaeolithic, but the other is certainly Aurignacian. They have been described by Gieseler.[31]

A further discovery takes us back to France. In 1933, R. Blanchard recovered from a rock-shelter at Saint-Germain-la-Rivière, near Fronsac (Gironde), a human skeleton which he presented to the State. The body of this Magdalenian, in a doubled up position and tinged with ochre, was protected by a heap of stone slabs. No anatomical description has yet been published.[32]

Finally, in 1937, C. Maviglia announced the discovery in the cave at San Teodoro, Sicily, of a burial with ochre containing a well preserved skeleton dating from a late phase of the Upper Palaeolithic. From 1938 to 1942 four other skeletons or fragments of skeletons were exhumed from the same cave. The whole of this material has been described by Graziosi.[33] Dolichocephalic or slightly mesocephalic, the skulls are more slender in shape than those of Cro-Magnon Men properly so-called, with a tendency towards the classical Mediterranean type.

[29] Martin, H., 'La frise sculptée et l'atelier solutréens du Roc' (*Archives de l'Institut de Paléontologie humaine*, Memoir 5, Paris, 1928); 'Caractères des squelettes humains quaternaires de la vallée du Roc (Charente); race de Chancelade' (*Bull. et Mém. de la Soc. d'Anthrop. de Paris*, 1927).

[30] Keith, A., *New Discoveries relating to the Antiquity of Man* (London, 1931, Chap. XXVII).

[31] Gieseler, W., 'Bericht über die jungpaläolithischen Skeletreste von Stetten ob Lontal bei Ulm' (*Verh. Ges. phys. Anthrop.*, VIII, 1937).

[32] Blanchard, R., *Découverte d'un squelette humain a Saint-Germain-la-Rivière* (*Gironde*) (Bordeaux, 1935).

[33] Graziosi, P., 'Gli uomini paleolitici della grotta di S. Teodoro, Messina. Antropologia' (*Rivista di Scienze preistoriche*, Vol. II, 1948).

Such are the principal data we possess for the study of the fossil Men of the Upper Pleistocene. A few other discoveries might be added, but either they consist of bone fragments barely sufficient to provide any accurate information, or else some doubt exists as to the conditions of their deposition. We may mention those at Bruniquel (Tarn-et-Garonne), La Madeleine (Dordogne), Gourdan (Haute-Garonne), Le Placard, near Vilhonneur (Charente), Lacave (Lot), Libos (Lot-et-Garonne), Freudenthal and Kesslerloch, near Schaffhausen in Switzerland, in the Prince John Cave, near Lautsch in Moravia, at Berghausen in the Grand-Duchy of Baden, at Hohlefels, near Happburg in Wurtemberg, and at Oundory and Chvalynsk, on the Middle Volga in the U.S.S.R.

To these osteological records we must now add evidences contributed by works of art depicting human beings, which we shall study separately.

With regard to the skeletons, which we shall consider first of all, the opinions of anthropologists are somewhat at variance. In all these Men of the Reindeer Age, some anthropologists distinguish varieties of only one race of *Homo sapiens*. Others are inclined to distinguish as many special types as there are specimens. We think that the truth lies between these two views. All this osteological material may, in short, be relegated to three types or races, closely akin to each other from the zoological point of view. We shall study them in succession and in their chronological order: the Grimaldi Negroids, belonging to the earliest part of the Reindeer Age; the Cro-Magnon Race and its varieties, belonging to the Aurignacian period; and the Chancelade type, belonging to the Magdalenian period.

THE GRIMALDI RACE

Its Geological Age

As its name indicates, this race was established by Professor Verneau upon evidences obtained from one of the Grimaldi caves, the 'Grotte des Enfants'. The human skeletons, found during this excavation by M. de Villeneuve, lay at three different levels. The two upper skeletons, like the skeletons from the other caves and like the famous 'Mentone Man', belong to the Cro-Magnon race, which we shall presently study. The two skeletons of the Grimaldi race lay at a lower level. Discovered on June 3, 1901, they were carefully exhumed and conveyed to the Monaco Museum.

It is important to study exactly the conditions of their embedding. A section of the cave-deposits of the 'Grotte des Enfants' is shown in Fig. 202. This cave deposit consists of a whole series of layers, superimposed to a depth of 30 feet, and chiefly composed of materials brought thither by human beings, and of cinders mixed with rock fragments accruing from the disintegration of the rocky walls; the floors of occupation distinguished by the excavators are merely zones showing more charring than the neighbouring zones. The whole of these cave deposits are Pleistocene, for bone-remains of the Reindeer are found even in the uppermost layers. This first

conclusion, determined by a study of the fauna, is one of the most important
from the point of view of a solution of the much discussed problem of the
age of the human skeletons found in all the Grimaldi caves.

The deepest layers, resting on the rocky floor of the cave and containing
Merck's Rhinoceros, must, in our opinion, be considered as forming a
transition from the Lower Pleistocene to the Mid Pleistocene.[34] The skeletons of Negroids, situated at a depth of 28 feet on a floor of occupation directly

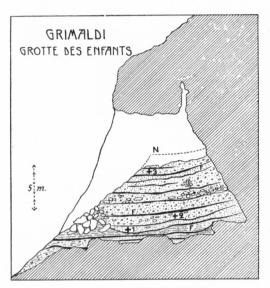

202 Section of the Grotte des Enfants

N, original level of the soil; F, layers of occupation; + 1, spot at which the Negroids lay
+ 2, + 3, spots at which the skeletons of Cro-Magnon types lay

above these deposits, must then belong to the Mousterian period, and this
is the conclusion at which we first arrived. Now, we have here to deal with
a human type which is quite distinct from that of Neandertal and exhibits
many characters common to certain African races of *Homo sapiens*, and this
co-existence in Western Europe, at one and the same geological period, of
two human forms so widely different would seem to be a fact of very great
importance.

But here we must make some reservations. M. de Villeneuve's observations, contained in his diary of the excavations, show that the Negroids
lay in a pit 2 ft. 6 ins. in depth. They were, therefore, contemporary, not
with the layer of occupation at the level of which they were encountered,

[34] Renewed excavations by Italian scientists in 1928, then in 1938 and the following years,
confirmed the existence of a Mousterian level with warm fauna in the lowest deposits in
several of the caves. But unfortunately no new skeleton was discovered. See Graziosi, P.,
'Gli Scavi dell'Istituto italiano di Paleontologia umana ai Balzi Rossi' (*Riv. Ingauna e
Intemelia*, Bordighera, Vol. V, 1939).

and which has been assigned to the Mid Pleistocene, but rather with a higher layer of occupation which marked the uppermost limit of the pit, and the products of which are already definitely Aurignacian in character. The Negroids are, therefore, Aurignacian, just like the Cro-Magnon Men. In addition to the change between the products of the Mousterian and the Aurignacian industries, now recognized by the best informed archaeologists, there would seem also to have been a corresponding, and no less important, anthropological change, and this conclusion appears to be best fitted to meet the present case.

It is none the less a fact that the Negroid skeletons date from the commencement of the Reindeer Age, a period bordering on the Mousterian, if not actually merging with it. This fact must not be lost sight of.

THE SKELETONS

We have just seen that the Negroid skeletons have been objects of burial. The first is that of an old woman, the second that of a young man of fifteen to seventeen years of age. They lay side by side, their bodies drawn up, their lower limbs much bent (Fig. 203), in the manner of Peruvian mummies. The skull of the young man was protected by a sort of cist, formed of undressed blocks of stone. There were also found the remains of a headdress and bracelets of shell work made from dog-whelk (*Nassa*) shells.

According to Professor Verneau,[35] whose important work we shall here summarize, 'these two ancient human beings differ appreciably from those who succeeded them (in the same cave, that is to say those of the Cro-Magnon type), and they exhibit the most striking points of resemblance to each other.' These two subjects, instead of attaining the great height of the other cave-dwellers of the Baoussé Roussé, scarcely exceed the average height of the French of our own day, 5 ft. 1.4 ins. in the case of the youth, 5 ft. 3 ins. in the case of the old woman.

When we compare the dimensions of the bones of their limbs, we see that the leg was very long in proportion to the thigh, the forearm very long in proportion to the whole arm; and that the lower limb was exceedingly long relative to the upper limb. Now these proportions reproduce, but in greatly exaggerated degree, the characters presented by the modern Negro. Here we have one of the chief reasons for regarding these fossils as Negroid, if not actually Negro.

THE SKULLS

The Negroid affinities are likewise indicated by the characters of the skull. These are large; the crania are very elongated, hyperdolichocephalic (indices 68 and 69), and, seen from above, they present a regular elliptically-shaped contour, with flattened parietal bosses (Fig. 204). The skulls are also very

---

[35] Verneau, R., *loc. cit.*, *Les Grottes de Grimaldi*, Vol. 1, Part 1, '*Anthropologie*'.

high, so that their capacity is at least equal to that of the average Parisian of our day: 1,580 cubic centimetres in the case of the young man, 1,375 cubic

203 The two skeletons of Negroids discovered by M. de Villeneuve in the Grotte des Enfants. Musée d'Anthropologie, Monaco. (After Verneau)

centimetres in the case of the old woman. The mastoid apophyses are small. The face is broad but not high, whilst the skull is excessively elongated from the front backwards; so that the head might be called unbalanced or dysharmonic.[36]

The forehead is well developed and straight; the orbital ridges project

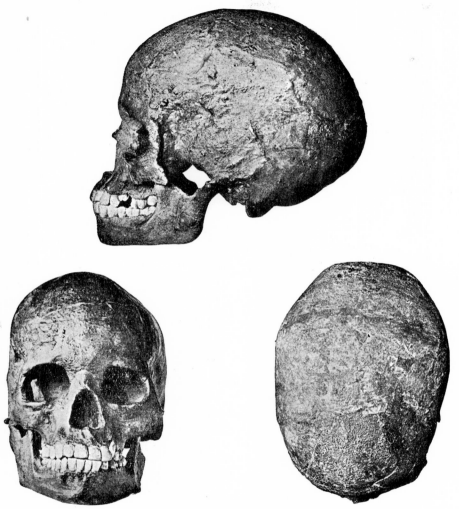

204 Skull of the young Negroid from Grimaldi, seen in profile, in full face and from above. One-third natural size. (After Verneau)

only slightly. The orbits are large, deep and subrectangular; their lower border is everted towards the front.

The nose, depressed at the root, is very broad (platyrrhinian). The floor of the nasal fossae is joined to the anterior surface of the maxillary by a

[36] In order to have *harmony*, vertical lengthening of the face should accompany the lengthening of the skull.

groove on each side of the nasal spine, as in Negroes, instead of being bordered by a sharp edge as in the white races. The canine fossae are deep.

The upper maxillary projects forwards in very marked fashion. This prognathism especially affects the subnasal or alveolar region. The palatal arch, though only slightly developed in breadth, is very deep (Fig. 205).

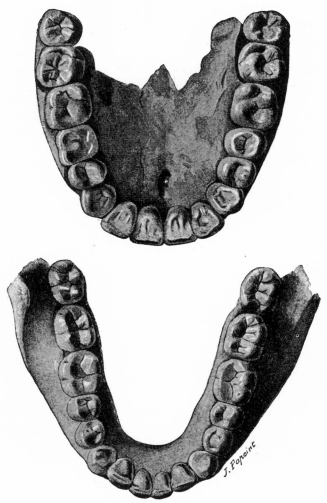

205 and 206 Upper and lower jaws of the young Negroid from Grimaldi. Natural size. (After Albert Gaudry)

The jaw is strong, its body very thick; the ascending branches are broad and low. The chin is not greatly developed; a strongly marked alveolar prognathism, correlated with the upper prognathism, gives it a pronouncedly receding appearance (Fig. 206).

The majority of these characters of the skull and face are, if not Negritic, at least Negroid. Some of them may be regarded as indicating inferiority from the morphological point of view.

DENTITION

The dentition of the young individual strikes one at first sight by its unusual size. Its greatest resemblances are with the dentition of the Australian aborigines, which has retained many primitive characteristics. The dental arches are less widely divergent than in the higher races. The alveolar borders are more elongated; and the development of the teeth and of their cusps is in proportion to this prolongation. So we find that the morphology of the molars retains several simian characters like those found in the fossil types we have already examined, as is the case in the modern primitive races with large dentitions. All the upper true molars have four well-developed cusps, even the hindermost, which in civilized races has only three (Fig. 207). All the lower molars have five quite distinct cusps, even the second and third, which, in the white races, usually have only four (Fig. 208).

Albert Gaudry,[37] when examining this dentition, was struck by the narrowing of the fore part of lower jaw at the level of the premolars and canines (Fig. 206). In this he sees an indication of inferiority in agreement with the marked prognathism of the lower jaw, the consequence of which was to leave less room for the development of the tongue and for its free forward movement.

THE LIMB BONES

We have seen that the proportions of the limbs and of their several segments are Negroid proportions. Verneau recognized that 'in the vertical direction of the haunch bones, in the curve of the iliac crest, in the reduced dimensions of the great sciatic notch, the pelvis of the old woman differs from the pelvis of the modern European female, and resembles, on the contrary, that of a Negress.'

The shaft of the femur is rather strongly bent, and the tibiae exhibit a certain degree of retroversion of the upper head. These characters, which we have already studied in Neandertal Man, are here, however, much less marked.

AFFINITIES AND SURVIVALS

To sum up, in the most ancient skeletons from the Grotte des Enfants we have a human type which is readily comparable to modern types and especially to the Negritic or Negroid types. It would be interesting to go further than Verneau, with a prudence that we can readily appreciate, ventured, and to endeavour to define even more closely his comparisons with

[37] Gaudry, A., 'Contribution à l'histoire des Hommes fossiles' (L'Anthropologie, XIV, 1903).

present-day types. For our part, we have been greatly struck by the resemblances these Grimaldi Negroids bear to the group of South African tribes,

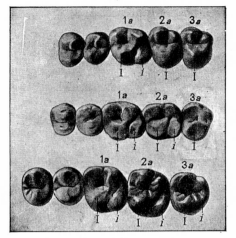

Frenchman

Australian

Negroid

207 Comparison of the upper left molars of the young Negroid, of an Australian and of a Frenchman. Natural size. (After A. Gaudry)

1*a*, 2*a*, 3*a*, first, second and third true molars; I, inner cusp of the first lobe; *i*, inner cusp of the second lobe, present in all the molars of the fossil.

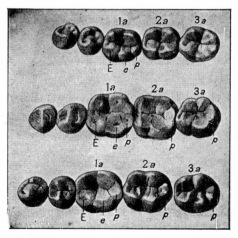

Frenchman

Australian

Negroid

208 Comparison of the lower left molars of the young Negroid, of an Australian and of a Frenchman. Natural size. (After A. Gaudry)

1*a*, 2*a*, 3*a*, first, second and third true molars; E, external cusp of first lobe; *e*, external cusp of second lobe; *p*, posterior cusp present in all the true molars of the Australian and of the fossil Man, and particularly well developed in the latter.

the Bushmen and the Hottentots. Comparisons which we have been able to make with the material at our disposal, in particular with the skeleton of the Hottentot Venus, have led us to note, for instance, the same dolichocephalic character, the same prognathism, the same flattening of the nose, the same development of the breadth of the face, the same form of jaw, and the same great size of teeth. The only differences are to be found in the stature and perhaps in the height of the skull. Professor Sollas of Oxford also made similar observations.[38]

This comparison between two groups of human beings, so widely separated at the present day both in time and in space, seems to be confirmed by the discovery of the fossil Man of Asselar—which has undeniable affinities on the one hand with the fossil Negroids of Grimaldi, and on the other with modern Hottentot and Bantus[39]—and also, as we shall presently see, by an examination of the steatopygian statuettes of women yielded by some of the oldest deposits of the Reindeer Age.

Verneau has investigated the survivals of the Grimaldi race at different prehistoric periods. He has first of all compared this type with the Cro-Magnon, which succeeded it in place. 'At first sight', he says, 'the two races appear to differ greatly from each other; but on examining them in detail, we see that there is no reason why they should not have had some ties of kinship.' Verneau even declares that the Grimaldi Negroids 'may have been the ancestors of the hunters of the Reindeer Age'.

Verneau likewise discovered, in both prehistoric and modern races, survivals or reappearances of the Grimaldi types.

'In Brittany, as well as in Switzerland and in the north of Italy, there lived in the Polished Stone period, in the Bronze Age and during the early Iron Age, a certain number of individuals who differed in certain characters from their contemporaries', in particular in the dolichocephalic character of their skull, in possessing a prognathism that was sometimes extreme, and a large grooved nose. This is a matter of partial atavism which in certain cases, as in the Neolithic Breton skull from Conguel, may attain to complete atavism. Two Neolithic individuals from Chamblandes in Switzerland are Negroid not only as regards their skulls but also in the proportions of their limbs. Several Ligurian and Lombard tombs of the Metal Ages have also yielded evidences of a Negroid element.

Since the publication of Verneau's memoir, discoveries of other Negroid skeletons in Neolithic levels in Illyria and the Balkans have been announced. The prehistoric statues, dating from the Copper Age, from Sultan Selo in Bulgaria are also thought to portray Negroids. In 1928 René Bailly found in one of the caverns of Moniat, near Dinant in Belgium, a human skeleton of whose age it is difficult to be certain, but which seems definitely prehistoric. It is remarkable for its Negroid characters, which give it a resemblance to the skeletons from both Grimaldi and Asselar.[40]

[38] Sollas, W. J., *Ancient Hunters* (3rd Ed., London, 1924).
[39] Boule, M. and Vallois, H., 'L'Homme fossile d'Asselar' (*Arch. de l'Institut de Paléontologie humaine*, Memoir 9, Paris, 1932). For further details see the chapter of this book on Africa.
[40] Bailly, R., 'Sur un squelette à caractères négroïdes trouvé à Moniat, Belgique' (*XVe Congrès int. d'Anthr. et d'Archéol. préhist.*, Paris, 1931). See also *Revue anthropologique*, 43rd Year, Nos. 4–6, 1933.

It is not only in prehistoric times that the Grimaldi race seems to have made its influence felt. Verneau has been able to see, now in modern skulls and now in living subjects, in the Italian areas of Piedmont, Lombardy, Emilia, Tuscany, and the Rhone Valley, numerous characters of the old fossil race. The persistence or reappearance of these characters, which anthropologists have long recognized without arriving at any understanding of them, are explained by the facts of atavism. 'That we may still find at the present day so many traces of a racial type having characters recalling those which I have observed in the Grimaldi race', declares Verneau, 'must of necessity have been due to the fact that this race was formerly represented in our country by a whole group.' And he adds: 'We must therefore admit that an almost Negro element lived in South-Western Europe towards the Mid Quaternary Era, between the Spy race and the Cro-Magnon race.'

THE CRO-MAGNON RACE

This race derives its name from the locality where, in the circumstances recounted above, the remains of five human bodies were found—an old man,[41] two adult men, a woman and an unborn infant. These remains, first investigated by Broca and Pruner-Bay,[42] represent the prototypes of the fossil human race recognized, described and named by de Quatrefages and Hamy.[43]

We have seen how discoveries made in different regions have revealed the existence of this race throughout a great stretch of Europe, and in archaeological conditions which indicate methods of burial and funeral rites of very great uniformity. Among these discoveries the most important is represented by the series of ten skeletons exhumed successively from the various caves of the Baoussé Roussé. The first few skeletons, discovered by Rivière, were studied by de Quatrefages and Hamy. The succeeding ones, discovered in the course of Abbo's work and the excavations of the Prince of Monaco, form the subject of a masterly monograph by Verneau.

It is now easy to define the Cro-Magnon race by certain general characters. Some readily observed differences accord with different beds or different regions, but such differences fall within the limits of those existing at the present day between individuals or, at most, between varieties of the same race.

THE CRO-MAGNON SKELETONS

To begin with, let us take as types the original specimens from Cro-Magnon, and in particular the skull of the old man, who exhibits the characters of the

---

[41] In reality, it is an adult aged fifty years at the most. The term 'old man' by which it has become customary to describe it is far from accurate. See on this subject Vallois, H., 'La durée de la vie chez l'Homme fossile' (*L'Anthropologie*, XLVII, 1937, p. 499).

[42] In 'Reliquiae aquitanicae' (*Bull. de la Soc. d'Anthrop. de Paris*, 1868).

[43] *Crania ethnica*, pp. 45–98.

race in an especially clear, if not indeed even in a somewhat exaggerated degree (Fig. 209).

The skull is dolichocephalic (cephalic index = 73.7) and very large (cranial capacity = 1,590 cubic centimetres). The cranial vault is low. Seen from above the brain-box exhibits a pentagonal contour, due especially

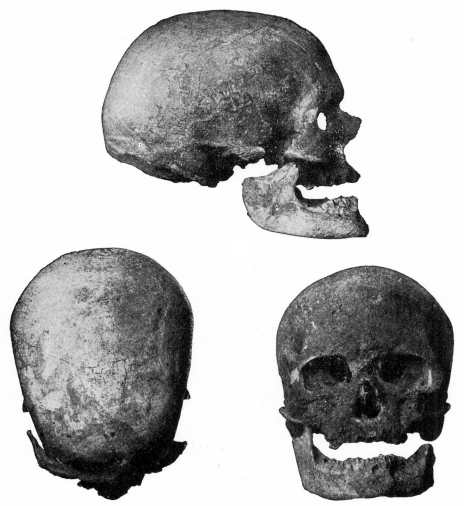

209 Skull of the 'Old Man' from Cro-Magnon, seen in profile, from above and full face. One-third natural size. Anthropological Gallery, Musée de l'Homme

to the marked projection of the parietal bosses. This is the so-called *dolichopentagonal* form of certain anthropologists. Seen in profile, we observe the forehead rising above relatively slight superciliary ridges; then the vault is developed in a regular curve in the anterior and middle regions, whilst the parieto-occipital region forms a broad flattened area succeeded by the projection of the nape. 'Thus', says de Quatrefages, 'in this savage contemporary of the Mammoth, the skull presents in a high degree all the characters regarded as indications of an intellectual development of the most advanced kind.'[44]

The face, no less remarkable, is relatively flat and very broad, whilst the skull is narrow and long. The proportions of the head are dysharmonic (see note, page 287). Below the wide high frontal bone, arched in the centre, open the orbits, likewise very wide, with almost rectilinear margins forming a quadrilateral outline. The cheek-bones are strong and prominent. On the other hand the nose is narrow, long and fine, *leptorrhinian*; the nasal bones project forwards. The upper maxillary, withdrawn to the level of the dental arches, exhibits a somewhat pronounced prognathism. The roof of the palate is relatively narrow, is shallow, and bears a median projection.

The long bones point to great height (5 ft. 11.6 ins.) and an athletic physique; their muscle imprints are strongly marked. In the femur the *linea aspera* is so developed as to form a kind of prominent column. The tibia is flattened like a sabre-blade, a *platycnemic* tibia. This characteristic, absent in Neandertal Man, seems to be fairly general in the Cro-Magnon race.

The Grimaldi Skeletons

Verneau's examinations of the fine series of skeletons from the Baoussé Roussé put him in possession of new facts. He was able to study nine skulls,

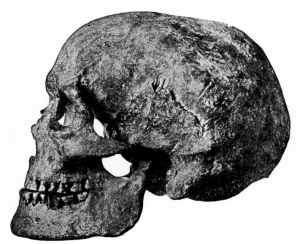

210 Skull of large male individual from the Grotte des Enfants, seen in profile
One-third natural size. (After Verneau)

eight male and one female, all belonging to the Cro-Magnon type (Fig. 210). These skulls exhibit a certain degree of variation, but, according to Verneau,

[44] Quatrefages, A. de, *Hommes fossiles et Hommes sauvages* (Paris, 1884) p. 65.

the differences do not exceed the individual variations to be met with in relatively homogeneous groups.

All the skulls are remarkable for their great size, due partly to the great stature of the individuals. There exists a striking lack of harmony between the skull, which is dolichocephalic, and the face, which is both flat and broad. The flattened parieto-occipital area, found in the Cro-Magnon skulls, is always present. In all the specimens, the face shows the essential characteristics of the type: transverse enlargement due to the development of the cheek-bones and zygomatic arches, rectangular orbits, leptorrhinian nose, etc. The strong jaw has a prominent chin, triangular in shape.

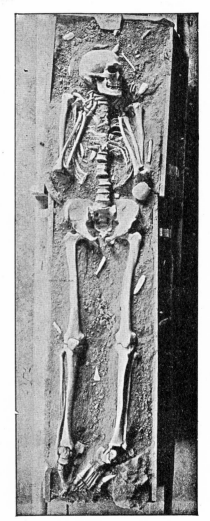

But to these general characters there are added here certain peculiarities constituting a variant of the type. The parietal bosses are less pronounced, and, in consequence, the pentagonal form of the skull, seen from above, is somewhat different; the occiput is less prominent, and the sub-nasal prognathism tends to disappear. 'These peculiarities', says Verneau, 'can in no way justify us in separating the Men from the Baoussé-Roussé from the Vézère type. . . . The old man from Cro-Magnon exhibits this type in exaggerated form.'

Thanks to the numerous specimens at his disposal, Verneau was able to re-examine the problem of the stature of the Men of Cro-Magnon type. Broca had estimated the stature of the old man at 5 ft. 10.8 ins. Rivière had calculated the height of the three adults, whose skeletons he had found, as varying from 6 ft. 0.7 ins. to 6 ft. 8.7 ins. According to Verneau, these figures are too large. Those obtained by him vary from 5 ft. 10.4 ins. to 6 ft. 4.4 ins. for five male adults, giving an average of 6 ft. 1.5 ins. The Grimaldi cave-dwellers must still be regarded, even after this

211 Skeleton of the large male individual discovered by M. de Villeneuve in the Grotte des Enfants. Musée de Monaco. (After Verneau)

correction, as men of very great height (Fig. 211) who were also exceedingly strong.

They exhibited a very marked elongation of the forearm in relation to the whole arm, and particularly of the leg in relation to the thigh; their upper limbs were very long in contrast with their lower limbs; the trunk was of remarkable breadth at the level of the shoulder. 'In the proportions of their limbs', writes Verneau, 'as well as in the transverse development of the upper portion of their chest, the Grimaldi men differ from Europeans, and are more akin to the Negro races.'

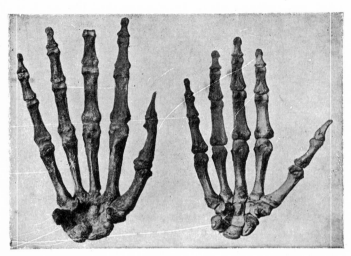

212 Hand of the large individual from the Grotte des Enfants and of a modern individual
5 ft. 7½ in. in height, photographed to the same scale
One-third natural size. (After Verneau)

On the other hand, the pelvis has no Negro characteristic. 'On the contrary, the well-developed iliae and the harmony of its curves render it as fine a form as that of the white races in which it is most highly developed.'

The femora, as in those from Cro-Magnon, here show signs of remarkable strength. The ridge (*linea aspera*), broad and prominent, may really be described as a column, and is always accompanied by a *hypotrochanterian fossa*. This structural arrangement gives rise to a certain antero-posterior flattening of the shaft below the trochanters, that is to say, to a *platymeric* femur.

The tibiae are equally strong: their shafts are more or less flattened transversely. This character of *platycnemia*, less marked in some bones, is, in the case of others, as marked as in the old man from Cro-Magnon.

The hands are large, corresponding to the general build of the skeleton; the metacarpals are relatively longer and the fingers relatively shorter than in the case of a modern Frenchman (Fig. 212). These characteristics are exactly reproduced in the handprints in the Castillo cave, in the Cantabrian Pyrenees.[45] The feet are remarkable for the length of the heel. The

[45] Sollas, W. J., 'Cro-Magnon Man: Imprint of his Hand' (*Nature*, May 7, 1914).

footprints they have left in certain caves show that the proportions of the feet were comparable to those of modern Men.[46]

OTHER EVIDENCES: VARIETIES OF THE TYPE

Bone-remains of the Cro-Magnon race have been collected in many parts of Western Europe. To this race de Quatrefages and Hamy attribute a large number of finds, apart from those at Cro-Magnon and Mentone; the skeleton from Paviland, in England; skulls from Engis and Engihoul, in Belgium; and more or less complete skulls from Aurignac, La Madeleine, Grenelle, Bruniquel, Laugerie-Basse, Solutré, and Gourdan, in France. To these must now be added a skull from the Grotte du Placard, at Vilhonneur in Charente; the skeleton from Les Hoteaux in the Ain; that from Combe-Capelle in the Dordogne; skeletons from Brno (Brünn) and Lautsch in Moravia; the skeletons from Obercassel and Stetten in Germany; the fine series of skeletons from the Beni-Segoual, in Algeria,[47] etc.

Even if we confine ourselves, as we should, to the anatomical specimens in this long list which are fairly complete and well preserved, it is easy to see that they often differ quite markedly from the morphological prototype from Cro-Magnon, and thus indicate a very pronounced degree of variation in the race that bears this name.

We have seen that the Cro-Magnons from the Côte d'Azur sometimes differ slightly from those from the Vézère (the general shape of the skull is less pentagonal, prognathism less pronounced).

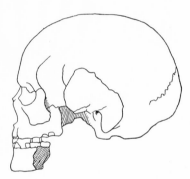

213 Profile of a skull from the Grotte du Placard. One-fourth natural size. (After Hamy)

Hamy already observed that the skull from Le Placard (Fig. 213) differs from the Dordogne type in possessing a cephalic index which is almost sub-brachycephalic.[48]

According to Depéret, Arcelin and Mayet,[49] the truly Aurignacian skeletons from Solutré, while they exhibit what may be regarded as the fundamental characteristics of the typical forms of Cro-Magnon Man, differ from them in certain particular features, notably in having a cephalic index (79) which renders them mesocephalic bordering on brachycephalic. The Men of Solutré, therefore, had rounder heads than those of the Vézère or Grimaldi.

In the following examples the differences are even greater.

[46] Vallois, H., 'Les empreintes de pieds humains des grottes préhistoriques du Midi de la France' (*Palaeobiologica*, IV, 1931, p. 79).

[47] See chapter on Africa, below.

[48] Hamy, E., 'Nouveaux matériaux pour servir à l'étude de la Paléontologie humaine' (*Congrès intern. d'Anthrop.*, Paris, 1889).

[49] *Loc. cit.* (see p. 273).

The skull from Combe-Capelle, first described by Klaatsch,[50] who made of it a new species (*Homo aurignacensis*), has been studied by numerous anthropologists. Mochi considered that it possessed Australoid characters, because of its strongly marked superciliary arches. According to Giuffrida-Ruggeri,[51] this skull is more dolichocephalic, more prognathic, and more platyrrhinian or flat-nosed, and therefore shows Ethiopian affinities. Mendes Corrêa[52] shares this opinion, while Szombathy[53] holds that the Combe-Capelle skeleton, despite its relatively small height (5 ft. 5.7 ins.) and these special characters of its skull, must be attributed to the Cro-Magnon race.

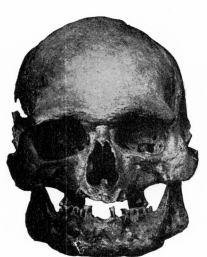

The Magdalenian skeletons from Obercassel are of much smaller stature, especially the woman's (4 ft. 10.2 ins.). The brain box is elongated and displays a sagittal crest. The male skull possesses marked eyebrow ridges. In general appearance, seen from in front (Fig. 214), it resembles the Chancelade skull, which is approximately the same age. But in the opinion of Bonnet, who has described them, the Obercassel skeletons also exhibit a number of characters of the Cro-Magnon type, which might be explained by racial intermingling.

214 Skull of the male individual from Obercassel, seen full face. One-third natural size. (After Bonnet)

There remain the fine series of Moravian skulls and skeletons, from Brno, Predmost, etc. In them the differences are still more pronounced. Even their affinities have been very much disputed. They have been designated successively *Homo predmosti*, the 'Brünn race', the 'Loess race', and 'Eastern Cro-Magnons', indicating that they are a race which, towards the east, impinged upon the western and southern race of Cro-Magnon. According to Matiegka's excellent study,[54] the shape of the skulls is here more elliptical than pentagonal; their vault is loftier and at the same time carinate. The development of the superciliary ridges is such that it may go so far as to approach the Neandertalian conformation. There is sometimes an occipital chignon (Fig. 215). Some of these structural features differ, as may be seen, from those of the Cro-Magnons. They have

[50] *Loc. cit.* (see p. 281).

[51] Giuffrida-Ruggeri, V., 'Quattro crani preistorici dell'Italia meridionale. . .' (*Archivio per l'Antr. e la Etn.*, XLV, 1916).

[52] Mendes Corrêa, A. A., 'A posição sistematica do esqueleto de Combe-Capelle' (*Trabalhos da Soc. Portug. de Antrop. e Etnol.*, VI, Part 2, 1933).

[53] Szombathy, J., 'Gegen die Überschätzung des *Homo aurignacensis* Hauseri Klaatsch' *Mitteilungen der anthr. Gesells. in Wien*, LVII, 1927).

[54] *Loc. cit.* (see p. 278).

led to the 'Loess race' being regarded as morphologically and genetically intermediate between Neandertal Man and modern types. But the tall stature of the Predmost subjects, a whole series of characters of their limb bones (platymeric femora with a third trochanter, extremely platycnemic tibiae, deeply channelled fibulae, etc.) and above all the structure of the face contradict this conclusion and link them up with the true Cro-Magnons.

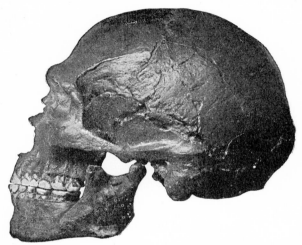

215 Skull of the male individual No. 3 from Predmost, seen in profile
One-third natural size. Photographed from a cast

So that, in Matiegka's view, if the Predmost skulls—to which he adds those from Brno, Combe-Capelle and Obercassel—can be situated midway between the Neandertalians and modern Man, there can be no question of the genetic relationships invoked by other authors. And, although he preserves the appellation *Homo predmosti*, in memory, it would seem, of his friend Maska, Matiegka does not hesitate to write: 'I think that the Predmost skulls represent a homogeneous type allied to the well known Cro-Magnon type, of which they are simply a variation.'

Such divergences of opinion testify, above all, to the difficulties of such a subject. They are also to be explained by different turns of mind, certain anthropologists having a tendency to link everything together, and others to keep everything apart.

Obviously, the Cro-Magnon race, in the broad sense, is exceedingly heterogeneous. We must carefully distinguish between its chief aspects, and there is no reason, in principle, why these aspects should not be designated as sub-races or sub-types. But in practice this is very difficult, because the differential characteristics are generally of less value than the common characteristics; furthermore, they form a more or less continuous scale of modifications running in different directions. Such are the so-called 'Neandertaloid' characters, the degree of development of which is so variable, even between individuals from the same stratum, and which must be considered rather as relics of a primitive ancestral state, common to all the races. This being so, where are we to place the points of separation?

One would expect that by arranging the various evidences according to their relative ages it would be possible to observe differences connected with this chronological relationship and therefore evolutionary in character. In fact, we find nothing of the sort. The Men who have preserved the most primitive characteristics, such as those of Predmost and Combe-Capelle, cannot be much older than those of Cro-Magnon or Grimaldi, while we find these same primitive characteristics in the Magdalenian, that is to say far more recent, skeletons from Obercassel.

There is certainly no harm in giving a special name to the Predmost-Combe-Capelle-Obercassel group, as being the most distinct, and calling it the Predmost 'variety' or 'sub-type', this term having the advantage of recalling its original designation. We shall have occasion later on, when dealing with Africa, to describe another parallel variety, that of Mechta, remarkable for its tall stature, great strength, large, primitive-looking skull, and broad nose.[55]

But, while we spare no effort to make a detailed analysis of its variations, we must on no account forget the profound unity of the great race which we have been studying in its various aspects.

In short, from the osteological point of view, the true Cro-Magnons may be considered as a median type, around which there already gravitate variations, due probably to the influence of varying geographical environments, and perhaps also to racial intermixture. But as a whole they really form one stock, a fine race which, as de Quatrefages has said, played an important part over a considerable area and throughout a considerable period of time.

SURVIVALS

This race did not come to an end in France with the termination of Quaternary times. As we shall see later, it not only survived during the Neolithic age, but, even in our own day, it still appears sporadically in different parts of France, especially, according to Dr. Collignon, in the Dordogne (Fig. 216).

De Quatrefages and Hamy[56] have drawn attention to its existence in Dalecarlia (Southern Sweden), where its representatives form a special group, very different from the rest of the population. This type, the 'Dal race' as it was later called, was subsequently reported from various regions of Germany, especially Westphalia and Lower Hessen. In the latter district it can even be traced without a break from the Polished Stone period to the

[55] Boule, M., Vallois H. and Verneau, R., 'Les grottes paléolithiques des Beni-Segoual (Algérie)' Part II (Archives de l'Institut de Paléontologie humaine, Memoir 13, 1934).

[56] Crania ethnica, p. 91.

present day.[57] Many individuals in this area do indeed display a series of characteristics—square face, deep-set eyes whose upper lids are as though hidden beneath the orbital arch, distinct detachment of the lateral edge of the frontal bone from the temple, horizontal line of the lower margin of the mandible, etc.—which correspond to what one would expect to find in descendants of the Cro-Magnon race.

In another direction, Verneau has been able to trace this race throughout Spain; it is found in burials, dating from more and more recent times the

216 Cro-Magnon type still persisting in the Dordogne. (From photographs by Dr. Collignon)

further one travels southwards. Fleure has observed a curious survival of this type in one county of Wales.

Broca noted the presence of structural affinities between the Basques, the Kabyles and the Guanchos. De Quatrefages and Hamy proved that a fair number of craniometric characters present in the cave-dwellers of Périgord are also to be met with in the pure-blooded Kabyles, and these characters have been noted in remains collected in prehistoric tombs in Algeria. Deniker related to the Cro-Magnon type his dark, mesocephalic, tall race which is at present spread along the Atlantic and Mediterranean seaboards of the Iberian Peninsula, for which reason he named it the Atlanto-Mediterranean race.

But it is among the Guanchos of the Canary Islands that the Cro-Magnon type has been best preserved. This statement, which we owe to de Quatrefages and Hamy, has been confirmed by Verneau's researches in the Canary archipelago, where the foundations of the population are formed of the Guancho elements; that this is derived from the Cro-Magnon race, or rather from its African variety from Mechta, is proved by resemblances in the skulls, which are sometimes identical. Verneau has even discovered among the modern islanders implements such as were formerly used by our ancient Dordogne hunters.

[57] Perret, G., 'Cro-Magnon-Typen vom Neolithikum bis Heute' (*Z. f. Morph. und Anthrop.*, XXXVII, 1937).

THE CHANCELADE RACE

The Site

The discovery at Raymonden, near Chancelade, to which we have already referred, was made and carried through under excellent scientific auspices. The bed proved to be very rich in archaeological and artistic objects. The fauna, identified by A. Gaudry, comprises, among other interesting species, the Greenland Seal. The human skeleton was examined by Professor Testut, of the University of Lyons. Ten years ago one of the present writers made a further study of this skeleton and reported his clarification of certain points. All this valuable material is preserved in the Museum at Périgueux, where it was arranged by Féaux, one of the fortunate investigators at Chancelade.[58]

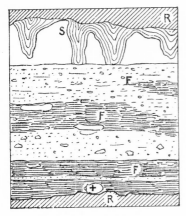

217 Section of the rock-shelter at Chancelade. (After Féaux)

R, rock, floor and roof of shelter; F, floors of occupation; +, human skull; S, stalactites.

The geological arrangement of the bed is extremely simple, consisting of three Magdalenian layers of occupation, alternating with gravels and silts, and forming a total thickness of about 5 ft. 3 ins. The lower floor of occupation lies directly upon the rock-surface, and the human skeleton rested in the lower part of it (Fig. 217).

The skeleton, found on October 1, 1888, lay on its left side. The arms were raised; the left hand was placed under the head, the right hand under the left side of the lower jaw; the lower limbs were bent; the feet were, in consequence, drawn up towards the lower part of the pelvis, and the knees were just touching the jaw. Such a constrained position recalls that of certain Peruvian mummies, and Testut advanced the opinion that the Chancelade Man 'might also have undergone similar treatment, and have been firmly tied up with cords or flexible lianas, and perhaps even been sewn in some kind of a sack made of an animal's skin, all in order to reduce the body to the smallest size so that it should occupy the smallest possible space. A similar method of burial is found among a great many ancient and modern peoples, particularly in the case of modern Eskimoes.'

As in the Mentone burials, the body seems to have been powdered over with haematite iron-ore, which coloured red not only the bones but also the surrounding earth.

[58] Hardy, M., 'La station quaternaire de Raymonden' (*Bull. de la Soc. histor. et archéol. du Périgord*, 1891). Testut, L., *loc. cit.*, see p. 276. Féaux, M., *Catalogue du Musée du Périgord*, (Périgueux, 1905): Vallois, H., 'Nouvelles recherches sur l'Homme fossile de Chancelade' (*L'Anthropologie*, XL, 1947, p. 65).

Let us glance at the chief results of the anthropological examination.

THE SKELETON

The skeleton is that of a man who died between the ages of thirty-five and forty years.[59] This man was of small stature: Testut estimated his height at 4 ft. 11 ins., but this figure is based on an error of assessment and it

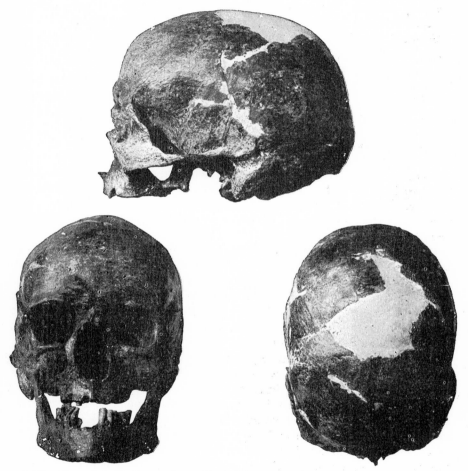

218 The Chancelade Skull, seen in profile, full face and from above. One-third natural size.

ought to be 5 ft. 3 ins. Even when thus corrected, the height differs considerably from that of the Cro-Magnon type.

The state of preservation of the skull leaves much to be desired, but it has been carefully reconstructed (Fig. 218). It is markedly dolichocephalic

[59] *L'Anthropologie*, XLVII, 1937, p. 514.

(cephalic index 72), and remarkably lofty. Its capacity, estimated at 1,710 cubic centimetres, greatly exceeds the average of present-day skulls, even of Europeans.

'Seen in profile, the Chancelade skull exhibits all the characters belonging to the higher races.' Above the slight superciliary ridges, the broad, somewhat bulging forehead rises at first almost vertically; the line of the profile then slopes backwards and is continued in a regular curve. The parietal bosses are very marked. The occipital region presents an almost perpendicular surface. The mastoid apophyses are remarkably well developed.

Seen full face, the skull is characterized by the height of the forehead, and by the unusual height of its median area, which gives to the general aspect the appearance of a high and narrow arch.

The face is very broad and very high, so that the skull appears to be well-balanced or harmonious. We may recall the fact that the ill-proportioned or dysharmonic skulls of the Cro-Magnon type have a broad but squat face.

The cheek bones are strongly developed and prominent; the orbits are wide; Testut ascribed a great height to them, but this was only a false appearance due to an error of reconstruction, and the difference from Cro-Magnon Man is far less than was supposed. The nose is long and narrow (leptorrhinian), and the upper jaws show no subnasal prognathism. The alveolar borders, lacking teeth, surround a palate of medium width and elliptic in form.

The lower jaw is narrow and strong, and remarkable for the breadth of its ascending branches. The chin forms a very broad and prominent projection. The whole external appearance testifies to a considerable development of the muscles of mastication. A special characteristic is the presence of a bony ridge on the inner surface of the bone, the *torus mandibularis*, to which no parallel is found except in the skulls of various living Arctic peoples. The molar teeth were powerful.

The upper limbs were relatively long, longer than those of modern Europeans, longer even than those of Negroes. Their bones, massive and thick-set, like the skeleton as a whole, indicate a vigorous frame and strong muscles; so that, to judge from their insertions, the supraspinatus, infraspinatus, deltoid, great pectoral, great dorsal, and great round muscles, all of which are attached to the humerus and play an important part in the act of climbing, were specially developed. The same applies to the lower limbs, to the gluteus maximus, the posterior muscles of the thigh, and, as a whole, to all the posterior muscles of the leg, which are the active factors in the erect position and in walking.

The femora are a little more bent than in modern Europeans. Like those of Cro-Magnon, they have the linea aspera formed like a column or rod, and a hypotrochanterian fossa. The upper ends of the tibiae are markedly bent backwards, in consequence of which 'in the upright position the knees must have projected more prominently forwards than in modern races.'

These tibiae have the shaft flattened in a transverse direction: they are slightly platycnemic.

Chancelade Man had large feet, which in the usual position were turned inwards. The first metatarsal, corresponding to the great toe, was distinctly separated from the second toe, a little like that of the apes and exactly like that of Neandertal Man. The foot of our fossil Man, as in the case of some

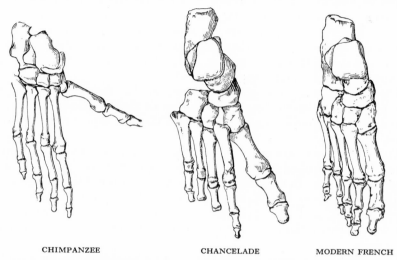

CHIMPANZEE   CHANCELADE   MODERN FRENCH

219 Skeleton of foot of Chimpanzee, Chancelade Man and a modern Frenchman from Lyons. About one-fourth natural size. (After Testut)

native races, could probably play the part of a grasper, able to grip objects between the first two toes (Fig. 219).

COMPARISONS

We are very poor in representatives of the fossil Chancelade race. Hervé believed that we could attribute to it the skulls from Laugerie-Basse, classified by de Quatrefages and Hamy as Cro-Magnon in type. The skeleton of the cave-dweller from Sorde also exhibits these points of resemblance. Even the female skull from Le Placard, in spite of its sub-brachycephalic character and its close relationships with the female skulls of the Cro-Magnon race, must, according to Hervé, be added to the small Chancelade group and must confirm the homogeneity of the Magdalenians.[60] The skeletons from Obercassel, which are likewise Magdalenian, although they belong to the Cro-Magnon type seem to show some of the characteristics of the Chancelade skeleton (see p. 281).

According to N. Martin,[61] the skeletons discovered by him in a rock-shelter in the Roc Valley (Charente), and regarded as Magdalenian, resemble

[60] Hervé, G., 'La race des troglodytes magdaléniens' (*Revue de l'École d'Anthrop.*, III, 1893).
[61] *Loc. cit.* (see note p. 281).

the Chancelade skeleton by their small stature (about 5 ft. 1 in.) and by the characters of their skulls, which are dolichocephalic, ovoid in shape, and show a sagittal ridge. Unfortunately, the facial characters, particularly important in determining the species, are virtually unknown.

The position is the same as regards the female skeleton from Cap Blanc (see p. 281).

Some anthropologists think that the two types, Cro-Magnon and Chancelade, do not belong to different races.

It is certainly a fact that among the three types we have just described, the Grimaldi Negroids, the Cro-Magnon Men, and the Chancelade Man, there is a certain number of common and fundamental characters, which bear witness, as we have already said, to the unity and at the same time to the variability of *Homo sapiens fossilis*. But they are not, on that account, to be confused, and Testut effectively brought out the differences, as between Cro-Magnon and Chancelade.

Whilst the Chancelade reindeer hunter was of quite small stature, about 4 ft. 11 ins. in height, the famous 'old man' from Cro-Magnon attained an almost gigantic height. The skulls have a broad face, but while the Cro-Magnon face is much reduced in height, that from Chancelade is remarkably lofty; the difference is considerable. The orbits of the old Cro-Magnon man take the form of two rectangles, greatly elongated in a transverse direction; those of the Chancelade man have a quadrilateral shape, the height differing little from the breadth. It is evident that the general appearance of these two cave-dwellers of the Upper Palaeolithic must have been very different.

Testut has also clearly shown the resemblance of the Chancelade skeleton to the skeletons of the Eastern Eskimoes, who still live in a wild state amid the snow of Labrador and Greenland, and who, in all respects, represent a very ancient race. 'Like the Chancelade Man, the Eskimoes are decidedly dolichocephalic; like him, they have a high skull, prominent sagittal ridge, a face at once very wide and very high, and orbits almost round in form. We also know that the Eskimoes have a large head and are of small stature. . . .'

Sollas,[62] and Morant[63]—the latter, it is true, with certain reservations—have defended this interpretation, the chief interest of which lies in the fact that it confirms a comparison which the prehistorians Hamy, Gervais and Dupont made long since on the strength of archaeological and ethnographical evidences, and of the resemblances between the physical environments. As long ago as 1870, Hamy said of the modern Arctic peoples that they 'seem to be akin to the Quaternary cave-dwellers of our countries. They carry on into our own times, in polar regions, the *Reindeer Age* of France, Belgium, and Switzerland, with the same zoological and ethnographical characters, etc.'[64]

[62] Sollas, W. J., 'The Chancelade Skull' (*J. of the Roy. Anthr. Inst.*, LVII, 1927).

[63] Morant, G. M., 'Studies of Palaeolithic Man. I. The Chancelade Skull. . . .' (*Annals of Eugenics*, I, 1926).

[64] Hamy, E., *Précis de Paléontologie humaine*, p. 366.

This theory, shared by Pruner-Bey, Boyd-Dawkins, and Hervé, was re-vived by Professor Sollas of Oxford. According to this scholar, a study of the modern Eskimoes, of their habits, their implements, and their artistic efforts, confronts one with an array of facts in favour of the existence of an actual relationship, which is so admirably confirmed by the Chancelade skeleton. The Cro-Magnon race may formerly have had relations with the Chancelade race, similar to those to be observed at the present day between the Algon-quins and the Eskimoes. The Palaeolithic peoples seem to have gradually taken possession of the circumboreal regions by way of the Behring Straits and the Aleutian Islands.[65]

The theory of an anatomical relationship advanced by Testut, Sollas and Morant was vigorously disputed by A. Keith, who went so far as to describe it as 'extravagant'. In his view, Chancelade Man was not a Mongo-loid, but a true European.[66] A similar opinion was reached by H. Vallois, who compared Chancelade Man, once his corrected measurements were available, with all the various groups of Eskimoes at present known and not only to the Greenlanders, as had been done hitherto. A large number of differences then appear which had escaped the notice of previous authors. In Chancelade Man the orbits are much lower, the cheek-bones are less prominent, the lower jaw is narrower; there is complete orthognathism, whereas the Eskimoes show a very pronounced alveolar prognathism; the infra-nasal grooves so typical of the latter are absent; the nose is much more prominent, etc. Chancelade Man is unquestionably not an Eskimo. On the other hand, he differs from the other Men of the Upper Palaeolithic far less than used to be thought.

This conclusion accords with the opinion of certain anthropologists in the United States, such as Boas and Chamberlain,[67] who regard the Eskimoes as a race of American origin. Far from having come from Northern Asia, they may have set out from an ancient centre of distribution in the interior of Canada, whence they spread towards the maritime regions they occupy in our own day. As for the ethnographic resemblances, they are easily explained by a similarity in the conditions of life and the use of the same materials, reindeer horn, bone and ivory. These similarities would constitute a simple case of convergence unconnected with any direct relationship. Not so very long ago, de Laguna observed that Eskimo art bears no closer resem-blance to that of the Upper Palaeolithic than any other art of simple content.[68]

We shall only mention, in passing, Girod's[69] opposite theory of 'the

[65] Sollas, *Ancient Hunters* (3rd Ed., 1924) pp. 591–594.

[66] Keith, A., *The Antiquity of Man* (2nd Ed., Vol. I, London, 1925) pp. 82–86.

[67] Chamberlain, A. F., 'Quelques problémes ethnographiques et ethnologiques de l'Amérique du Nord' (*L'Anthropolog.e*, XXIII, 1912).

[68] Laguna, F. de, *The Archaeclogy of Cook Inlet, Alaska* (The University Museum of Phila-delphia, 1934).

[69] Girod, P., *Les invasions paléolithiques dans l'Europe occidentale* (Paris, 1900).

Eskimo invasion', which, to use a popular expression, is a case of 'putting the cart before the horse'.

HUMAN FIGURES

Let us now examine the works of art contemporary with the Men whose skeletons we have studied. Judging from the accuracy of many of their animal drawings, this new source of information should be of great assistance to us. The artists of the Reindeer Age did, indeed, sometimes carve or engrave portraits of their fellows; but, unfortunately, they were unskilful in this form of art, and this is particularly true of the engravers. The sum total of the anthropomorphic figures of Quaternary art already forms a series of considerable importance from the point of view of the number and variety of subjects dealt with; but in its evident inaccuracy or lack of skill in drawing, this series is in contrast with the collection of animal figures, which are not only very numerous but amongst which real works of art abound. The majority of the engraved or sculptured portraits of fossil Man are most often simply childish caricatures, and many of these human personages seem to be dressed in animal masks which conceal their true features. In the absence of any work of art of really outstanding quality on which we might consequently have relied, we must be cautious in the interpretation of certain characters or contours, which, far from representing real morphological features, may only be the result of unskilful execution or an attempt at stylization.

With these reservations, let us examine the principal evidences.

The Reindeer Age was of long duration, and in the course of it art, like industry, underwent an evolution; this evolution has been studied by Piette and Breuil.[70] The former thought that the sculpture of statues in full relief preceded engraving. But Breuil has shown that this idea is correct only in a general way and in regard to the art of movable objects, while, so far as mural art is concerned, it applies with still less exactness. None the less, sculptures are more numerous during the most ancient period of the Reindeer Age (Aurignacian), and engravings attain their maximum development, in number as well as in quality, during the last phases of this Age (Magdalenian).

AURIGNACIAN SCULPTURES

However this may be, Aurignacian deposits of different countries, far apart from each other, have yielded a certain number of very realistic statuettes or bas-reliefs.

There are, first of all, objects in Mammoth ivory, taken by Piette[71] from

[70] Breuil, H., 'L'évolution de l'art quaternaire et les travaux d'Édouard Piette' (*Revue archéol.*, 1909).

[71] Piette, É., 'La station de Brassempouy et les statuettes humaines de la période glyptique' (*L'Anthropologie*, VI, 1895).

the Brassempouy Cave in Landes, the most important of which are here reproduced (Fig. 220).

Here we see, along with the head of a young woman, known as the 'hooded figure', some mutilated statuettes representing torsos and bodies of men or

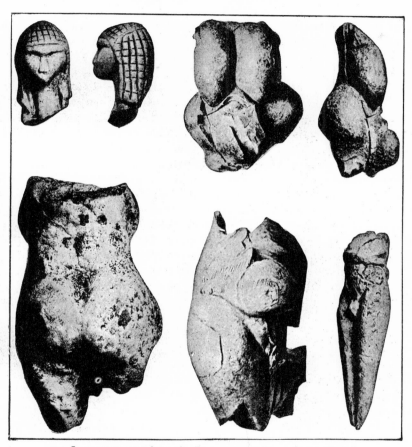

220 Ivory statuettes from the Brassempouy Cave. (After Piette)

Above, to the left, 'hooded figure', full face and profile, slightly reduced. Above, to the right, damaged female body, seen full face and in profile, about four-fifths natural size. Below, to the left, female body, known as a 'dagger haft', about four-fifths natural size. Below, in centre, the 'Venus de Brassempouy', reduced by one-fourth. Below, to the right, 'belted figure', reduced by one-fifth

women. One of these statuettes, known as the *Venus of Brassempouy*, or *La Poire*, must have been a fine specimen, if we may judge from the delicacy of the modelling of the portions remaining intact. Another, regarded by Piette as the haft of a dagger, is a female body, remarkable for the exuberance of its forms. A third 'Venus' is more elegant in style. The 'belted figure' probably represents the lower part of the body of a man.

There are, in the next place, the statuettes known as the 'Mentone', or better the Grimaldi statuettes. They were found at different times by the collector, Julien, in the Barma Grande cave; and although their authenticity was for long disputed, it is now admitted by all competent observers. The statuettes from this locality, instead of being made of ivory, are carved from a soft mineral—steatite or soap-stone.[72] We here reproduce the most interesting of them (Fig. 221). Along with a very rude model of a head and a statuette of a man, there are five almost complete female statuettes, all remarkable for the great development of the breasts, the hips, and the genital parts.

In 1909, Szombathy[73] published the photograph of a curious figure from Aurignacian settlements in the Willendorf loess, $12\frac{1}{2}$ miles from Krems in Lower Austria. The statuette, $4\frac{1}{3}$ ins. in height, was carved from a piece of limestone, and its surface retained some traces of red painting. It represents a nude woman of massive proportions, with enormous breasts, protruding belly, and full hips (Fig. 222). The head is covered by a mop of hair, represented by concentric lines, and re-divided by markings at right angles to these primary lines. This coiffure almost completely conceals the face, no part of which is even indicated. The arms, which are extremely slender and are ornamented by bracelets, are folded over the chest. The thighs and legs are thick, short, and fat, and the genital region is distinctly portrayed. The general appearance is very realistic, the workmanship most skilful.

Two years afterwards, in 1911, Dr. Lalanne,[74] who for several years had been excavating the great deposit at Laussel in the Dordogne, discovered there a very curious bas-relief, representing two persons lying down and facing each other (a representation of birth or perhaps rather of mating). In the following year three other bas-reliefs were brought to light; a fourth was stolen from Dr. Lalanne by his head workman, and sold to the Berlin Museum through the agency of Professor Verworn of Bonn. We here reproduce the two finest of these sculptures.

The first bas-relief is very skilfully executed. It measures $18\frac{1}{8}$ ins. in height and represents a nude woman, holding in her right hand a bison's horn (Fig. 223). The head is represented only by a vague outline, but, on the other hand, the remainder of the body is carefully treated. Here, again, we find enormous, elongated, and pendulous breasts, a prominent but well-modelled abdomen, with folds of fat and carefully drawn *mons veneris*. The hips are stout, with marked iliac and femoral prominences; the general appearance is fleshy and adipose. The thighs are full, the legs slender and short. The arms are slender and well modelled; the fingers on the hand are indicated. The whole surface of this bas-relief, apart from the head, which

[72] Reinach, S., 'Statuette de femme nue découverte dans une des grottes de Menton' (*L'Anthropologie*, IX, 1898). Piette, E., 'Gravure du Mas d'Azil et statuettes de Menton' (*Bull. de la Soc. d'Anthrop. de Paris*, 1902).

[73] Szombathy, J., 'Die Aurignacienschichten im Loess von Willendorf' (*Korrespondenzblatt der d. Gesells. für Anthrop.*, XL, 1909).

[74] Lalanne, G., 'Bas-reliefs à figurations humaines' (*L'Anthropologie*, XXII, 1911, and XXIII, 1912).

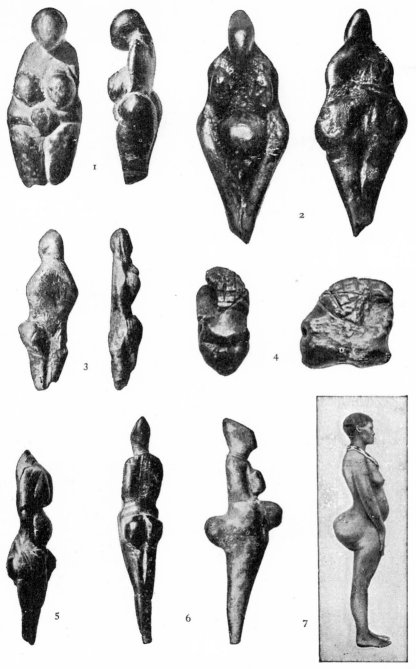

221 Statuettes in steatite from the Mentone or Grimaldi Caves (1–7). Natural size. From photographs. Musée de Saint-Germain. 7, Modern Bushman woman, profile

seems to have been crushed, is delicately worked and even polished, and some traces of red paint are still to be found upon it.

The second, and more damaged, figure again represents a nude woman.

222 Willendorf Statuette, front view and profile. Half natural size. Photograph from a cast

223 (left) Bas-relief from Laussel, representing a naked woman seen full face
One-sixth natural size. (After G. Lalanne)

224 (right) Bas-relief of a man from Laussel. One-sixth natural size. (After G. Lalanne)

The head is vaguely worked, the hair is executed in the manner of the female statuettes from Brassempouy and Willendorf. The greatly enlarged breasts resemble those of the preceding bas-relief, while the prominent belly ends below in a triangular projection. The hips must have been very large, but they are very much abraded, as are also the upper parts of the thighs. A portion of the arms may still be distinguished.

The third bas-relief, $15\frac{3}{4}$ ins. high, is a three-quarter length figure of a man, contrasting in its graceful form with the massive figures of the women (Fig. 224). Unfortunately this work of art is also incomplete. The head is lacking, as well as the greater portions of the arms and the feet. The proportions are graceful. The trunk and loins are bent, the legs are placed as though the individual had been in the act of drawing a bow. Two parallel lines mark a belt around the body.

In 1922 a discovery of a new human figure was made by M. and Mme. de Saint-Périer[75] in the Grotte des Rideaux, at Lespugue in the Haute-Garonne. It consists of a statuette in mammoth ivory, well preserved, almost complete and of such beauty as to establish it as a queen amongst the Aurignacian 'Venuses' (Fig. 225). It is almost 6 ins. in height. In general outline its graceful form takes the shape of an all but regular lozenge, the upper apex occupied by the small head, the lower by the attenuated legs. It presents the general structural characters of the works of art already described, as well as their peculiar features. Thus the head, covered with rather short hair, which partially hides a face without features, possesses the graceful outline of certain heads from Mentone and Brassempouy. The slender, well-defined neck and the flat chest are also found in the Mentone specimens. The arms, standing out slightly from the body, are slender like those of the Willendorf statuette, and are posed and executed in exactly the same fashion. The long, full breasts, shaped like leather bottles, hang over the abdomen and recall one of the Brassempouy ivories. The buttocks are enormous, not specially prominent behind but greatly enlarged sideways. The lower part of the abdomen is damaged, so that the sexual parts are absent. Thighs and legs are tapered as in the Willendorf and Laussel specimens; the feet are barely indicated by slight forward projections. But what distinguishes this statuette from all others is the presence of a sort of garment, a waist-cloth, covering the back of the thighs below the buttocks. This rudimentary garment seems to be made of vertical strips or straps starting from a transverse cord and ending below in a fringe.

M. and Mme. Saint-Périer were so good as to present this superb specimen of Palaeolithic art to the Palaeontological Gallery of the French National Natural History Museum.

Since the last edition of this book, other productions of the same kind have been found not only in France, but also in Italy, Central Europe, Russia and as far away as the centre of Southern Siberia, that is to say over a distance

---

[75] Saint-Périer, Dr. René de, 'Statuette de femme stéatopyge découverte à Lespugue (Haute-Garonne)' (*L'Anthropologie*, XXXII, 1922).

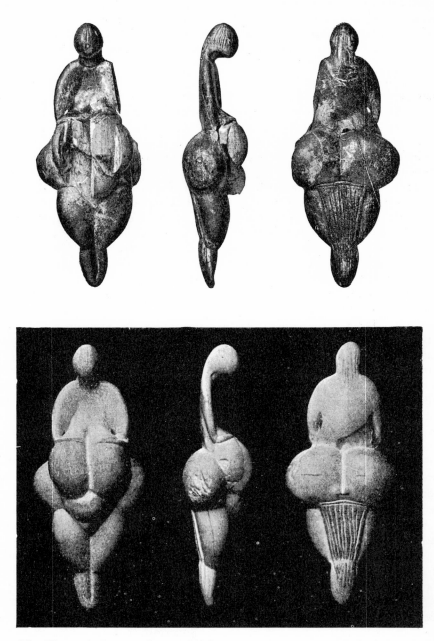

225 The 'Vénus de Lespugue', seen full face, in profile and from the back. Above, the
statuette as it was found. Below, the statuette restored by the author (plaster cast)
Half natural size. Musée de l'Homme

of about 5,000 miles. We shall only discuss the most important of these.[76]

In France there is the charming calcite statuette, unfortunately mutilated, found by chance in a rut in the road near Sireuil (Dordogne). In spite of the obscurity surrounding its origin, Breuil and Peyrony[77] consider it to be Aurignacian. Although the subject is young, as indicated by the slender

226 Stone statuette from Savignano, seen full face, in profile and from the back About half natural size. (After P. Graziosi)

torso and the shape of the breasts, the figure is nonetheless steatopygous.

In Italy there is another female statuette, of serpentine, found at Savignano, near Modena, the origin of which is uncertain. Larger in size (9 ins.), this sculpture has been discerningly compared by Vaufrey[78] to the statuettes from Grimaldi. It, too, is distinctly steatopygous (Fig. 226). But this characteristic is missing from the statuette, likewise female, found in 1940, at

[76] On this subject, see Kuehn, H., 'Menschendarstellungen im Paläolithikum' (Z. für Rassenkunde, IV, 1936). Passemard, L., Le statuettes féminines paléolithiques dites Vénus stéatopyges, (Nîmes, 1938).

[77] Breuil, H. and Peyrony, D., 'Statuette féminine aurignacienne de Sireuil, Dordogne' (Revue anthropologique, XL, 1930).

[78] Vaufrey, R., 'La statuette féminine de Savignano sur le Panaro' (L'Anthropologie, XXXVI, 1926).

Chiozza,[79] under stratigraphic conditions that were unfortunately also very inconclusive.

In Germany the Linsenberg settlement, near Mainz, has yielded, along with curious bone objects, two female statuettes of sandstone that recall the beautiful specimen from Willendorf.[80]

A series of other statuettes was found by C. Absolon, between 1928 and 1934, in the great loess bed at Vistonice in Southern Moravia. The finest of them, which seems to be made of clay and powdered bone, also has the same general outline as the Willendorf statuette, with very wide hips and a head on which the face is barely indicated. Another depicts the lower half of a female body; a third, a male or female head with a well drawn profile.[81]

Moving eastwards, we come first to Mizyn, in the government of Chernigov in Russia. We shall mention only the objects of mammoth ivory found by Volkov in a splendid Aurignacian settlement. Most of these sculptures are very difficult to interpret: they have been taken for phalic symbols, birds, or highly stylized human figurines. The decorations on these objects, with their meander patterns and 'Greek borders', carry us away from Western Europe.[82]

Two Russian localities even further away from us—Kostienki, near Voronezh, and Gagarino, near Tambov—bring us more or less back to the European style.

The mammoth ivory statuette from Kostienki[83] is extremely adipose, with voluminous, pendulous breasts and thin arms (Fig. 227).

Gagarino is a site in the open air, or rather at the bottom of a hut with walls reinforced by slabs of stone. Six small female statuettes of ivory have been found there, at least two of them very reminiscent of similar productions from Willendorf and Mentone. As in the latter, the arms are thin and rest on the breasts.[84]

Finally, 2,000 miles further east, in the middle of Siberia, we again find analogous artistic productions in the archaeological deposit at Malta, near Krasnoyarsk.[85] This deposit yielded about ten bone figurines, the majority of them slender in shape. They are very different in appearance from the European specimens and may not be of the same age. Brought together from districts far apart and corresponding to the most ancient phase of the Reindeer

[79] Graziosi, P., 'La Venere di Chiozza' (Studi etruschi, Vol. XVII, 1943).

[80] In Vaufrey, R., 'Les progrès de la Paléontologie en Allemagne' (L'Anthropologie, XLI, 1931).

[81] Kuehn, H., 'Neue Funde eiszeitlicher Kunst in Mähren' (Ipek, 1934).

[82] Roudinksy, M., Industrie en os de la station paléolithiques de Mizyn interpretée par Volkov (Kiev, 1931) (in Ukrainian, but with captions to the figures in French).

[83] Reinach, S., 'Une nouvelle statuette féminine en ivoire de Mammouth' (L'Anthropologie, XXXIV, 1924, p. 346).

[84] Zamyatnin, S., 'Gagarino' (Bull. of the Acad. of the History of Material Culture, Sect. 88, 1934).

[85] Golomshtok, E. A., 'Trois gisements du Paléolithique supérieur russe et sibérien' (L'Anthropologie, XLIII, 1933).

Age (Aurignacian), this small collection of some fifty artistic productions is remarkable for the association of characters which give it a general appearance of considerable uniformity, almost, indeed, a family likeness. These statuettes

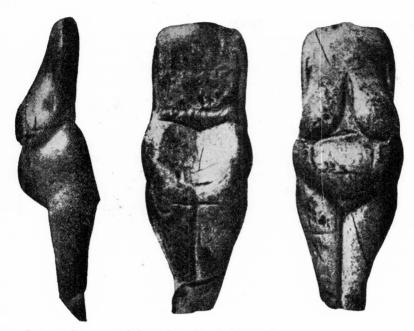

227 Statuette in mammoth ivory from Kostienki, seen in profile, from the back and full face. Approximately natural size

or bas-reliefs must, therefore, translate with some fidelity the general characters of the form of their models. We may, then, place a certain amount of reliance on the information they contribute.

THEIR INTERPRETATION

We say 'a certain amount', because occasionally writers have gone too far in their interpretation of them, as, for example, when Piette attempted to calculate the cephalic index of the 'hooded figure' from Brassempouy.

The following facts must be definitely recognized.

In almost every case the head is scarcely blocked in; the hair is often represented, sometimes by simple parallel lines, as at Lespugue, generally by criss-crossing strokes forming a chequered pattern, as at Willendorf, in the Dordogne, on the Côte d'Azur, and in the Pyrenees. We may interpret this feature, also found in primitive Egyptian art, as a type of hairdressing, an arrangement in narrow plaits, or in short tresses or small tufts, such as are found in modern Negro or Negroid races, particularly of the Bushman and Hottentot tribes whose hair is grouped in little bunches. Or, on the other hand, the pattern may be looked upon as representing a net, similar to the hair-nets made of shells found on several of the Grimaldi skeletons. Perhaps both practices were in use.

The features of the face are always obliterated or roughly represented, even in the hooded figure from Brassempouy. Lalanne thought he traced, on his bas-reliefs, elongated faces, with prominent cheeks and pointed chins. Such an interpretation may perhaps be admitted without difficulty, for in its vague terms it does not stand in any great contradiction with the osteo-logical characters of contemporary skulls. On the other hand, however, the Grimaldi head has really a Negroid appearance.

The female bodies are for the most part short and massive; the breasts very large, long, cylindrical, and pendulous; the belly is prominent, with rolls of adipose tissue sometimes overhanging the pubes. The hips are greatly developed, fleshy enough even to amount to true steatopygia; the thighs are likewise fleshy, sometimes with projecting ridges of fat; they are supported by slender legs. The upper limbs, on the contrary, preserve a certain degree of delicacy. The sexual parts are always strongly emphasized; the *mons veneris* is large and well defined. We can recognize in *La Poire* from Brassempouy and in the statuette from Willendorf a development of the nymphae (*labia minora*) similar to the 'apron' of Bushman Women.

These structural characters have been variously interpreted by pre-historians. True *steatopygia* (i.e. fatty development of the buttocks in a backward direction) occurs in only a few cases (Mentone, Gagarino); in the majority of cases we see *steatomeria* (i.e. fatty development of the hips in a lateral direction) and sometimes simply more or less generalized obesity. The exaggerated emphasis on the genital parts and the secondary sexual characteristics are said to possess 'aesthetico-erotic' significance or to con-tribute a sort of homage to some fertility goddess. Here the fanatical believers in the magic significance of primitive art once more find grist for their mill. All these questions have been clearly expounded and summarized in a lecture delivered by M. Luquet to the French Institute of Human Palaeontology.[86]

RESEMBLANCE TO THE BUSHMEN

This association of characters has been compared with that now or formerly exhibited by Bushman women, in whom steatopygia has been regarded as classic since the work of Cuvier on the 'Hottentot Venus' in the French National Natural History Museum. Quaternary male figures likewise agree in their general morphology with the male Bushman, in possessing a slender body. Together with Dr. Lalanne in France, Professor Sollas in England, Dr. Péringuey at the Cape and others, we have several times had occasion to lay stress on this resemblance, which is of considerable interest.

We know now that the ethnography of South African tribes presents many striking similarities with the ethnography of our populations of the Reindeer

[86] Luquet, G. H., 'Les Vénus paléolithiques' (*Journal de psychologie*, 31st Year, 1934) with bibliography. See also Passemard, L., *loc. cit.*

Age. Not to speak of their stone implements which, as we shall see later, exhibit great similarities, Péringuey has told us that in certain burials on the South African coast 'associated with the Aurignacian or Solutrean type of industry', rows of circular discs made from ostrich egg-shell, and round plates of bone or of shells, perforated for stringing, accompany the skeletons of women and of children; one of these necklaces exactly resembles those found with the Mentone skeletons.[87]

Bushman art is extraordinarily like that of our caves. As in France and Spain, the pictures of animals are also of higher quality than the human figures, and many of the latter wear an animal mask and a long tail. The two centres are united by a long, connected series of works of art, from France to the Cape by way of Spain, North Africa, the Sudan, the Chad and the Transvaal. This almost uninterrupted series leads us to regard the African continent as a centre of important migrations, which at certain times may have played a great part in the stocking of Southern Europe. Finally, we must not forget that the Grimaldi Negroid skeletons show many points of resemblance with the Bushmen skeletons.

They bear no less a resemblance to that of the fossil Man discovered at Asslar in mid-Sahara, whose characters led us to class him with the Hottentot-Bushmen group.[88]

It does not seem, in the present state of our knowledge, that the Bushmen were descended from our Aurignacians, but perhaps the latter were descended from the ancestors of the Bushmen, who must be the survivals of a very ancient race. The relationship of these two groups cannot be denied, however far apart they may be in time and space. The most reasonable course, it would seem, is to admit that they are descended from a common primitive stock, which must have spread towards the centre or the north of the African continent, and whose branches have developed in different directions, morphologically and geographically, while retaining a common fund of ethnographical survivals. In any case, no explanation based simply on phenomena of convergence seems to be sufficiently far-reaching to cover such a mass of consistent data.

MAGDALENIAN SCULPTURES

Let us now glance at the anthropomorphic images belonging to a more recent period, the Upper or Magdalenian period of the Reindeer Age. Their value from an anthropological point of view is very small, as may be seen from the examples here reproduced, selected from the best or, let us say, the least bad specimens.

The two statuettes, one from Laugerie-Basse (Vibraye Collection in the French National Natural History Museum), the other from the Mas

[87] Péringuey, L., 'The Bushman as a Palaeolithic Man' (*Transactions of the Royal Society of South Africa*, V. 1915).

[88] Boule, M., and Vallois, H., 'L'Homme fossile d'Asselar (Sahara)' (*Archives de l'Institut de Paléontologie humaine*, Memoir 9, 1932). See chapter on Africa.

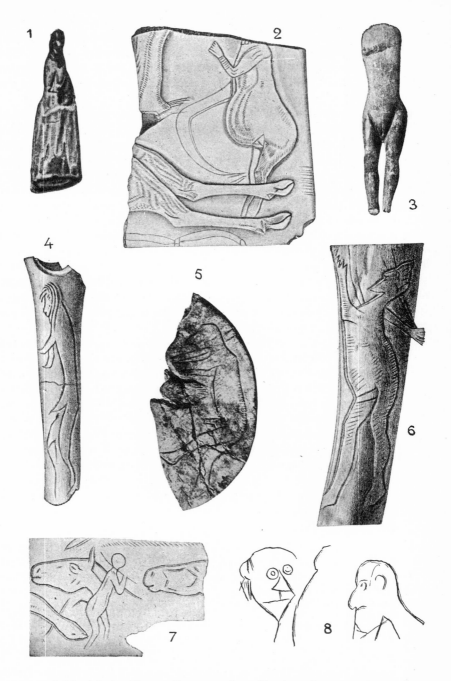

228 Magdalenian Human Representations. (See legend on opposite page)

d'Azil (Piette Collection at Saint-Germain), resemble certain idols, fetishes, or amulets of savage tribes and could never be regarded as portraits. The first, known as *Vénus impudique*, is in ivory (Fig. 228, No. 3), and differs markedly from Aurignacian statuettes in its more slender outlines. The second, carved from the root of an incisor tooth of a horse, is an even coarser work (Fig. 228, No. 1). Piette laid far too much stress upon the study of the features.

Another production from Laugerie-Basse is an engraving in low relief on a sunk background, representing a pregnant woman beside the hind legs of a reindeer (No. 2). It is the 'Woman with the Reindeer' of Abbé Landesque. The creator of this bas-relief was certainly skilful, for the legs of the reindeer are perfectly rendered; but the drawing of the woman's body is quite mediocre. As it is highly probable that the two subjects were engraved by the same artist, we have here yet another proof of the lack of skill of the artists of the Reindeer Age in reproducing the human body. The woman is adorned with a necklace and bracelets. The only anthropological fact of interest relates to the development of the body hair, clearly indicated on all the abdominal surface.

The Petersfels Cave, near Engen, in the southern part of the Grand-Duchy of Baden, contained a rich Magdalenian stratum that yielded several pendants made of jet. Two of these, 1.2 and 1.6 inches in length, seem to represent highly stylized steatopygous women.[89]

The line engravings are still poorer or more rudimentary; that discovered by É. Lartet at La Madeleine, representing a man between two horses may be taken as an example (No. 7). Such also is the famous 'Hunting the Aurochs' discovered by Massénat at Laugerie-Basse, where the aurochs is much better drawn than the man with the absurdly pointed skull (No. 6). Much more curious is a human scene engraved on bone and found by M. de Saint-Périer[90] in a Magdalenian level in the cave of Isturitz (Basses-Pyrénées). It is composed of two individuals (Fig. 229). The first is a naked woman, massive in shape but in no way steatopygous; she is decked with a necklace and anklets, and by this feature as well as by her marked hairiness and general posture recalls the 'Woman with the Reindeer'. An arrow is engraved on her right thigh. Below the woman is the upper part of a man's body,

[89] Peters, E., *Die altsteinzeitliche Kulturstätte Petersfels* (Augsburg, 1929).

[90] Saint-Périer, R. de, 'Deux œuvres d'art de la grotte d'Isturitz' (*L'Anthropologie*, XLII, 1932).

Legend to Fig. 228

1, Incisor of horse, the root of which has been carved into a female figure, from the Mas d'Azil in Ariège; 2, engraving on reindeer antler, known as 'The Woman with the Reindeer', from Laugerie-Basse in Dordogne; 3, the 'Vénus impudique' in ivory, from Laugerie-Basse; 4, engraving on reindeer antler from Gourdan in the Haute-Garonne; 5, engraving on disc of bone from Mas d'Azil; 6, portion of an engraving on reindeer antler known as 'Hunting the Aurochs', from Laugerie-Basse; 7, engraving on reindeer antler from La Madeleine; 8, engraving on the wall of Marsoulas cave in the Haute-Garonne.

Nos. 1, 2, 4 and 7 are after Piette; No. 3 is a photograph of the original in the French Nat. Hist. Museum; No. 8 after Breuil.

which is also ornamented with a necklace and bangles. The head is plainly
à caricature. The two arms are bent and raised, like those of the woman, in
an attitude of supplication or prayer. The arrow seems to indicate that the

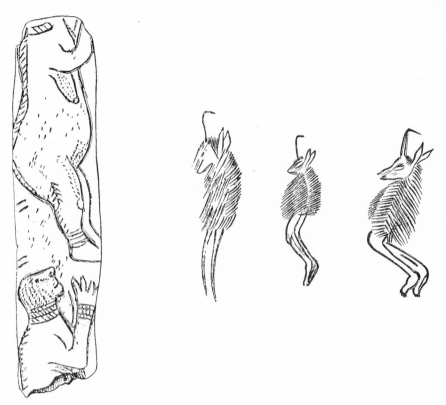

229 (left) Human scene engraved on bone from the Isturitz Cave. Natural size
(After R. de Saint-Périer)

230 (right) Human figures with chamois heads, an engraving on bone from the Teyjat rock-
shelter in the Dordogne. Natural size. (After H. Breuil)

composition possesses a magical significance; it may also be an expression
of amorous desire.

Other drawings are more grotesque still; such as the odd creature carved
on a round bone disc from the Mas d'Azil, in which Piette attempts to see
the figure of a monkey, because of its muzzle-like face (No. 5). It is probable
that here, as at Gourdan (No. 4), Marsoulas (No. 8), Teyjat (Fig. 230),
Altamira and elsewhere, we have a man wearing a mask in the form of an
animal's head, either in order to indulge in dancing or in certain ceremonies,
or more readily to stalk game, as certain native peoples still do or formerly
did, such as the Australians, Bushmen, and others. There are also some
simple caricatures recalling the drawings of children.

As regards its artistic value, which is in striking contrast to the foregoing figures, an exception must be made for the astounding sculptured frieze, representing, life-size, three naked women without either the upper part of the torso or the extremities of the limbs, found a few years ago in the rock-shelter at Angles-sur-l'Anglin (Vienne) by Mlle de Saint-Mathurin and Miss D. Garrod (Fig. 231). Executed with a remarkable realism and a striking

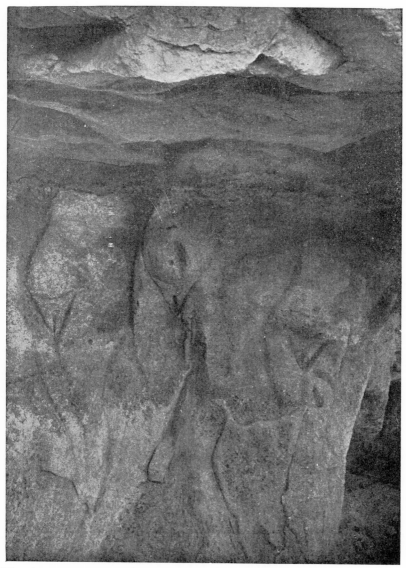

231 The three 'Venuses' from the shelter in the Roc aux Sourciers at Angles-sur-l'Anglin. One-fourth natural size. (After S. de Saint-Mathurin and D. Garrod)

232 Panel from the frieze at Minateda in Spain, representing a fight, and various subjects belonging to other, earlier and later, periods. About one-sixth natural size. (After H. Breuil)

perfection of line, these bas-reliefs are much less stylized than the majority of Palaeolithic Venuses. The same shelter had yielded shortly before a large number of engraved fragments, one of them bearing the drawing of a human head which is the finest representation of this type recovered from the whole Upper Palaeolithic.

To the laborious investigations of Breuil and his disciples at Madrid,[91] Spain has yielded many human representations painted on rock. The frescoes at Alpéra, Cogul, Minateda, etc. (Fig. 232), in many respects so curious, are more interesting from the ethnographical than from the anthropological point of view. Breuil asserts that they are the products of an art 'which evolved parallel to the development of our Reindeer Age', and he notes their close resemblance to the rock paintings of South Africa.

CONCLUSIONS

To sum up, in France the Men of the Upper Pleistocene, that is to say, of the Reindeer Age, belong to a new type, greatly superior to the preceding types, and by its every characteristic justifying its inclusion in the general mass of modern *Homo sapiens*. Their general features are sufficiently uniform to induce certain anthropologists to group them under the common name of the *Cro-Magnon race*. But there is also a certain diversity of characters, and this agrees well with those movements of populations which variations in industry also enable us to envisage.

We have been able to distinguish fairly easily, and without resorting to too subtle methods of analysis, three principal types which seem to have succeeded one another in France: the Grimaldi, the Cro-Magnon-Predmost and the Chancelade. These three types seem to us to be varieties, following each other in time, and more or less differentiated, of one general, widely-spread dolichocephalic form, of the origin or even the provenance of which we still know nothing. The extremely interesting fact is that they show affinities with each of the three great divisions of modern Man: Negroes, Whites, and Yellows. To each of the populations which can be grouped thus, there correspond a fairly special industry and art, although, as a whole, the general aspect of the Reindeer Age forms a very homogeneous unit which appears, so far as latter-day knowledge extends, greatly isolated both in time and in space.

Comparisons between the Men of the early Reindeer Age, that is, the Aurignacians or at least the first of the Aurignacians, and certain modern groups, long since led to the admission that these prehistoric Men were African in origin. The presence and the persistence of an industry partially

[91] Breuil, H., and Cabré, J., 'Les peintures rupestres du bassin inférieur de l'Ébre' (*L'Anthropologie*, XX, 1909). Ibid, and Serrano, P., 'Les abris del Bosque à Alpera' (*L'A.*, XXIII, 1912). Breuil, H., 'Les roches peintes de Minateda, Albacete' (*L'A.*, XXX, 1920). Ibid,. *Les peintures rupestres schématiques de la péninsule ibérique* (4 vols., Lagny, 1933 and 1935). Cabré, J., 'Las Cuevas de los Casares y de la Hoz' (*Arch. esp. de Arte e Arqueologia*, No. 3, 1934). Obermaier, H., 'Nouvelles études sur l'art rupestre du Levant espagnol' (*L'A.*, XLVII, 1937).

analogous to the Aurignacian in Africa and particularly in North Africa (where it has been designated the *Capsian* industry); the uninterrupted chain, across the whole of the Dark Continent from north to south, of an art developed on cave-walls or rocks; the really extraordinary resemblances between the art of the South Africans and our prehistoric art; the evidence obtained by Breuil's remarkable work and observations in Spain of transition stages between Aurignacian and Magdalenian art on the one hand and on the other the less naturalistic and more diagrammatic art of more southern regions, as well as the Neolithic art of Susa;—all these facts plead in favour of this hypothesis. Nowadays we are less categorical, and recent investigations tend to suggest that the industry of Aurignacian Man originated in an unspecified Asian centre. Thrusting in successive waves towards both Europe and Africa, it is thought to have given the various facies of the Aurignacian and the Capsian industries. But, even when seen in this light, there are nevertheless close affinities between the two. All the facts are at one in breaking down the isolation of our Reindeer Age and leading us to admit the existence of broad relationships with countries and peoples whose prehistory has hardly yet begun to be unveiled.

Moreover, the three great types of the Upper Palaeolithic do not necessarily share the same origin. The Grimaldi Negroids are certainly African—a fact which is not in formal contradiction with the opinion of Verneau who considered them as indigenous, for indigenousness must necessarily have a beginning somewhere.

The Cro-Magnons established themselves in the Mediterranean countries, and spread widely throughout Western and Southern Europe and also, through the Mechta type (see below, Chap. XI), North Africa. If they no longer correspond exactly to any living ethnographical group, their various characters are today still to be recognized, more or less clearly, scattered here and there among the populations of many countries. They seem to represent an ancient stock which is not yet exhausted.

The Chancelades represent a group evolved in a somewhat different direction, probably beneath more northern skies. Towards the end of Pleistocene times they seem gradually to have supplanted, more or less, the Cro-Magnon group, and later, at the dawn of modern times, to have withdrawn northwards at the same time as the Reindeer, under the pressure of new invaders.

We cannot hide from ourselves the fact that these conclusions are still vague and uncertain. It will be necessary to submit them to the test of new excavations, and these must be undertaken with an absolutely clear understanding of the great anthropological problems to be solved, and not with the sole aim of making collections of archaeological objects.

———— CHAPTER NINE ————

THE MESOLITHIC PERIOD

THE Men of the Reindeer Age, as we have just seen, already belonged to modern mankind both in structure and in mental characteristics. So that even as early as the dawn of our present geological, or *Holocene*, Period (see p. 49), modern Man was definitely established, and had been so for a long period of time; and now the role of palaeontology is ended. Henceforth the task falls to anthropologists and archaeologists to pursue the study of human groups throughout the countless migrations and changes which preceded the historical events related in ancient manuscripts.

DIFFICULTY OF THE TASK

This linking up of Palaeolithic times with Neolithic times, of Neolithic times with the Metal Ages or Prehistoric times, and of these again with Historic times, is full of the most difficult problems. At the present time these problems can only be approached, and even that with hesitation, in Europe, the Near East and North Africa, the only regions regarding which sufficiently abundant data has been accumulated. Further, in regard to the relatively recent Periods of our prehistory, as well as in regard to more ancient geo- logical Periods, we barely know more than the final results of events, the origins or starting points of which, at least in the majority of cases, are to be found in more distant countries, still almost unexplored from our point of view. The light which will one day illumine the great questions raised by a study of prehistoric times will come only after we have gained sufficient knowledge of Asia and of Africa; for to the palaeontologist these two conti- nents represent the great laboratories of life in the Ancient World. They must also have been the great centres of development of successive human- ities, from those most primitive types which were still akin to the animal to those which saw the dawn of the great civilizations.[1]

[1] In thus expressing ourselves we are viewing things broadly and from a naturalist's point of view. The movements of the tide of humanity have been, at least in the blind alley of the European peninsula, movements of flux converging on a centre. These movements have sometimes been followed by a sort of backwash or drift from the centre; but such move- ments, more limited in extent, can only be directly observed in protohistoric or historic times, when the populations of Europe had reached a higher degree of culture.

This book is essentially a palaeontological work, and we could now draw it to a conclusion, ignoring everything which relates to the Neolithic and Metal Ages; for these, though to the historian they represent prehistory, are to the palaeontologist only the conclusion of a history, that of the evolution of the human kind. It seems to us, however, that many of our readers might be disappointed did they fail to find here a summary of the known facts bearing on the transition from the vague Humanity of geology to the Humanity of history. And we decided to write this chapter in an attempt to join 'the two ends of the chain', without too much thought of the many and diverse difficulties to be encountered. It is a relatively easy matter to make a catalogue or to arrange a scheme (more or less formal or artificial) of observed facts or of relics, to arrange them geographically or in objective categories. But to give a synthetic account of all such scattered facts with a view to reconstructing a series of events, and that in the spirit of a naturalist, is a risky business. In excusing our effort, we wish to say that we ourselves are the first to realize the rashness and imperfection of the attempt we are about to lay before the reader.

THE HOLOCENE PERIOD:

ITS DIVISION

The *Holocene* Period, which we have now reached, well deserves the other name of *Recent*, also given to it by geologists. Its topography is that of today; it possesses the same wild animals and plants, to which are now added the domestic animals and cultivated plants. In the new civilization we actually see the dawn of the civilizations of history. It coincides with the arrival in Europe of the first Round-Headed or Brachycephalic Men.

The subdivisions of the geologist, the palaeontologist and the anthropologist are now in perfect agreement, and from the outset of prehistoric studies, as we have seen, they were clearly understood and established. The Pleistocene of the geologist is the Palaeolithic of the prehistorian; the Holocene of the geologist begins at exactly the same time as the Mesolithic of the archaeologist. The Holocene Period is divided in the following manner:

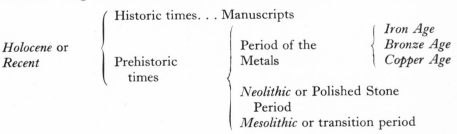

We should greatly exceed the limits of our subject were we to enlarge on the archaeological characters and subdivisions of the main stages of prehistoric times. For such information we refer our readers to special works on the subject.[2] It will suffice if we draw attention to certain important points.

COMPARATIVE CHRONOLOGY OF PREHISTORIC AND HISTORIC TIMES

At the outset it must be clearly understood that the expressions *historic times* and *prehistoric times* have a different chronological value in different countries. We, in France, consider that history really begins with Julius Caesar—that is to say, but a short time before the Christian era; in the northern countries, however, its beginnings are much later, while in the East, on the other hand, they date back for some 6,000 years.

So it comes about that, during the prehistoric stages of the Polished Stone and Metal Ages, there cannot be, even in Europe, chronological agreement between the successive archaeological fashions of different countries, such as the correlations we have been able to allow, not, however, without the strictest reservations, in Palaeolithic times. Thus in the East, the Neolithic Age, at least in its beginnings, seems to be contemporary with the end of our Mesolithic. Copper, bronze, and iron had been known and made use of in Egypt thirty centuries before they were employed in Central Europe. Yet in the valley of the Nile, the Metal Ages overlap historic times, while with us their beginnings are lost in the darkness of prehistoric times.

Facts of the same kind may still be observed or were formerly to be observed in various parts of the globe: in America, in the Oceanic Isles and in Australia, where European colonists were to be found settled among peoples who had remained at the Stone Age state of culture.

The Neolithic represents an almost universal phase, which everywhere seems to have been of long duration. It is very difficult to estimate the date of its beginnings, which appear to have taken place chiefly in Asian regions that are still unexplored, and may have been the result of the convergence of cultural elements born in isolation.[3] Montelius considered that it dated back 20,000 years in Egypt, a greatly exaggerated estimate. Nowadays, dates of 8,000 to 10,000 years (6,000 to 8,000 B.C.) are accepted for the ancient Egyptian localities of Fayum and Badari. The Neolithic of Susa, which is more advanced, with axes of copper, is certainly more recent. But the lower levels at Anau, in Russian Turkestan, seem older. Arthur Evans believed that in Crete the beginnings of the Neolithic went back 14,000 years; this figure must be reduced to 10,000 or 8,000 years. In our regions we may place the appearance of Polished Stone at 5,000 or 4,000 years ago. Here it persisted for about 2,000 years; for the Metal Ages, which began in the East 3,000 to 5,000 years before our era, did not originate in the West till about 2600 B.C.

[2]   Déchelette, J., *Manuel d'Archéologie* (Paris, 1908–14). Burkitt, M. A., *Our Early Ancestors* (Cambridge, 1926). Goury, G., *L'Homme des cités lacustres* (Paris, 1931). Peake, H., and Fleure, H. J., *The Corridors of Time* (Vols. 3 to 9, Oxford, 1927–1936). Hawkes, G., *The Prehistoric Foundations of Europe to the Mycenian Age* (London, 1940). Childe, V. G., *The Dawn of European Civilization* (4th Ed., London, 1947).

[3]   Vayson, A., 'L'existence d'une vague néolithique mondiale' (*L'Anthropologie*, XLIV, 1934, p. 719); 'La question des origines du Néolithique' (*L'A.*, XLVII, 1937, p. 683).

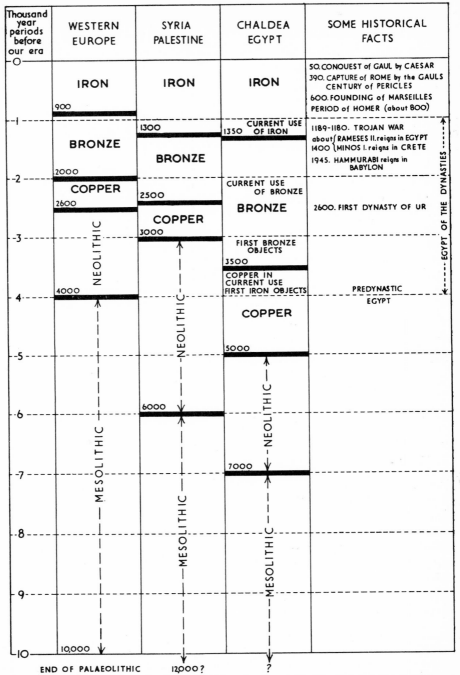

233 Indication of the comparative chronology of the Prehistoric, Protohistoric, and Historic
times in Western Europe, the Near East, Egypt, and Chaldea

The Iron Age, which is also more ancient in the East, lasted in Gaul from 900 B.C. till the Roman conquest. The accompanying table (Fig. 233), the dates in which have been taken from various sources,[4] summarizes the chief chronological facts relating to this subject.[5]

PALAEOLITHIC AND NEOLITHIC

In all respects the close of the Palaeolithic Age differs from the Neolithic Age, as is shown in the following table, wherein the chief characteristics of the two periods are summarized.

End of Palaeolithic	*Neolithic*
Climate colder than today	Climate like that of today.
Fauna still comprising numerous extinct or emigrated species.	Fauna identical with that of present day.
Dolichocephalic Men, nomads and hunters. Rudimentary social groups.	Dolichocephalic and brachycephalic Men, herdsmen and cultivators. More advanced social life.
Mainly cave-dwellers.	Dwellers in the open. Huts and lake-dwellings.
No domestic animals nor cultivated plants.	Domestic animals and cultivated plants; cereals, textiles.
Stone industry dressed only. No pottery.	Stone industry dressed and polished. Mines worked. Pottery. Cloth woven.
No stone erections.	Primitive architecture, megalithic monuments: dolmens, menhirs.
Strong artistic feeling, denoting contemplative mind.	Rudimentary artistic feeling. Practical utilitarian mind.
Primitive religious ideas.	More complicated religious ideas and burial rites. Graves more elaborate and monumental.

The contrasts disclosed by this table are extremely striking. The Neolithics appear as the first Men who succeeded in breaking away from a passive attitude towards their physical environment, who attempted to render nature subservient to their needs by exploiting the forests, cultivating the plains and capturing animals, in order to make of them valuable auxiliaries. Hence a new upsurge of the spirit of invention. Hence, too, new

[4] Communications made to the *Congrès intern. d'Anthrop. et d'Archéol. préhist.* (Monaco and Geneva) by Montelius, A. Evans, Hoernes and others. Also: Morgan, J. de, *Recherches sur les origines de l'Égypte* (Paris, 1896); *Les premières civilisations* (Paris, 1909); *L'Humanité préhistorique* (Paris, 1921). Peake, H., and Fleure, H. J., *Peasants and Potters* (Oxford, 1927).

[5] After the commencement of the Ages marked by the knowledge of metals the dates of an absolute chronology are furnished by the historical documents of Egypt and Chaldaea. With the aid of the latter we can, by degrees, establish dates for other countries by means of archaeological comparisons. The most ancient historical date known is that of the introduction in Egypt of the Sothic calendar, 4,236 years before our era.

social organizations leading to fixed agglomerations of dwellings, that is to
say, to true villages. We cannot lay too much stress on the moving grandeur
of the changes that must have taken place in order to turn the more or less
nomadic hunters of the Palaeolithic into cultivators, the first peasants living
on their crops, henceforth attached to a soil which fed them and which
therefore gave them, for the first time, the idea of a Country. We are in the
presence of a major stage in the evolution of Humanity, at the very origin
of true civilizations. This stage can only be compared with that, infinitely
older, of the conquest of fire.

Transition from Palaeolithic to Neolithic:
Mesolithic

As, in archaeological layers, the Neolithic levels are often separated from
the Palaeolithic by the intercalation of a sterile bed, indicating a more or
less lengthy period without occupation, prehistorians have long maintained
that the two great divisions of the Stone Age are separated by a blank, sometimes described as a gulf, corresponding to a complete transformation or
revolution. More moderate opinion on the subject was content to regard it
as a mere hiatus in our knowledge.

It was clear that if the Neolithic Age shows a completely new order of
things, particularly the arrival of peoples with quite different industries,
customs and sometimes physical characteristics from those of the last
Palaeolithic peoples, then, in accordance with the general principle of
continuity, the break could not have existed everywhere; sometime or other
the transition period would appear less obscure. That was what happened.
Following J. de Morgan,[6] the name *Mesolithic*, although not altogether
satisfactory, has been generally adopted for this transition period, which
was unknown less than half a century ago and now comprises several archaelo-
ogical facies, the interest of which is all the greater because of their extremely
widespread distribution throughout the three continents of the Old World.
They have also been the subject of very numerous investigations.

Azilian

The earliest in date were those of Piette in the cave at Mas d'Azil (Ariège).
During the years 1887–1889, this eminent prehistorian explored a series of
river deposits of archaeological interest on the left bank of the Arize, a rapid
stream which flows through the vast tunnel forming the Cave of Mas d'Azil.
The accompanying figure illustrates a section of these deposits, as recorded
by Piette in 1889. From top to bottom there was revealed (Fig. 234):

The lower layers (1 and 2) represent the later Pleistocene deposits; they
belong to the end of the Reindeer Age, to the Magdalenian period. The
upper formation (5) corresponds to the modern period, from Neolithic

[6] Morgan, J. de, *Les premières civilisations* (Paris, 1909) p. 136.

5. Masses and blocks of rock detached from the roof of the cave. Here were found Gaulish objects, Bronze Age objects, and, towards the base of the layer, polished stone axes and Neolithic pottery. Depth varied from 6 to 10 feet.

4. Banded masses of ashes, with beds of charcoal and innumerable snailshells. Polished stone implements, pebbles worn with usage at the points. Fragments of pottery. Variable depth.

3. Bed of cinders, reddish incinerated earth, and charcoal, with modern wild fauna. Red Deer and Beaver abundant; not the slightest trace of Reindeer. Flat perforated harpoons of deer-horn (Fig. 235). Painted pebbles (Fig. 236); some pebbles polished at ends, etc. The upper part consists of an ancient surface (a.s.) marked by a line of stones; in the lower part are beds of ashes (ch). Depth 4 ins. to 2 ft. 7 ins.

2. Great deposit of silt from the neighbouring river, made up of hundreds of laminae, and cut up by several ashy lines of incinerated earth. In these layers of occupation the Red Deer abundant, Reindeer rare; harpoons of red deer and reindeer antlers; needles and artistic engravings. Total depth about 11 ft. 6 ins.

1. Earth mixed with pebbles, almost barren, resting on the calcareous rock (R) of the cavern. Depth, about 4 ft. 7 ins.

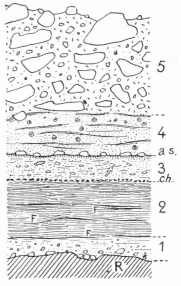

234 Section of archaeological layers in the left bank of the Mas d'Azil Cave. (For a description of the layers see accompanying text)

times to our own day. The intermediate layers (3 and 4) cover the well-known hiatus between Palaeolithic and classic Neolithic times: layer 4 represents the dawn of Neolithic times, while layer 3, containing coloured pebbles, is really the transition layer. It corresponds to a particular period well named by Piette[7] the *Azilian* period.

To our mind the majority of archaeologists are mistaken in wishing to place this Azilian period in Palaeolithic times, and in calling it *Epipalaeolithic*. As one of us pointed out, as long ago as 1889,[8] the Azilian, though not yet Neolithic, is no longer Palaeolithic; it is a period apart, with a special facies, and the facies is that of transition, initiating a state of affairs which is to lead, little by little, to the new world of the Neolithic and Metal Ages.

From the geological or stratigraphical point of view, this transition is obvious; from the palaeontological point of view it is no less clear, since the fauna of the Azilian layer, from which the Reindeer is absent, is identical with the wild fauna of the present day and does not yet contain any trace of domestic animals. Transition—we do not say direct succession—is also evident from the archaeological point of view, for along with flint implements resembling those of the Magdalenian period, we find innumerable

[7] Piette, É., 'Un groupe d'assises représentant l'époque de la transition entre les temps quaternaires et les temps modernes' (*Comptes rendus de l'Acad. des Sc.*, February 25, 1889). And several memoirs, notably in *L'Anthropologie*, VII, XIV.

[8] *Congrès intern. d'Anthrop. et d'Archéol. préhist.*, Paris, 1889, p. 209.

334

microlithic flints and the first products of stone-polishing. Though harpoons of deer-antler still persist, their form and substance are different. Products of artistic expression are no longer present, for the colouring of the pebbles

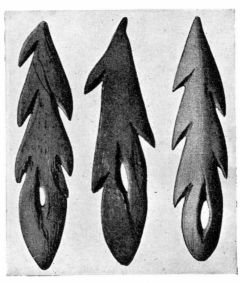

235 Flat harpoons of red deer antler from the Mas d'Azil Cave. Three-fourths natural size. (After Piette)

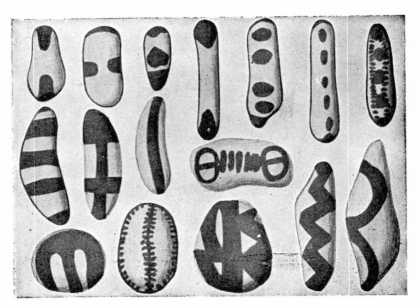

236 Coloured pebbles from Mas d'Azil. (After Piette)

has nothing in common with Palaeolithic paintings. It would be difficult to imagine a set of conditions more expressive of transition than those we have just enumerated.

These conclusions were at first not well received by the prehistorians whose ideas they upset. It was not long, however, before these conclusions were confirmed. The *characteristic fossils* of the Azilian period, together with flat harpoons and coloured pebbles (Figs. 235 and 236), were soon after discovered in other deposits in the Cantabrian and French Pyrenees, Ande, Gard, Dordogne, Drôme, Switzerland, Bavaria and Denmark, in Britain as far north as Scotland and perhaps in Russia.

TARDENOISIAN

Other material proofs of the existence of a transition period have been found in many countries. In the first place, a special implement industry came to light in France to the products of which the name 'pygmy flints' was given because of their small size; they are geometrical in shape—triangles, lozenges, trapeziums, segments of circles, etc. (Fig. 237). G. and A. Mortillet[9] considered that this industry—which they named *Tardenoisian*, after Tardenois, a small district in what used to be Picardy, where it is well represented—belonged to the Lower Neolithic. Since that time, the Tardenoisian has been the subject of many researches both in France and outside. Of the work done in France we must mention, after Octobon's numerous typological studies,[10] an interesting discovery made by Coulonges that showed, for the first time, a Tardenoisian industry firmly in place between the Magdalenian and the Neolithic.[11] In this respect, the deposits at Sauveterre-la-Lémance are comparable with those at Mas d'Azil.

Outside France, this curious microlithic industry (often accompanied by large-scale elements) has been studied by many prehistorians, who have greatly extended its known area of distribution. Today this includes France, Belgium, Holland, Great Britain, Germany, Poland, Russia, Spain, Portugal, Italy, the whole of Africa, Syria, India, Ceylon and Australia. It has been possible to establish a number of archaeological subdivisions in the Tardenoisian, since it presents considerable variations. At the same time, some idea has been formed of its origin. On the one hand, for example, it has been noted that in Europe the microlithic industry seems to be partially derived from the Aurignacian technique. On the other hand, its extreme abundance in the whole of Africa, after the Upper Palaeolithic or Capsian, suggests it originated in the south, or at least was imported thither on a large scale.

[9]   Mortillet, G. de, *Formation de la nation française* (Paris, 1879) p. 250. Mortillet, A. de, 'Les petits silex taillés à contours géométriques. . .' (*Revue de l'École d'Anthrop.*, 1896).

[10]   Octobon, 'La question tardenoisienne' (*Bull. de la Soc. préhist. de France*, after 1922, *passim*); 'Réflexions sur l'hiatus: ses deux aspects, paléo-mésolithique et méso-néolithique' (*Festschrift für Otto Tschomi*, Fravenfeld, 1948).

[11]   Coulonges, L., 'Les gisements préhistoriques de Sauveterre-la-Lémance, Lot-et-Garonne' (*Arch. de l'Inst. de Paléont. humaine*, Memoir 14, 1935).

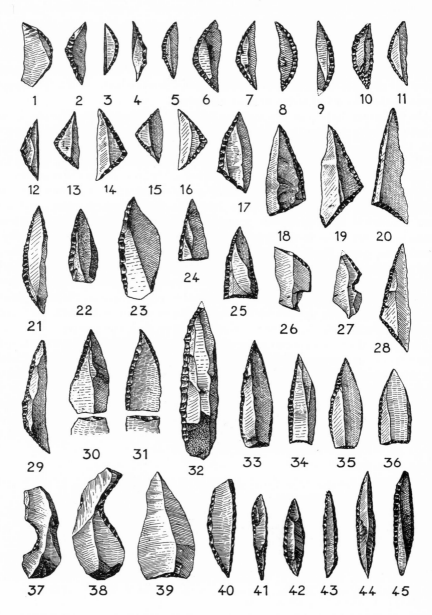

237 Tardenoisian microliths from the bed at Piscop, Seine-et-Oise. Natural size
(After Giraud, Vaché and Vignard)

1 to 11, 21 and 29, half-moons and segments of a circle; 12 to 20, 28, triangles; 22 to 25,
30 to 36, 39, points from Tardenois; 37, 38, grooved pieces; 40 to 45, points from Sauveterre.

In this connexion, the excellent investigations carried out by Vignard[12] at Sebil, in Upper Egypt, are of exceptional interest. It seems as though here the microlithic and geometric industry was born on the spot, through a slow evolution of the local Mousterian. Sebil must have been its birthplace, or rather one of its birthplaces.

The majority of Tardenoisian deposits are surface beds, sometimes with a limestone base. The most instructive are those which lie in the upper levels of the fillings of caves or rock-shelters.

On the other hand, on the coasts of Denmark, France and Portugal, we have long been familiar with artificial mounds, composed of earth, cinders, and floors of occupation, containing, scattered everywhere, innumerable shells of edible molluscs, bones of animals, implements of flint—trapezium-shaped microliths and larger flints known as 'paring-knives' (tranchets)—and of bone, as well as pottery. They are sites of ancient settlements, to which Danish archaeologists, who have carefully studied those in their own country,[13] have given the name kjökkenmöddings (or better, kjökken-möddinger), which is to say kitchen middens. This industry is now called Erteböllian, after Ertebölle in Jutland, one of the most important sites. The presence of the domestic dog and of pottery in the kitchen middens of Denmark led to their being ascribed to a very early phase of the Neolithic. But nowadays the best-informed prehistorians place them in the late Meso-lithic, corresponding approximately to the extreme end of the Maglemosian, while the Portuguese heaps of sea-shells seem to be a trifle older.

In France there is a special form of industry resembling that of the Danish Erteböllian, the first phases of which are undoubtedly contemporary with the Mesolithic and which is often regarded as belonging to the earliest phase of the Neolithic. This is the industry known as Campignian, because it is well represented in the foundations of huts at Campigny, near Blangy-sur-Bresle (Seine-Inférieure). The characteristic implements are paring-knives (tranchets) and picks; there are no polished axes, but coarse pottery is known.[14]

MAGLEMOSIAN

If the question of the Mesolithic was first raised in France, it is in the North of Europe that it has been most scientifically studied.[15]

In the first place, we owe to Danish prehistorians our knowlege of another and important aspect of the Mesolithic, the Maglemosian, of which the

[12] Vignard, E., 'Une nouvelle industrie lithique: Le Sébilien' (Bull. de l'Inst. français d'Archéol. orientale, XII, Cairo, 1923).

[13] Early works by Steenstrup, J., Worsaae. A fine, more recent book by Madsen, Muller, S., Neergaard, Petersen, Rostrup, Steenstrup, R. J. V., and Winge, H., Affalsdynger fra stenalderen i Danmark (Copenhagen, 1900).

[14] Salmon, P., d'Adult du Mesnil, G., and Capitan, L., 'Le Campignien' (Revue de l'École d'Anthrop., 1898). See in particular the important monograph by Nougier, L. R., Les civilisations campigniennes en Europe occidentale (Le Mans, 1950).

[15] An excellent account, with bibliography, in Clark, J. G. D., The Mesolithic Settlement of Northern Europe (Cambridge, 1936).

type is found in the peat-bog or great fen (*maglemose* in Danish) of Mullerup on Seeland.[16]

This is a culture whose centre is in Denmark and which spread chiefly to Southern Sweden, the Baltic zone as far as Esthonia, and even to Britain. The Maglemosian industry, which is rich and very varied, shows that its possessors were specially adapted to a forest life. Pike-fishers and bird-hunters, they lived in small groups in the vicinity of lakes, rivers and marshes. Along with Tardenoisian microlithic flints, sometimes found still attached to throwing weapons of bone or wood, there is an industry of larger flints—paring-knives, axes, adzes, hammers and pebbles with edges worn by rubbing. The industry in wood was no less developed and includes clubs, axes, helves, oars and what seem to be dog-sleighs. The horns of deer (Red Deer, Roe Deer, Moose) and bones were used to make pierced staves, a great variety of harpoons (Fig. 238), fish-hooks, and the like. Many of these objects are decorated with designs that are almost always purely geometric and carried out in a rather special manner. No pottery or truly polished stone has ever been found, but the Dog was already domesticated.

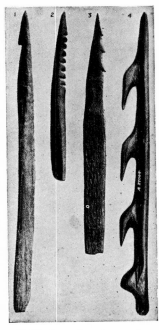

238 Maglemosian bone harpoons from the Island of Seeland. One-third natural size. (After J. Clark)

In particular, we must briefly summarize the excellent studies of the chronology and climatology of post-glacial times made by Scandinavian scientists.

On the one hand, thanks to the *varve* method (see p. 63), geologists have been able to determine the duration of several successive phases of the general retreat of the ice, from the epoch of their maximum advance to the south of Berlin (about 40,000 years ago) to the moment when they occupied no more than their centres of origin in the Scandinavian mountains (about 10,000 years ago).

On the other hand, these geologists disclosed to us the geographical and topographical changes that took place during the same period in the North of Europe under the double influence of eustatic movements of the sea-level of a general nature (see p. 33) and of movements of an isostatic, or orogenic, nature that were more local in character (Fig. 239).

Thus we know that after the regions of Denmark and the extreme South of Sweden had been freed from ice, the site of the Baltic was occupied by

[16] Sarauw, G. F. L., 'En stenalders boplads i Maglemose ved Mullerup' (*Aarboger for Nordisk Oldkyndighed*, 1903, and also in *Prähistorische Zeitschrift*, 1911 and 1914).

a sea which was more extensive than the present Baltic and communicated along a wide front with the North Sea. This 'sea with *Yoldia*', which was arctic in temperature, dated, according to de Geer, from about 10,000 years ago (8000 B.C.).

PERIODS	PHYSICAL GEOGRAPHY CLIMATE	FOREST FLORA	FAUNA	INDUSTRIES
NEOLITHIC 3000 B.C.	SUB-BOREAL CLIMATE	AS AT PRESENT	DOMESTIC ANIMALS	POLISHED STONE
MESOLITHIC UPPER 5000	SEA WITH LITTORINA / ATLANTIC CLIMATE / WARM AND DAMP / CLIMATIC OPTIMUM	OAK FOREST MIXED WITH ELM AND ALDER	DOG / ELK RARE / REINDEER EXTINCT	ERTEBÖLLIAN / CAMPIGNIAN / MIDDLE TARDENOISIAN
MESOLITHIC MIDDLE 6800	LAKE WITH ANCYLUS / BOREAL CLIMATE / WARM AND DRY / CONTINENTAL	PREDOMINANCE OF BIRCH AND PINE (PINE PERIOD) DEVELOPMENT OF HAZEL	DOG / ELK NUMEROUS / LAST REINDEER	MAGLEMOSIAN / MIDDLE TARDENOISIAN
MESOLITHIC LOWER 8300	SEA WITH VOLDIA THEN BEGINNING OF LAKE WITH ANCYLUS. PRE-BOREAL CLIMATE PROGRESSIVE RISE IN TEMPERATURE	BIRCH, PINE AND WILLOW	REINDEER AND OTHER EARLIER FORMS BUT NO MORE LEMMING	AZILIAN / LOWER TARDENOISIAN
END OF THE PALAEOLITHIC B.C.	SUB-ARCTIC CLIMATE	BIRCH AND DWARF WILLOW	STEPPE AND TUNDRA FAUNA / LEMMING	

239 Approximate chronology of Mesolithic times in Northern Europe. (Partly after J. Clark)

The retreat of the glaciers was virtually at end when an upward movement of the earth, or emersion, little by little broke the links between the

Baltic and the North Sea, and around 7500 B.C. the former became a stretch of fresh water, the 'lake with *Ancylus*'.

Some 2,500 years later, towards 5000 B.C., a new marine transgression transformed the *Ancylus* lake into a 'sea with *Littorina*' rather more extensive and more saline than the present Baltic. The establishment of this latter, in about 3000 B.C., marks the end of Mesolithic times and the advent, in these regions, of a true Neolithic.

The variations in climate correlative with these geographical changes have been revealed by palaeobotanical researches, some of them carried out long ago, based on the examination of the vegetative organs of plants preserved in the peat-bogs, others, more recent, on the analysis of pollen. The latter make it possible to obtain statistics of the principal components of the forests coeval with the strata studied from an archaeological point of view. In this way, precise data have been established as to climatic conditions during each of the various phases of the Mesolithic.[17]

The arctic and subarctic conditions corresponding to the first movements of retreat of the Scandinavian *inlandsis*, with a tundra fauna and flora, were succeeded by a less harsh period, called *Pre-Boreal*, which permitted the formation of peat-bogs and forests composed almost exclusively of Willows, Birches and Pines. This was the epoch of the *Yoldia* sea. The mean temperature then rose rapidly, during the epoch of the *Ancylus* lake: this was the *Boreal* period, followed by the *Atlantic* period, which was warm and humid and corresponded to the *Littorina* sea. During this period the mean temperature for July rose to 63° F, a figure comparable to that which now characterizes the North-West of France. This 'climatic optimum', which dates from 6000 B.C., was accompanied by a great development of forests of Oaks, Limes, Elms, Hazels and other plants, whose area of distribution extended much farther north than it does today. Then the climate became drier (the *Sub-Boreal* phase), and after a few further vicissitudes, of a secondary nature, we come to historical times.

Of the various Mesolithic facies we have just described, the Azilian, probably the most ancient, may be contemporary, in the South of France, with the *Yoldia* sea in the North. The Tardenoisian, sometimes observed in position on top of the Azilian, corresponds approximately to the whole extent of the Mesolithic and continues into the Neolithic. The Maglemosian levels, dating from the 'Pine Age', occupy the land that had emerged from the sea and now bordered the *Ancylus* lake. It is a forest facies of the Tardenoisian with a few characters that seem to indicate a prolongation of the Azilian period in the North of Europe. The Erteböllian, from the Danish kitchen middens, is a coastal facies of the Maglemosian, very highly developed at the time of the maximum extension of the *Littorina* sea. It therefore corresponds to the 'climatic optimum'. The French Campignian, very

[17] On this subject, see Dubois, G., 'L'analyse pollinique des tourbes et son application à l'étude du Quaternaire et de la Préhistoire' (*L'Anthropologie*, XLII, 1932). Lehman, J. P., 'L'analyse pollinique en Suède, d'après les travaux de von Post' (*Ann. de Paléontologie*, XXXV, 1949).

similar to the Erteböllian, is confined to the initial stage of the Neolithic in France.

A Preliminary Study: Races and Peoples

Before taking up again the chronological thread of human prehistory where we left it, we must, in order to simplify the continuation of our account, summarize the state of our anthropological knowledge regarding the modern peoples of Europe with whom this account will finally land us.

We have just written '*anthropological* knowledge', because, as a matter of fact, historians and geographers consider only peoples or nationalities; but anthropologists, who are first and foremost naturalists, must deal only with *races*. This word being used, not in the literary sense, which is generally metaphorical in meaning, but in its true sense, the general biological sense and the physical sense, that of a variation of the species more or less fixed by heredity.

For a long time now certain clearsighted men in the historians' camp, and in the naturalists' as well, have laid stress on the extremely vexatious confusion which has arisen from the use of the words race, people, nation, language, culture or civilization, but the distinctions and the appropriate uses of these different expressions have not yet penetrated into the minds even of the enlightened public. Even today the most distinguished and most academic authors, when dealing with human classifications, use quite indiscriminately and in a completely wrong sense the word *race*, when they would express themselves more correctly in speaking of their horses and dogs.

We must really impress on our minds the fact that the *race*, by which we mean the continuity of a physical type transmitting blood relationships, represents an essentially natural group, possibly having and, as a rule, actually having nothing in common with the people, the nationality, the language, and the customs, which correspond to purely artificial groupings of no anthropological significance and connected only with those historical events of which they are the products. Thus there is no Breton *race*, but a Breton *people*; no French *race*, but a French *nation*; no Aryan *race*, but Aryan *languages*; no Latin *race*, but a Latin *civilization*. De Quatrefages wrote: 'A people changes its language, its customs, its crafts, sometimes in a relatively short period; it cannot with the same rapidity lose its stature, its colour, and the form of its skull.'[18] The result is that maps, essentially

[18] An example of the extraordinary confusion which may result from a purely literary terminology is shown by the use of the word *Celtic*, which signifies to some people a language, to others a special civilization, and which is often used, rightly or wrongly, as synonymous with Gallic; to the mind of certain authors it represents the blond type, of great stature and elongated skull, found in the north; according to others it should be applied to the dark type, of small stature and round head, belonging to the Central Plateau or the Alps. Anthropologists agree that it would be best to leave this expression to the archaeologists and historians. 'Ethnographical names are the bugbear of anthropology', said Salomon Reinach, and with good reason.

multi-coloured and changing, of peoples, nations, or languages, cannot bear and never do bear any resemblance to a map of races.

It is really very difficult to make a racial map, because of the multiple movements of peoples which have taken place over the whole of Europe since the end of Palaeolithic times, and because of the innumerable crossings of every kind which have resulted.[19]

'The anthropologist who undertakes a history of the human races', said de Quatrefages again,[20] 'is faced with a task exactly similar to that of the zoologist who attempts to set forth the races of one of our domestic species.' It must be added that in the case of Man the problem is even more difficult, because crossings take place by chance and no longer under the influence of rational selection. The commingling of races has been both more intense and more haphazard. So it is that in anthropology, more than in systematic zoology, and more in Europe than elsewhere, the race can scarcely represent anything but an abstraction, a sort of ideal type, around which are grouped variations resulting from combinations, or rather from associations of characters borrowed from different primitive elements.

'Neither the type nor the race, in the present state of mankind, are objective realities,' said Topinard.[21] This is not to say, however, that the search for this ideal physical type is altogether an idle pursuit. We can still perceive individuals or groups of individuals who have remained more akin to their original stocks, either through having escaped, by isolation, from outside influences, or through possessing in themselves a combination of dominant characters similar to that of the ideal type.[22]

In practice, we may define as races those human groups which possess in common the same physical characters, taking as some of the most important, stature of body, form of skull and face, and colours of eyes and hair.

THE RACES OF EUROPE

For half a century, anthropologists have devoted themselves to laborious investigations in an attempt to rediscover or reconstruct those primitive physical types which represent in Europe the common stock, a stock now overlaid by successive ethnographical alluvials, reshuffled again and again. Thousands of living individuals and skeletons have been examined, studied,

[19] There can be no doubt that great movements of peoples took place during Palaeolithic times, and that in great part they were correlated with the migrations of faunas, for, in these remote ages, Man was less independent of the influence of physical phenomena than he later became. But we still have no means of tracing these movements, which, moreover, were limited by the geographical conditions of the Pleistocene Period. In Mesolithic and Neolithic times, which are closer to our own day, communications between Europe and Asia became much easier and the great migrations stand out more clearly. Thanks to the development of his industry, Man shook himself free more readily from physical conditions: his massed movements hardly ever originate except from his own will or from that of his leaders.

[20] Quatrefages, A. de, *Histoire générale des races humaines*, p. 188.

[21] Topinard, P., *L'Homme dans la Nature*, p. 43.

[22] We must, in fact, distinguish permanence of type from permanence of characters, the latter being much more frequent than the former.

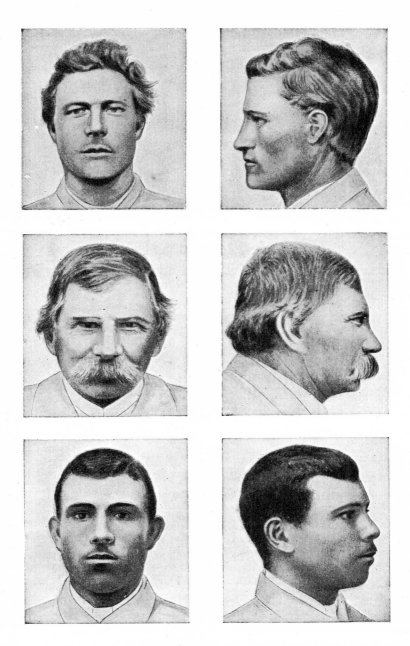

240 Representatives of the three physical types of Europe, full face and in profile. Above, **Nordic** race (Norwegian). In centre, Alpine race (Austrian). Below, Mediterranean **race** (Sicilian). (After Ripley)

measured, with a view to deciding the blood affinities and natural descent of each. In France, Broca, de Quatrefages and Hamy, Topinard, Collignon, and Deniker have published important works on this subject. England, Germany, Italy and Scandinavia have been the centres of similar enquiries.[23] The American anthropologist Ripley has written a book of the highest value, illustrated by many maps, on *The Races of Europe*. These maps, like those of Deniker, present a medley of colours and figures, which clearly reflect at first glance the extraordinary complexity of the human mosaic in the European region.

The conclusions of the most eminent French anthropologists differ from each other as regards the number of divisions or subdivisions adopted, as well as in the terminology used and in certain other details of secondary importance; but they agree in distinguishing three main groups, which are likewise admitted by Retzius, the Swedish worker. These three great subdivisions of the species or race of *White Man*,[24] the only divisions which we need examine for the purpose we have in view, are as follows:

	Dolichocephalic (long-headed)	Fair, of large stature . . 1.	Nordic race
Homo sapiens albus		Dark, of small stature . . 2.	Mediterranean race
	Brachycephalic (round-headed) . . 3.		Alpine race Dinaric race East-European race

THE NORDIC RACE

The first of these types is characterized by having a long dolichocephalic skull, long narrow face, straight fine aquiline nose, large stature, blue eyes, fair hair, and rosy skin.

At the present day it is widespread in the north of Europe, round the North Sea and the Baltic Sea, in Scotland, in the north and east of England, in the east of Ireland, in Flanders, Holland and Denmark, North Germany, the Baltic Provinces, Russia, the coasts of Finland, and especially in Norway and Sweden. It is also found, less pure or in sporadic groups, throughout a wide belt encircling the outer limits of the area we have just mentioned; so far as France is concerned, in the basin of the Seine, and especially in Normandy.

This is the type which the great Swedish naturalist, Linnaeus, had in view when he referred to his *Homo europaeus*. Following the example of

[23] For bibliography, see Deniker, J., *Races et peuples de la terre* (Paris, 1900; 2nd Ed., 1926). Ripley, W. Z., *The Races of Europe* (London, 1900). Coon, C. S., *The Races of Europe* (New York, 1938). Vallois, H., *Les races humaines* (3rd Ed., Paris, 1951).

[24] All Europeans are white, with the exception of a few enclaves; they belong to *Homo sapiens albus* (see p. 72). It is this group, species or race which we must subdivide into races or sub-races.

certain anthropologists, we might reserve this term for the small section of mankind we have just described. But for various reasons, we consider it better to use Deniker's term *nordicus*. And if we wish accurately to define this first type, in a monogenistic sense, we must say: *Homo sapiens albus nordicus*. For convenience in speaking and writing, and without in any way prejudicing the question of monogenism or polygenism, we shall simply say *Homo nordicus*. It is useful to know, however, that the following terms also correspond more or less closely to this designation: the *Scandinavian* race, Ripley's *Teutonic* race, or the *Germanic* race of numerous authors, the *Kymric* race of Broca, the *Homo indo-europaeus dolichomorphus nordicus* of Giuffrida-Ruggeri, etc.

THE MEDITERRANEAN RACE

The second type is also characterized by a dolichocephalic skull and long and narrow face, but in this case the stature is small or medium, the body slender, the nose larger, the eyes are very dark, the hair black or brown, and the skin swarthy.

At the present day it occupies the whole surrounding area as well as the islands of the Mediterranean Sea: the Iberian Peninsula, the South of France, Provence, Corsica and Sardinia, Italy southward of Rome, Sicily, the shores of the Aegean Sea, and North Africa. Mixed or in a sporadic state, it is found on the Atlantic coast of France and in the west of the British Isles, particularly in Wales.

It is often described by the very expressive name of *Homo mediterraneus*, which corresponds to the *Mediterranean branch* of Sergi, the *H. meridionalis* of Wilser, the *Homo indo-europaeus dolichomorphus mediterraneus* of Giuffrida-Ruggeri, the *Ibero-insular* race of Deniker, and to the Iberians of historians.[25]

BRACHYCEPHALIC RACES

This third group is clearly distinguished from the first two by the shape of its head. For a long time it was thought to correspond to only one type, which was described as small and thickset, with a broad, round face, a rather broad nose, light or dark brown eyes, and hair black or chestnut.

This was the *Homo alpinus* of the classical anthropologists, the *Homo indo-europaeus brachymorphus alpinus* of Giuffrida-Ruggeri, the *Occidental* or *Cévenole* race of Deniker, the *Celtic* or *Rhaetic*, *Celto-Slav*, *Arverne*, *Laponoid*, and *Armenoid* races of other authors. Driven like a wedge between the Mediterranean and Nordic races, it was thought to occupy the greater part of Russia, Asia Minor, the Balkans, Bohemia, Switzerland, the Western Alps, the Central Massif and the South-West of France, the Cantabrian coast, and North Italy.

[25] Along with Deniker, we can distinguish as a sub-race or sub-type an Atlanto-Mediterranean group, mesocephalic and of large stature, limited to certain points on the Atlantic and Mediterranean coasts of France, Spain and Northern Italy. We mention it here because it has been claimed as a survival of the Cro-Magnon race.

Today we know that the European brachycephalics do not all belong to the same race. We must distinguish three which seem to justify the title of independent races: the *Alpine* race, which answers to the foregoing description, but is limited to the central and western parts of the brachycephalic area of Europe; the *Dinaric* race, also dark, but extremely tall and with a dysharmonic head, which lives mainly in the Balkans; and the *East-European* race, also called the *Eastern* or *East-Baltic* race, which is of medium

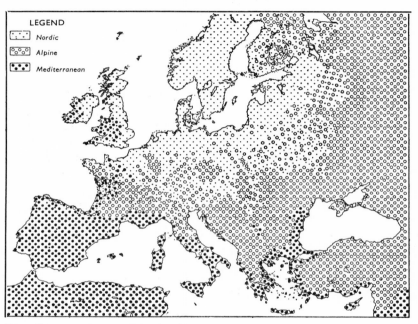

241 Very diagrammatic map of the distribution of the three principal European racial groups.
(After Ripley and Madison Grant)

In this map the designation 'Alpine' covers the three brachycephalic European races

height, with prominent cheek-bones, very fair hair and light eyes, and is chiefly found in Poland and in Central and Southern Russia.

Needless to say, this modern geographical distribution of the three principal physical types, which we have succeeded in disentangling from the European ethnographical medley, is only diagrammatic. Their limits are far from being clearly defined; there are imperceptible transitions from one region to the next; there are also intrusions of all sorts, islets all but swamped in a different mass. There are in particular innumerable combinations of characters, producing gradual transitions from one type to the other, and we have seen that this could not but be so. But, in view of the goal we are striving to reach, we must treat the subject broadly. From this standpoint we consider that the disentangling and elucidating of these three principal European types is a real conquest of anthropology.

To sum up, as the accompanying map (Fig. 241) shows, the distribution of these races follows the general lines of the physical geography of our continent, while it is quite independent of its political geography. The three names which we have adopted, *Nordic*, *Mediterranean*, and *Alpine*, describe this distribution well. The Nordic is the man of the northern countries with their harsh climate, misty horizons, and long, pale nights; the Mediterranean type of the southern countries is also the product of his environment, of an easy life in a warm climate and bright sunshine; the Alpine type is the result of an age-long adaptation to mountainous and barren regions. Each of these three physical types also possesses psychical characters on which we shall not lay stress here, but which will emerge in the course of this account.

After this digression, the utility of which the reader will readily perceive, let us return to our main subject, and try to form an idea, from the osteological evidences now in our possession, of the physical characters of the peoples that lived in Europe during the ages of transition from the end of the Palaeolithic to the beginning of the Neolithic.

AZILIANS AND MAGLEMOSIANS

Beginning with what we believe to be the earliest phase of the Mesolithic, we must first record that Piette collected at Mas d'Azil human bone-remains coloured red. They are too fragmentary to enable us to determine the chief characters of the race they present.

Not far from Mas d'Azil, at Montardit (Ariège), there lies a small cave known as the 'Trou Violet'. Here, in 1924, Ida and Paul Vaillant-Couturier[26] found two burials belonging to the Azilian period and each containing a skeleton.

A study of these human remains, which were severely damaged, was published seven years later by R. Sawtell.[27] They belonged to two adult male individuals. Small in stature (5 ft. 2 ins.), these Pyrenean Mesolithics had oval, slightly mesocephalic heads with a high vault and low capacity (1,389 cubic centimetres). They bear considerable resemblance to the skull from Kaufertsberg in Bavaria, also Mesolithic, which we shall discuss later.

It seems that the skull of a child of seven or eight that was found in 1927 by Gaillard, Pissot and Cote[28] in a deposit—originally believed to be Magdalenian—of the prehistoric shelter at La Genière (Ain) should be ascribed to the same period. This skull, which was in very poor condition, exhibited certain Negroid characters.

[26] Vaillant-Couturier, I. and P., 'La grotte azilienne du "Trou Violet", à Montardit, Ariège' (*L'Anthropologie*, XXXVIII, 1928).

[27] Sawtell, R., 'Azilian Skeletal Remains from Montardit (Ariège)' (*Papers Peabody Museum of Amer. Archaeol. and Ethn.*, XI, 1931).

[28] Gaillard, G., Pissot, C., and Cote, J., 'L'abri préhistorique de La Genière, à Serrières-sur-Ain' (*L'A.*, XXXVII, 1927). Peyrony, D., 'Mise au point au sujet du squelette préhistorique de La Genière, Ain' (*L'A.*, LIII, 1949).

Before describing more important palaeo-anthropological discoveries, we must first say a few words about older, but unfortunately not very valuable, finds made in the countries of the North, otherwise so rich and so well studied from an archaeological point of view.

The Maglemosian locality of Stangenäs, in Bohusland, Sweden, yielded in 1843 remains of two human skeletons reduced to a skull-cap and a few limb bones indicating a tall stature. They were studied by numerous authors. Fuerst, the most recent, found that the skull-cap, which was distinctly dolichocephalic, bore a resemblance to that of Cro-Magnon Man. He considered that it represented a variety of the Nordic race, of which Stangenäs Man was the oldest representative known on Scandinavian soil.[29] It is important to add that, if the geological age of the deposit (a beach of the *Ancylus* lake) is certain, doubt exists as to the contemporaneity of the skeletons, which might have come from a more recent burial.

Other human bone-remains were extracted later from two neighbouring Danish peat-bogs, Svaerdborg and Mullerup, on the island of Seeland. Their fragmentary state and the youth of the majority of the individuals to whom the remains belonged greatly diminish their scientific interest. Thus the descriptions given of them by Danish anthropologists are contradictory. While Nielsen[30] finds in them persistent Neandertal characteristics, which is manifestly mistaken, his colleague Arnborg[31] declares that there is nothing to distinguish the Men of the old Danish peat-bogs from the majority of living Europeans.

A few similar discoveries have been made at various places in North Germany, but the uncertainty as to their age deprives them, in our eyes, of any scientific value. An exception should perhaps be made in favour of two skulls dredged, along with objects of Mesolithic age, from Lake Pritzerber, not far from Brandenburg. These skulls are dolichocephalic. Reche[32] considers them to be Nordic and to display affinities on the one hand with Chancelade Man, and on the other with the first Neolithics in Silesia and Bohemia.

Rather better dated from a chronological point of view are two skulls collected by J. Butter from the sands and gravels near Deventer in Holland, which seem to be coeval with the Boreal period. They are both dolichocephalic, with a low, very slightly carinate vault and narrow forehead. In only one was the face present, and this was dysharmonic with the cranium.[33] An incomplete skull-cap found some distance from this spot, at Hengelo,

[29] Fuerst, C., 'Strangenäskraniets renässans' (*Fornvännen*, XX, 1925).

[30] 'Squelettes humains du plus ancien âge de la Pierre découverts dans les tourbières de Svaerdborg and Mullerup' (*Mém. de la Soc. roy. des Antiquaires du Nord*, 1920–24).

[31] Arnborg, J., 'Fragments of mandibles and isolated teeth of Men of the oldest Stone Age in Denmark' (in Danish in *Vidensk. Medd. fra Dansk naturhist. Foren*, Vol. 1925).

[32] Reche, O., 'Die Schädel aus der Ancyluszeit vom Pritzerber See' (*Arch. f. Anthr.*, XXI, 1925).

[33] Vallois, H., 'Les ossements humains de Koerhuisbeek près Deventer, Hollande' (*Verh. nederl. Akad. Wetenschappen*, Vol. XL, 1943).

although it was slightly Mesocephalic, appeared to be of the same physical type.[34] A comparison of these Dutch 'Maglemosians' with Ofnet Man, whom we shall discuss later, shows a resemblance to the dolichocephalic type from the Bavarian bed.

Before we leave this series of unimportant or inadequately dated osteological evidences, we will add a few words concerning other human bone-remains discovered in Great Britain and summarily described by Keith.[35] Of five skulls found at different times in Aveline's Hole, near Bristol, three are dolichocephalic and two brachycephalic. In 1925, an extremely well preserved skull, even more brachycephalic than those from Aveline's Hole, was found at the entrance to the large and celebrated Kent's Cavern in South Devon. Unfortunately, the age of these various specimens has not been clearly established, and the same is true of a skull found in 1894 in Mac-Arthur's Cave, near Oban, in Scotland.

On the other hand, the human bone-remains unearthed in 1928 in Kilgreany Cave, near Dungarvan, County Waterford, Ireland, were clearly in their original position; they belonged to several individuals and dated from the Upper Palaeolithic or Mesolithic period. One well preserved skull is dolichocephalic, with a short, broad face and narrow nose. Its affinities seem to be with the forms of the Continental Upper Palaeolithic.

We shall discuss the Mesolithic Men of Palestine when we deal with Asia; let us say at once that they display resemblances to the European Mesolithics, particularly with those from Mugem, in Portugal, described below.

OFNET MAN

We now come to osteological evidences that are far more important than the foregoing, of clearly established age, and consequently much more instructive.

Ofnet Cave, near Nördlingen, in Bavaria, was excavated in 1907 and 1908 by R. Schmidt. Its deposits comprised a series of layers of the Reindeer Age, overlaid by a deposit of Azilian age. Two shallow pits or trenches contained a large number of human skulls, enveloped in a mass of red ochre, having their jaws intact and arranged concentrically close to each other, as if in a nest, with their faces turned towards the west. The large trench contained twenty-seven skulls, the small one six (Fig. 242). The skulls of women and children, which were most numerous, were decorated with the canine teeth of deer and perforated shells, similar to those from Mas d'Azil. A great many of the skulls bore the marks of blows, and this, together with the fact that, apart from some cervical vertebrae, there was no trace of the

---

[34] Florschutz, F., van Vlek, I., van den Broek, A., Bursch, F., 'The Pleistocene Human Skull from Hengelo' (*Ibid.*, XXXIX, 1936).

[35] Keith, A., *New Discoveries relating to the Antiquity of Man* (London, 1931).

other parts of the skeleton, leads us to suppose that these individuals were beheaded after a violent death.[36]

It was possible to achieve a more or less satisfactory reconstruction of some twenty skulls, which already present an extraordinary mixture of types. There are dolichocephalic forms, brachycephalic forms, and intermediate forms (the cephalic index ranging from 70 to 89). The first (five individuals)

242 Burial in the smallest trench at Ofnet. (After a drawing by R. Schmidt)

have long faces, harmonious in their proportions; they thus differ from the dolichocephalics of the Cro-Magnon race. Schliz regards them as belonging to the group of *Homo mediterraneus*. The second, eight in number, represent the most ancient brachycephalics known with certainty, the first arrivals of *Homo alpinus*. The remaining eight, which are mesocephalic, are held by the German author to be products of crossing, which is far from proven.

Since then, the Ofnet material has been studied at intervals by various anthropologists, notably by Scheidt,[37] who at the same time described a new skull found in 1912 at Kaufertsberg, near Lierheim, in a bed not far from Ofnet and of the same age. All authorities are agreed in proclaiming the heterogeneity of this collection of Bavarian Mesolithic bone-remains,

[36] Schmidt, R. R., *Die diluviale Vorzeit Deutschlands* (Stuttgart, 1912); the third part containing anthropological notes by Schliz, A. See also Breuil, H., 'Le gisement quaternaire d'Ofnet' (*L'Anthropologie*, XX, 1909). Mollison, T., 'Zeichen gewaltsamer Verletzungen an den Ofnet-Schädeln' (Anthrop. Anz., XIII, 1936).

[37] Scheidt, W., *Die eiszeitlichen Schädelfunde aus der grossen Ofnet-Höhle und von Kaufertsberg bei Nordlingen* (Munich, 1923).

and in distinguishing the same three groups according to their cephalic indices. Differences between the various authors relate to the affinities of each of these groups with other fossil or living races, to their subdivision into secondary groups, and to the problematic role of crossing in the formation of the mesocephalic group. The true dolichocephalics have been compared with certain types from the Upper Palaeolithic and occasionally even regarded as Nordics. The mesocephalic skulls, including that from Kaufertsberg, display a marked resemblance to those from Téviec which we shall discuss shortly.

Three skulls, probably of Azilian age, found in 1938 in one of the caves of the Hohlenstein, in the Swabian Jura, and also buried in isolation with a few cervical vertebrae, offer a striking resemblance to the majority of the individuals from Ofnet.[38] The same is true of a skeleton discovered at Bottendorf, in Saxony, in a stratum that was undoubtedly Late Mesolithic (beginning of the *Littorina* sea), which possessed a dolichocephalic and dysharmonic skull.[39]

MUGEM MAN

Great mounds of sea-shells accompanied by a Tardenoisian industry and very rich in human skeletons have long been known in the low-lying valley of the Taugs at Mugem, in Portugal, especially in the small hills known as Cabeço d'Arruda and Moita de Sebastião. The old discoveries were described in 1865.[40] But the osteological evidences were seriously studied for the first time twenty years later, by Paula e Oliveria.[41] He was followed by several other authors, in particular Mendes Corrêa.[42] Although examination was confined to a very limited number of individuals, all investigators agree in recognizing the existence of two quite distinct types.

The first, much the more numerous, is dolichocephalic, small in stature (about 5 ft. 3 ins.), with a dolichocephalic skull that is high and narrow (hypsistenocephalic) and of poor cranial capacity; the face is long, of harmonious proportions, and slightly prognathous; the eyebrow ridges are projecting and the nose of medium breadth. This is the 'Mugem race' of Quatrefages, and the *Homo afer*, var. *taganus* of Mendes Corrêa, who finds

---

[38] Gieseler, W., 'Anthropologischer Bericht über die Kopfbestattung und die Knochentrümmerstätte des Hohlensteins im Lonetal' (*Verh. der D. Gesellschaft für Rassenforschung*, IX, 1938).

[39] Heberer, G., and Bicker, F., 'Der mesolithische Fund von Bottendorf a. d. Unstrut' (*Anthrop. Anz.*, XVII, 1940).

[40] Pereira da Costa, F. A., *Da existencia do homen em epochas remotas no valle do Tejo. Primeiro opusculo: Noticia sobre es esqueletos humanos descobertos no Cabeço da Arruda* (Lisbon, 1865)

[41] Paula e Oliveira in É. Cartailhac's fine work, *Les âges préhistoriques de l'Espagne et du Portugal* (Paris, 1886).

[42] Mendes Corrêa, A. A., 'A propos des caractères inférieur de quelques crânes préhistoriques du Portugal' (*Arch. de Anat. e Antrop.*, III, 1917); 'Origins of the Portuguese' (*Amer. Journ. of Phys. Anthrop.*, II, No. 2, 1919); 'Nouvelles observations sur l'*Homo teganus*' (*Revue anthropologique*, XXXIII, 1923). See also Ataide, A., 'Novos esqueletos umanos dos concheiros mesoliticos de Muge' (*C. R. du premier Congrès du Monde portugais*, Lisbon, 1940).

in it what he regards as archaic characters, Negroid and Australian, and believes that we have here very ancient representatives of *Homo mediterraneus*, possessing Ethiopian traits and in no way descended from the Cro-Magnon type. According to this view, the race evolved progressively during the Neolithic period under the influence of higher peoples more closely related to the modern Portuguese, amongst whom traces of this race may occasionally be discovered as survivals.

The second type, represented by only a few skulls, has been described as brachycephalic and is said to belong to *Homo alpinus*. One of the skulls belonging to this group exhibits Mongoloid features in the face.

In 1930 one of us re-examined the Mugem bone-remains and extended this examination to all the specimens preserved in the Museum of the Geological Survey of Portugal, most of which had never before been studied.[43] Like his predecessors, he noted that the great majority of the individuals belonged to a dolichocephalic type whose characters he detailed as follows: medium cerebral capacity, with a high vault, a face of moderate length and less in harmony with the skull than had previously been stated, a nose of medium breadth, in some cases a more or less accentuated sub-nasal prognathism and a well marked chin. A certain number of these characteristics recall the great Cro-Magnon race, and more particularly the Combe-Capelle type and the Eastern Cro-Magnons. Other features give the Mugem dolichocephalics a resemblance to the present-day Mediterranean group, an important conclusion to which we shall return later.

As for the so-called brachycephalic skulls, these are far less numerous than the foregoing and all present *post mortem* deformations, which largely explain their shape. Detailed examination reveals that in reality they were at most mesocephalic. There seems no justification for regarding them as a separate group; 'it is very probable that these mesocephalics are only a variant of the true dolichocephalics.'

TÉVIEC MAN

Téviec is a granite islet near the Quiberon peninsula (Morbihan), where, superimposed upon an emerged beach that is probably Pleistocene, there is an interesting settlement with burials of Mesolithic age, admirably explored by Marthe and Saint-Just Péquart.[44] It represents a kind of kitchen midden with burials dating from a time when the island of Téviec was linked to the nearby mainland, in consequence of a fall in the sea level probably contemporary with the *Ancylus* lake, that is to say at a period when part of the present English Channel was dry and England was widely joined to the Continent. Palaeontological and archaeological evidences agree in showing that the Téviec Mesolithics were at one and the same time fishers and

[43] Vallois, H., 'Recherches sur les ossements mésolithiques de Mugem' (*L'Anthropologie*, XL, 1930).
[44] Péquart, M. and St-J., 'Un gisement mésolithique en Bretagne' (*L'Anthropologie*, XXXVIII, 1928); 'La nécropole mésolithique de Téviec' (*Ibid.*, XXXIX, 1929).

hunters of mammals (Deer, Wild Pig, etc.) and birds. They must have shared features of both the Tardenoisians and the Maglemosians. They had already domesticated the Dog, but they seem to have been totally ignorant of polished stone and pottery.

The arrangement of the burials, ten in number and without fixed orientation, varied considerably. One of the most curious was formed by a heap of red deer antlers enveloping or crowning the human bone-remains (Fig. 243). These graves contained from one to six skeletons of men, women

243 One of the Mesolithic burials at Téviec, with crowns of stag's antlers
(After M. and Saint-Just Péquart)

and children. The bodies were all found in a doubled-up position with the legs forcibly bent. The bones had been sprinked with red ochre, like those of so many skeletons from the Upper Palaeolithic. They were likewise accompanied by various objects of stone or bone and decorated with shells.

The human skeletons from Téviec were prepared and studied at the French Institute of Human Palaeontology.[45] They comprised 15 adults— 7 men and 8 women—aged between twenty and forty-seven years; a girl between fourteen and sixteen years; and 7 children from nil to five years. By virtue of their number and their excellent state of preservation, these

45 Péquart, M. and St-J., Boule, M., and Vallois, H., 'Téviec, station-nécropole mésolithique du Morbihan' (Arch. de l'Institut de Paléontologie humaine, Memoir 18, Paris, 1937).

evidences are of exceptional value for the study of Mesolithic peoples.

The following are the principal characters of the adults. The skulls present a massive appearance. The crania are thick and relatively large (average cerebral capacity approximately 1,550 cubic centimetres). Their cephalic index, from 70 to 80, indicates moderate dolichocephaly or mesocephaly. The cranial vault is high, distinctly carinate, with an almost oval contour. The supra-orbital arches are moderately developed. The forehead is wide and rounded. The mastoid apophyses are short, the zygomatic arches slight. The face is broad and low, with rectangular orbits, a mesorrhinian nasal aperture and a wide palate. The lower jaws are powerful with a projecting chin. The teeth are large with certain primitive characters in the structure of the true molars. There are a few rare cases of caries.

Téviec Man's stature was small: an average of 5 ft. 2 ins. in the male individuals and 4 ft. 11 ins. in the females. The skeleton as a whole is generally rather slight.

We are happy to add that the majority of the osteological evidences from Téviec have been presented to the French Institute of Human Palaeontology by M. and Mme. Péquart. These skilled investigators have discovered, on the neighbouring island of Hoëdic, a similar layer to that on Téviec with bone-remains and burials of exactly the same type.[46]

A few other French discoveries remain to be mentioned. First, there is a complete and perfectly preserved human skeleton extracted in 1928 by MM. Niederlender and Lacam from a Mesolithic deposit in the cave of Cuzoul, near Gramat (Lot.). This skeleton, which has been given by its finders to the French Institute of Human Palaeontology, is dolichocephalic with a face of harmonious proportions; its characters are intermediate between those of Téviec Man and Mugem Man.[47] This seems also to be true of two other skeletons unearthed shortly before 1939, the study of which was interrupted by subsequent events—one of them discovered by Dr. Jude at Rochereil, in the commune of Grand-Brassac (Dordogne), the other of Azilian, or possibly Magdalenian, age found by M. Desrut in the little cave of Le Cheix (Puy-de-Dôme). A fourth skeleton, found earlier not far from Les Eyzies, on the Barbeau Rock, could not be examined.

More recently, L. Coulonges unearthed a skull from a Mesolithic stratum on the Allan Rock, near Sauveterre-la-Lémance (Lot-et-Garonne). It was slightly mesocephalic and many of its characters recalled those of the inhabitants of Téviec.

Finally, to complete this list of finds whose number has so notably increased during the last twenty years or so, we must mention the discovery in the Crimea, in the caves of Murza Koba and Fatma Koba, of skeletons contemporary with an Azilian or Tardenoisian industry: of rather tall

---

[46] Péquart, M. and St-J., 'La nécropole mésolithique de l'île de Hoëdic, Morbihan' (*L'Anthropologie*, XLIV, 1934).

[47] Lacam, R., Niederlender, R., and Vallois, H., 'Le gisement mésolithique du Cuzoul de Gramat' (*Arch. de l'Institut de Paléontologie humaine*, Memoir 21, Paris, 1944).

stature, they are dolichocephalic with a dysharmonic face and low orbits.[48] They have been compared with Cro-Magnon Man.

Conclusions

Comparative study of all the material we have just been examining enables us to arrive at certain general conclusions, which must, however, be regarded as only provisional.[49]

Without being pygmies, as has sometimes been said, almost all known Mesolithics are of small stature (with an average height of about 5 ft. 3 ins. in the men).

This is their only common character. According to their cephalic structure, they may be divided into four types, as follows:

Brachycephalics	. . . . . .	1.	*Ofnet*
Dolicho-Mesocephalics { dysharmonic { True Dolicho-cephalics .	2.	*Ofnet*
	Mesocephalics .	3.	*Téviec, Hoëdic, Kaufertsberg, Ofnet*
harmonic	4.	*Mugem, Palestine*

Brachycephalics are very rare. Since we must rule out those from Mugem, we see that they really exist only at Ofnet, where they appear to constitute the very first representatives, in Western Europe, of a new group with a broad, short head. Their origin raises a question which will be dealt with later.

The second type consists of the true dolichocephalics from Ofnet, who were probably tall; no doubt we should also include in this group Koerhuisbeek Man and perhaps also various other specimens which have been compared, not without reason, to the living Nordics, of whom they are said to be the earliest representatives.

The third, mesocephalic, type from Téviec—to which Hoëdic Man, some skulls from Ofnet and the Kaufertsberg skull belong—while it preserves certain morphological features of the Men of the Reindeer Age, especially of the Chancelade race, constitutes a truly new element possessing intermediate characteristics, like the Mesolithic period itself. This type was produced not, as has been claimed, by crossing with brachycephalics—who did not yet exist in Europe—but by the transformation of ancient dolicephalics under mesological or other influences. Types two and three seem to be closely linked by the dysharmonic character of their skulls.

The fourth type, clearly dolichocephalic, differs from the two preceding groups by having a narrower and longer face, which is consequently more harmonious in its proportions. It includes Mugem and Palestine Man.

[48] Debetz, G., 'Tardenuazskij kostjak iz navesa Fatma-Koba v Krymu' (*Anthrop. Journal,* Leningrad, 1936, No. 2).

[49] For details of these comparisons, see Boule, M., and Vallois, H., in 'Téviec' (*Arch. de l'Institut de Paléontologie humaine*, Memoir 18, Paris, 1937).

While still possessing certain Aurignacian characters, the Men of this group bear a striking resemblance to the great Mediterranean race.

Thus, with the advent of recent or post-glacial times, indigenous races of the Upper Palaeolithic were compelled to follow the Reindeer in its retreat towards the north, at the same time undergoing modifications; while in southern countries an expansion of the short, dolichocephalic types took place. We already see unfolding a picture of the distribution of modern European races, especially through the intrusion of the first brachycephalics and the diffusion of the Mediterranean type. Examination of Neolithic remains will help us to envisage the development of this new state of things, by showing us its growing complexity as well as an increasing diversity of types according to the country of their habitation.

NEOLITHIC RACES:

RELATIONSHIPS OF THE THREE GREAT TYPES

Unfortunately these evidences, although very numerous, are not so informative as we could wish. We have in particular skulls, but the indices of of these do not always allow of a precise definition of the race to which they belong. Complete skeletons, which would have enabled us to determine the stature of the peoples, are much rarer. And we can hardly learn anything of the characters founded upon the skin or nature of the hair.

In a general review of the great accumulations of statistical data collected by anthropologists, but neglecting details and adhering only to the main lines, we find two general facts emerge:[50]

1. In the first place, we note the simultaneous presence in every country of varied physical types, long heads, short heads (Fig. 244), and intermediate (or mesocephalic) forms of head. This emphasizes still more strongly the important change in the distribution of the human types, which was suggested in deposits belonging the Mesolithic period.

2. The relative proportions of each of these elements vary with the regions examined, and these proportions are such that they really enable us to define the relationship of the chief modern physical types. And here again, notwithstanding that we take this new standpoint, the Neolithic appears as the dawn of modern times. Though, of course, new and important changes still follow, the main features of this primary division persist. Using as a basis purely anthropological grounds and avoiding a detailed consideration of archaeological data, which would involve us too deeply, we shall give here some facts relating to the different European countries.

In France, the evidence is very abundant. More than fifty years ago, Salmon completed an enumeration of 688 Neolithic skulls found in that country.[51] Fifty-eight per cent. of these skulls are dolichocephalic, 21 per

[50] On this question as a whole, see Vallois, H., *Le néolithique et les premiers âges des Métaux* in *Historia Mundi* (Berne, 1952).

[51] Salmon, P., 'Dénombrement et types des crânes néolithiques de la Gaule' (*Revue de, l'École d'Anthrop.*, 1896). See also Hervé, G., 'Les brachycéphales néolithiques' (*Ibid.* 1894 and 1895). Vallois, H., *Anthropologie de la population française* (Paris, 1943).

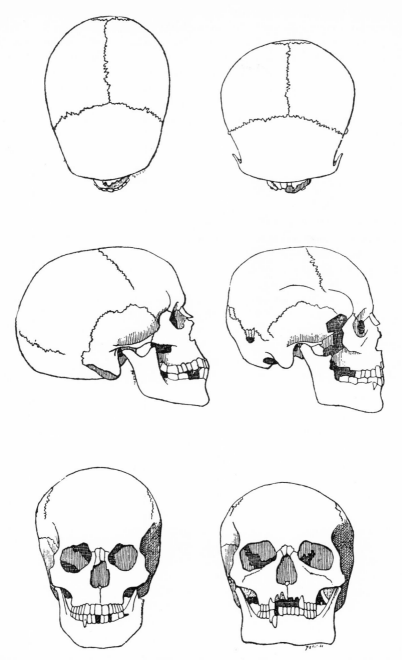

244 Dolichocephalic and brachycephalic skulls seen from above, in profile and full face. From covered passage in the Mureaux (Seine-et-Oise). One-fourth natural size (After Dr. Verneau)

cent. are brachycephalic, and 21 per cent. are intermediate. The dolicho-cephalics are thus greatly in the majority, but it becomes apparent that the number of brachycephalics begins to increase gradually from the beginning to the end of Neolithic times. These first brachycephalics are universally accepted as identical with the type of *homo alpinus* which was found at Ofnet.

What were the dolichocephalics? Some clearly belong to the Cro-Magnon type, which, far from disappearing at the close of the Palaeolithic, persisted for long in different regions. In the Cévennes, for example, numerous bones taken by Dr. Prunières from certain burial caves in the Lozère show that,

at the beginning of Neolithic times, the peoples of this reg-ion still preserved many feat-ures of the Men of the Upper Palaeolithic. In other caves, some brachycephalics appear, as well as new dolichocepha-lics with longer faces harmon-izing with the cranium, a characteristic that leads us to ascribe them to the Mediter-ranean race.

245 Human vertebra pierced by a Neolithic arrow-head, from a cave in the Lozère. Natural size. Prunières Collection, in the Anthropological Gallery of the Musée de l'Homme.

There can be no doubt regarding the contemporaneity of these brachyephalics and the old Palaeolithic dolicho-cephalics, since several of the skeletons exhumed by Dr. Prunières still bear, in their bones, the Neolithic arrows which pierced them (Fig. 245), and which show that they must have been the victims of the Neolithic invaders whose skulls are found in the dolmens.[52] But the invasion of these mountainous regions must have been slow and incomplete, for, speaking generally, Neolithic brachycephalic skulls remain for a long time extremely rare in the Cévennes; they become numerous only in the Bronze Age. A little farther south, at Montouliers in Hérault, Neolithic skulls, according to L. Mayet, are still Cro-Magnon in type, with a slight brachycephalic admixture.[53] The same is true in the Vaucluse according to Gagnière, and Dr. Marquié has observed the same rarity of brachycephalics in Aveyron.[54]

[52] Dr. Prunières scattered his numerous notes throughout different publications, parti-cularly those of the *Association française pour l'avancement des Sciences*. The anthropological material was studied chiefly by Broca (*Congrès intern. de Bruxelles*, 1872, p. 182). See also Quatrefages, A. de, *Hommes fossiles et Hommes sauvages*, pp. 99 and 105.

[53] Mayet, L., 'Les Néolithiques de Montouliers' (*L'Anthropologie*, XXIII, 1912).

[54] Marquié, M., 'Étude sur l'anthropologie de l'Aveyron' (*Thèse de Médecine*, Toulouse, 1939). For Hérault, see also Vallois, H., and Marquié, M., 'Ossements humains proto-historiques de la région du Pic Saint-Loup, Hérault' (*Bull. et Mém., Soc. d'Anthr. de Paris*, 1940).

The artificial caves of the Marne, explored by de Baye, show the same association of types. Among the skulls examined by Broca and de Quatrefages many still resemble the Cro-Magnon type, others are brachycephalic and these show mixed characters resulting from crossing. It is the same in Franche-Comté where, according to Piroutet, the brachycephalics become preponderant during the Bronze Age. But here it is a question of tall individuals who might be referred to the Dinarics.

In the Duruthy cave at Sorde, in the department of Landes (see p. 274), the Neolithic skulls from the upper portion of the bed are similar to the skull from the base of the deposit dating from the Reindeer Age; while at Monaco, the Neolithic skulls examined by Verneau[55] are mainly brachycephalic, accompanied by rare individuals still exhibiting affinities with the Cro-Magnon type, so well represented in this region in Palaeolithic times.

Thus, while we still find practically all over France at this period dolichocephalic types with short (dysharmonic) faces, who may be regarded as modified descendants of the Men of the Upper Palaeolithic, at least two new elements appear alongside them: brachycephalics belonging in the vast majority to the *Homo alpinus* type, and dolichocephalics with long faces, the representatives of a new element which we observed emerging after the Mesolithic. The latter must rather be grouped with the Mediterranean type, which seems from this period onward to have predominated in the regions where it still prevails.

In Italy, Neolithic skulls are very mixed, sometimes the brachycephalic, sometimes the small-sized dolichocephalic type predominating. The latter case is particulary noticeable in the basin of the Po, where round heads are most numerous at the present day.[56] But in Sicily and Sardinia a very large majority of Neolithic and Bronze Age skulls exactly resemble the skulls of modern Sardinians and Sicilians.[57] From the most remote prehistoric times Malta, Crete and Greece were also peopled by the Mediterranean type to which were later added some brachycephalics, who became predominant in Crete towards the end of the Bronze Age; and Sergi declares that the Ancient Egyptians, who were identical with the Libyans, are only a branch of the Mediterranean family.[58]

We have seen this same type appear in the Iberian peninsula at the period of the kitchen middens of Mugem. De Paula, already cited in this connexion (p. 351), tells us, moreover, that in the caves and Neolithic burials of Portugal the dolichocephalic type of Mugem still predominates, with, however, very

[55] Verneau, R., and Villeneuve, L. de, 'La grotte des Bas-Moulins' (*L'Anthropologie*, XII, 1901).

[56] Puccioni, N., 'Appunti sui resti scheletrici umani del giacimento del Belverde' (*Arch. per l'Antr. e la Etn.*, XLII, 1933).

[57] Ardu-Onnis, E., 'Restes humaines préhistoriques de la grotte de San Bartolomeo, près Cagliari' (*L'Anthropologie*, XV, 1904).

[58] Sergi, S., *The Mediterranean Race: A Study of the Origin of European Peoples* (London, 1901). Falkenburger, F., 'La composition raciale de l'ancienne Égypte' (*L'Anthropologie*, LI, 1947).

wide individual variations; although in certain beds of the same age the Cro-Magnon type is found. The brachycephalic type of Mugem likewise appears in certain Neolithic stations, where it shows all the characters of the Neolithic brachycephalics of France.

On the other hand, Verneau has found representatives of the Cro-Magnon race in the Neolithic deposits of Oviedo and Segovia, as well as of Andalusia. Jacques, on examination of the material yielded by the excavations of Siret in the south-east of Spain,[59] distinguished, in a series of Neolithic and Bronze Age skulls, a first group resembling the Cro-Magnon type, a second group composed of brachycephalics, a third group resembling the Mugem Men (Mediterranean type), and finally a fourth group, resembling the Basque peoples of Spain. As a whole, the dolichocephalic Mediterranean type appears to predominate in the Iberian peninsula.

In Belgium and Holland, there is the same mixture of round heads, long heads and mixed forms produced by crossing (such as the Furfooz skulls). The dolichocephalics are classified by various authors as belonging sometimes to the Cro-Magnon type, sometimes to the Mediterranean type.[60]

In the British Isles a very clear distinction has long been recognized. The Neolithic burials in long barrows enclose only dolichocephalic skulls: 'Long barrows, long skulls', is the saying. As soon as bronze makes its appearance, the tumuli become round in form and the skulls found are brachycephalic: 'Round barrows, round skulls.' Here, in the extreme west of Europe, for reasons readily understood, the first brachycephalic migrations were later in taking place. According to the majority of authors,[61] the Neolithic dolichocephalics, small in stature, with long faces and narrow noses, belong to the Mediterranean type, although Morant holds them to be true Nordics. They still play an important part in the ethnographical constitution of Great Britain and Ireland. The brachycephalics, who temporarily invaded them, had broad faces and belonged partly to the Alpine stock and partly to another type, having strongly marked superciliary arches and a tall stature, which is found at the same period in Denmark, where it bears the type name of Borreby; it has been placed in the Dinaric group. Nowadays, their traces have been almost wholly obliterated.[62]

In Switzerland the facts are somewhat different. As in most Western European countries, the dolichocephalics exist alone at the beginning of the Neolithic. But the brachycephalics very rapidly supervene, and very

[59] Jacques, V., 'Les races préhistoriques de l'Espagne' (*Congrès de Paris*, 1889).

[60] Fraipont, J., 'La Belgique préhistorique et protohistorique' (*Bull. de l'Acad. roy. de Belgique*, 1901). Houzé, É., 'Les Néolithiques de la province de Namur' (*C. R. Congrès Arch. et Hist. de Dinant, Namur*, 1904). Bork-Feltkamp, A. van, 'Anthropological Research in the Netherlands' (*Verh. Kon. Akad. van Wetenschappen*, XXXVII, 1938).

[61] Morant, G., 'A Preliminary Classification of European Races based on Cranial Measurements' (*Biometrika*, XX, B, 1928). Cameron, J., *The Skeleton of British Neolithic Man* (London, 1934).

[62] Keith, A., 'The Bronze Age Invaders of Britain' (*Journal of the Roy. Anthrop. Inst.*, XLV, 1915).

soon they predominate almost exclusively. It is generally accepted that they were the builders of the lake cities so charactersitic of the Swiss Neolithic.[63] This assertion has been contested and it is possible that pile-dwellings were originated by the dolichocephalics.[64] It is at least indisputable that the brachycephalics of the *Homo alpinus* group were responsible for their extraordinary development.

In the Mid-Neolithic period the dolichocephalics reappear. Mingled with the mesocephalics, they just about balance the brachycephalics. In the period of transition from the Polished Stone to the Bronze Age they even become predominant, according to Schenk. The important series of burials at Chamblandes, near Lausanne, recalls the Cro-Magnon type, but the skeletons are of small size and in certain characters resemble the Grimaldi Negroids.[65] These burials, moreover, present a new element. Side by side with the skeletons of the small dolichocephalics, two skulls exhibit the characters of the northern race; and Pittard tells us that, towards the end of the Neolithic period, there arrived in Switzerland men of tall stature, with elongated skulls and narrow noses, whom he is able to classify as belonging to the type of *Homo nordicus*. It must also be added that there were found at Schweizersbild, near Schaffhausen, the bone-remains of some individuals of very small stature, almost pygmies, who Kollman would have us believe played a considerable part in the development of the human races,[66] but who are regarded by the majority of anthropologists as being only dwarfs whose skeletons lay side by side with those of other individuals of normal stature.

Nevertheless, the fact remains that even in the Neolithic period or rather at the end of the Neolithic period, the anthropological complexity which now exists in Switzerland becomes clearly noticeable. Here, for the first time, we recognize the presence of representatives of the big dolichocephalic peoples of the North. These become more and more numerous as we pass towards Central and Northern Europe.

In Central Europe, Neolithic remains are generally dolichocephalic.[67] In the south-west of Germany a primitive type, which can be grouped with the Mediterranean race, is mingled with a long-faced element, certainly Nordic, which predominates in the north and east of the country and which is also found in Bohemia, Silesia and the Bavarian area, where it is correlated with

[63] Pittard, E., *Les races et l'histoire* (Paris, 1924) p. 181. Schalginhaufen, O., *Die Anthropologie der Steinzeit der Schweiz* in Tschumi, O., *Urgeschichte der Schweiz*, Vol. I (Frauenfeld, 1949).

[64] Vouga, P., 'Le Néolithique lacustre ancien' (*Recueil de travaux publiés par la Fac. des Lettres de Neuchâtel*, XVII, 1934).

[65] Schenk, A., 'Les sépultures et les populations préhistoriques de Chamblandes' (*Rev. de l'École d'Anthrop. de Paris*, 1904); *La Suisse préhistorique* (Lausanne, 1912).

[66] Kollmann, J., 'Die Pygmäen und ihre systematische Stellung innerhalb des Menschengeschlechts' (*Verhandl. naturforsch. Ges. in Basel*, XVI, 1902).

[67] Scheidt, W., *Die Rassen der jüngeren Steinzeit in Europa* (Stuttgart, 1921). Bounak, V., 'The Craniological Types of the European Neolithic' (in Russian) (*Acad. of Sciences of the U.S.S.R., Inst. of Ethnography*, Vol. I, 1946).

a particular culture, that of the caliciform vase. This group is generally described as Alpine, but some authors classify it with the Dinaric type. Another group is observed in the northernmost part of Germany and also in Denmark; characterized by strongly marked superciliary arches and a tall stature, this is the Borreby type no doubt resulting from the crossing of the dolichocephalics, descended from the Men of the Upper Palaeolithic, with the Alpine brachycephalics. Many dolichocephalics, however, continue to exist side by side with them.[68]

It is again the Nordic type or related forms that we meet in Hungary. Brachycephalics only make their appearance later, in the so-called Danubian period. According to Giuffrida-Ruggeri, in the Illyrian and Danube regions dolichocephalic skulls are also very numerous at even the most remote periods; they gradually decrease in number and almost entirely disappear in many regions on the descent of the Alpine peoples from the mountains to the plains.[69]

If we penetrate into Russia, we see that in the south-west, in Ukraine, Volhynia, and also in Poland, dolichocephalics of great stature are more or less dominant in the Neolithic 'khurgans' or tumuli; and farther north and east, we find only dolichocephalics. Bogdanov has shown that the most ancient races of Central Russia (inhabitants of settlements on the shores of Lake Ladoga described by Inostranzeff) had long heads and faces like the modern inhabitants of Sweden.[70]

Finally, in the Scandinavian peninsula, the phenomenon is still more marked. Certain skulls from Neolithic burials are brachycephalic and conform to the Danish type from Borreby, but the majority resemble those of modern Swedes. The skeletons indicate a tall stature and robust frame. Scandinavia at this period was already populated by the direct forebears of the modern populations who best represent the ideal type of *Homo nordicus*.[71]

Thus, even at the end of the Neolithic period, it is possible to recognize, in its broad outlines, the geographical distribution of the three principal physical types which anthropologists have been able to distinguish by studying the numerous varieties or sub-races, the amalgamation of which forms the ethnographical constitution of present-day Europe.

The Metal Ages

Contemporaneous with the Metal Ages, both protohistoric and historic, there occurred other movements of peoples and other interminglings, leading to the complexity apparent to us today.[72]

[68] Broholm, H., 'The Bronze Age People of Denmark' (*Acta archaeologica*, XIII, 1942).

[69] Giuffrida-Ruggeri, V., 'Contributo all'antropologia fisica delle regioni dinariche e danubiane' (*Arch. per l'Antrop. e la Etnol.*, XXXVIII, 1908).

[70] Bogdanov, A., 'Quelle est la race la plus ancienne de la Russie?' (*Congr. intern. d'Anthrop.*, Moscow, 1912).

[71] Fuerst, C., 'Zur Kraniologie der schwedischen Steinzeit' (*Handl. Svenska Vetenskapsakademiens*, XLIX, Stockholm, 1912).

[72] Bowen, E., 'The Racial Geography of Europe at the Dawn of the Age of Metal' (*J. of the R. Anthrop. Inst.*, LXI, 1931).

We know very little of the Copper Age (also called the Eneolithic or Chalcolithic period), though many burials and monuments from the close of the Neolithic period must belong to it. It seems as though the constitution of the so-called Aryan family of languages, corresponding to a culture that was the work of several racial elements,[73] dates from the Copper Age.

In the Bronze Age the practice of cremation was gradually substituted in many regions for that of inhumation, and this practice is highly prejudicial to anthropological study. Speaking generally, the Bronze Age in Western Europe, particularly in France, may be characterized (from the point of view of our studies) by the arrival of new and extensive inundations of brachycephalic peoples. The bronze industry seems then to have been imported into Western Europe by Men of the Alpine or Dinaric type, though this does not necessarily mean that they were its inventors.[74] These new floods of brachycephalic peoples penetrated at this period into the British Isles, where they are commemorated by round barrows, containing round-headed individuals.

On the other hand, the tall dolichocephalics of the Nordic type survive in Russia and in the Scandinavian peninsula, which may already be regarded as their ancient fatherland, and in which tombs of the Bronze Age still sometimes contain their fair hair. Furthermore, we see them penetrating in numbers into the Rhine valley, into Switzerland and Southern Germany, where already they are found in those Iron Age tombs which are arranged in rows, the so-called *Reihengraeber*.

Towards the end of the Bronze Age, the brachycephalics reappear in Switzerland and in the north of Italy; there they are very pure, and once more predominate numerically.

On the other hand, the Eastern Mediterranean region, Crete, where the Aegean civilization flourished, Malta, Sicily, Southern Italy and the Iberian peninsula remain the strongholds of the Mediterranean element, which continues largely to predominate there. Cyprus, on the contrary, was peopled at this period, according to Fuerst, by a strong majority of brachycephalics of Armenoid type.[75]

---

[73] Poisson, G., *Les Aryens* (Paris, 1934).

[74] The problem of the origin of metallurgy is one of the most controversial problems of prehistoric archaeology. There is, *a priori*, no reason to suppose that the discovery of metals and their alloys may not have been made independently at different periods and in different countries. But this hypothesis is not readily supported by our present knowledge. All the evidence seems to be in favour of an Asiatic origin (on Cyprus and in the mountains of Eastern Asia, according to J. de Morgan and Déchelette). The dates of the appearance of the metals in the different countries of the East and in Europe (see p. 329) show that they spread, generally speaking, from the east westwards, and from the south northwards. Step by step with this diffusion, one after another the mining centres of each country, as it was invaded, contributed in their turn towards new manufactures. [See Morgan, J. de, 'Note sur les origines de la métallurgie' (*L'Anthropologie*, XXXII, 1922, p. 487).]

[75] Fuerst, C., 'Zur Kenntnis der Anthropologie der prähistorischen Bevölkerung der Insel Cypern' (*Lunds Univ. Arsskrift*, XXIX, 1933).

The Iron Age[76] corresponds to the maximum expansion of the Nordic race: 'a new metal in the hands of a new race', said Hamy, speaking of France, where the tall fair dolichocephalics imported with them the civilization of the first Iron Age, termed *Hallstattian*, from the name of the famous necropolis at Hallstatt in Austria. The Nordic peoples now penetrated everywhere along the great rivers, and thus hemmed back and isolated the massive brachycephalic mountain races. These warlike invaders landed on the coast of the British Isles, and spread over Belgium and the North of France; attracted by the sunny, wine-producing regions, they reached Spain by the valleys of the Loire and Garonne, and Northern Italy through Switzerland. They prospered in the valley of the Danube, which they overflowed in various directions as far as Macedonia, Greece, Asia Minor, and perhaps even as far as Turkestan and India.

On the other hand the brachycephalic peoples, thus bounded and constrained, annexed territory elsewhere. In Russia they drove back the Nordic peoples, even reaching the Norwegian coast. In Central and Western Europe they occupied all the mountainous regions and spilled over into the neighbouring plains of Hungary, Bohemia, Bavaria and the whole of South-West France. Constricted in their turn, the Mediterranean races were confined to the coastal zones of the Mediterranean, together with the Iberian peninsula and Southern Italy. But they left behind numerous vestiges in the regions they were forced to abandon, the most important of which inhabited the West of Great Britain and the area south of Moscow.

THE ANCIENT PEOPLES IN HISTORY

Up to this point, all these peoples remain nameless to us. But now, by means of the oldest texts, confused and vague though these too often are, we can attempt to identify the first historical groups from an anthropological point of view. It must be clearly stated, however, that the ancient peoples whose names have come down to us, such as the peoples of ancient Gaul, were in many cases already highly mixed as regards physical type. Camille Jullian, in his excellent *Histoire de la Gaule*, says eloquently: 'Away behind the tribes of the seventh century B.C. there lies a great mass of human lives, of sex relationships, of formations and disintegrations of States, and of invasions by land and sea, a confusion of languages, types, and customs which baffles all analysis.'

The task, therefore, is full of difficulties and pitfalls. And yet we may make some comparisons which both anthropologists and historians are

---

[76] The origin of iron is no less obscure than that of bronze. G. de Mortillet regarded it as African. In the opinion of J. de Morgan, it was Asiatic. The most ancient objects of iron we know of were yielded by a predynastic Egyptian tomb and therefore date from about 4,000 years before our era. But we have seen that, before 1500, there could be no question of the existence of an Iron Age in Egypt.

able to accept, at least provisionally, as a result of their respective studies.[77]

We may consider as belonging to the type *Homo nordicus* the whole series of peoples who, during a long series of centuries, successively and periodically invaded Great Britain, France, and Central and Southern Europe. And, first of all, we believe, come the great majority of Celts[78] or Gauls, who formed the powerful 'Celtic Empire' of prehistorians and dominated Europe. It was they who seized Rome in 390 B.C.; who invaded Thrace, whence, though checked for a short period by Alexander, they soon invaded Macedonia and Greece, laying waste everything in their path, seizing the treasures of the Delphian temple under the leadership of their chief Brennus (in 279 B.C.), and who finally, 'coveting Asia', crossed the straits and installed themselves in Phrygia (Galatia).

Later, the invaders came definitely from the north, and were called Belgians, Cimbrians and Teutons, Germans, Goths, Franks and Normans. These peoples represent each a fresh thrust of that race in which may also be grouped the Umbrians, Achaeans, Dorians, Cimmerians, the closest modern relations of whom are probably the Circassians, and others.

To the type *Homo mediterraneus* must be attributed the old peoples of Northern Africa, the Egyptians and Libyans, as well as the Phoenicians, the Pelasgians, Aegeans, Etruscans, the oldest Ligurians, the Phocians of Marseilles and the Iberians.

To the brachycephalic group belonged the ancient peoples of Western Asia, the Accadians and Sumerians (?), and the Hittites, to whom perhaps may be added the Sarmatians; the Slavs, whose invasions took place from the 4th to the 9th centuries of our era, and who, along with the Mongols, finally expelled the Nordic peoples from the greater part of the Russian region.

Once more it must be recalled that these are and can only be approximate determinations, for the majority of the names just mentioned apply to ethnographical groups which are already intermixed, and which we can only describe from the anthropological standpoint by the predominant element. We are all aware that, after the first Celtic invasions, there soon arose peoples known as the Celto-Iberians, Celto-Ligurians, Celto-Scythians, Celto-Thracians, Gallo-Greeks, and so on. Sometimes even the old ethnographical names signify a more complex mixture. It is clear, for instance, that the 'Celtic Empire' of prehistorians was not composed solely of representatives of *Homo nordicus*, and that, later on, the Gauls or Celts described by Caesar

[77] On the one hand, see Deniker, *Races et peuples de la terre*. Ripley, *The Races of Europe*. Coon, *The Races of Europe* (copious bibliography). And on the other hand, Arbois de Jubainville, D., *Les premiers habitants de l'Europe* (Paris, 1894). Dottin, G., *Les anciens peuples de l'Europe* (Paris, 1916). Pittard, E., *Les races et l'histoire* (Paris, 1924). Kappers, A., and Parr, L., *An Introduction to the Anthropology of the Near East* (Amsterdam, 1934).

[78] It must not be forgotten that by the majority of French anthropologists the Celts are regarded as brachycephalic. We have already drawn attention to this confusion (see note, p. 341). But there is no doubt that Celt and Gaul are really synonymous from the historian's point of view.

included types other than those of the original Gauls; the armies of Vercing-etorix were composed cf very heterogeneous masses of humanity and included in their ranks representatives, more or less pure or more or less mixed, of the three principal physical types now blended together in the French nation.

The Mongoloid or Hunnish invasions on the one hand, and the Arab or Saracen invasions on the other, occurred later, still further complicating this extraordinary human mixture, although they have left only relatively slight traces in France.

ORIGIN OF THE THREE GREAT RACES

How much can we learn or hazard regarding the probable origin of the three great races? We have seen that, at the end of the Palaeolithic period, the countries of Western and Central Europe were peopled by dolichocephalics, which are sometimes grouped under a general term as the 'Cro-Magnon Race', but which, in addition to possessing common morphological features, already showed notable differences, such as we see in the Grimaldi Negroids and the types of Cro-Magnon, Chancelade and Combe-Capelle. In this stock close search must be made among characters still somewhat generalized, in order to discover the ancestors of the two groups of dolichocephalics which subsequently became differentiated.

Homo nordicus is a great product of the North, but he cannot have origi-nated outside Europe. At the present time his centre of dispersal appears to have been Scandinavia; but this, none the less, is purely illusion, for during the Palaeolithic period, Sweden, being covered with ice, was inaccessible. The cradle of the Nordic race must be sought farther south in countries which have always remained free of ice, or from which the glaciers retreated at an early stage.[79]

Several anthropologists have considered that the Nordic peoples were directly descended from Cro-Magnon Man, and more particularly from the 'Men of the Loess'. But these two groups have nothing in common apart from their great stature; in other respects they differ greatly and are not to be confounded. Some anthropologists take the view that only certain Nor-dics, distinguished by their broader faces, in dysharmonic proportion to the cranium, and sometimes regarded as a special variety—the Dal sub-race—are descended from the Cro-Magnons. A number of other authors agree with Sergi and Giuffrida-Ruggeri in thinking that the Nordic dolicho-cephalics of the Danubian region and the khurgans of South Russia are the true ancestors of the modern Nordics, who represent 'the Mediterranean type transported into the North'. Yet other hypotheses have been advanced, placing the birthplace of the Nordic peoples on the southern shores of the

[79] On this subject, see Giuffrida-Ruggeri, V., *Su l'origine dell'Uomo* (Bologna, 1921). Saller, K., 'Die Entstehung der nordischen Rasse' (*Z. für Anat. u. Entw. gesch.*, LXXXIII, 1927). Perret, G., 'Cro-Magnon-Typen vom Neolithikum bis Heute' (*Z. für Morph. u. Anthr.*, XXXVII, 1937).

Baltic, in Western Siberia, in the steppes of Turkestan, or on the plateaux of Iran. To these suppositions must be added others of an ethnological order, according to which the Nordics introduced the Aryan languages into Europe and, at the same time, the Indo-European civilization.

Recent investigations by Schreiner,[80] based on a methodical examination of modern and ancient Nordic skeletons, have scotched all these hypotheses. They have shown that *Homo nordicus* is a comparatively recent product, resulting from the superimposition, at the beginning of the Neolithic and towards the base of the Danish peninsula, of a local element formed by the descendants of the Men of the Upper Palaeolithic and a mixture of invaders from the South—various dolichocephalics mixed, up to a point, with small Neolithic brachycephalics. It was only after a second migration that the Nordics reached Scandinavia, which they occupied so solidly that today this region gives the impression of being their country of origin. The inter-minglings which marked their formation explain the heterogeneous character of the modern Nordics. They show the error of theories that sought to link this race with the importation of a particular language.

Homo mediterraneus of European countries is a product of the South; he belongs to the main mass of the dark dolichocephalic peoples who occupy North Africa, a large part of Western Asia, and the shores of the Mediter-ranean, and who sometimes exhibit certain Ethiopian affinities where their regions border on those of the black races.

It is very probable that Europe owes the importation of Neolithic culture, megalithic structures, and perhaps also the discovery of primitive industries in metal, to *Homo mediterraneus* of North Africa and Asia Minor. It was in the countries which he inhabited, and at the juncture when he was ex-clusively predominant, that the great Oriental civilizations of Egypt, Chaldea and Sumeria were born and developed. He therefore played a part of the first importance in the origin of our Western civilization. According to Giuffrida-Ruggeri, *Homo mediterraneus* must have arisen through the crossing of an equatorial or proto-Ethiopian type with a more northern type like that of Cro-Magnon.[81] This is pure supposition, for everything leads us to believe in the high antiquity of the Mediterranean type, the origin of which is undoubtedly linked with the Palaeolithic stock at the eastern extremity of the Mediterranean basin.

The European brachycephalics are generally regarded as of Asiatic origin. They belong to the immense brachycephalic stock of Central Asia, which comprises both white and yellow races (Mongols). According to this hypo-thesis, the starting-point of the early brachycephalic peoples on their march to Western Europe was the Ural-Altai region. They then possessed certain Mongoloid characters, which they seem gradually to have lost in their

[80] Schreiner, K., 'Crania Norvegica, II' (*Institutet for sammenlignende Kulturforskning*, Series B, XXXVI, 1946).

[81] Giuffrida-Ruggeri, V., 'Quattro crani preistorici dell'Italia meridionale e l'origine dei Mediterranei' (*Archivio per l'Antrop. e la Etnol.*, LXV, 1916).

progress westwards. Their migration must have commenced after the end
of the glacial period, at the same time as that of the fauna of the steppes of
their native country. At first this migration took place slowly, rather by a
gradual infiltration than by a regular invasion. Later, towards the end of the
Neolithic period, it seems to have taken place in greater mass. *Homo alpinus*,
in particular, suddenly becomes very numerous in France in the Bronze
Age. Their present distribution, the result, as we have seen, of repeated
migratory movements, clearly indicates their origin. They form, as it were,
a vast procession, enormous at the point of departure, that is to say in Asia,
but, on its way from East to West, gradually decreasing and tapering off
altogether as it approaches French Brittany. Here is pitched the apex of the
triangle, hemmed in between the origin of the fair dolichocephalics from the
North (*Homo nordicus*) and that of the dark dolichocephalics from the South
(*Homo mediterraneus*).

The foregoing hypothesis, which was for long the generally accepted
theory, faces one very serious objection. The earliest brachycephalics are
localized in Western Europe; farther east, in Central Europe and Russia,
we find during the same period only dolichocephalics. How, then, can it be
claimed that the brachycephalics came from the East? Since, on the other
hand, they cannot have come from the Near East or North Africa either—
regions which are also devoid of brachycephalics during the Neolithic period
—we are constrained to regard the brachycephalics of Western Europe as
indigenous.

Recent investigations have shown that the shape of the skull is much less
stable than used to be believed; it may vary quite rapidly within certain
limits. On the other hand, we know that the Men of the Palaeolithic were
either dolichocephalic or mesocephalic. Brachycephalia therefore appeared
secondarily and no doubt through mutation. The Mesolithic skulls from
Ofnet are the first known representatives of the new type that was to develop
rapidly during the Neolithic and the Metal Ages, first in Western Europe,
and only later in Central and Southern Europe. There is nothing, moreover,
to prove that this phenomenon occurred once only and at one single point
in time. It is possible, indeed very probable, that Asiatic brachycephalia
is independent of that in Europe. In any case, *Homo alpinus* certainly developed on the spot and in Western Europe, starting from the Ofnet type.

CONCLUSIONS

Such, reduced to its main features, is the picture which, with the slight
resources at its disposal, modern anthropology has been able to sketch of
the intermingling and transformations undergone by the groups of peoples
who contended for the possession of the territories of Europe, from the end
of Palaeolithic times onwards.

This bird's-eye view, in spite of its diagrammatic character, is probably
inaccurate in many points. But, if it has no other merits, at least it is exclusively based on the idea of race, in the true sense of that word, and not

in the sense too often attributed to it by historians and even by certain anthropologists; it is drawn from the naturalist's point of view, and so, being more in conformity with biological laws, it may perhaps also throw more light on the subject.

We are thus led to view from another angle, from a standpoint presenting fresh perspectives, the succession of events which prehistory and history seek to construct regarding Humanity. So we can better appreciate, among the many factors which shape the evolution of peoples, those which arise directly from general biological principles, and in particular the double influence of heredity and environment, those profound and persistent forces which often remain concealed under an accumulation of influences more purely human in origin, perhaps of equal importance, yet undoubtedly more superficial and ephemeral.

CHAPTER TEN

THE FOSSIL MEN OF
ASIA AND OCEANIA

Now that we have discussed fossil Man in Europe, it would seem that a still greater task remained to be accomplished, for the surface of our own continent is but a very small portion of the total land surface of the globe. But the truth is that beyond France and its neighbours, the palaeontology of Mankind is still deficient.

It is indeed the case that, all over the world, there have been collected archaeological evidences of a remote past prior to historical times, often dating even from geological times, but, beyond Europe, no country has yielded a collection of facts comparable to that which has just been described. The majority of the archaeological evidences found outside Europe consist of isolated and scattered finds; and these come from deposits hardly studied at all from the stratigraphical point of view, so that their relative chronology is far from being established, except in certain rare localities. In such circumstances, we must be doubly careful in interpreting ethnographical facts, and must keep in mind that resemblance does not always signify contemporaneity or descent. In certain parts of a continent the Stone Age seems to date as far back into the past as in Europe; in other places, even in the same continent, this Age persists to the present day.

Palaeontological evidence is even less abundant than archaeological evidence—in fact, there is still very little respecting fossil Man. Discoveries of skulls or skeletons have been made, especially in the two Americas, but they possess neither the high antiquity nor the importance attributed to them. Indeed the majority have not been able to withstand critical examination; so that, leaving Europe out of account, human palaeontology can present only a relatively poor catalogue.

ASIA AND MALAYSIA

We shall first discuss Asia, of which Europe is only an appendage—hence the expression Eurasia, which is often used to designate the largest continental unit on the earth. Relations between Europe and Asia must, *a priori*, have been closer than their relations with other continents. Hence remote and mysterious Asia has at all times been invoked for the solution of the most obscure problems. Thus Asia was credited with the chief role in populating our globe, in the origin, evolution—both moral and physical—and dispersion of the various groups of Mankind: *Officina gentium* it has often been called. Is this notion of Asia as the cradle of Humanity a mere 'Oriental mirage'? Let us admit that even modern science often turns its eyes in this direction, in the hope of seeing some light blazing forth upon many obscure points respecting biological life on our planet. We have reason to believe that Asia played a great part in the progressive evolution of the higher Primates and, consequently, of our most remote ancestors. What we have said concerning the fossil Great Apes of the Siwaliks, and concerning *Pithecanthropus* and *Sinanthropus*, only confirms this opinion.

At the present time Asia is made up of a nucleus formed by very high plateaux (Pamir, Tibet) dominated by the Himalayas, whose peaks rise to more than 27,000 feet. Round this central mass, the 'roof of the world', are set great peninsulas, Europe, Arabia, India, Indo-China, and vast plains, such as Siberia, furrowed by mighty rivers. Finally, in the interior, there are large deserts and closed areas of water like the Caspian and Aral Seas. The flora and fauna present wide variations, ranging from those of the tundras in the extreme north and the Siberian steppes, with their excessively continental climate, to those of the Indian jungles, which are tropical in character, and passing on the way through those of the high plateaux and icy peaks.

The ancient geographers, aware only of the outward appearance of things, believed that the oldest part of the continent was the mountainous nucleus, around which successive accretions had produced the lower areas. Geology tells us exactly the opposite. It reveals that towards the end of the Primary Era the oldest parts of Asia consisted, on the one hand, of a Sino-Siberian continent (also known as the continent of *Angara*, after a Siberian river) and, on the other, where India lies today, of an ancient platform, the remains of a very ancient continent, called *Gondwana*, that ran from Brazil to Southern Africa, Madagascar, Australia and India. Between these two continental areas stretched a vast sea, a primitive Mediterranean, the *Tethys* or *Mesogea*, which persisted for a long time at precisely the point now occupied by high mountain ranges (the Himalayas and the Alps), whose rise dates only from the middle of the Tertiary Era. These great orogenic thrusts were naturally followed by a phase of demolition accompanied by all the vicissitudes of the Ice Ages. The significance of these facts, which we cannot develop here, will not escape those engaged in studying the evolution of the great Primates and the formation and diffusion of successive human types.

At the present time, Asia displays all sorts of human types. It seems, first, like the great fatherland, if not the original home, of the enormous stock of the yellow races—Mongols, Ugrians and Eskimoes. But there are also white races like the brachycephalic Assyroids and the dolichocephalic Arabs, not to mention the curious Ainus lost on a few Japanese islands. The Negro or Negroid races are represented by the Dravidians of India and the Negritos of Malaysia All these races may be divided into sub-races which penetrate one another and intermingle in a complicated manner and which it is not always easy to distinguish, because of innumerable crossings.

In all the habitable countries of the great continent of Asia we find mementoes of the Stone Ages, and everywhere legends and superstitions are attached to them; just as in Europe, stone weapons are looked upon as products of the heavens, as residues of thunder, or are made use of in magic rites to cure diseases.

We shall now deal, region by region, with the principal archaeological acquisitions and palaeontological discoveries.

WESTERN ASIA

The first scientific discoveries were made in Asia Minor, where the coast is simply a continuation of our Mediterranean coast, and where, consequently, it is not surprising to discover facts similar to those of the most ancient European prehistory.

In 1864, Louis Lartet[1] rediscovered in Libya a prehistoric settlement found thirty years before by Botta, the contents of which, animal bones and dressed flints, resembled exactly those of the Périgord settlements, which his father, Édouard Lartet, was just then beginning to make known. Since that time, Palestine and the whole of Syria have been visited by many archaeologists. Excavations have been carried out in caves or in deposits in the open, and collections have been made. The prehistoric localities already mapped out or described in this part of Western Asia by Richard, Cazalis de Fondouce, Morestin, Arcelin, Chantre, de Morgan, Zumoffen, Blanckenhorn, Arne, Desribes, Neophytus, Neuville, Mallon, Day, Rhotert, and others were soon numbered by hundreds.

From the archaeological point of view, all the forms of weapons and implements of our Stone Ages have been found there: Chellean and Acheulean (Fig. 246), Mousterian, Aurignacian and even Mesolithic types. The Neolithic deposits are no less rich in polished axes and arrowheads similar to our own.[2]

The undisturbed Palaeolithic settlements, as in Europe, are accompanied by an ancient fauna, including extinct or emigrated species. The bone breccias, containing dressed flints, are sometimes composed of hard rocks, like those of our French caves, and in the days of classical antiquity these breccias were used as building stones. The Romans constructed a road across the breccias of Ras el Kelb in Phoenicia. At various times, the presence

---

[1]   Lartet, L., 'Note sur la découverte de silex taillés en Syrie' (*Bull. de la Soc. géolog. de France*, 2nd Ser., Vol. XXII, 1865).

[2]   Zumoffen, G., 'L'âge de la Pierre en Phénicie' (*L'Anthropologie*, VIII, 1897); *La Phénicie avant les Phéniciens* (Beirut, 1909). Neophytus, Brother, 'La Préhistoire en Syrie-Palestine' (*L'Anthropologie*, XXVIII, 1917). Neuville, R., 'La Préhistorique de la Palestine' (*Revue biblique*, XLIII, 1934). Haller, J., 'Aperçu sur l'état actuel de nos connaissances de la préhistoire de la Syrie et du Liban' (*Notes et Mém., section géolog., Délég. franç. Liban*, IV, 1944).

in ancient gravels of dressed stones of very archaic appearance has been noted. Schaeffer found 'hand-axes' in the Pleistocene alluvials of the Orontes, and Passemard in those of the Euphrates. Father Bergy recovered flints of Mousterian workmanship in old marine beaches and the consolidated dunes surmounting them.[3] Their entire geological bearing points to the fact that these deposits, like those in Europe, date from remote Quaternary times.

At the commencement of the Neolithic period the physical conditions were those of the present day. Neolithic deposits, which are very abundant,

246 Dressed flints from Syria. (After F. J. Arne)

are not always on the surface, but to find them at any depth one must seek at the base of the *tells*, artificial hills formed by the rubbish of towns and villages of classic or prehistoric antiquity, sometimes on top of Mesolithic deposits, as at Jericho. These facts, and others besides, successfully refute the obsolete ideas of classical archaeologists, who declared that our Palaeolithic could not be more ancient than the old Chaldean or Egyptian civilizations.

Discoveries, at first localized in Syria, were not long in spreading and increasing in number. As early as 1878, Cartailhac[4] was able to compile an

---

[3] Bergy, P., 'Le Paléolithique ancien stratifié à Ras-Beyrouth' (*Mélanges de l'Université Saint-Joseph*, Beirut, 1932).

[4] Cartailhac, É., 'L'âge de la Pierre en Asie' (*Congrès des Orientalistes*, 3rd Meeting, Lyons, 1878).

inventory of the Stone Age discoveries in Asia, and since that date the inventory has greatly increased. Here we can describe only the most important facts.

Asia Minor and Persia, with their mountains and high plateaux, in great part covered during the Pleistocene Period with ice and snow, are very poor in Palaeolithic remains. Here J. de Morgan explored, without result, great quantities of ancient alluvial deposits carried down from the mountains. But he was more fortunate in the low plains, where some settlements contain both Palaeolithic and Neolithic remains. More recently A. Kansu announced the discovery of Chellean remains near Ankara, and Mousterian relics have been found at various other places in the same region.[5] A cave containing a Mousterian industry was explored by D. Garrod in Southern Kurdistan, and C. Coon studied several caverns in the Iranian plateaux whose deposits range from the Mid-Palaeolithic to the Mesolithic. A Lower Palaeolithic industry of Levalloisian type was reported in Southern Arabia.[6] Neolithic remains are to be found everywhere, at Sinai, in Arabia, in Iran, in Mesopotamia, and as far as Susa, where they were discovered by the fine excavations carried out by J. de Morgan and Mecquenem.

THE NEANDERTALIANS OF PALESTINE

During the last twenty-five years, systematic investigations have been carried out in Palestine, on the one hand by an Anglo-American expedition under the successive direction of Turville-Petre and Miss Garrod, and on the other by M. Neuville, French Consul at Jerusalem, under the auspices of the French Institute of Human Palaeontology. The Anglo-American investigations concerned various caves at Galilee and on Mount Carmel, those of Neuville related to grottoes in the desert of Judaea, a few miles from Bethlehem, and also in the immediate neighbourhood of Nazareth. They led to the discovery of numerous human remains belonging to various ages, the most ancient of which are remarkable for their resemblance to European Neandertal Man.

The stratigraphical and archaeological side of these important explorations has formed the subject of a considerable number of publications and, in particular, of two large memoirs, one by Miss Garrod and Miss Bate, and the other by R. Neuville.[7] The sequence observed in all the Palestinian caves is as follows.

[5] Pfannenstiel, M., 'Die altsteinzeitlichen Kulturen Anatoliens' (*Istanbuler Forschungen*, XV, 1941).

[6] Caton-Thompson, G., and Gardner, E., 'Climate, Irrigation and Early Man in the Hadramaut' (*The Geographical Journal*, XCIII, 1939).

[7] Garrod, D., 'Fouilles paléolithiques de Palestine' (*Bull. de la Soc. préhist. française*, 1930, p. 160); 'The Stone Age of Palestine' (*Antiquity*, 1934); 'A New Mesolithic Industry: the Natufian of Palestine' (*Journ. of the Roy. Anthrop. Inst.*, 1932). Garrod, D., and Bate, D., *The Stone Age of Mount Carmel. Excavations at the Wady-el-Mughara*, I (London, 1937). Neuville, R., 'Le Paléolithique et le Mésolithique du désert de Judée' (*Archives de l'Inst. de Paléontologie humaine*, Mem. XXIV, 1951).

The deepest layers contain an industry called 'Tayacian', which is only a facies of the Acheulean. Above this come Mousterian industries, including a 'Levalloisian' facies already containing scrapers and gravers reminiscent of our Upper Palaeolithic. These oldest deposits are succeeded by several levels of a clearly Aurignacian character, the upper part of which may here represent the Magdalenian of Western Europe. The series continues with various Mesolithic beds (Miss Garrod's *Natufian*) surmounted by deposits from the Metal Ages. One cannot help being struck by the close analogy of this sequence with that in European countries.

Changes of climate and fauna, as Miss Bate observed, took place in the course of development of these various stone industries. The most ancient, Acheulean and Mousterian, strata contain the bone-remains of great extinct species, such as the Hippopotamus and Rhinoceros, indicative of a warm, subtropical climate. After the disappearance of these pachyderms, a fauna of ruminants, deer and antelopes, develops, denoting a phase that was still temperate but damper. During the Aurignacian, or Upper Palaeolithic, the climate became drier, the deer diminish and the antelopes increase. The Mesolithic contains only the present species of wild animals.

Some of these caves yielded human remains. They belong essentially to two periods, the Acheuleo-Mousterian and the Mesolithic. We shall first consider the most ancient.

The first discovery which drew attention to these investigations was that, in 1925, of the famous 'Galilee skull', extracted by Turville-Petre from an Acheuleo-Mousterian level in the cave of Mugharet-el-Zuttiyeh, situated in the ravine of Wadi el'Amed, north-west of the Sea of Galilee or Lake Tiberias.[8]

This anatomical specimen, which was limited to a few fragments (frontal bone, right cheek-bone, right wings of the sphenoid) and immediately strikes the observer by its strongly marked orbital arches (Fig. 137, p. 210), was studied by Keith.[9] To his mind this skull, which he ascribed to a woman, is patently of the Neandertal type, but certain differences of detail lead him to suppose that it may be a variety or race of this type.

Far more complete and informative are the evidences discovered somewhat later in the caves of Mount Carmel by Miss Garrod and McCown, on the one hand, and in the Nazareth region by MM. Neuville and Stékelis, on the other. All are of Mousterian or Acheuleo-Mousterian age.

The Mount Carmel discoveries were made, during the years 1931 and 1932, in the two caves of Et-Tabun ('Cave of the Oven') and Mugharet es Shkül ('Cave of the Kids') near Athlit. The former yielded a female skeleton (the 'Tabun woman') and a human lower jaw and femur. From the second,

[8]   Turville-Petre, F., 'Excavations of Two Palaeolithic Caves in Galilee' (*British School of Arch. Jerusalem*, Bull. 7, London, 1925).

[9]   'Report on the Galilee Skull' (in 'Researches in Prehistoric Galilee'; publ. of the *Brit. School of Arch. Jerusalem*, London, 1927); *New Discoveries Relating to the Antiquity of Man* (London, 1931).

which was much richer, there were unearthed the remains of six individuals, men and children, enclosed in an extremely hard breccia from which it was difficult to extract the bones, whose state of preservation left much to be desired. These evidences were studied by Keith and McCown.[10]

The Tabun woman was found lying on her side, her legs slightly bent. She is short (5 ft.) and has a small, mesocephalic skull (cephalic index 78) possessing a cerebral capacity estimated at only 1,271 cubic centimetres. The eyebrow arches are very developed and form a positive visor. The forehead is sloping and the face shaped like a muzzle, as in the Man of La Chapelle-aux-Saints. The lower jaw has no chin. The resemblance of these characters to those found in the Neandertalians in Europe is borne out by other features of the skeleton, such as the powerful thorax, the curvature of the bones of the upper arm with a considerable space between the bones, pronounced curve of the femur, marked retroversion of the upper head of the tibia, and so on. But alongside these characteristics there are others which recall modern Man, in particular the relative loftiness of the cranial vault and the rounded shape of the occipital bone. We therefore see characters belonging to *Homo neandertalensis* side by side with those of *Homo sapiens*.

The same mixture occurs again in the Shkül skeletons, with the difference that here the Neandertalian characters are less numerous and less pronounced. Thus the best preserved, No. 5, has a stature of 5 ft. 10 ins. The skull, which is large, has a capacity of 1,518 cubic centimetres; the forehead is much more vertical than in the Tabun woman and the height of the cranial vault is comparable to that of modern Man. Unlike the Neandertalians, the orbits are low and the mastoid apophysis very developed; the lower jaw possesses a chin and the occipital bone is completely rounded. Finally, the thorax is narrow and the limb bones long and slender. And yet this same man has eyebrow ridges that project to form a visor; his palatal vault is even wider than that of any known Neandertalian, and his cervical vertebrae repeat the curious disposition of the Mousterian Man from La Chapelle-aux-Saints.

In their earlier publications Keith and McCown deduced the existence of two types, one primitive and closely resembling, if not identical with, the European Neandertals, which was the Et-Tabun type, the other more evolved and similar to Cro-Magnon Man, which was the Es-Shkül type. Today they have abandoned this distinction, having reached the conclusion that Neandertalian and recent characters exist side by side in all the Mount Carmel skeletons, the only difference being that the proportion between the two sets of characters is not the same in each individual. It follows that certain skeletons, like the Et-Tabun woman, more closely resemble *Homo neandertalensis*, while others, like Es-Shkül skeleton No. 5, tend more strongly towards *Homo sapiens*; but as all stages of transition exist between the two, any division would be artificial. This must definitely be regarded as an intermediate group. Comparing it with the various known Men of the

[10] Keith, A., and McCown, T., *The Stone Age of Mount Carmel, II: The Fossil Human Remains from the Levalloiso-Mousterian* (Oxford, 1939).

Upper Palaeolithic, we see that it most closely resembles, on the one hand, the Neandertalians of Krapina, and on the other, the Cro-Magnon Men from the Grimaldi caves.

This conclusion is confirmed by the evidences collected in 1934 and 1935 by MM. Neuviile and Stékelis from the cave of Jebel Kafzeh, near Nazareth. Roughly contemporary with those from Mount Carmel, they comprise the skeletons or skeletal remains of five individuals, adults and children. These fragments, which are still being studied at the French Institute of Human Palaeontology, are also badly damaged; but it has been possible to reconstruct at least one skull in a satisfactory manner, and this may be considered one of the best preserved of all those belonging to this period so far found in Palestine (Fig. 247). It has a very large capacity (about 1,560 cubic centimetres) and a slightly dolichocephalic index (73.7). The eyebrow ridges

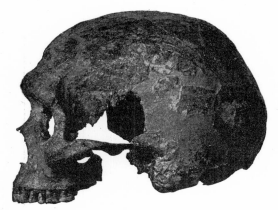

247 Skull of Skeleton No. 5 from Kafzeh, seen in profile. One-third natural size

project in a visor, but the cranial vault is lofty, and the occiput shows no trace of the chignon characteristic of the European Neandertals. Two Neandertalian characters which it does possess are the broadening of the nose, the skeleton of which continues on either side into the upper jawbone without any groove, and the extraordinary development of the palate. Nevertheless, the 'facial muzzle' is only slightly in evidence, and the orbits are low, as in Cro-Magnon Man. We find the same combination of primitive and recent features that is so striking in the Mount Carmel skeleton.

The study of all these Acheuleo-Mousterians from Palestine therefore brings us face to face with a group that is morphologically intermediate between *Homo neandertalensis* and *Homo sapiens*. Of the former it possesses at least three characters: the supra-orbital visor, the special arrangement of the malar bone with a massive orbital apophysis, and the great development of the palatal vault. Of the latter it has the relatively lofty cranium and the shape of the occipital bone. Other dispositions fluctuate between the two types.

The idea of interbreeding between Neandertal and Cro-Magnon Man springs to mind, but Keith and McCown have ruled out this explanation. It would presuppose that the two groups which gave birth to Palestine Man both existed before the latter and in clearly differentiated form. This is difficult to imagine. The two authors prefer to regard all these individuals as forms in the process of differentiation in the direction of *Homo sapiens*. Perhaps they are not the direct ancestors of the Upper Palaeolithic Men we know, but at least they indicate that the transformation of Neandertal Man into modern Man, if it did not take place in Europe, may have happened elsewhere. This is a conclusion of the utmost importance.

Keith and McCown gave these Palestine Men the name *Palaeoanthropus palestinus*, which cannot be approved. The term *Palaeoanthropus* was created for Mauer Man, of which we have only a lower jaw. It cannot be applied to Neandertal Man, and even less to a group that so closely resembles *Homo sapiens*. Palestine Man may be considered a very highly envolved variety of Neandertal Man; that is as far as one can go.

Outside Palestine, some remains of limb bones have been found by Coon in a level containing a Levalloisian industry in the cave of Behistun, on the Iranian plateau.[11] They are said to show pronounced Neandertalian characteristics.

THE NATUFIANS

The Upper Palaeolithic, although well represented in Palestine, has so far yielded only a small number of isolated human bone-remains of no great interest.

It is different with the upper deposits of certain formations containing microlithic industries—Miss Garrod's 'Natufian'. This eastern Mesolithic, remarkable for its small sculptures of animals, differs from the European Mesolithic in one vital respect: although they were not yet acquainted with either polished stone or pottery, and consequently cannot be regarded as Neolithics, the Natufians practised agriculture. They may have been the first Men to cultivate corn, a discovery which earns them a place of honour at the origin of the great Mediterranean civilizations.

The levels of this period are very rich in human bone-remains, so much so that we can speak of veritable cemeteries. From 1928 to 1931 Miss Garrod recovered the remains of 45 individuals, adults and children, from the cave of Shukbah, and of 87 from that of Mugharet-el-Wad on Carmel.[12] From a third bed, Erq-el-Ahmar, south of Bethlehem, Neuville obtained in 1931 the remains of 6 or 7 individuals.[13]

At Mugharet-el-Wad the bodies had been buried in a more or less forcibly bent position and decked with all sorts of ornaments—Elephant's Tooth

[11] Coon, C., 'Cave Explorations in Iran, 1949' (*Museum Monographs, University of Pennsylvania*, 1951).

[12] Garrod, D., 'Mesolithic Burials from Caves in Palestine' (*Man*, 1931).

[13] Neuville, R., 'Le Préhistorique de la Palestine' (*Revue biblique*, XLIII, 1934).

shells, pendants of bird's bones, pierced teeth, and so on. Unfortunately, the condition of the majority of skeletons was too bad to permit of detailed study.

According to Keith,[14] the chief characters of those individuals unearthed by the British expedition that were sufficiently well preserved for study are as follows: Medium height (average in men 5 ft. 3 ins., in woman 5 ft.); skull dolichocephalic or mesocephalic, very lofty; face low and not very broad; sub-nasal prognathism; nasal aperture high and wide; nasal bones broad and flat, like those of Negroes; extraction, in the women, of one or two of the median incisors from the upper jaw; undeveloped lower jaw. One 'very striking' character is the strong development of the bones of the lower

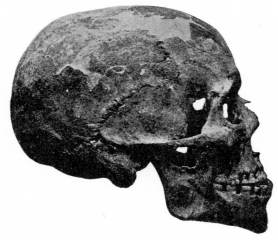

248 Skull No. 2 from Erq-el-Ahmar, seen in profile. One-third natural size

limbs in comparison with those of the upper limbs, which are relatively much slighter.

Keith declares that the Natufians cannot be identified with any living race, but that they none the less represent a branch of the great Mediter-ranean stock. Their affinities are with the Neolithics of Malta, and above all with the predynastic Egyptians. He adds that they must have practised cannibalism.

Neuville entrusted the study of the bone-remains from Erq-el-Ahmar to one of us.[15] Only one skull, that of a woman, is well preserved (Fig. 248). It displays a great resemblance to those of the foregoing beds, bearing witness of the physical unity of the Natufian type. A few differences may, however,

[14] Keith, A., *New Discoveries relating to the Antiquity of Man* (London, 1931); 'The Late Palaeolithic Inhabitants of Palestine' (*Proc. of the First Intern. Congress of Prehist. and Protohist. Sciences*, London, 1932, p. 46).

[15] Vallois, H., 'Les ossements natoufiens d'Erq-el-Ahmar' (*L'Anthropologie*, XLVI, 1936).

be noted relating to the more marked development of the eyebrow arches, reduced breadth of the nasal bones, and slighter prognathism.

If these Natufians are compared with the various types of European Meso-lithics,[16] it is easy to recognize that they bear the most numerous and closest resemblances to those from Mugem in Portugal—the farthest away geo-graphically speaking—and not to those from Téviec, Ofnet and elsewhere (see p. 355). This is not surprising, since at Mugem, too, we see the appear-ance of the great Mediterranean stock. Thus during the Mesolithic, and at the two extremities of the Mediterranean, we note the first signs of the race that is to play such an important part in the subsequent population of the whole basin of this sea. And it is not without importance to remark that neither in Palestine nor in Portugal do we yet observe the presence of brachycephalics.

The periods which succeed the Natufian have been named by Neuville *Tahunian* and *Ghassulian*. They already mark the appearance of metal, and with them we enter proto-history. It will be sufficient to say that at this stage we meet true representatives of the Mediterranean race, with all their classical morphological features.[17] At this point in time, the race is clearly implanted on the seaboard of Palestine and the Lebanon, where it persists right down into historical times.

SIBERIA

When we come to Siberia we are again in direct contact with Europe, but this time via Russia. During the last twenty years or so the scientists of this country have published numerous works, unfortunately rather inaccessible, on the most ancient prehistory of their vast empire.[18]

In Siberia, as in Northern Russia, the Lower Palaeolithic is still unknown, probably because geographical conditions rendered this region uninhabi-table until towards the end of the Ice Age. The same does not hold true in respect of the Upper Palaeolithic. The most numerous observations have naturally been made along the most populated zone of the Trans-Siberian Railway, at the foot of the great Central Asian massif, and in the high valleys of the Obi, the Yenisei, the Lena, and so on.

In 1896 Kashchenko discovered at Tomsk, on the banks of the Obi, in a sort of loess accompanied by worked flints, the carcase of a mammoth that had been dismembered and half carbonized. He believed he had found the relics of a Pantagruelian repast dating from Siberia's Quaternary times.

[16] Boule, M., and Vallois, H., in 'Téviec' (*Arch. de l'Inst. de Paléont. humaine*, Mem. 18, 1937).

[17] Vallois, H., 'Les ossements humains de la nécropole énéolithique de Byblos' (*Bull. du Musée de Beyrouth*, I, 1937).

[18] For Russia in Europe, see the long and extremely useful outline by Golomshtok, E. A., 'The Old Stone Age in European Russia' (*Trans. of the Amer. Philos. Soc.*, New Series, Vol. XXIX, Part II, Philadelphia, 1938) (very numerous illustrations). For Russia and Siberia, see Field, H., 'Contributions to the Anthropology of the Soviet Union' (*Smith-sonian Miscellaneous Collections*, CX, 1948).

The Pleistocene formations of the Yenisei, round Krasnoyarsk, have been studied by Savenkov, de Baye, Volkov, Merhart and Auerbach.[19] The most important locality, that of Aphontova-Gora, is a Palaeolithic settlement *in situ* on a high terrace of the Yenisei, 45 to 60 feet above the river. The gravels of this terrace, used for ballast, are overlaid by a deposit of silt or loess, which contains a rich Pleistocene fauna, including the Woolly Rhinoceros, Mammoth and Reindeer. Worked stones are found in abundance at the bottom of the silt-deposits, where they lie upon the gravels; they include implements fashioned of quartzite pebbles, dressed on one or both surfaces in the Mousterian or Chellean manner (Fig. 249), as well as scrapers

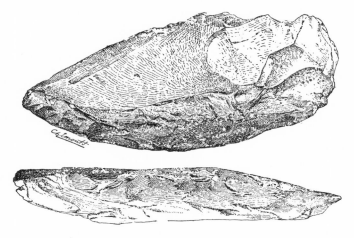

249 Quartzite scraper from Aphontova-Gora. Natural size
(After de Baye and Volkov)

and blades of flint. Along with these stone objects were others of bone, reindeer antler and mammoth ivory. This layer, essentially Palaeolithic in character, and similar, from a geological point of view, to our European alluvial and loess beds, is quite independent of the Neolithic of that region, of which characteristic evidences may be found in the layers of vegetable soil covering the loess.

East of Krasnoyarsk, in Trans-Baikalia, the district of Irkutsk and the banks of Lake Baikal have been visited by various investigators. On Mount Verkholensk, near Irkutsk, Petri explored a bed in the loess, similar to the foregoing, that was rich in worked flints, blades, scrapers and leaf-shaped points, accompanied here by a series of bone harpoons with lateral barbs like those of the European Magdalenian. Another settlement, at Malta, in the loess of an alluvial terrace of the River Bielaya, was studied by Mr.

[19] Savenkov, 'Sur les restes de l'époque paléolithique dans les environs de Krasnoyarsk' (*Congrès intern. d'Anthrop. et d'Archéol. de Moscou*, Vol. I, 1892). Baye, Baron de, and Volkov, 'Le gisement paléolithique d'Afontova-Gora' (*L'Anthropologie*, X, 1899). Merhart, G. von, 'The Palaeolithic Period in Siberia...' (*Amer. Anthropologist*, XXV, 1923).

Gerasimov of Irkutsk Museum. The characteristics of its industry in stone and bone suggest that this deposit is older than any of the foregoing. It is remarkable for the great quantity of carved and engraved objects, ornaments of bone or mammoth ivory, and above all for the female figurines or statuettes obtained from it, to which reference has already been made (see p. 317). It also yielded the skeleton of a child, coloured red and decked with ornaments.

Still farther west, in the valley of the Onon, Rudenko found other deposits of a similar nature. Finally, at the eastern end of the Trans-Siberian Railway, the loess at Skotovo, near Vladivostok, also contains Palaeolithic flints. The same seems to be true of the rich deposits of bone-remains of Quaternary animals in Northern Manchuria, especially on the River Sungari.

Farther north, in Eastern Siberia, near Oleminsk, the deposits bordering the Lena contain flint arrow-heads and implements of mammoth ivory, simple relics of a Stone Age which still exists or formerly existed among those circumpolar populations whose territories we have just reached.

From an anthropological point of view, the discoveries are still very scanty. Until a few years ago, the oldest skeletons unearthed in this vast area went back no further than the Neolithic. If they tell us nothing about the first inhabitants of Northern Asia, at least they reveal the occurrence of changes of population. The majority of these remains, in fact, belong to different races from those now occupying the regions in which they were discovered.

Thus various skulls from prehistoric settlements in Trans-Baikalia are dolichocephalic: they resemble the skulls from the khurgans or tumuli of Southern Russia, and are entirely different from the modern brachycephalic types of the region.

On the other hand, the khurgans of Siberia, of various ages, contain skulls differing greatly in form. Along with specimens resembling those of the Mongols and Ostiaks, there are dolichocephalic forms similar to those from the Russian khurgans.[20] The American anthropologist Hrdlička[21] is convinced that in the khurgans of Siberia, Mongolia and Tibet skeletons have been discovered representing the race which peopled America.

Of far greater importance is the discovery made by the Russian archaeologist Okladinov, between 1938 and 1939, in the little cave of Teshiktash to the north of Baysun, in the Soviet republic of Uzbekistan,[22] of a human skeleton contained in a level with a characteristic Mousterian industry

[20] Zaborowski, S., 'Les kourganes de la Sibéria occidentale' (*Bull. de la Soc. d'Anthrop. de Paris*, 1898).

[21] Hrdlička, A., 'Restes, dans l'Asie orientale, de la race qui a peuplé l'Amérique' (*Congrès intern. d'Anthrop. et d'Archéol. préhistoriques*, Geneva, 1912); 'Crania of Siberia' (*Amer. J. Phys. Anthrop.*, XXIX, 1942).

[22] Okladinov, A., 'Les recherches de la grotte paléolithique de Techik-Tach' (*Acad. Sci. U.S.S.R., Uzbekistan Section*, Series I, Part I, 1940). Debetz, G., 'Sur les particularités anthropologiques du squelette humain obtenu dans la grotte de Techik-Tach' (*Ibid.*).

almost identical with that of Western Europe. The skeleton belonged to a child of about eight years; the bones were partially scattered and surrounded by a circle of goat's horn pegs. The skull, which was well restored, has been studied by Debetz. It was notable for the thickness of its walls and also for its capacity (1,490 cubic centimetres) which is much higher than one would expect in a child of eight. The supra-orbital torus is already in evidence. The forehead is receding, although less so than in the majority of Neandertalians. The face, which is very orthognathous, is no more developed in relation to the cranium than is the case with the children of modern races. The orbits are of normal size. The canine fossae are barely indicated and the nose is remarkably broad. The lower jaw, devoid of chin, is strikingly massive. One character Debetz stresses is the great size of the teeth, the dimensions of which are intermediate between those of the various Neandertalians and of *Sinanthropus*.

The interest of this discovery, made in a region in which we were previously unaware even of the existence of a Mousterian culture, is very great. The scientists who have studied the skeleton all agree that it certainly belonged to a true Neandertalian. In some of its characters, however, such as its great cranial capacity and the relative loftiness of the calvarium, it differs from what we are accustomed to find in European Neandertals, and Weidenreich advanced the hypothesis that it more closely resembled the Mount Carmel forms. In any case, all these new discoveries, whether in Palestine, Iran or Turkestan, show the great eastward extension of one of the most characteristic types of ancient Humanity.

EASTERN ASIA

We can deal here only with the relatively lowlying and habitable regions of Eastern Asia, since the mountain ranges and the highest plateaux are unexplored from our point of view. Mongolia, Manchuria, Korea, Japan and China are all more or less rich in prehistoric relics; but until 1923 nothing was known from these countries older than the Neolithic, though the relics of this period, which include shell-mounds and kitchen middens similar to those in Denmark as well as the remains of ancient villages and megalithic monuments, are exceedingly interesting.[23]

In 1923 and 1924, on an expedition organized by the Institute of Human Palaeontology at Paris, É. Licent and Father Teilhard de Chardin explored Ordos, a district of China enclosed within the great loop of the Hwang-Ho or Yellow River and bordering in the north upon the Gobi Desert. This expedition made the prehistory of Asia richer by an important discovery— that of the Chinese Palaeolithic. It brought back a considerable collection of objects methodically obtained and accompanied by extremely exact stratigraphic and palaeontological observations. The results of the study

[23] See especially Torii, R., and Torii, K., 'Études archéologiques et ethnologiques' (*Journal of College of Science*, XXXVI, Tokyo, 1914). Andersson, J. G., *Children of the Yellow Earth* (London, 1934).

of this material are embodied in a memoir published by the French Institut
of Human Palaeontology.[24]

From a stratigraphic point of view, the investigations of Licent and Teilhard afforded a more exact knowledge of the famous Chinese loess, its
composition and its relations with other geological formations. In particular
they revealed the existence, below the loess, of an older Pleistocene level,
represented by red silts (Fig. 250).

These lower silts or *red earths* (*terra rossa*) correspond to an extremely long
period. Marked at its commencement by a progressive lifting of the soil,

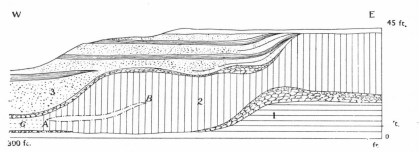

250 Section of the main Palaeolithic layer of occupation at Choei-tung-k'eou in the Ordos
Desert. 1, 'red earth', early Quaternary; 2, 'yellow earth', Chinese loess; 3, post-loessic
river deposits; AB, Palaeolithic layers of occupation
(After E. Licent and Father Teilhard de Chardin)

this period was an erosion phase which produced terraces and caverns. It is
the period of the bone fissures of South China, where we find a fauna of
Indo-Malaysian origin with the Gibbon, the Orang and the teeth of the
mystifying *Gigantopithecus* (Fig. 83), of which we have spoken above. During
this period Japan became an island, but a land-bridge still linked China with
Formosa and the Philippine islands.

Sinanthropus, whose duration we have seen to be considerable, dates from
the red silt phase; but he seems to have been the only representative of the
Hominids during the whole of the latter, for, outside the Choukoutien
region, not the least archaeological trace of human presence has been found
either in North or South China. It may be, however, that some of the
quartzite implements from the gravels at the base of the overlying yellow
earths originated in the eroded and reshuffled deposits of red earth.

The loess itself, or layer of *yellow earths*, which may be up to 200 feet
thick, forms a vast mantle, frequently reshuffled, that covers the red silts
and corresponds essentially to a cold, dry climate. The richest hauls of palaeontological material have been recovered from the bottom or close to the
bottom of this layer. These include two almost complete skeletons, one of

[24] Boule, M., Breuil, H., Licent, É., and Teilhard de Chardin, 'Le Paléolithique de la
Chine' (*Arch. de l'Inst. de Paléontologie humaine*, Mem. 4, 1928). For more recent works see
Pei, W., 'Palaeolithic Industries in China' in McCurdy, G., *Early Man* (Philadelphia, 1937).
Teilhard de Chardin, 'Early Man in China' (*Inst. de Géo-Biologie*, VII, Peking, 1941).

a woolly rhinoceros, and the other of a hemione or wild ass, obtained for the French Museum of Natural History. Taken as a whole, the mammalian fauna of the Chinese loess bears sufficient resemblance to that of the European loess to justify the assertion that they are contemporaneous.

The products of the stone industry were studied by Breuil. The Palaeolithic levels excavated by Teilhard appear under well established conditions that are always the same, some of them being human settlements with layers of occupation situated at depths of 200 feet below the surface of the loess. Others lie at all levels, right up to the surface. The extreme northern and southern deposits are 300 miles apart. The area covering all the fossil-bearing sites studied extends over no less than 12,000 square miles. The two most important deposits are those in the ravines of Choei-tung-k'eou (Fig. 250) and Sjara-osso-gol, in the south of Ordos.

The Palaeolithic of the Chinese loess resembles that of Europe and other parts of the world: the same needs, making the best of the same raw materials, inevitably created everywhere the same range of rudimentary implements. We therefore have here the same Mousterian cores, discs, points and scrapers, the same blades more or less retouched to make scraping-knives, gravers and borers, together with numerous microlithic forms. The fact that many of these worked stones repeat those of the European Mousterian industry is entirely in accordance with geological and palaeontological findings (Fig. 251). In China, as in Siberia, however, this Mousterian industry is accompanied by elements which, in Europe, are characteristic of the Upper Palaeolithic, that is to say of the Reindeer Age. But is it not to be expected that the phenomena of human palaeontology do not recur the world over in the order observed in a few French provinces? If prehistoric archaeologists seek to keep their local classifications rigid, they will incur the same reproaches as were levelled last century against certain geologists, who considered that the geology of every country ought to be modelled on that of the Paris Basin.

The archaeological facts observed at Ordos, in the middle of the continent of Asia, tend to prove that the real origins of some of our Palaeolithic industries must be sought elsewhere than in the European cul-de-sac. Thus in China it would seem that we are confronted by one of those industry-centres in which were elaborated products that were gradually disseminated, in successive stages, as far as the extremities of the peninsulas. In the light of this hypothesis, which is no longer a mere illusion, Asia appears as a great centre of diffusion of human industries which are among the most ancient of all.

It would be of the greatest interest to know the physical characters of the old stone-dressers of Ordos. In spite of all their efforts, Licent and Teilhard were only able to discover isolated fragments that were quite useless.

The only fossil human remains dating from the yellow-earth period come, like those belonging to the preceding phase, from Choukoutien. On top of the great bed in which the bone-remains of *Sinanthropus* were found, was a

251 Dressed flints from Choei-tung-k'eou. Natural size
(After E. Licent and Father Teilhard de Chardin)

cavity separated from the other fissures, the 'Upper Cave', filled with
deposits of yellow clay and containing a rich fauna of more recent appearance
and probably of late Upper Pleistocene age, together with a very poor
collection of stone implements which was, however, accompanied by numerous objects of adornment—pierced deer and fox teeth, shells, red-painted

stones, and so on.[25] The absence of certain types of industry, frequent at the same period in Mongolia and Manchuria, suggests the hypothesis of a southern origin. From the heart of this formation, Pei collected the remains of several skeletons belonging to adults and children of both sexes, concerning three of which Weidenreich published a brief study.[26]

The skull of an old man, very dolichocephalic with a low vault and marked eyebrow ridges, is thought to present certain analogies with that of Cro-Magnon Man, but the presence of Mongoloid characters in the face lead the author to regard it as rather a primitive form of Mongol. Of the two others, both female, one is thought to resemble the Melanesian type of New Guinea, while the other appears to resemble the skull of a modern Eskimo woman. Thus, at this early period, these ancient inhabitants of the Upper Cave at Choukoutien display an unexpected mixture of races. Weidenreich thinks they might represent the ancestors of the Amerindian peoples already on the march towards the New World. It is very strange.

Weidenreich, moreover, does not rule out the possibility that the old man is at the same time a very remote forerunner of the modern Chinese. But the latter do not appear until much later, and then abruptly, with all their anthropological characters already well marked. Thus the Neolithics of the Yang-shao period, possessing a polychrome pottery and dating from about 5,000 years ago, recovered by Anderson from Kansu and Honan and studied by Black, 'already belong to a type essentially similar to that of the Northern Chinese'.[27]

The foregoing facts relate to China. We are even less well informed about Japan, a country in which only one deposit containing dressed stones, of Palaeolithic type and associated with the bone-remains of extinct species (*Elephas namadicus*), has been reported; this is in the south of Hondo Island. It is still doubtful whether it really belongs to the Pleistocene.[28] All the other prehistoric settlements in Japan are certainly of Holocene age.

The skeletons exhumed by Matsumoto[29] from kitchen middens containing a Neolithic industry, which are very frequent on the Japanese coast, present —with differences that enable us to distinguish at least three types—a basis of common characters which gives them a similarity to the Ainus, but they

[25] Pei, W. C., 'The Upper Cave Industry of Choukoutien' (*Palaeontologia Sinica*, N.S., No. 9, Peking, 1939).

[26] Weidenreich, F., 'On the Earliest Representatives of Modern Mankind recovered on the soil of East Asia' (*Peking Nat. Hist. Bull.*, XIII, 1939, p. 161).

[27] Black, D., 'A Study of Kansu and Honan Aeneolithic Skulls and Specimens from later Kansu Prehistoric Sites. . .' (*Palaeontologia Sinica*, Series D, VI, Part I, Peking, 1928). See also Andersson, J., 'Researches into the Prehistory of the Chinese' (*The Museum of Far Eastern Antiquities*, XV, 1943). Teilhard de Chardin and Pei, W., 'Le Néolithique de la Chine' (*Institut de Géo-Biologie*, X, Peking, 1944).

[28] Schnell, I., 'Prehistoric Finds from the Island World of the Far East . . .' (*Museum of Far Eastern Antiquities*, No. 4, Stockholm, 1932).

[29] Matsumoto, H., 'Notes on the Stone Age People of Japan' (*American Anthropologist*, XXIII, No. 1, 1921).

bear an even greater resemblance to certain Men of the Late Palaeolithic and Neolithic periods in Europe.

SOUTHERN ASIA:

INDIA

In the present state of our knowledge, Southern Asia appears far richer in archaeological evidences than Eastern Asia. Since the rise of the Himalayas, India seems to have been inhabited first by numerous Anthropoid Apes and then by Man himself. The oldest Stone Ages in this region are, in fact, represented by a number of deposits, some of which date from a remote geological past; and an almost uninterrupted sequence may be observed running from these obscure periods down to modern times.

The presence of dressed stones in ante-Quaternary deposits has sometimes been recorded. Noetling, for example claimed to have found them in a supposedly Pliocene conglomerate in Central Burma; but these were probably only natural eoliths. Yet if there is one region in the world where the existence of a human or pre-human form may one day be demonstrated it is Southern Asia, which was once vaster than it is today and where life has always been so prolific.

Over almost the whole of India, stones dressed in the Palaeolithic fashion are to be met with on the surface of the soil. In 1866, Foote[30] discovered dressed quartzites of almond shape in the laterite[31] deposits on the outskirts of Madras, the formation of which dates at least from Pleistocene times (Fig. 252). Since that time, many discoveries of this kind have been made. Seton-Karr puts the age of the quartzites from the laterite deposits at 250,000 years.

Other dressed stones have been found *in situ* in the ancient alluvials of many streams, such as the Nerbudda (or Narbada), the Godavari, the tributaries of the Kistna and others, as well as in caves in the Karnul district. The fauna accompanying the relics is for the most part composed of extinct species, several of which date from Pliocene times. Here the problem of the antiquity of man confronts us under the same aspect as in Europe.[32]

The museums in the chief towns of India already possess rich collections of prehistoric objects of all sorts, catalogues of which have been published.

Products of stone industries exactly similar to those of our Chellean, Acheulean, Mousterian, Aurignacian, and even Solutrean periods are wide spread on the surface soil, especially in South-East India. The neighbourhoods

[30] Foote, R. B., Various publications, principally in the *Congrès intern. d'Arch. et d'Anthrop.*, 1868, p. 224.

[31] Laterite is a red clayey earth, formed by the decomposition of underlying rocks, and is very widespread in tropical regions.

[32] Mitra, P., *Prehistoric India* (2nd Ed., Calcutta, 1927). See also Krishnaswamy, V., 'Stone Age India' (*Ancient India, Bull. Archaeol. Survey of India*, III, 1947).

of Madras and Cuddapah, which are particularly rich in this respect, constitute a region where the technique was gradually perfected, and which became a great centre of dispersal for Palaeolithic culture.

During the last twenty-five years a team of geologists and archaeologists of various nationalities—de Terra, Teilhard de Chardin, Paterson, Movius —have undertaken a comparative study of the Quaternary deposits of China

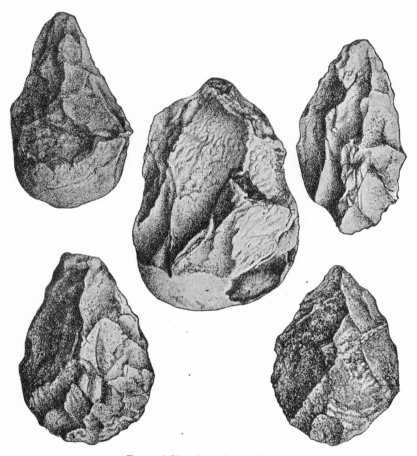

252 Dressed flints from India. (After Ball)

and Southern Asia. They have sought to link up the alluvial formations of India with the ancient moraines of the Himalayas described by Danielli on the one hand, and with analagous formations in Burma, China, Malaysia and even Java on the other. Some of them have also endeavoured to establish a correlation with the glacial phenomena of Central Europe. But the hypothetical element in such attempts is all the greater because it is not certain that the Himalayan glaciations followed the same rhythm as those of Europe.

The findings of all these investigations have been embodied in important memoirs.[33] The following are the essential conclusions.

The three main Himalayan Ice Ages of Kashmir are paralleled, in the region of the Punjab and the Himalayan foothills, by three quite distinct formations.

The most ancient, homologous to the upper layers of the Siwaliks, is formed of gravels and clays devoid of any industry. Hitherto considered to be of Upper Pliocene (Villafranchian) age, it is held by modern geologists to date from the Lower Pleistocene.

The next formation begins with gravel mixed with lumps of conglomerate, often inclined or even vertical. This level contains large quartzite flakes, not retouched, and considered by de Terra and Movius to be the most ancient known industry in India, contemporary with the last Himalayan Ice Age. This is the *Pre-Soan* industry. The upper section of this formation is furrowed by a channel filled with pebbles, corresponding to an inter-glacial period and containing numerous bifaces of Chellean and Acheulean types. At the same time core implements, known as choppers and chopping-tools and characteristic of a new industry, the *Soan*, make their appearance. This pebble-filled channel is coeval with the lower alluvial systems of the Narbada and the Godavari, which contain the same worked objects.

The topmost formation is represented by the gravels and grey silts of Potwar and covers a long span of time, lasting until the end of the Pleistocene Period and corresponding to the Chinese loess and the upper layers of the Narbada. The industry is still well-developed Soan.

The same authors have sought to establish a link between India and China via Burma.[34] The highest terrace of the Irawadi (360 feet above the present river) has a laterite soil and is also steeply inclined. It is attributed by de Terra and Movius to their Lower Pleistocene. The middle terraces (200 and 100 feet), formed of gravels with *Elephas namadicus*, contain—especially around Pagan—a Palaeolithic bearing boulders and rhyolithic tufas as well as silicified woods (Movius's *Anyathian*). The characteristic implements are still choppers, accompanied by a few rare flakes with smooth butts. The lower terraces, some of them post-glacial, contain stone artefacts of more recent date, occasionally even Neolithic.

On the basis of these investigations, Movius has put forward the suggestion that two great and completely different archaeological provinces should be distinguished in the Lower Palaeolithic of the Old World. The

[33] Teilhard de Chardin, 'Notes sur la paléontologie humaine en Asie méridionale' (*L'Anthropologie*, XLVII, 1937, p. 23, and XLVIII, 1938, p. 449). Terra, H. de, and Paterson, T., 'Studies on the Ice Age in India and associated Human Cultures' (*Carnegie Institution of Washington*, No. 493, 1939). Movius, H., 'Early Man and Pleistocene Stratigraphy in Southern and Eastern Asia' (*Papers Peabody Mus. Amer. Arch. and Ethn.*, XIX, 1944); 'The Lower Palaeolithic Cultures of Southern and Eastern Asia' (*Trans. Amer. Phil. Soc.*, XXXVIII, 1949).

[34] Terra, H. de, and Movius, H., 'Research on Early Man in Burma' (*Trans. Amer. Phil. Soc.*, XXXII, 1943).

first, which embraces Europe, Africa and South-West Asia, is that of the classical hand-axe industries, the Chellean and Acheulean of Europe and their African counterparts. The second, which embraces the Indo-Malaysian peninsula and China, is characterized by the absence of hand-axes and their replacement by choppers and chopping tools. The industry found with *Sinanthropus* at Choukoutien belongs to this second typological complex, so the author wonders whether the whole eastern province is not bound up with the Prehominians, while the western province, with its bifaces, corresponds to a different Humanity, more primitive from every point of view. The available evidence is still far too incomplete to support such a hypothesis and, in any case, the division between the two cultural groups proposed by Movius seems much less clear-cut than this author asserts.

The caves in the Karnul region, still imperfectly explored, have yielded implements resembling those of our Magdalenian, although they seem to date from a more ancient period. There can still be distinguished in India a late Palaeolithic phase—represented by pygmy flints, Tardenoisian in form from Banda and the Vindhyan Hills—which passes without break into the Neolithic period.

Discoveries of cave paintings and engravings are now relatively numerous and of a most interesting nature.[35] Red paintings on rocks situated near Singanpur, in the Raigahr district, represent hunting scenes and dances with masked figures, resembling those at Cogul in Spain. One of them depicts Kangaroos, animals now restricted to Australia. Rock engravings at Ghatsila, in the Singbhurn district, are remarkable for their Australian character. According to Mitra, these facts point to the existence of an ancient Indo-Australian culture extending from the Upper Palaeolithic to the Neolithic.

Cockburn discovered numerous paintings in the caves in the Mirzapur district. Here hunting scenes show men, armed with harpoons having stone shaftheads, attacking rhinoceroses (Fig. 253). They may be attributed to the end of the Palaeolithic period, represented in this area by Capsian and Aurignacian industries. In the Bellary district, more than twenty groups of animal drawings and hunting scenes with men armed with javelins and shields are known, and these are probably Neolithic.

Neolithic relics are to be found throughout almost the whole of Southern Asia. In India, the district of Bellary was a great centre during this period and is the site of many large Neolithic cinerary tumuli. In the north-east of Baluchistan there are artificial mounds containing stone implements and bronze weapons. Polished axes, arrow-heads, etc., have been collected in abundance in India as well as in Indo-China. As for the many megalithic monuments in the Deccan, and those which are to be found even in the mountains of Assam, we shall do no more than record their presence in passing.

[35] See in particular Anderson, C. W., 'The Rock Paintings of Singanpore' (*Journ. of Behen and Orissa Research Soc.*, 1918). Mitra, p., *Op. cit.*, p. 410.

The island of Ceylon has been studied from an anthropological standpoint by F. and P. Sarasin, who found in the caves where the wretched Veddahs used to live, and still live, quartz implements resembling those of our own Magdalenian Palaeolithic industry.[36] According to Wayland, the Palaeolithic of Ceylon comprises coarse forms passing to Mousterian and Aurignacian forms, which pass in their turn to Mesolithic microliths, all of which represent a period previous to the arrival of the Veddahs.[37]

253 Painting from cave in the Mirzapur district representing a rhinoceros hunt. (After Mitra)

The whole vast territory of India has unfortunately not yet yielded the least fragment of a truly fossil Man. The few skull finds reported by Mitra, in his work on the prehistory of the peninsula already cited, are very inconclusively dated and it is very unlikely that any of them go farther back than the Neolithic or Eneolithic.

First there is the Bayana skull, found at a depth of 40 feet during the construction of a bridge over the River Gumbhir, in the Ganges basin. Keith[38] attributed it to the race still living in the country. The same is true of the skull from Sialkot, in the Indus basin, probably retrieved from a burial. It does not differ in any way from the skulls of the present inhabitants of the Punjab. By contrast, the skulls from the megalithic burial ground at

[36] Sarasin, P. and F., *Ergebnisse naturwissenschaftlichen Forschungen auf Ceylon, IV: Die Steinzeit auf Ceylon* (Wiesbaden, 1908).

[37] *Spolia Zeylanica*, Vol. XI, Part 41, 1919. See also *Nature*, August 7, 1926.

[38] *Journ. of the Anthrop. Soc. of Bombay*, XI, 1919.

Aditannallur, in the Tinnevelly district, are remarkable for their hyper-dolichocephaly, their platyrrhinia and other characters of the Veddah type which must once have been far more wide-spread than they are today. On the other hand, according to Guha,[39] the majority of the skulls from the famous Eneolithic sites of Mohenjo-Daro and Harappa in the Indus valley, dating from 3000–4000 B.C., are dolichocephalic with a lofty vault and long, narrow face, accompanied—especially at Harappa—by some brachycephalic Armenoids, who were probably later arrivals.

These meagre evidences are very little in comparison with what we may expect. Prehistoric anthropological investigations in India have a splendid future before them.

INDO-CHINA

The prehistory of French Indo-China has been the subject of numerous works by Mansuy, Mlle Colani, Patte, Fromaget, and others.[40]

The Palaeolithic is still unknown there. In Northern Laos, Fromaget and Saurin recorded 'raw or crudely worked pebbles of Pleistocene or even Pliocene age' which seem, however, to have been simply the products of nature.[41] More positive results were obtained by excavating caves and shell-mounds mixed with kitchen refuse. In 1906 Mansuy observed north-west of Langson, beneath a Neolithic level containing polished axes with a shoulder, the presence of a cruder industry almost or completely unpolished. Later, he extracted from the lower beds in the caves of the limestone massif of Bac-Son still coarser implements (Fig. 254), amygdaloids polished only at the cutting level, scrapers which in many cases resembled those of the European Early Palaeolithic, and polishers showing curious grooves arranged in pairs. But this *Bacsonian*, subsequently rediscovered at many other places in Indo-China—and of which Mlle Colani's *Hoabhinian* is only one of the facies—is dated by a fauna comprising none but living species. It cannot be older, at the most, than Mesolithic or 'Pre-Neolithic'. At this level there have been unearthed human skeletons, which we shall discuss in a moment.

F. Sarasin[42] described, from certain caves in Siam, a very crude Palaeolithic, often Eolithic in appearance, which seems to be roughly contemporary with the Bacsonian of Indo-China. More recently, van Heeckeren has recorded in the old gravels of the Lower Mekong[43] a chopper industry,

[39] Guha, B., *Racial Affinities of the Peoples of India*, 1935.

[40] *Bull. et Mém. du Service géologique de l'Indochine* (passim). See also Mansuy, H., 'La Préhistoire en Indochine' (*Publ. de l'Exposition coloniale*, Paris, 1931). Verneau, R., 'Les récentes découvertes préhistoriques en Indochine' (*L'Anthropologie*, XXXV, 1925). Patte, É., 'L'Indochine préhistorique' (*Revue anthropologique*, 1936).

[41] Fromaget, J., and Saurin, E., 'Note préliminaire sur les formations cénozoïques et plus récentes de la chaîne annamitique septentrionale' (*Bull. du Serv. géolog. de l'Indochine*, XXII, Part 3, 1936).

[42] Sarasin, F., 'Recherches préhistoriques au Siam' (*L'Anthropologie*, XLIII, 1933).

[43] Heeckeren, H. van, 'Prehistoric Discoveries in Siam, 1943–1944' (*Proc. of the Prehistoric Soc.*, XIX, 1948, p. 24).

254 Stone implements from the lower strata of caves in the Bac-Son Massif. About half natural size. (After R. Mansuy)

1, crudely dressed rhyolite implement preserving part of the original surface of the pebble; 2, 2bis, quartzite amygdaloid dressed by striking off large flakes; 3, scraper of greenish cornelian retouched at the edges; 4, 4bis, pebble polished over a very small area at one end.

while in the Malay Peninsula, on the River Perak, Dr. Collings of the Singapore Museum found, below gravels and volcanic tufas, an abundant collection of worked stones, also of the same type.[44]

[44] 'Pleistocene Site in the Malay Peninsula' (*Nature*, September 24, 1938).

The only human remains so far discovered come from the north of Indo-China. Only one specimen is a true fossil: a lower molar found by Fromaget and Saurin in phosphatic deposits containing an 'Orang fauna' identical to that of the fossil-bearing fissures of South China and, like them, of Lower Pleistocene age. Man, or at least a Hominian, must therefore have lived in this region a very long time ago.

The many skulls recovered from Bacsonian and Hoabinhian deposits have not yet been fully described. The first studies, by Verneau,[45] remain the most accurate. They concern three skulls from the lower layers of Pho-Binh-Gia, remarkable for their dysharmonic proportions, which give them a resemblance to our great Cro-Magnon race. Very different from the Mongolians, they are closely related to the Indonesian race, that is to say the race which preceded the Malays in the Asiatic archipelago. According to Mansuy and Colani, 15 to 16 other skulls from the caverns of Dong-Thuoc, Lang-Cuom, Lang-Gao and Cho-Ganh are also very different from the Mongols. Some must be grouped with the Indonesians, while others, which are dolichocephalic and have very lofty vaults, possess the essential characteristics of the Melanesians of New Guinea (Papuans). One and possibly two show Australoid features.

In the rock-shelter of Tam-Pong in the Annamese Range, and in a layer which they consider Mesolithic, but which is perhaps only late Neolithic, Fromaget and Saurin found a skeleton that constitutes 'a sort of prototype' and combines Ainu, Polynesian, Papuan and Australoid characters. Other skeletons from this cave or from the cave near Southern Tam-Hang, all dating from the Lower Neolithic, closely resemble those of certain living Negritos (on the Andamans). The four lateral incisors had been extracted from the adult skulls of this type as a mutilation carried out during life.

Finally, Patte recovered from the cave of Minh Cam in Annam, from a more recent level than the Bacsonian, the skull of a young individual in which he found the typical Negrito characters clearly marked.

All these discoveries show that important racial changes took place in Indo-China during prehistoric times. The Melanesians, who were present in the peninsula at the time of the Bacsonian culture, are thought by Mansuy to have subsequently given place to the Indonesians. The latter were joined during the Upper Neolithic by the true Mongolians. As for the Negritos, who are now localized in the Philippine Islands, they, too, long had representatives in Indo-China. Thus Huxley guessed right when, in 1863,[46] he drew attention to the similarities of skulls found in a shell-mound on the Malay Peninsula with those of the New Guinea Papuans and the Australians.

The sum total of palaeoanthropological facts from Southern Asia definitely confirms an interesting idea which purely archaeological date gave us reason

[45] Verneau, R., 'Les crânes humains du gisement préhistoriuqe de Pho-Binh-Gia, Tonkin' (*L'Anthropologie*, XX, 1909).

[46] Huxley, T., 'On the Human Remains found in the Shell-Mounds' (*Trans. of the Ethnolog. Soc. of London*, 1863).

to expect: namely, that in the course of its prehistory Asia, like Europe, was the scene of many great changes of population. Long and patient research will be required to bring order into the chaos.

MALAYSIA

The East Indian, or Malay, Archipelago was not separated from the Asiatic continent until the Quaternary Era. Before this period the chain of the Sunda Islands prolonged the Indo-Chinese peninsula towards Australia, whose much older isolation dates from the beginning of the Tertiary. All these Malaysian islands deserve the name 'Asiatic archipelago' which is sometimes given to them, for their prehistory bears a notable resemblance to that of Indo-China, not only from its archaeological aspect, but also as regards the meagre information we possess concerning the characteristics of their ancient populations.

The inhabitants of these islands were still living in the Stone Age a few centuries ago, so that the numerous Stone Age relics found on them have no chronological value. Nevertheless, some archaeological facts are worthy of mention.

Thus in a shell-mound on the east coast of Sumatra, near Medan, van Stein Callenfels[47] collected a series of amygdaloid specimens, of Palaeolithic facies, but generally belonging to the uniface type of the choppers and sometimes accompanied by grinders and mullers dyed with red colour. He found the same industry, which bears a striking resemblance to the Bacsonian of Indo-China, in the caverns of Malacca. It has since been recorded in Borneo on Celebes and in the Philippines. This Malaysian 'Pre-Neolithic' was, therefore, spread across a whole vast province of the Far East.

In the south-east of Java, on roughly the same meridian as the famous locality of Trinil, there is a karst region with alluvial terraces from which von Koenigswald extracted, in 1935, at Pajitan, an abundant collection of choppers and chopping-tools, comparable to those from the lower Anyathian of Burma. There are also true bifaces reminiscent of those from Madras in India.[48] This industry, which has since been recorded all along the south coast of the island as far as the meridian of Batavia, has been compared with the lower Soan. The geological age of this archaic Palaeolithic does not seem yet to have been clearly established.

The palaeontological discoveries are considerably more important. According to F. and P. Sarasin, Ceylon, Sumatra and the Celebes seem to have been inhabited, at a remote period, by a primitive race of small stature, probably a simple variety of the Negrito type, upon the antiquity and wide distribution of which in ancient times de Quatrefages laid such stress in his writings.

---

[47] Publications inaccessible. See abstract of a letter from the author in *L'Anthropologie*, XXXVII, 1927, p. 229. See also Heine-Geldern, R., 'Die Steinzet Südostasiens' (*Mitt. Anthrop. Ges. in Wien*, 57, 1927).

[48] Koenigswald, G. H. R. von, 'Early Palaeolithic Stone Implements from Java' (*Bull. of the Raffles Museums*, Series B, No. 1, Singapore, 1936).

D. Sanchez y Sanchez[49] described a human skull found in the town of Manilla in the Philippines at a depth of 8 to 10 feet in the subsoil, which is formed by the alluvial deposits of the Rio Pasig. He found certain Negrito characters in it, and ascribed it to a Pre-Negrito race, naming it *Homo manillensis*. Unfortunately, it is impossible to date this bone relic.

Java, celebrated in the annals of palaeontology for the *Pithecanthropi* from Trinil and Sangiran, the story of which we have related at length, has been the subject during recent years of geological investigation accompanied by important discoveries in the field of human palaeontology.

In 1921 Dubois described two human skulls found by him at Wadjak in 1890, prior to the discovery of *Pithecanthropus*, in a limestone terrace over-hanging an ancient lake.[50] It was not accompanied by any industry but only by the bones of animals belonging to Java's present fauna. They cannot, therefore, be very old. Their pronounced state of fossilization nevertheless indicates that they are Pleistocene.

The first, Wadjak I, is that of a woman; the second, Wadjak II, is that of a man. They are both dolichocephalic, very different from the Malay type, and, though of more robust appearance, have all the characters of Australian and Tasmanian skulls: keeled cranial vault, scaphocephalic; receding fore-head; superciliary ridges prominent; low orbits, etc. (Fig. 255).

Wadjak I is exceptionally large for a woman (length, 200 millimetres; breadth, 145 millimetres); its capacity may be estimated at 1,550 cubic centimetres, a figure which is very much higher than the maximum capacity of the Australians and Tasmanians and also exceeds the average for European women. Wadjak II is still larger, having a capacity of 1,650 cubic centimetres. The face is prognathous, the nose broad and flat; the upper dental arch overlaps the lower arch.

The jaws, fashioned after the Australian type, are massive, as strong, according to Dubois, as the jaw of Heidelberg Man.

It was the first time skulls of such character had been recorded outside Australia. *Homo wadjakensis* is a Proto-Australian, indicating that the latter had their origin in Eastern Asia. No doubt he is not very different from the Men who must have inhabited the other islands of Malaysia and the Indo-China peninsula at about the same period. He must be grouped with the Australo-Melanesians of the Bacsonian levels in Southern Asia. The sum total of the discoveries made during the last twenty-five years in the whole region that runs from Tonkin to Java reveals an ancient and very great extension of a human type possessing very primitive characters which are today more localized.[51]

[49] Sanchez y Sanchez, D., 'Un craneo preistórica de Manila' (*Mem. R. Soc. Españ. Hist. Nat.*, XI, 1921).

[50] Dubois, E., 'The Proto-Australian Fossil Man of Wadjak, Java' (*Kon. Akad. van Wetenschappen te Amsterdam, Proc.*, XXII, 1921).

[51] Stein-Callenfels, P. van, 'The Melanesoid Civilisation of Eastern Asia' (*Bull. of the Raffles Museum*, Series B, No. 1, Singapore, 1936).

This seems to be confirmed by Mijsberg's study of a skull obtained from a rock-shelter at Goewa Lawa and also of the Australo-Melanesian type.[52] But a more important discovery was shortly to be reported.

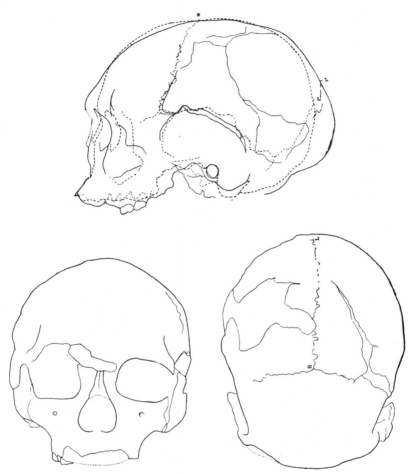

255 Wadjak Skull I, seen in profile, full face and from above. One-third natural size. On the profile of this skull (above) the profile of a typical modern Javanese skull has been superimposed to show the differences. (After Dubois)

NGANDONG MAN

Twenty miles downstream from Trinil the banks of the Solo present ancient terraces; these are the fluviatile beds of Ngandong, considered to be the upper limit of the Pleistocene formations of Java.

In 1931–32, the Java Geological Survey unearthed from the lower sections of these beds, which are rich in fossil bone-remains, five human crania or

[52] See *L'Anthropologie*, XLIV, 1934, p. 182.

parts of crania, without facial bones, but so obviously remarkable that the Director of the Survey, W. Oppenoorth,[53] felt called upon to make of them a new sub-genus of Hominian, *Javanthropus*. Similar specimens were found later, notably by von Koenigswald,[54] so that today we possess 11 crania or more or less important fragments of crania and 2 tibiae, all well mineralized and collected *in situ* within an area of about 150 by 300 feet. The results of their study were embodied in several works, among them an important monograph, a posthumous and unfortunately unfinished work by F. Weidenreich.[55]

In the same terrace, Oppenoorth collected some dressed stones and chalcedony flakes, most of them uncharacteristic, as well as rounded stones very similar to those found in Mousterian deposits in Europe and thought to be throwing stones. Stags' antlers, apparently worked, were regarded as pickaxes, and the same horizon, but at another locality, yielded a flat harpoon.[56] The whole of this industry is very meagre and, above all, very difficult to interpret.

Five of the crania are in a fairly good state of preservation; two of them have the base intact. The other specimens are very fragmentary but evidently belong to the same morphological type. This type, which ·is very homogeneous, at first sight resembles that of Neandertal by a whole series of primitive characters (Fig. 256): extremely thick cranial wall, supra-orbital arches joined to form a visor; forehead very receding, sloping and flat; vault depressed; powerful occipital ridge; small mastoid apophyses. It is very remarkable for the contrast between the large dimensions of the cranium (No. 5, a man's, measures 221 millimetres in length) and the relatively low volume of its cerebral capacity (about 1,300 cubic centimetres; two other crania, belonging to women, have capacities of 1,150 and 1,200 c.c. respectively). The cephalic index varies between 71 and 80; Skull 11 represents the average with 75, the same index as that of the Man from La Chapelle-aux-Saints.

But there are certain differences. The most striking is the structure of the occipital bone, the squamous portion of which is clearly divided into two surfaces that are strongly bent—almost at right angles—at the level of a pronounced occipital ridge, which overhangs the flat lower surface or nuchal plane. This conformation, which we shall meet again in almost identical shape in the Rhodesian skull, is doubtless no more than an exaggeration of

---

[53] Oppenoorth, W., 'Homo (*Javanthropus*) soloensis, een plistoceene Mensch van Java' (*Wetenschappelijke van den Dienst van den Mijnbouw in Ned. Indie*, No. 20, Batavia, 1932); 'The Place of *Homo soloensis* among Fossil Men' (in *Early Man*, Philadelphia, 1937).

[54] Koenigswald, G. H. R. von, 'Ein neuer Urmensch aus dem Diluvium Javas' (*Centralblatt Min.*, etc., Stuttgart, 1933, No. 1).

[55] Dubois, E., 'Racial Identity of *H. soloensis* Oppenoorth. . .' (*Kon. Akad. van Wetenschappen te Amsterdam*, Proc., XXXIX, 1936). Vallois, H., 'Le Javanthropus' (*L'Anthropologie*, XLV, 1935). Kappers, A., 'The Endocranial Casts of the Ehringsdorf and *Homo soloensis* Skulls' (*Journ. of Anatomy*, LXXI, 1936). Weidenreich, F., 'Morphology of Solo Man' (*Anthrop. Papers Amer. Mus. Nat. Hist.*, XLIII, 1951).

[56] Stein-Callenfels, P. van, 'L'industrie osseuse de Ngandong' (*L'Anthropologie* XLVI, 1936). In the opinion of von Koenigswald (1951) this was really a spearhead.

that displayed by *Sinanthropus* and especially *Pithecanthropus* (Fig. 74). It is normal in the Great Apes and, according to Dubois, may be observed in the skulls of recent Australians. In addition, the occipital foramen seems to be set farther back than in modern Man and partially encroaches upon the nuchal plane of the bone, so that it faces downwards and backwards. This morphology, about which there is something brutish, denotes that the head was bent forward in an attitude resembling that of the Anthropoids.

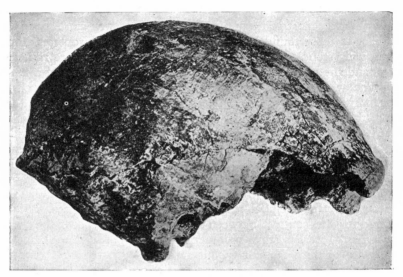

256 Ngandong Skull I, see in profile. Half natural size. (After W. Oppenoorth)

Another important character of these Ngandong crania consists in the fact that their maximum width is not situated at the level of the mastoid process, as in *Pithecanthropus*, *Sinanthropus* and the Apes, nor much higher up in the parietal region, as in Man, but in an intermediate region which is, however, closer to the former than to the latter. This resemblance to the Prehominians of Java and Peking is also manifest in other peculiarities of the supra-orbital visor, the auditory meatus and the frontal sinuses. Finally, Kappers drew attention to the similarity of the endocranial cast to that of *Sinanthropus*. Solo Man is thus a more primitive type than Neandertal or Rhodesian Man.

We are therefore led to ask ourselves whether the fossil Men of Ngandong could not be considered the direct descendants of a Prehominian form, notably that which preceded them on the soil of Java itself—*Pithecanthropus*. This hypothesis, which was contested by Dubois, has been defended at length by Weidenreich, who believed that Ngandong Man is only a more evolved form of *Pithecanthropus* possessing a larger brain. His true name ought to be *Pithecanthropus soloensis*. From the palaeontological point of view this hypothesis is very defensible. It accords witl. the chronology, for a considerable lapse of time must have separated the beginning of the Trinil beds, containing *Pithecanthropus*, which are now folded and have little connexion with the present topography, and the deposition of the horizontal river terraces of Ngandong, which form an integral part of the present topography of the Solo valley. But it is also possible to take the view that, precisely by virtue of his evolution, Ngandong Man has moved sufficiently far away from *Pithecanthropus* to be regarded as a different type. He gives us a glimpse of the mechanism through which the Prehominians gave birth to Neandertals, and may be placed, beside the latter and parallel with Galilee and Rhodesian Man, in the great species of *Homo neandertalensis*, of which he represents simply a special race. In any case, as Oppenoorth thought, there is no justification for creating a new genus nor even a new species.

Some authors have felt that Ngandong Man must be regarded as the ancestor of Wadjak Man and, through him, of the Australians. If he resembles the latter in certain respects, he presents, on the other hand, quite marked differences from the former. Any hypothesis of this kind seems, in any case, premature as long as we do not know the facial characters of these very ancient Javanese.

Thus the little we know about Asian prehistory enables us to assert that it goes back, at many points, as far into the past as in Europe, and perhaps even farther. The facts we have just enumerated also reveal a diversity indicative, in general outline, of a succession of epochs or states comparable to the European sequence: Palaeolithic, Neolithic, Metal Ages. There is doubtless no synchronism, but there is *homotaxia*. A day will come when science will be able to establish, for every major region of Asia, a more detailed sequence, with parallels between one region and another. The task is considerable, on the scale of the largest of the continents, but the splendid discoveries made in the last few years lead us to hope for still finer ones. Who would have foreseen, only thirty-five years ago, the discovery of the Palestine Neandertalians, *Sinanthropus* or the various fossil Men of Java?

AUSTRALIA

GENERAL NOTES

Australia is the smallest, but the most peculiar of the continents. Massive in shape with few indentations, it is separated from New Guinea in the north by the Torres Strait and is extended southward by Tasmania. High mountains—the Blue Mountains and the Australian Alps—rise on its Pacific coast and look out towards the west, in the direction of the Indian Ocean, across immense plateaux and plains with a central depression and vast deserts.

Everything about this continent strikes the naturalist as strange and archaic in character. Its vegetation, comprising tree-ferns, cycads, araucarias, palms, mimosas, eucalyptus and prickly scrub, recalls that of the Secondary

Era. In the surrounding seas are found the corals, the *Trigonia* and *Nautili* of our Jurassic and Cretaceous seas. In its rivers still lives *Ceratodus*, that curious amphibious fish which was first discovered in the Triassic deposits of Europe. The dry land is peopled by a very peculiar mammalian fauna, composed—apart from the Monotremes, belonging to a primitive and still reptilian type—almost wholly of forms remaining at the marsupial stage. This fauna, therefore, forms a legacy from Secondary times, which, nevertheless, has been considerably enlarged and diversified. The indigenous human populations likewise belong to one of the most primitive of modern races.

The majority of these general features of Australia may be explained by its geological and palaeontological history. The larger part of its land surface remained above water during the Primary and Secondary Eras. At first Australia was united to a vast Antarctic continent, including South Africa, Madagascar, India, and what geologists call the *continent of Gondwana*. The latter soon began to break up; it seems that, during the Cretaceous period there was still some temporary communication with Asia through the solid lands of the Malay Archipelago, but after the end of the Cretaceous period, or at the commencement of the Tertiary Era, Australia became isolated in much its present form. Thus there have remained, imprisoned on an immense island, the flora and fauna which were then dominant throughout the world. As this isolation seems to have lasted, more or less completely, up to our own time, the organized life of Australia has been compelled to continue its own evolution in its own area, borrowing very little from the rest of the world, and gradually assuming its present aspect. This independent evolution, carried on in a very special direction, has produced the extraordinary diversity of marsupial mammals, some of which, not so long ago, attained to gigantic size.

MODERN AUSTRALIANS

It is very difficult to explain the settlement of Australia by Man, who can only have been one of the latest comers, unless we believe, with Schoetensack, that Australia is the place of origin of our species, a supposition which seems hardly admissible.[57]

When the first European navigators disembarked in Australia and Tasmania, they found there men of strange and miserable appearance, cannibals, and they immediately compared them with monkeys: 'tailless Chimpanzees', said the English. The Tasmanians no longer exist; they were annihilated by the 'black war' waged upon them by the settlers, and also by alcohol, syphilis, and pulmonary phthisis. The Australians are still numerous. They have been carefully studied from every point of view, and appear to us now to be far removed from the wild brutes spoken of by the first explorers.[58]

[57] Schoetensack, O., 'Die Bedeutung Australiens für die Heranbildung der Menschen aus einer niederen Form' (*Zeitschrift für Ethnologie*, XXXIII, 1901).

[58] See especially Spencer and Gillen, *The Native Tribes of Central Australia* (London, 1899); *The Northern Tribes of Central Australia* (London, 1904); *Across Australia* (London, 1912, 2 vols). Spencer, *Native Tribes of the Northern Territory of Australia* (London, 1914).

In spite of many points of difference, corresponding to the various regions of Australia, the common features of Australians are sufficient to stamp a type forming a very distinct sample of primitive Humanity (Fig. 257). Its general characters may be summarized as follows: stature below average; skin chocolate brown; considerable body-hair; hair on the head curly, wavy

257 Different types from the Arunta tribe. (After Spencer and Gillen)

or even straight; skull long and of moderate capacity; forehead rather receding; superciliary arches prominent; nose very broad and depressed at the root; more or less marked prognathism; pelvis narrow in women.

At one time it was thought that several layers could be distinguished among the Australians, the most ancient of which, possessing Negroid characters, was related to the Papuans of New Guinea, while the most recent, with more Europoid features, resembled the Veddahs of Ceylon and certain Pre-Dravidians of the Indian mainland.

Contrary to this opinion, most authors now admit that the overwhelming majority of Australians belong to one very homogeneous type which represents, among all living races of Men, a race apart. The Tasmanians, who were distinguished by their tendency to brachycephaly and their woolly hair, certainly constituted a different type. According to the majority of authors, they must be regarded as a very specialized variety of Melanesians; their

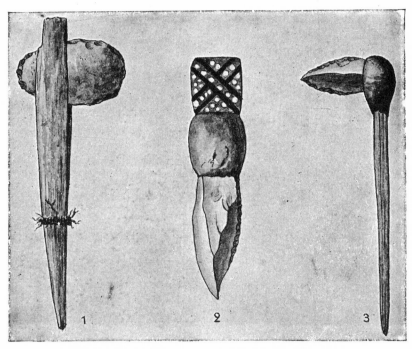

258 Weapons from Central Australia (Warramunga tribe). 1, Stone axe fitted into the branch of a tree, split and tied by means of a thong of horsehair. 2, Stone knife with shaft of decorated wood held together with resin. 3. Stone pick with shaft of wood, split and held together with resin. (After Spencer and Gillen)

resemblance to certain groups of the latter, such as the Baining of New Guinea, is striking.

We can readily understand with what eager interest anthropologists have studied these Men, for in certain of their physical characters they recall our fossil Men, and they live in conditions similar to, if not the same as, those in which our Palaeolithic peoples must have lived. They are indefatigable hunters, immensely agile and skilful tree-climbers; they live in families and tribes, naked or dressed in the skins of animals, in natural shelters or huts of branches, feeding on fruits, roots, reptiles, insects and honey. They are unacquainted with pottery. Their stone weapons often resemble our dressed flints from Saint-Acheul and Le Moustier (Fig. 258); their throwing weapons resemble those of our hunters of the Reindeer Age (boomerangs and spear-throwers); they use religious or magical objects, *churingas*, which may be compared to the coloured pebbles from the Mas d'Azil. They ornament their rock shelters or caves with paintings, not unlike those of our prehistoric caves; and similar drawings of hands, sometimes with the same mutilation of the fingers, are to be found (Fig. 259). These tangible evidences

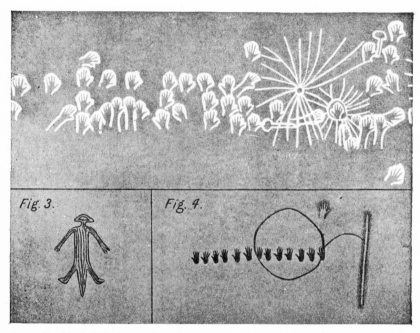

259 Australian Rock-Paintings. Above, hands traced in white round the outline, and various signs. Below (3) a man, and (4) red hands joined by a line and a circle to a boomerang. (After Matthews)

of a primitive culture are related to the social customs, religious or magical, which may still be studied on the spot, and which, on the basis of analogy, have sometimes been attributed to our cave-dwellers.

Thus prehistorians have endeavoured to draw extremely interesting comparisons between our Palaeolithic ancestors and the modern Australians. Professor Sollas has traced these analogies in a most vivid picture.[59]

[59] Sollas, W., *Ancient Hunters and their Modern Representatives* (3rd Ed., London, 1924). Comparisons of this kind are always extremely interesting, but by themselves they are not sufficient to prove the close relationship of peoples who exhibit them. In fact, ethnographical resemblances often result simply from the fact that similar necessities everywhere require similar means to meet them. The Australians certainly resemble our Palaeolithic peoples in their implements and customs, but we now know, contrary to the opinion long held, that they differ completely in physical characters (see p. 253).

The study of human palaeontology in Australia ought, therefore, to be particularly informative. Unfortunately the data are still very meagre.

Let us examine the matter first from the archaeological standpoint.

ARCHAEOLOGICAL EVIDENCES

Products of a stone industry are not lacking in Australia; on the contrary, they are very abundant. All the museums, especially that at Melbourne, are rich in stone implements, some polished, others simply flaked. Among them are to be found most of the types upon which our European historians based their classifications, from 'eoliths'[60] to large and beautiful polished axes, passing through the Chellean to the Mousterian forms, Aurignacian and Magdalenian blades and knives, and even pygmy flints.[61]

But in Australia these various forms are contemporary; they were all in use at the time of the arrival of the first Europeans, and as they are collected on the surface, there is scarcely any method available for distinguishing recent from more ancient objects.[62] Perhaps examination of the patina would justify us in making some distinction, but this method would only allow of vague evaluations.

Professor Howchin[63] described a collection of quartzites, rudely dressed and bearing a resemblance to the products of the Tasmanian stone industry. The bed from which they were obtained is situated in the desert to the south of the McDonnell Ranges, exactly in the centre of Australia, and it occurs in conditions which seem to indicate great antiquity.

One or two discoveries of axes from the depths of alluvial deposits have been announced, but the facts have been recorded very indefinitely, and there is ground for scepticism when, following Keane, we consider that the exploration of auriferous gravels, carried out over hundreds of square miles, has not yet yielded any conclusive evidence.

The only certain finds of an industry in situ seem to be those of Hale and Tindale,[64] made in the course of excavations on the island of Tartanga, in the Murray River in South Australia, and in a rock-shelter not far from this island. Here there were a number of levels, of which the most superficial

[60] Noetling, F., 'Notes on the Tasmanian amorpholiths' (*Proc. Roy. Soc. of Tasmania*, 1906/7, and *L'Anthropologie*, XIX, 1908, p. 645). Jones, F., and Campbell, T., 'A Contribution to the Study of Eoliths. . .' (*J. of Roy. Anthrop. Inst.*, LV, 1925).

[61] Howchin, W., *The Stone Implements of the Adelaide Tribe of Aborigines now extinct* (Adelaide, 1934).

[62] Führer-Haimendorf, C. von, 'Zur Urgeschichte Australiens' (*Anthropos.* XXXI, 1936). Noone, H., 'Some Aspects of Aboriginal Stone Culture' (*Mankind*, III, 1923, p. 136). A fine critical review of the present state of the question, with a complete bibliography, will be found in Mahony, D., 'The Problem of the Antiquity of Man in Australia' (*Memoirs of the Nat. Mus. Melbourne*, XIII, 1943, p. 7).

[63] Howchin, W., 'On the Occurrence of Aboriginal Stone Implements of unusual Type in the Tableland Regions of Central Australia' (*Trans. and Proceed. of the Roy. Soc. of South Australia*, XLV, 1921).

[64] Hale, H., and Tindale, N., 'Notes on some Human Remains in the Lower Murray Valley, South Australia' (*Records S. Austr. Museum*, IV, 1928, p. 145).

contained implements identical with those of the modern Australians, while the deeper ones held numerous shells along with burnt stones suggesting hearths and an industry of patinated flint with thick scrapers and scratchers. Despite the thickness of the deposits, which reached 13 feet in the rock-shelter, this latter industry does not appear particularly primitive. A child's skeleton accompanied by some fragments of bones was found in the same layers. It was distinguished by the great size of the palate and teeth. Hale and Tindale attribute it to a primitive type of Australian.

On the eastern and southern coasts of Australia, there are many shell- and ash-mounds similar to our kitchen middens. In them are found rudely

260 Skeleton of *Diprotodon australis*. One-fiftieth natural size. Palaeontological Gallery of the French National Museum of Natural History

worked stones and bones, but neither pottery nor arrowheads. And yet, since the extent and the bulk of these artificial mounds are sometimes considerable, we may suppose that their formation took some appreciable time and that they date from a fairly remote period.

The study of the art of the rock-paintings leads to the same conclusions. Engravings and paintings are very common in the district where caves and rock-shelters are found. Many of these drawings, which represent all kinds of animals and men, sometimes grouped in definite scenes, are the work of the contemporary tribes. But there are some which are obviously more ancient, and Matthews[65] believes it possible to distinguish two kinds of artistic productions, which must be attributed to two different races. According to Basedow,[66] the rock paintings of the Flinders Mountains must be very ancient, for they are as patinated as the rest of the rock upon which they are engraved. They have besides a special character, and the present native tribes of the region believe that they are the work of their ancestors. Having compared this patina with that of certain Egyptian monuments of

[65] Matthews, 'Rock Paintings and Carvings of the Australian Aborigines' (*J. of Roy. Anthrop. Inst.*, XXIV, 1895; XXVII, 1898).

[66] Basedow, H., 'Aboriginal Rock Carvings of Great Antiquity in South Australia' (*J. of Roy. Anthrop. Inst.*, XLIV, 1914).

5,000 years ago, Basedow finds it to be at least equally developed. Further, certain drawings represent foot-marks which can only be attributed to extinct animals: to *Genyornis*, a giant bird, to *Diprotodon*, a gigantic marsupial, complete skeletons of which have been taken from the deposits of Lake Callabonna (Fig. 260). Here, then, is a very ancient geological record.

Some of the discoveries are more definitely palaeontological in character. At one time it was thought that there were undoubted traces of a fossil Man, dating perhaps from Tertiary times. In 1898, Archibald, Director of the Varnambool Museum in Victoria, announced the discovery of footprints on slabs of sandstone of marine origin, obtained from a depth of 60 to 200 feet. These concretionary sands represent an ancient beach, on which kangaroos, dingoes, and emus had been wont to wander. Among the tracks of these animals there appeared others which, it seemed, could only have been those of a man, who, walking and seating himself upon the yielding sand, had left upon it the imprints of his feet and buttocks. These imprints were studied later by the German palaeontologist, Branco,[67] who was struck by their narrowness. Some years afterwards, Noetling,[68] while travelling in Tasmania, observed on the snow long tracks, arranged in pairs, and so closely resembling the supposed human tracks on the Varnambool sandstones that they might have been mistaken for them. But these tracks, which were remarkably narrow, had been made by kangaroos. This observation appears to be conclusive.

For long it has been well known that in Australia there are fairly numerous deposits containing fossil animals, dating from Pleistocene and even from Pliocene times: bone caves such as the Wellington Caves in New South Wales, or alluvial deposits such as those of Lake Callabonna. These deposits have yielded a host of most curious creatures, particularly the giant marsupials, *Nototherium*, *Diprotodon* (Fig. 260), and *Thylacoleo*, but not the smallest dressed stone has ever accompanied the remains of these vanished creatures. A human tooth was believed to have been found here, but it was subsequently proved to be that of a kangaroo.[69] Nevertheless, certain facts hold out grounds for hope. De Vis recognized on one side of *Nototherium* certain marks which may be attributed to human agency. The Dingo or native dog, which must have arrived in Australia at the same time as its master, has left fragments of its skeleton in these bone deposits.

THE TALGAI SKULL

Matters stood at this unsatisfactory stage when, in 1914, at the time of the outbreak of the First World War, the British Association for the Advancement

---

[67] Branco, W., 'Die fraglichen fossilen menschlichen Fussspuren. . .' (*Zeitschrift für Ethnologie*, XXVII, 1905).

[68] Noetling, F., 'Bemerkungen über die angebliche Menschenspur. . .' (*Centralblatt für Mineralogie*, 1907).

[69] Etheridge, R., 'Antiquity of Man in Australia' (*Records of the Australian Museum*, XI, 1916/17). Finlayson, H., *Nature* (April 14, 1948).

of Science met at Sidney and was thrilled by Messrs. David and Wilson's account of the discovery of a human fossil skull, found near Talgai, on the Darling Downs in Queensland. This fossil has since been the subject of various communications; it was described by S. A. Smith[70] in a memoir of which we here give a summary.

The discovery of the skull dates as far back as 1884. It was found by an old workman at a depth of about 8 feet. The deposit which contained it was laid down by a brook, the Dalrymple Creek, and is formed of two layers. The upper layer consists of black vegetable soil, and rests upon a layer of reddish brown clay containing calcareous nodules. It seems that the skull was taken from the top of this second layer. No other fossils were found there, but bones of *Diprotodon*, *Nototherium*, *Megalania* and others, have been obtained from similar formations laid down by other streams in the neighbourhood of Talgai. The remains of these extinct animals are in the same state of fossilization as the human skull, which was entirely encrusted with ferruginous calcareous matter, within as well as without. When freed from the soil, and after having been treated and prepared for examination, it still seemed much fossilized, and was badly cracked and very fragile. The facial portion is better preserved than the cerebral, which has the appearance of a mosaic of bone fragments (Fig. 261). The density of a fragment of the parietal bone is 2.79 (instead of 2.28 to 2.30 as in modern bones), and it does not consist of more than 3.60 per cent. of organic matter.

The skull belonged to a male, aged from 14 to 16 years. The different profiles superimposed upon the profiles of various modern Australian skulls, corresponded with extraordinary accuracy. The Talgai skull is, therefore, essentially an Australian skull. Smith declares that, had it been found without the facial portion, no one would have regarded it as of any importance from the anatomical point of view.

The face also is Australian in type, but it presents more primitive features than modern skulls. The facial prognathism is striking. The forehead is receding, but has no pronounced superciliary ridges (probably on account of the youth of the subject). The orbit is large and quadrangular; the nasal bones arise from a deep hollow; the floor of the nasal fossae gradually merges in the supra-alveolar surface of the maxillaries, which are very large.

The form of the palate is very primitive,[71] and the molar series are almost parallel. The canines are enormous; the pointed summit of the crown exceeds by several millimetres the general level of the biting surface. Two worn facets have been produced by the contact of the canine with the lower premolar (Fig. 261, C). The arrangements of these facets differs from that normally seen in Man, and is more like that found in the skulls of young

[70] Smith, S. A., 'The Fossil Human Skull found at Talgai, Queensland' (*Philosoph. Transact. of the Roy. Soc. of London*, Series B, Vol. CCVIII, 1918).

[71] According to M. Hellman, however, this appearance is largely due to *post mortem* deformation. A reconstruction of the exact shape of the palate shows its resemblance to the palates of the living Australians and of Neandertal Man ('The Form of the Talgai Palate', *Amer. Journ. of Phys. Anthropology*, XIX, 1934.)

orangs and young gorillas, although there is no real diastema in the upper
jaw to accommodate the lower canine. The pre-molars and true molars are
very large.

The majority of these characters may be encountered separately in some
skulls of Tasmanians or modern Australians, but it would seem that they

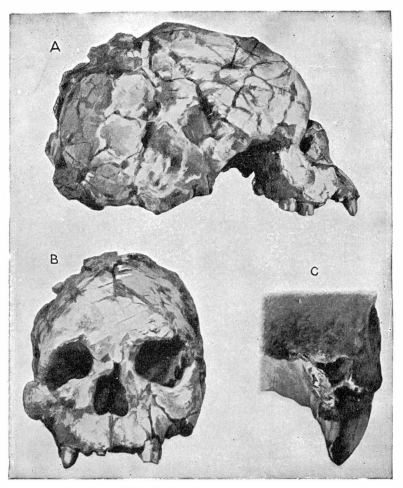

261 The Talgai Skull. A, seen in profile; B, full face. One-third natural size. C, upper right
canine tooth (enlarged). (After A. S. Smith)

have never been observed simultaneously and developed to such a degree,
in any individual case.

The Talgai Man is thus Australian and not Tasmanian in type; he represents a proto-Australian, who had long possessed a human brain, but whose
face retained much more brute-like relics of his origin.   Although the

geological age of the skull is difficult to determine exactly from its condition of fossilization, it may be regarded as Pleistocene. It is the first proof of the high antiquity of Man in Australia.

The Cohuna Skull

There seems no doubt that a certain number of human remains discovered in 1925–6, not far from the Murray River in the north of the state of Victoria, must be attributed to the same type. The most characteristic, which is at the same time the best preserved, is a skull without its lower jaw brought to light about ten miles away from the river near the town of Cohuna.

This skull was found in November 1925, during the digging of an irrigation channel. It was only two feet down and lay in a bed of sand of marine origin, which, according to Mr. Dunn, a government geologist, must be anterior to the Pleistocene, because no post-Pleistocene deposit was laid down in this region since it became dry land except a thin film of brownish-red sand, called *Mallee blown sand* and of modern age. At the point where the skull was found this surface formation was a foot thick, but elsewhere it is generally only 4 to 8 inches thick. The skull was not accompanied by any industry nor by any bone-remains of animals. The only proof of its antiquity is its state of mineralization, which is much greater than that observed in the skeletons from native burials and even comparable, according to Colin Mackenzie, Director of the Zoological Museum at Canberra, to that of the *Pithecanthropus* calotte. The specific weight of one fragment is 2.71; a chemical analysis has shown that it contains only 1 per cent. of organic matter.

No detailed description of this skull has appeared, apart from a note by T. Campbell and a brief paragraph devoted to it by A. Keith in one of his books.[72] From information supplied directly by Mr. Mackenzie, it appears that the skull, in excellent condition, belonged to an adult man in the prime of life. It is remarkable for the receding shape of the frontal region, the development of the supra-orbital torus, and the accentuation of the muscular insertions of the face. The bones of the calvarium are strikingly thick: 12 millimetres at the level of the bregma, 13 at the occipital, 23 at the glabella.

The volume of the cranial cavity is not great—1,260 cubic centimetres, according to Keith. The skull is 199 millimetres long and 131 millimetres wide, which gives it the extremely dolichocephalic index of 65.8. The vault is low. The face is broad and so is the nose, which is distinctly platyrrhinian. There is very pronounced prognathism, much more than in Talgai Man or the modern Australians. The dimensions of the palate are considerable: the distance between the outer edges of the two canines, that is to say the 'width of the muzzle', is 55 millimetres. The canines are even longer than those of the Talgai skull, and the molars are also very large.

[72] Keith, A., *New Discoveries relating to the Antiquity of Man* (London, 1931) p. 304. Campbell, T., 'A Suggested Reconstruction of the Missing Anterior Teeth of the Cohuna Specimen' (*Records South Australian Mus.*, VII, 1943, p. 235).

All these characters led Mr. Mackenzie to regard the Cohuna skull as representing a special race, different from that of Talgai and having a better claim than the latter to be considered the true Proto-Australian race. This view is not shared by all authors, however; some think that this skull is not essentially different from those of the modern Australians. Even its antiquity is thought to be very doubtful.[73]

The same characters, especially the great thickness of the calvarium, recur in various other skeletal remains, also mineralized, discovered subsequently either in the immediate vicinity of the Cohuna skull, or some distance away in the locality of Swan Hill. One particular calotte was the exact replica of that from Cohuna.

THE KEILOR SKULL

A new find, made in 1940, perhaps offers greater certainty. A workman unearthed from a sand-pit near the village of Keilor, ten miles north-west of Melbourne, at a depth of about 15 to 20 feet, a human skull and some bones. These remains were unaccompanied by any fauna or industry. It seems—but here again a stratigraphic check was only made very belatedly—that they were *in situ* and that there had been no reshuffling of the levels. Now, the deposit in which the sand-pit lies is part of a system of river terraces which Australian geologists agree in regarding as Pleistocene. Leaving on one side certain very hypothetical parallels with European glacial phases which have been drawn in this connexion, the terrace containing the human remains can be dated at least from the late Pleistocene.

This find was studied by J. Wunderly.[74] The skull, which lacks the lower jaw and is in a good state of preservation, is that of an adult man. Its capacity is considerable: 1,593 cubic centimetres. The vault is long and dolichocephalic, but, contrary to the great majority of living Australians, the eyebrow arches are not prominent. The face is low and so are the orbits, and the nasal bones do not have the compressed shape observed in the Tasmanians. The palate is wide and the teeth large. Finally, there is a certain prognathism. In Mr. Wunderly's view this skull combines Australian and Tasmanian characters in roughly equal proportions. He dates it from a period when the ancestors of the Tasmanians had not yet settled on their island.

A somewhat different interpretation has been advanced by Weidenreich.[75] This author draws attention to the extraordinary resemblance the Keilor skull bears to those from Wadjak described by Dubois. Not only are the dimensions and indices very similar, but the contours in the various planes can be almost exactly superimposed. The few differences noted, in particular the lesser massiveness of the Keilor specimen, might be of sexual

[73] Mahony, D., *loc. cit.*, p. 34.

[74] Wunderly, J., Adam, W., and Mahony, D., 'The Keilor Fossil Skull' (*Memoirs of the Nat. Mus. Melbourne*, XIII, 1943, p. 57).

[75] Weidenreich, F., 'The Keilor Skull: a Wadjak Type from Southeast Australia' (*Amer. J. of Phys. Anthr.*, N.S., III, 1945).

order. We have seen earlier that Wadjak Man must be regarded as a Proto-Australian. Keilor Man, in Weidenreich's view, is a representative of the same group who had already reached Australia.

In spite of the uncertainty surrounding all these discoveries, in spite of the lack of data regarding their geological bearings, they agree, as may be seen, in showing that a human type far more primitive than the Australians we know, who are undoubtedly its descendants, lived in the south-east of Australia at some time in the past. It must be very many centuries since the present-day Australians settled in their island, and despite having preserved many ancient characters they must have undergone in their new home transformations parallel to those of the higher races of the Eurasian continent.[76] The discoveries at Talgai, Cohuna and Keilor cast a first gleam of light upon the origin and evolution of the inhabitants of this vast country. But many more such discoveries remain to be made, in Australia and Malaysia, before the important anthropological problems presented by these regions can be solved.

[76] Did the Proto-Australians perhaps reach other territories? According to F. Fenner ['Fossil Skull Fragments of probable Pleistocene Age from Aitape, New Guinea' (*Records South Austr. Mus.*, VI, 1941, p. 335)], a fossil skull found at a depth of 10 feet in an ancient marine beach of the Aitape district of New Guinea, displays characters of the Southern Australian type.

CHAPTER ELEVEN

THE FOSSIL MEN OF AFRICA

AFRICA must have played as important a part as Eurasia in the origins and primitive history of Humanity.

Evidences of a long extended past have increased in number with the progress of exploration. In all those parts where investigation has been at all intensive traces have been found of a Stone Age and weapons and tools similar to those of our most ancient Palaeolithic have been collected. To begin with, they were found on the surface of the soil; then closer study revealed deep levels, beds in stratigraphical or palaeontological conditions allowing of chronological comparisons. Examination of these beds justifies the important conclusion, which may be applied to the whole continent, that the prehistory of Africa is at least as old as that of Eurasia.

From the geographical point of view, Africa forms a block without many indentations which has for a very long time possessed its present shape. It is essentially a country of plateaux in which the great mountain ranges are confined to the periphery, bordering more or less directly upon the coast. Unlike Europe and Asia, there are no huge continental massifs isolating the various regions, and communications between the latter are hindered by few natural obstacles. This must have greatly facilitated the migrations of prehistoric Men.

A remnant of the Africano-Brazilian continent, Africa seems to have gained its independence towards the middle of the Tertiary Era. Its separation from the neighbouring continents is today almost complete. It was less so in the past: it seems that the subsidence which gave birth to the Red Sea only dates from the end of the Tertiary; at the same period, land-bridges across the Mediterranean created communications between North Africa and Europe. Africa has, therefore, not always been in the position of an isolated continent. Large contributions of fauna reached it from Asia on several occasions, and certain exchanges took place with Europe. In the last of these contributions and exchanges the first Men no doubt took part.

The distribution of its fauna and flora divides Africa into two major regions, separated by the great desert zone of the Sahara: North Africa, which forms part of the *Palaeoarctic* province of the naturalists, and Central and Southern Africa, which constitute the main part of their *Ethiopian* province. The first is a Mediterranean territory, closely resembling Southern Europe, and like the latter its human population belongs to the white race. The second is totally different: this is the true Africa, the great Dark Continent. Here live the African Negroes properly so-called, with their various groups, the Sudanese, Bantus and so on; here, localized in the great tropical forest, is the primitive race that was once far more widespread and whose culture is still at the Stone Age—the race of the Bushmen; and alongside them lives the closely related race of the Hottentots.

Geology, palaeontology and prehistory combine to tell us that there was a time when this division of Africa into Palaeoarctic and Ethiopian zones did not exist, or was less pronounced. It was only by degrees that the various regions of Africa assumed the different aspects they now present. Before it dried up the Sahara was no desert, that is to say no barrier, but a bridge; the subtropical Ethiopian fauna extended over North Africa. Man lived in every part: dressed stones, identical with those of the oldest European Palaeolithic, are found exactly alike at a great many points, forming an almost continuous chain from the extreme north to the extreme south of the continent.

Then climatic changes took place of which prehistoric Man was a witness. But they did not consist in a simple process of growing progressively drier. They were more complex. In certain regions, such as East Africa, we shall see that it has been possible to disclose successive phases of great rains and aridity. Knowledge of these 'Pluvial' and 'Inter-Pluvial' periods has greatly facilitated the chronological interpretation of the archaeological deposits, but the problem of their relationship to the Ice Ages of the northern hemisphere, often posed, has not yet been solved.

Concurrently with these variations in climate, the geography of Africa also underwent changes. A great phase of volcanic activity appeared towards the beginning of the Quaternary. It was accompanied by foldings of the soil and subsidences. Many faults were produced; the deep depressions which were to give birth to the great lakes of East Africa were completed; the gorges of various rivers were hollowed out. Archaeological deposits attest the fact that Man was a witness of all these phenomena, many of which doubtless influenced his prehistory.[1]

EGYPT

Egypt has been studied by archaeologists from the days when the idea of prehistory scarcely existed. In 1867 Worsaee recorded the first dressed flints, which Arcelin, Hamy, and Lenormant compared to European flints, confirming the existence of an Egyptian Palaeolithic phase, far older than the oldest monuments of classical Egypt. Delanoue, John Evans, and Haynes supported this conclusion, which was for a long time contested by

[1] On Africa in general, see Breuil, H., 'L'Afrique préhistorique' in *Cahiers d'Art* (Paris, 1931). Leakey, L., *Stone Age Africa* (Oxford, 1936) (contains a bibliography).

Egyptologists. The latter, unnecessarily impressed by the thousands of years of Egyptian history, a period which barely counts from the geologist's point of view, retained their mistaken views regarding questions of origin. To refute the idea of the Palaeolithic phase, they laid stress on the fact, quite accurate in itself, that the use of flint implements had lasted for a long time after the first dynasties. But there are flints and flints. The honour of establishing the

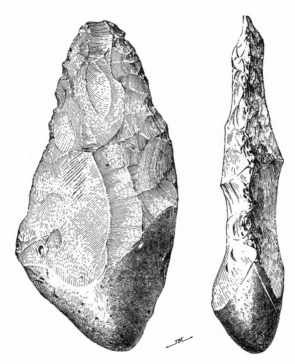

262 Dressed flint from the vicinity of Thebes in Egypt. Two-thirds natural size
(After J. de Morgan)

distinction, and of proving definitely the existence, the importance and the geological antiquity of the Stone Age in Egypt belongs chiefly to J. de Morgan.[2]

The first finds were made on the surface of the soil or in alluvial deposits of indefinite age. Later investigations led to the establishment of a stratigraphy; furthermore, they showed that there was a general parallel between the stone industries of Egypt and those of Europe (Fig. 262). Thus G. Caton-Thompson and E. Gardner found in the Kharga oasis, at a depth of 30 feet under tufas corresponding to a period of great humidity between

[2] Morgan, J. de, *Recherches sur les origines de l'Égypte: L'âge de Pierre et des Métaux* (Paris, 1896).

two dry periods, an Acheulean industry clearly *in situ*.[3] But it is to Sandford and Arkell[4] that we owe the most important discoveries.

While studying the cliffs that border the valley of the Nile in Upper Egypt, these authors noted the presence of a succession of gravel terraces, related to the progressive sinking of the river and extending over a length of several hundred miles between Aswan and Asyut. The highest, which date from the end of the Pliocene to the beginning of the Pleistocene, contain no industry; but the four lowest contain dressed stones comparable, save for a few details, with the classic implements of the European Lower Palaeolithic. The correlation is as follows: 100-foot terrace, Chellean; 50-foot terrace, Acheulean; 30- and 10-foot terraces, old Mousterian and typical Mousterian. All these industries continue southwards, and Arkell recorded an important Chellean level in the immediate neighbourhood of Khartoum.

The Upper Palaeolithic does not exist in Egypt in the form in which we know it in Europe, but Vignard recorded a very curious industry, particularly evident in the Sebil region, 500 miles south of Cairo, to which he gave the name *Sebilian*.[5] Here we can see the progressive transformation of a Mousterian flake industry into a Mesolithic industry of microliths (Fig. 263). Three layers have been distinguished: the first corresponding to a phase of silting-up during which the Nile, submerging the lower terrace, rose 110 feet, while the third saw the establishment in Egypt of the desert climate which prevails there today. There is no doubt that the last period was roughly contemporary with the European Mesolithic and late in date.

The Neolithic is widely represented in Egypt, and a whole series of industries have been attributed to it. The investigations of G. Caton-Thompson and E. Gardner have made it possible for us to follow the evolution of some of these at once from the archaeological, geological and climatological points of view. They pass imperceptibly to the Eneolithic, through which we come to the Predynastic period.

Thus Egypt now appears to us a corner of the African continent where Man established himself during the Lower Palaeolithic and which he has occupied ever since. But human palaeontology has so far provided almost no information regarding these first inhabitants of the Nile Valley. The only known true fossil remains are, in fact, a few skull fragments found by Sandford in the Lower Sebilian at Kom Ombo. They have not been published, but their finder notes their close resemblance to the Predynastic Egyptians.

[3] Caton-Thompson, G., and Gardner, E., *The Desert Fayum* (London, 1934).

[4] Sandford, K., and Arkell, W., 'Paleolithic Man and the Nile Valley in Nubia and Upper Egypt' (*The University of Chicago Oriental Inst. Publications*, XVII, 1933). Sandford, K., 'Paleolithic Man and the Nile Valley in Upper and Middle Egypt' (*Ibid.*, XVIII, 1934). Sandford, K., and Arkell, W., 'Paleolithic Man and the Nile Valley in Lower Egypt' (*Ibid.*, XLVI, 1939). A good general survey of recent works on Egypt is to be found in Huzzayin, S., 'The Place of Egypt in Prehistory. . .' (*Mémoires présentés à l'Institut d'Égypte*, XLIII, 1941).

[5] Vignard, E., 'Une nouvelle industrie lithique, le Sébilien' (*Bull. de la Soc. préhistorique française*, 1928).

A. Smith Woodward[6] described a fossil skull found 200 miles south of Khartoum, in the reshuffled deposits of the Nile, and dating from about 5,000 years ago, which would not place it farther back than the Neolithic. It consists of a moderately brachycephalic cranium, and in Smith Woodward's opinion is an ancestor of the living Bushmen, comparable up to a point

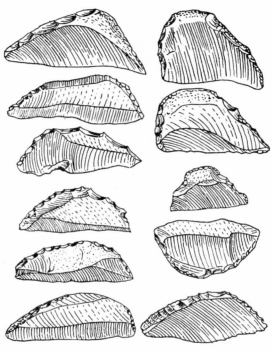

263 Sebilian industry. Forms showing the transition from the Mousterian-type flake to the half-moon. Two-thirds natural size. (After Vignard)

with the Boskop skull, of which we shall speak later. This view can only be accepted with reserve.

Much better known, on the other hand, are the Neolithics and Predynastics of Egypt properly so-called, several of whose burial grounds have been discovered. Small and dolichocephalic, they belong to the Mediterranean race which, at the same period, also already existed in the Near East and was making its appearance in Europe. It still forms the basis of the Egyptian population. Thus the race that at present predominates in Egypt was already in position during the Polished Stone Age and perhaps even the Upper Palaeolithic, if Sandford's observations are confirmed. A remarkable example of anthropological continuity despite the vicissitudes of history!

6   Smith Woodward, A., 'A Fossil Skull of an Ancestral Bushman from the Anglo-Egyptian Sudan' (*Antiquity*, 1938).

Barbary

Lesser Africa, or Barbary, has long yielded many clear evidences. In 1875, Bleicher[7] discovered dressed stones after the type of Saint-Acheul in a Pleistocene alluvial deposit at Ouzidan, near Tlemcen. Some years afterwards, Pomel, Tommasini, and Pallary described the Palikao or Ternifine deposit in the region of Mascara.[8] In this area stones dressed by the hand of man, Chellean and Mousterian in form, are to be found, along with numerous bone-remains of vanished or emigrated mammals, especially those of the extinct species *Elephas atlanticus*. The deposit at Aboukir, near Mostaganem, and the rich settlement on Lake Karâr, also in the province of Oran, exhibit similar palaeontological features.[9]

In 1887, Dr. Collignon[10] observed, in ancient alluvials in the neighbourhood of Gafsa, in Tunisia, several superimposed layers containing relics of various stone industries, the oldest of which is identical with our Chellean industry.

Then and since, a great number of places, caves, rock-shelters, or settlements in the open, have been investigated throughout the whole of North Africa. Among the works which have been published must be mentioned those of Smith and Graziosi on Libya; of J. de Morgan, Capitan and Boudy, Gobert, Reygasse, Latapie, Vaufrey, Passemard, etc. on Tunisia; of Pallery, Doumergue, Debruge, Flamand, Reygasse, Vaufrey, Marchand, Balout, etc., on Algeria; and of Pallary, Punchon, Campardou, Antoine, Neuville and Ruhlmann, etc., on Morocco.[11]

The oldest phase of Palaeolithic culture in North Africa resembles in every feature that of the ancient Palaeolithic of Europe and Asia. Chellean, Acheulean and Mousterian are to be found there with their characteristic implements (Fig. 264). In many of the beds the industries are mixed up, reshuffling of the alluvial deposits and corrosion of the surface soils having destroyed the original stratigraphy. Certain authors deduced from this that all these cultures were contemporaneous. This conclusion was incorrect. More accurate investigation has shown that here, as in Europe, they are independent, and they have been found superimposed at several sites. One

---

[7] In *Matériaux*, X, 1875, p. 196.

[8] Tommasini, 'Gisement chelléen de Ternifine, en Algérie' (*Bull. de la Soc. d'Anthropologie de Paris*, 1883). Pallary, P., and Pomel, M., 'La station quaternaire de Palikao' (*Matériaux*, XXII, 1888).

[9] Boule, M., 'Études paléontologiques et archéologiques sur la station paléolithique du lac Karâr' (*L'Anthropologie*, XI, 1900).

[10] Collignon, Dr. 'Les âges de la Pierre en Tunisie' (*Matériaux*, XXI, 1887).

[11] For bibliography see *L'Anthropologie, passim*. As a general review, attention must be particularly drawn to the interesting synthesis written nearly fifty years ago by P. Pallary, 'Instructions pour les recherches préhistoriques dans le Nord-Ouest de l'Afrique' (*Mémoires de la Soc. historique algérienne*, III, 1909). See also Reygasse, M. 'Les âges de la Pierre dans l'Afrique du Nord' (in *Histoire et Historiens de l'Algérie*, Paris, 1931). Breuil, H., *loc. cit.* Wulsin, F., 'The Prehistoric Archaeology of Northwest Africa' (*Papers of the Peabody Mus. of Amer. Archael. and Ethnol.*, XIX, 1941).

of the most typical of these is at Gafsa, where the Mousterian lies above the Acheulean in an unconformable stratum: the deposits containing the latter industry are ancient alluvials, compressed into pudding-stones and sloping at an angle of 40° to 45°; they are covered in places by a layer of recent horizontal alluvials containing typical Mousterian implements.[12] A tectonic

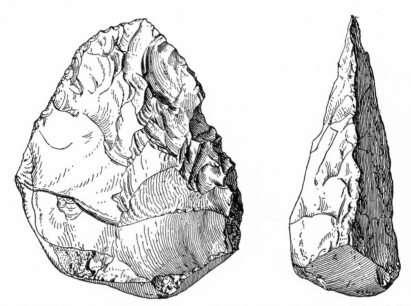

264 Dressed flint from Diabet, Morocco. Three-fourths natural size. (After Pallary)

upheaval took place between the two periods, clearly marking one off from the other.

C. Arambourg has recently recorded the discovery in the fluvio-lacustrian deposits of Saint-Arnaud, near Setif,[13] of polyhedral or vaguely spheroid pieces of hard limestone that bear every sign of having been deliberately dressed. In the same beds are to be found *Mastodon*, *Elephas meridionalis* and *Hipparion*, that is to say an extremely archaic fauna generally attributed to the Villafranchian. The Saint-Arnaud industry would therefore seem to date from the extreme base of the Pleistocene, and it can undoubtedly be compared to the *Pebble Culture* which we shall meet in East Africa. This discovery shows that Man was present in Barbary from the very beginning of the Quaternary Era.

In various North African settlements the Mousterian is continued by a special industry, in which the classical artefacts of this epoch are accompanied

[12] Vaufrey, R., 'Les plissements acheuléo-moustériens des alluvions de Gafsa' (*Revue de Géographie physique*, V, 1932).

[13] Arambourg, C., 'Traces possibles d'une industrie primitive dans un niveau villafranchien de l'Afrique du Nord' (*Bull. Soc. préh. française*, XLVII, 1950, p. 348).

by tanged arrowheads analogous to those observed in the Neolithic, as well as by blades, scrapers and rudimentary borers, which show a tendency towards the forms of the Upper Palaeolithic. This is the *Aterian* of Reygasse,[14] named after the settlement at Bit el Ater in Southern Constantine, where the Aterian level was *in situ* in a Pleistocene geological bed.

All these old Palaeolithic industries are occasionally found, notably in Algeria, in the lower layers of cave-fillings. Here they are contained in red clays comparable to those of the same period in European caverns. They are contemporary with a mammalian fauna that is partially extinct and of Europeo-Asiatic origin. They correspond to a more humid climate than the present one.

The Aterian certainly occupied an important part of the period that corresponded to the European Upper Palaeolithic. The two industries which succeed it and develop more or less parallel to one another, the *Capsian* and the *Ibero-Moorish*, represent both the end of the Upper Palaeolithic and the beginning of the Mesolithic. They are known through many deposits. The Capsian[15] which received its name from J. de Morgan and is the same as Pallary's *Getulian*, is met with in caves and rock shelters and on the surface of the soil. Especially typical of this period are some curious sites in Tunisia and the department of Constantine called snail-shell mounds (*escargotières*), artificial deposits where, alongside innumerable snail-shells mixed with cinders and some bone-remains of animals, there are found an abundance of implements made of flint, many of them microlithic (Fig. 265), bone and the shells of ostrich eggs.

Certain analogies between the Capsian industry and the French Aurignacian have led to the belief that the latter is of African origin. This notion must be abandoned. Typologically, the Capsian is more evolved than the Aurignacian. It is certainly later in date. The resemblances are much more easily explained in terms of a common origin: they represent two currents which, starting from the east of the Mediterranean, followed a parallel course along the opposite shores of this sea.

The Capsian does not extend over a wide area; it is localized in Southern Tunisia and the region bordering on the department of Constantine along the whole of the coast, from the Gulf of Gabes to Morocco, we find another industry, the *Ibero-Moorish*, whose artefacts are also largely microlithic, but without geometrical flints and without gravers.[16] Likewise correlated with

[14] Reygasse, R., 'Nouvelles études de palethnologie maghrébine' (*Recueils des Notices et Mémoires de la Soc. archéolog. de Constantine*, 1919–1922). Caton-Thompson, G., 'The Aterian Industry: its Place and Significance in the Palaeolithic World' (*Journ. of the Roy. Anthrop. Inst.*, LXXVI, 1946).
[15] Morgan, J. de, Capitan, L., and Boudy, P., 'Études sur les stations préhistoriques du Sud-Tunisien' (*Revue de l'École d'Anthr. de Paris*, XX, 1910, and XXI, 1911). Gobert, E., 'Notes et recherches sur le Capsien' (*Bull. de la Soc. préhistorique de France*, 1910). Vaufrey, R., 'Notes sur le Capsien' (*L'Anthropologie*, XLIII, 1933). Passemard, E. and L., 'Le Capsien de la Table Ouest dit "Abri Clariond" à Moularès, Sud-Tunisien' (*Préhistoire*, VIII, 1940).
[16] Gobert, E., and Vaufrey, R., 'Deux gisements extrêmes d'Ibéro-Maurusien' (*L'Anthropologie*, XLII, 1932).

deposits in caves or snail-mounds, it used to be considered later than the Capsian; it has now been proved to be contemporary. It is even possible that it began earlier.

The Capsian and Ibero-Moorish pass imperceptibly into a Neolithic that begins with a phase of numerous geometric flints resembling those of our Tardenoisian. But there are already polished stones and pottery. The

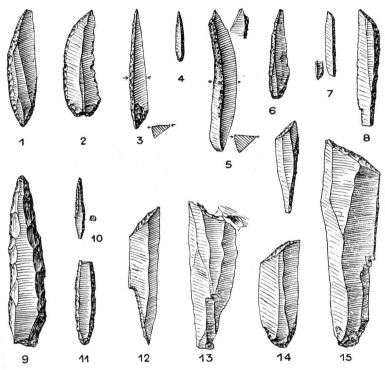

265 Dressed flints, chiefly microliths, from the El-Mechta bed; typical Capsian. Two-thirds natural size. (After R. Vaufrey)

1 to 8, various types of blades with a curved back; 9 to 11, blades with two chipped cutting edges; 12 to 15, blades with oblique truncation

authentically Neolithic elements in this period seem to have been borrowed from Egypt, whose culture was then far more advanced. Their progressive development produced the true Neolithic.

Many engravings on rock have been found in Southern Oran and Tripolitania. Some writers attributed them to the Upper Palaeolithic in their desire to establish yet another parallel with the European Aurignacian. The researches of R. Vaufrey have finally put paid to this hypothesis.[17] The

[17] Vaufrey, R., 'L'art rupestre nord-africain' (*Archives de l'Institut de Paléontologie humaine*, Mem. 20, 1940).

oldest of these engravings do not appear to be earlier than the Neolithic. The most recent date from a period very near the present. No direct connexion can be established between these drawings and those of the Dressed Stone Age in the caverns of the South of France.

ATLANTHROPUS

Barbary has yielded quite a number of skulls and skeletons from Stone Age deposits; but their value was long doubted. Some of them came from snail-shell mounds (*escargotières*), artificial hillocks which have often served as Berber burial places. Others were found in deposits whose stratigraphy was not well established. The anthropological description of all these specimens was generally incomplete. All this lack of accurate information finally cast discredit on them.

The discoveries made during the last thirty years have reopened the question. The first to cite, not only because they afforded the most ancient human remains yet known for North Africa, but also because of the striking resemblance which these remains bear to those of the Prehominians, were made in Algeria, in the Ternifine or Palikao deposit. .

Three years ago, on resuming excavations carried out last century in this deposit, MM. Arambourg and Hoffstetter brought to light from the bottom of a bed of sand corresponding to an ancient lake an extremely primitive fauna and industry. The fauna contained numerous extinct forms: *Elephas atlanticus*, *Rhinoceros simus*, a *Machairodus*, a *Phacocherium*, nearly related to the giant forms of the Lower Pleistocene of East Africa, and many hippopotami and giraffes. The industry was characterized by implements of quartzite and sandstone of a primitive Chelleo-Acheulean type reminiscent of the lower levels at Oldoway. All this places the Ternifine deposit in a very ancient period of the Quaternary, possibly synchronous with the second glaciation or at least with the second interglacial period.

In the deepest part of the sand-pit, almost or completely in contact with the underlying Tertiary substratum, MM. Arambourg and Hoffstetter found, in July 1954, two lower jaws of a primitive human type. The following year they recovered from the same stratum a third lower jaw together with a parietal bone. Only a preliminary description of these various specimens has so far appeared.[18]

The jawbones (Fig. 266) are remarkable for their great massiveness. The ascending rami are powerful with the region of the angle truncated; the lower margin is extremely thick. There is no chin and the symphysis is receding; its lingual surface possesses genial apophyses but there also exists, as in the Anthropoids, a small genio-glossal fossa. The imprints of insertion of the digastric muscle face virtually downwards, as in Heidelberg and Neandertal Man. The molars and especially the premolars, on the other

[18] Arambourg, C., 'L'Atlanthropus de Ternifine' (*Libyca*, II, 1954); 'Une nouvelle mandibule d'Atlanthropus du gisement de Ternifine' (*Comptes Rendus Acad. Sci.*, October 3, 1955); 'Le pariétal de l'Atlanthropus mauritanicus' (*Ibid.*, October 10, 1955).

hand, are striking for their large size and low crowns. On their outer surface, the premolars show a *torus cingularis* as in *Sinanthropus* and *Pithecanthropus*. Also like the latter, the two tubercles of the first molar are set obliquely, and not transversely as in modern Man. The pattern of the grooves of the molars has preserved a primitive type.

The parietal bone is remarkable for its thickness, the slightness of its

266 Jawbone of *Atlanthropus mauritanicus*, seen in profile. Two-thirds natural size

curve, which suggests that the cranial vault was low, and the presence on its inner surface of a Sylvian crest as in *Sinanthropus*.

All these characters clearly mark off the Ternifine fossils from living Men and even from Neandertal Man, and at the same time give them a resemblance to *Pithecanthropus* and *Sinanthropus*. This is, therefore, a new form, which its discoverers have named *Atlanthropus mauritanicus* and which, according to them, represents for Africa an evolutionary stage analogous to that of *Pithecanthropus* and *Sinanthropus* for the Far East. Like these two forms, *Atlanthropus* belongs to the Prehominians. Hence this group would appear not to have been limited, as previously thought, to Asia and Java, but to have extended as far as North Africa. The importance of the Ternifine discovery is evident. Nevertheless, we must not generalize too hastily. By various characters, *Atlanthropus* is more evolved than *Pithecanthropus* and even *Sinanthropus*. The identity between them is far from absolute. That *Atlanthropus* represents an exceedingly primitive form, the most primitive yet found in North Africa, is undeniable; but there is still too little evidence to assert with complete confidence that it should be classed with the Prehominians.

RABAT MAN

Along the Atlantic seaboard between Rabat and Casablanca there stretches a tall cliff of what is known as Rabat sandstone, corresponding to ancient consolidated dunes overlying an old marine beach. Geologists are not agreed as to the exact age of this sandstone, but it certainly dates from at least the Mid Pleistocene.[19] It is therefore contemporary with our Mousterian and possibly older. In 1933 human remains were found in this sandstone near Rabat.[20]

The remains of Rabat Man are unfortunately very limited. There seems

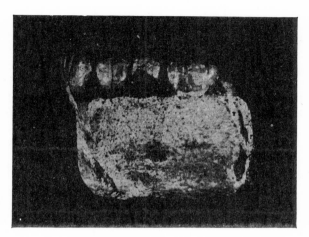

267 Side view of the Rabat Jaw in its matrix of Quaternary gravel. Natural size
(After J. Marçais)

to have been a complete skull, which was destroyed by the explosion of a mine and of which the only serviceable fragments are part of the palatal vault together with the anterior segment of the lower jaw.[21] Their archaic appearance is very pronounced (Fig. 267). The lower jaw is very robust and devoid of chin. The palate is very wide and concave. The teeth are extremely large, and many of their characters recall those found in *Sinanthropus*: in particular, there is a basal torus (*cingulum*) on the canines and lower pre-molars, and the lingual cusps of these latter teeth are remarkably developed. Rabat Man certainly belonged to a different type from modern Man. Although it is impossible to be definite, we may suppose that he was at a stage of evolution analogous to that of Neandertal Man and perhaps even more primitive.

Even more meagre are the few relics found in 1939 by B. Howe and H. Movius in one of the Caves of Hercules, near Tangier. Here, at a depth of 20 feet and in a sterile bed underlying a bed containing an already very

[19] See in particular Neuville, R. and Ruhlmann, A., 'De l'âge de l'Homme fossile de Rabat' (*Bull. et Mém. de la Soc. d'Anthropologie de Paris*, 1942). Choubert, G. and Marçais, J., 'Le Quaternaire des environs de Rabat et l'âge de l'Homme de Rabat' (*C.R. Acad. Sci.*, June 9, 1947).

[20] Marçais, J., 'Découverte de restes humains fossiles dans les grès quaternaires de Rabat, Maroc' (*L'Anthropologie*, XLIV, 1934).

[21] Vallois, H., 'L'Homme fossile de Rabat' (*C. R. Acad. Sci.*, November 26, 1945).

evolved Mousterian industry, there was the fragment of a child's upper jaw with two teeth, and a molar from an adult individual. These fragments were studied by M. Senyuerek.[22] Their characters link them directly with Neandertal Man.

MECHTA MAN

We do not yet know the Men of the Aterian, but we are much better informed about the ensuing period. The discovery by C. Arambourg, in 1928, of an important Ibero-Moorish ossuary in the cave of Afalou-bou-Rummel, near Bougie, made it possible for the first time to study a number of skeletons from this period that were archaeologically well dated.[23] In the course of this study a methodical revision was made of the various human remains previously found in Barbary. It showed the existence in this region of a special type, very similar to Cro-Magnon Man of the European Upper Palaeolithic. This is the *Mechta type*, named after the snail-shell mound of Mechta-el-Arbi, where its first representatives were observed. Its general dispositions are very characteristic.

Mechta Man was tall, 5 ft. 6 ins. on the average, while some individuals reached 5 ft. 11 ins. His shoulders were broad and he had long forearms and legs.

The skull is strikingly coarse and brutish in appearance (Fig. 268). The cranium, which is very thick and large, is pentagonal in shape and has an index that varies between dolichocephaly and mesocephaly. The cranial vault is lofty with no trace of flatness. The eyebrow arches are remarkably developed and join at the glabella in a projection that runs from the centre of one orbit to the centre of the other; below them, the root of the nose is strikingly depressed. The mastoid apophyses are enormous; the occipital bone often displays the transverse ridge or torus.

The face is short and broad, clearly dysharmonic with the cranium. The rectangular orbits are always very low and set well apart. The nose projects strongly, but the nasal aperture is wide and often platyrrhinian. The palatal vault is also wide. The lower jaw is powerful with lateral angles that project far outwards; the chin is well marked.

There is another character of a different kind: all the individuals examined had undergone an artificial mutilation of the front teeth consisting of the extraction of the two upper median incisors, and sometimes also of the lateral or the lower incisors.

The Mechta type is well represented among the skeletons from Afalou-bou-Rummel, but it is also to be seen over a large part of ancient Barbary. It is to this type that we must attribute a skull brought to light more than forty years ago by Debruge in the little cave of Ali-Bacha, west of Bougie,

[22] Senyuerek, M., 'Fossil Man in Tangier' (*Papers of the Peabody Mus. of Amer. Archeol. and Ethnol.*, XVI, 1940).

[23] Arambourg, C., Boule, M., Vallois, H., Verneau, R., 'Les grottes paléolithiques des Béni-Segoual, Algérie' (*Archives de l'Institut de Paléontologie humaine*, Mem. 13, 1934).

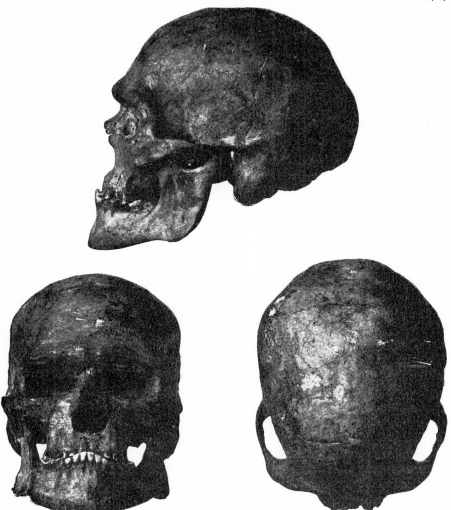

268 The Mechta Type: skull of individual No. 12 from the cave of Afalou-bou-Rummel, seen in profile, full face and from above. One-third natural size. (Collections of the French Institute of Human Palaeontology)

and originally ascribed to Neandertal Man, while others saw in it a 'pure Berber type'.[24] The industry accompanying it, the nature of which was long in dispute, is Ibero-Moorish, like that of Afalou. A number of skeletons extracted from caves or snail-shell mounds in various parts of Algeria, accompanied by an Ibero-Moorish industry or an industry that is still

[24] Delisle, F., 'Note sur les ossements de la grotte d'Ali-Bacha' (*Assoc. fr. pour l'avancement des Sciences*, Congrès de Montauban, 1902); 'Deuxième note sur les ossements humains de la grotte d'Ali-Bacha' (*Congr. intern. d'Anthrop. et d'Archéol. préhistoriques*, Monaco, Vol. I, 1906).

Neolithic but in the Ibero-Moorish tradition, also belong to the Mechta type.[25] So does a skull found a few years ago by A. Ruhlmann in the little grotto of Dar-es-Soltan, near Rabat, in a deposit belonging to the final phase of the Palaeolithic and overlying an Aterian level.[26] This type therefore extended as far west as the Atlantic Ocean.

It was long thought that Mechta Man was also to be met with in the Capsian. The recent investigations of Balout[27] tend to show that the few Capsian deposits in which he appears—the snail-shell mound of Mechta-el-Arabi in particular—belong to an end-phase of this period, manifestly influenced by the Ibero-Moorish phase. In the Capsian proper we meet another, more evolved type, bearing some resemblance to the Mediterranean race. This type seems to continue into the Neolithic and may possibly have come from East Africa.

However that may be, and judging by the finds already made, Mechta Man may well have been the dominant, if not exclusive, element throughout the whole period corresponding to the end of the Upper Palaeolithic in North Africa. It is doubtless he who was the bearer of the Ibero-Moorish culture. This means that he played a fundamental role in the prehistory of these regions. What, then, is his anthropological significance?

The earliest authors grouped the Mechta Men with Neandertal Man, regarding them at least as Neandertaloids. This view, which was based only on the study of the very incomplete fragments then known, cannot be maintained. Mechta Man is part of the great group of *Homo sapiens*, and comparison with the other fossil Men of the Upper Palaeolithic shows evident resemblances to the Cro-Magnon race: the same tall stature, the same craniofacial dysharmony, the same great development of the superciliary arches, the same low orbits, and so on. There exist certain differences, however, one of the most marked of which is the height of the cranium in the prehistoric inhabitants of Barbary. Without confusing the latter with the Cro-Magnons proper, we may regard them as constituting an independent but related type, a race or sub-race—it matters little what precise designation they are given.

This parallel development of two related anthropological types on either side of the Mediterranean during the Upper Palaeolithic is not without interest. Taken in conjunction with what we said above concerning the similarities between the Aurignacian of Europe and the Capsian of Africa, it implies that Cro-Magnon and Mechta Man are both derived from the same stock, whose origin lay in the eastern section of the Mediterranean basin. They were two divergent branches, perhaps the first manifestations of *Homo sapiens* in the regions to which they penetrated, bringing with them

[25] Arambourg, C., Boule, M., Vallois, H., Verneau, R., *Loc. cit.*, pp. 189 ff.

[26] Vallois, H., 'Les restes humains de la grotte de Dar-es-Soltan' (in Ruhlmann, A., 'La grotte préhistorique de Dar-es-Soltan'. *Collection Hespéris*, XI, 1951).

[27] Balout, L. and Briggs, C., 'Mechta-el-Arbi' (*Travaux du Labor. d'Anthr. et d'Arch. préhistoriques du Musée du Bardo*, III–IV, Algiers, 1951).

new industries. But their degree of physical evolution was not the same and, in the sum total of his features, the African type is revealed as coarser and more primitive than the European.

We have seen, in an earlier chapter, that the Cro-Magnon race did not become extinct at the end of the Palaeolithic. A few of its descendants have survived in various places in Europe. On the other hand, Verneau's investigations proved that the old population of the Canary Islands, the Guanchos, who were still there in the 15th century at the time of the Spanish conquest, displayed a number of characteristics that gave them a striking resemblance to these fossil Men. This resemblance was explained by a migration of Cro-Magnon Men across Spain and Morocco. The discovery of the Mechta Men simplifies the problem. It is evidently among them, and not among the European Cro-Magnons, that we must seek the origin of the ancient inhabitants of the Canary Islands: they represent the survival, almost to our own day, of the Ibero-Moorish race that once peopled the whole of Barbary.

The Sahara

It is not without surprise that we find in the Sahara such extraordinary abundance of Stone Age antiquities. Since Abbé Richard, more than half a century ago, recorded the presence of dressed flints in Southern Algeria, such finds have been repeatedly made. Dozens of explorers have collected, in almost every part of this vast desert, innumerable stones shaped by flaking in various fashions, as well as polished axes, mortars, and very beautiful and delicate arrowheads; worked ostrich eggs cut into rings; pottery, etc. The deposits are chiefly found in the vicinity of springs, modern or ancient, and near river-beds now dried up, a fact which indicates that, in the Sahara, great changes of climate and of the conditions determining habitability have taken place at a relatively recent date.[28]

Unfortunately, almost all the relics thus collected have been found on the surface, and the most various forms are frequently observed at the same place and in the same stratum. Erosion by wind and water has destroyed the stratification and mixed up the industries. Artefacts resembling our Chellean, Mousterian and Neolithic flints have been recovered, but the distinction between them is purely typological, and the greater or lesser weathering of the specimens is the only guide we have to their antiquity. Undisturbed deposits are an exception.

The Chelleo-Acheulean industries are found almost exclusively in the Western Sahara, either under the dunes or on the rocky plateaux. In a few rare instances they are associated with a primitive fauna, characteristic of a damp climate—*Elephas antiquus*, Hippopotamus, Zebra, Crocodile, etc. The

[28] Chudeau, R., 'L'hydrographie ancienne du Sahara, ses conséquences biogéographiques' (*Revue scientifique*, 1921). Gautier, É., *Le Sahara* (Paris, 1928). Dalloni, M., 'Matériaux pour l'étude du Sahara oriental' (*Mission scientifique au Fezzan, Public. Inst. Rech. sahariennes*, Algiers, 1948).

most typical of these deposits is that of the Tihohaidin Erg or Sand-Hill, near the Tassili (Plateau) of Adjer, where numerous Acheulean bifaces were mingled with bone-remains of *Elephas antiquus* and the Hippotamus.[29]

The Mousterian is not very frequent in its typical form: what predominates in the whole of the Sahara, from Algeria to the Sudan and from Tripolitania to the Atlantic, is the Mousterian with tanged points—Reygasse's Aterian. It is directly succeeded by the Neolithic. There are no industries comparable with those of our European Upper Palaeolithic. Even the Capsian is missing, except on the borders of Algeria. It seems, therefore, as

269 Neolithic arrowheads from the Sahara. Natural size. (After E. F. Gautier)

though in the whole of this vast area the Mousterian had evolved *in situ* and finally produced the primitive Neolithic, the Upper Palaeolithic being represented by its Aterian phase.

This phase must have endured for a very long time. The abundance of deposits corresponding to it show that the Sahara was then very thickly populated. After a dry period, which must doubtless be attributed to the Mid-Palaeolithic, the climate once more became damp.

This humidity persisted throughout most of the Neolithic. During this period there were many lakes in the Southern Sahara, on the banks of which stood kitchen middens. The whole area of the desert is littered with innumerable arrowheads showing a great variety of shapes (Fig. 269). Their extraordinary frequency contrasts with the scantiness of arrowheads in the Algerian Neolithic, but polished stones are rare here.

Many engravings and paintings on rocks have been found in the Sahara. The number of discoveries has greatly increased during recent years. They are known from the Libyan desert, Hoggar, Adrar Ahnet, Fezzan, Tassili and Tagant.[30] There is general agreement in dividing them into two periods, one recent, subsequent to the introduction of the Camel, the other more ancient and termed Pre-Cameline. This older period bears witness to an age when the Sahara was still widely inhabited. Some of the species represented are extinct, like the Great Buffalo (*Bubalus antiquus*); others, such as

[29] Joleaud, L., 'Gisements de Vertébrés quaternaires au Sahara' (*Bull. de la Soc. d'Histoire naturelle d'Afrique du Nord*, XXVI bis, 1936).

[30] Flamand, G., *Les pierres écrites* (Paris, 1921). Monod, Th., 'L'Adrar Ahnet' (*Travaux et Mémoires de l'Inst. d'Ethnologie*, XIX, 1932).

the Rhinoceros, Elephant and Giraffe, have emigrated. But there is no need to go back to the Palaeolithic in order to explain the presence of these animals: as in Southern Barbary, these drawings are at most Neolithic. Hence they, too, have no connexion with the paintings and engravings of our European Palaeolithic.

THE ASSELAR SKELETON

In 1927 MM. Besnard and Monod of the Augiéras-Draper expedition discovered in the heart of the Sahara, in the basin and not far from the dried-up valley of the Tilemsi, once a tributary of the Niger, near the military post of Asselar, a fossil human skeleton. This skeleton was noteworthy for its high degree of fossilization, comparable to that of the Tertiary animals of European deposits. It lay in a sand and sand-stone formation of freshwater origin and containing, along with mollusc shells, many bone-remains of great fish, crocodiles and mammals, notably the Phacocherium.

These deposits therefore date from a period when the valley of the Tilemsi formed the bed of an important stream, while the land on either side supported a rich mammalian fauna. All this is very different from the conditions that obtain today and must certainly date from a more ancient period, either the end of the Upper Palaeolithic or at least the great damp phase of the kitchen middens at the beginning of the Neolithic.[31]

This skeleton was presented by M. W. Draper to the French Institute of Human Palaeontology and was made the subject of a detailed description.[32] Its various elements were embedded in a very hard sandstone gangue, which made the work of preparation exceedingly difficult. It belonged to a male individual who died at a fairly advanced age.

The skull (Fig. 270) was well preserved and filled with a deposit that formed an endocranial cast. It is distinctly dolichocephalic (cephalic index 70.9), with a lofty vault. The face is mesoprosopic, almost brachyprosopic, with cheek bones projecting forward and a flattened root of the nose. The skull is, therefore, dysharmonic. In profile, the face reveals a certain prognathism. The nose is platyrrhinian. The orbits are low and sub-rectangular in shape. The two median incisors were extracted from the upper jaw in youth—a similar mutilation to that observed in Afalou Man. The lower jaw possesses a slightly developed chin. The teeth are large and display archaic characters.

The skeleton as a whole reveals a stature of at least 5 ft. 7 ins. The limb bones are slender; their length is considerable in relation to the trunk; the forearms and shanks were particularly long in relation to the upper arms and thighs.

In all these characters Asselar Man exhibits incontestable Negro or Negroid affinities. This differentiates him from the present population of

[31] Monod, Th., 'Sur l'âge de l'Homme d'Asselar' (*Historia naturalista*, IV, Rome, 1946). Bonarelli, C., 'L'età geologica dell'uomo d'Asselar. . .' (*Riv. di Antropologia*, XXXV, 1947).
[32] Boule, M. and Vallois, H., 'L'Homme fossile d'Asselar, Sahara' (*Arch. de l'Inst. de Paléontologie humaine*, Mem. 9, 1932).

North Africa and the Sahara, no less than from the Palaeolithic Men of Mechta; he can only be compared with the races of Central and Southern Africa.

But a distinction must be made between these races. The Asselar skeleton

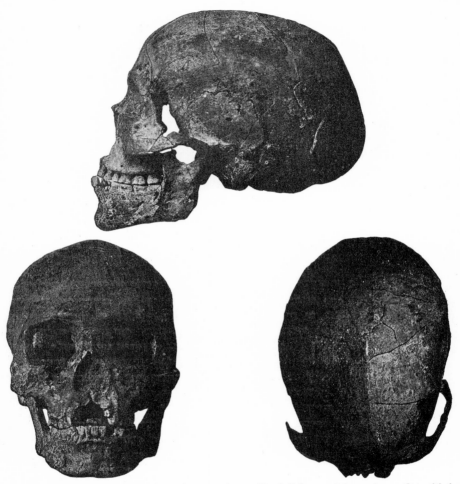

270 Skull of the Fossil Man of Asselar, seen in profile, full face and from above. One-third natural size. Collections of the French Institute of Human Palaeontology

is very different from the Sudanese Negroes properly so-called, and also from the Bushmen. It is with the Bantus, particularly those of South-West Africa, and with the Hottentots that it presents the most numerous points of likeness, without being more closely related to the one or the other: in its cranial characters it most closely resembles the former, in those of the face it bears the greatest likeness to the latter.

It may seem surprising to find that this fossil Man does not belong to any of the ethnic groups now inhabiting or surrounding the Sahara. It is even more astonishing to find him grouped with two races living in Southern Africa and therefore separated from him by more than half the continent. This shows that the present inhabitants of Southern Africa once had representatives to the north of the great tropical forest. At the same time, it proves that these representatives belonged to a generalized Negroid type, more primitive than the groups we know today. Moreover, Asselar Man presents certain affinities with the Negroid race of Grimaldi: perhaps this resemblance is due to a very remote common origin.

CENTRAL AFRICA

West Africa and the Sudan have yielded many relics. Hamy recorded some artefacts, mainly of Neolithic workmanship, from French and Portuguese Guinea, the Ivory Coast, the Gold Coast and Gabon.

Captain Duchemin has described tumult and megaliths in the valley of the Gambia. In the Senegal valley in French Sudan, de Zeltner[33] collected dressed stones, some of Palaeolithic workmanship, in superficial but usually clearly marked beds. Between Kayes and Timbuctoo, Dr. Decorse has observed and recorded the site of many Stone Age settlements. The Central Nigerian plateau, explored by Lieut. Desplagnes, is rich in Neolithic monuments and relics. According to Welcome, the Southern Sudan seems to be no less rich.

Dupont, Cornet, Stainier, Taramelli, Jacques, Deslisle, Cabu, Colette, Droux and Bergeaud, and others have described many series of Stone Age implements found in the Congo basin.[34] Here, as in the other great African territories, the raw material, the workmanship and the forms of the weapons or tools show the greatest diversity. Palaeolithic types, especially the amygdaloid (Fig. 271), are not absent. Always very crudely dressed, they are associated with polished axes and a microlithic industry which comprises, *inter alia*, trapeziums and arrowheads with a transverse cutting edge. Menghin has given to this complex, the value of which is variously interpreted and which is for some authors an entirely artificial creation, the name *Tumbian* and has emphasized its resemblance to the European Campignian. This analogy, which sometimes amounts to identity, has been verified by R. Vaufrey, who showed that the Tumbian also existed in the Senegal basin

[33] Zeltner, F. de, 'Notes sur le Préhistorique soudanais' (*L'Anthropologie*, XVIII, 1907). Laforgue, P., 'État actuel de nos connaissances sur la Préhistoire en Afrique occidentale française' (*Bull. Comité d'Études hist. et scientif. de l'Afrique occidentale française*, 1925).
[34] Bibliography in Delcroix, R. and Vaufrey, R., 'Le Toumbien de Guinée française' (*L'Anthropologie*, XLIX, 1939). See also Breuil, H., 'Le Paléolithique au Congo belge d'après les recherches du Dr. Cabu' (*Trans. R. Soc. South Africa*, XXX, 1944, p. 143). Janmart, J., 'Stations préhistoriques de l'Angola du Nord-Est' (*Diamang, Publ. culturais*, No. 1, Lisbon, 1947). Mortelmans, G., 'Coup d'œil sur la préhistoire du Congo belge' (*Bull. Soc. royale belge de Géographie*, LXXIII, 1949). Breuil, H., and Janmart, J., 'Les limons et les graviers de l'Angola du Nord-Est et leur contenu archéologique' (*Diamang, Publ. culturais*, No. 3, Lisbon, 1950).

271 Tumbian industry from the Ape's Cave, French Guinea. Half natural size
(After R. Vaufrey)

and in Guinea, where it is associated with pottery. In this author's view, it
is partly derived from the Neolithic with a Capsian tradition from the
Sahara. The Tumbian industry cannot, therefore, be very ancient. It goes
back, at most, to the last millennia before our era and cannot have come to
an end more than a few centuries ago.

No human remains have been found in Central Africa, for we cannot consider as such a skeleton recently unearthed in the gallery of an abandoned mine at Katanga, which does not differ in any practical respect from the Bantus of the region.[35] Soil conditions in the tropics, which make the preservation of bones difficult, lead us to fear that such finds will always remain a rarity.

ABYSSINIA AND SOMALILAND

In 1880 Revoil recorded the existence of Stone Age deposits in Somaliland, while du Bourg de Bozas noted their presence in Abyssinia in 1902. Various investigations have been carried out since then and have revealed a sequence

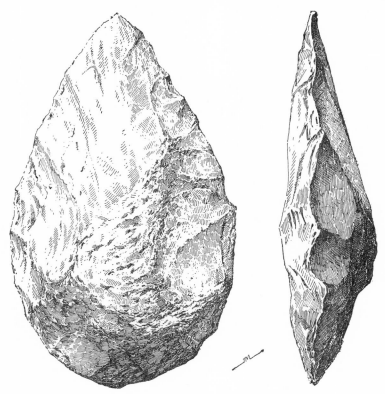

272 Quartzite implement from Somaliland. Two-thirds natural size. (After J. de Morgan)

of industries virtually identical with those of East Africa. But only very meagre data have so far been collected.[36]

Tools of Chellean and Acheulean type have been found on the surface in the north of British Somaliland (Fig. 272) and near Obock. Others, near

[35] Cabu, F., 'Introduction à l'étude de l'Homme de Likasi' (*Trans. Royal Soc. South Africa*, XXIX, 1942, p. 76). Drennan, R., 'Report on the Likasi Skeleton' (*Ibid.*, p. 81).

[36] See in particular Teilhard de Chardin, P., Breuil, P. and Wernert, P., 'Les industries lithiques de Somalie française' (*L'Anthropologie*, XLIX, 1940); 'Le Paléolithique du Harrar' (*L'A.*, LV, 1951).

Harrar, were contained in a clayey drift associated with fossil bone-remains.

Dressed stones of Mousterian type are numerous everywhere; they, too, are generally on the surface. Typologically, this Mousterian often gives birth to an industry very much like that of the Middle Stone Age of Southern Africa. It is this industry which here represents the Upper Palaeolithic—at

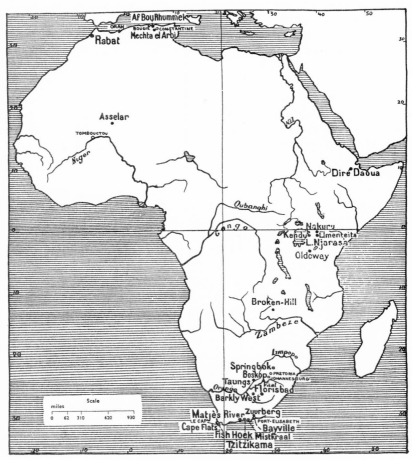

273   Map of the principal deposits of Fossil Man in Africa

least no other industry attributable to this period has been found up to the present.

A Microlithic and a Neolithic have been encountered on the surface at various places. They seem to have lasted until very recent times.

The only human skeletal relic discovered in Abyssinia was collected in 1932 by P. Wernert from the Porcupine Cave near Dire-Dawa, Harrar (Fig. 273). This was a fragment of a lower jaw, found in a bearing corresponding to evolved Mousterian, which must be considered, because of its very advanced state of fossilization, to be the same age as the industry accompanying it.[37] The specimen, which forms part of the collections of the French Institute of Human Palaeontology, is limited to the right part of the body of the jaw together with the corresponding molars and premolars. It displays a series of archaic features: very great massiveness of the body of the bone, absence of chin, receding shape of the rear face of the symphysis with a ridge projecting at the junction of the latter with the lower margin, elongated form of the digastric impressions on the lower margin of the mandible. The teeth are too much worn down for many of their characters to be in evidence, but they are strikingly large and the third molars are bigger than the second.

All these characteristics show that the Dire-Dawa jaw belonged to a far more primitive Man than living Men. Was he a Neandertalian? This cannot be definitely stated, but the characters of this specimen certainly accord with those of the few lower jaws of *Homo neandertalensis* known to us.

EAST AFRICA

The presence of dressed stone tools in East Africa was noted by J. W. Gregory as long ago as 1893, but systematic investigations were not undertaken until 1920. These were begun in Uganda by E. Wayland,[38] Director of the Geological Survey of that province, and continued in Kenya after 1926 by L. Leakey. On his own or with various helpers, among them J. Solomon, the geologist, the latter made a series of discoveries on the basis of which he drew up an archaeological, stratigraphical and palaeontological classification of the Pleistocene in this region.[39] The recovery of various human remains, some of which have been attributed to the very base of the Quaternary, added to the interest of these explorations, which seemed—in the course of a few years—to have brought an insight into East African prehistory comparable to our knowledge of the prehistory of Europe. Unfortunately this complex of information contained a certain number of hypotheses that have not been borne out by later research, and a great deal of investigation is still required. Many facts have stood the test of time, however, and these we must briefly outline.

The first, of a geological nature, rests on the existence in this part of East Africa of a number of lakes devoid of outlets and surrounded by old beaches at various levels, which make it possible to trace the successive changes in the water level. They constitute a sort of fossil rain-gauge, analogous to the great Pleistocene lakes of North America. On the other hand, a study of the deposits in the archaeological beds shows an alternation of subaerial and alluvial strata. High water levels in the lakes and alluvial

[37] Vallois, H. V., 'La mandibule humaine fossile de la grotte du Porc-Épic près Diré-Daoua, Abyssinie' (*L'Anthropologie*, LV, 1951).

[38] Wayland, E., 'The Stone Age in Uganda' (*Man*, XXIV, 1924); 'Rifts, Rivers, Rains and Early Man in Uganda' (*Journ. of the Roy. Anthrop. Inst.*, XIV, 1934).

[39] Leakey, L. S. B., *The Stone Age Cultures in Kenya Colony* (Cambridge, 1931); *The Stone Age Races of Kenya* (London, 1935); *Stone Age Africa* (London, 1936).

strata in the caves and rock-shelters correspond to periods of heavy rainfall, or 'Pluvial' periods, separated by 'dry' periods.

In Uganda, Wayland acknowledged the existence of two Rainy periods followed by a Post-Pluvial period. Leakey, after advancing several variations on this hypothesis, finally came to a rather different conclusion with the assumption of three Pluvials properly so-called followed by two periods that were only 'wet'. A long dry phase, accompanied by volcanic eruptions and movements of the earth's crust that caused subsidences of the soil, is supposed to have intervened between the first and second Pluvial. A great change of fauna took place at this juncture, and the majority of the archaic species from the base of the Quaternary, such as *Hipparion* and *Elephas antiquus*, then disappeared.

Wayland and Leakey wished to synchronize their Rainy periods with the Ice Ages of the Alps. Such an attempt is premature. There are even grounds for questioning whether the phenomena observed in closed basins like the East African lakes give an accurate picture of events and whether it would not be better, as O'Brien thinks,[40] to utilize the stratification of river terraces.

From the point of view of prehistoric archaeology, various industries have been recognized. The Lower Palaeolithic begins with an exceedingly primitive industry of crudely dressed pebbles, the *Pebble Culture*, which seems to correspond to the extreme base of the Pleistocene and represents a veritable Pre-Chellean phase. It is succeeded by a Chellean and an Acheulean roughly similar to those of Europe. In many places, such as the classic site at Olorgesaillie, they are on the surface. At others they are contained in alluvial deposits which Leakey attributes to his first two Pluvial periods together with the dry phase that separates them. One of the most typical localities is Oldoway Gorge, where a series of superimposed layers shows the progressive evolution of the industry from Pre-Chellean to an advanced Acheulean.

The Middle and Upper Palaeolithic, as we know them in Europe, are missing from East Africa. In their place we find a large number of industries, some of which appear in succession while others develop along parallel lines, and which have given rise to a proliferation of terms that often correspond only to local facies. Alongside forms that resemble the so-called Still Bay industry of South Africa, there are others which were first designated Aurignacian, but which are now, by general agreement termed Capsian,[41] although they are not absolutely identical with the Capsian of North Africa. The whole of this complex, which corresponds to both the Mousterian and the Upper Palaeolithic, stretches from the end of the second Pluvial to the end of the third.

[40] O'Brien, T. P., *The Prehistory of Uganda Protectorate* (Cambridge, 1939). Du Toit, A., 'Palaeolithic Environments in Kenya and the Union: A Contrast' (*South African Archaeol. Bull.*, II, 1947).

[41] Oakley, K., 'Le premier Congrès pan-africain de Préhistoire, Nairobi, 1947' (*L'Anthropologie*, LI, 1947).

Artefacts of Mesolithic type, accompanied by numerous microliths and pottery, correspond to the first Post-Pluvial wet phase. They all seem to be very recent. With the second damp phase polished axes make their appearance, but we also find iron implements. At this point we are already in the modern period.

AFRICANTHROPUS

A certain number of fossil Men have been discovered in East Africa. But the conditions under which they were found have not always been sufficiently well established, and the value of some of them has been disputed. Many hasty conclusions have subsequently had to be rectified.

In the almost unanimous opinion of all authors, the majority of these Men belong to *Homo sapiens*. The one exception to this is the type that has received the name *Africanthropus*. In spite of the uncertainty surrounding its true geological age, we shall consider it first.

In 1935 Dr. Kohl-Larsen recorded the discovery, on the shores of Lake Njarasa or Eyasi (Fig. 273), of fragments of human skull of an extremely primitive type.[42] These remains, which were heavily mineralized, lay half buried in a bed of sandstone that was normally submerged in the lake but had recently been exposed by drought. The same formation contained numerous bone-remains of animals, also heavily mineralized, very fragmented and black in colour. The most ancient, very much rolled from water-action, belonged to mammals characteristic of the Mid-Pleistocene in this region, among others, *Hipparion*. The rest, not rolled by water-action, were derived from a more recent fauna that was attributed to the second Pluvial. The human remains seem to have been contemporary with this fauna. They were accompanied by many dressed stones.

The remains comprised nearly two hundred pieces corresponding to two or three skulls. The brain-box of one of these was partially reconstructed by H. Weinert, who has given a detailed description of it.[43]

Of moderate size, its shape recalls that of both Neandertal Man and *Sinanthropus* (Fig. 274). Its most remarkable characteristic is the projection of the superciliary arches, which are joined into a visor as marked as in the Prehominians. As in the latter, the forehead is receding and the vault flat; the maximum width of the cranium is situated rather low down, though not as low as in *Sinanthropus*; the mastoid apophyses are extremely reduced in size. The foramen magnum seems to be tilted towards the back, as in the Great Apes. The cranial capacity is thought to be no more than 1,100 cubic centimetres, but this figure must be accepted with caution.

Several teeth and a fragment of the upper jaw, together with the lower

[42] Kohl-Larsen, L., 'Vorläufiger Bericht über den Fund eines mitteldiluvialen Menschen-restes im Njarasa-Graben, nördliches Deutsch-Ostafrika' (*Forschungen und Fortschritte*, XII, Berlin, 1936).

[43] Weinert, H., 'Africanthropus njarasensis' (*Ztschr. für Morphol. und Anthrop.*, XXXVIII, 1939).

margin of the nasal aperture, were also found. The few characters revealed by these agree with those of the skull-cap.

Weinert concluded from his examination that all these relics belonged to a being closely related to *Pithecanthropus* and *Sinanthropus*. He believed it to be a true Prehominian and gave it the name *Africanthropus njarasensis*. Certain of its dispositions, however, bear an even greater resemblance to those of Neandertal Man: the vault is rounded and not keel-shaped in a transverse direction; the occiput has not the highly special form seen in *Sinanthropus* and the axis of the petrous portion of the temporal bone is

274 Skull-cap of *Africanthropus*, seen in profile. One-third natural size
(After H. Weinert)

straight as in modern Man. The attribution of *Africanthropus* to the Prehominians cannot be considered final. This being might just as well be classed with the Rhodesian Man, of whom we shall speak later.

The above opinion, already expressed in the last French edition of this book, seems to be borne out by Leakey and Reeve's exploration of the site.[44] The deposit which contained the human remains is thought to be the same age as that which held the Oldoway skeleton, and the fauna is modern as regards the majority of its elements; *Hipparion* only appears in it as the result of reshuffling. As for the industry, it is that of the Middle Stone Age, as in the case of Rhodesian Man. All these facts do not speak in favour of the high antiquity of the so-called *Africanthropus*.

In a recent memoir, H. Weinert once more drew attention to Kohl-Larsen's discovery, in 1939, in an early Quaternary deposit some thirty miles north of Lake Eyasi, of jaw-fragments bearing teeth almost as large as those

---

[44] Leakey, L. and Reeve, W., 'Report on a Visit to the Site of the Eyasi Skull. . .Geological Report on the Site. . .' (*J. East Africa Nat. Hist. Soc.*, IV, 1946).

of the Javan *Meganthropus*.[45] He is convinced that this is an African form of *Meganthropus*. But this conclusion would also seem premature.

THE OLDOWAY SKELETON

The other fossil Men of East Africa incontestably belong to *Homo sapiens*. The most ancient discovery dates from 1913.[46] It was that of a complete skeleton in an excellent state of preservation unearthed by Dr. Reck in the Oldoway Gorge, on the borders of the Seregenti plain, in what was then German East Africa. According to its finder this skeleton is of very great antiquity. The question is worth examining in some detail.

The wall of Oldoway Gorge is about 300 feet high and shows five strata, one above the other. The lowest, No. 1, is composed of limestone tufas containing artefacts of Pre-Chellean type, with a very primitive fauna including the genera *Dinotherium*, *Hipparion* and *Elephas*.

Stratum No. 2, more alluvial in nature, contains a species of *Hipparion* and a variety of *Elephas* (*E. antiquus recki*) accompanied by large Chellean implements. The human skeleton was found in the upper section of this stratum.

Above this, Strata 3 and 4 contain a fauna consisting of 50 per cent. extinct species. The artefacts in these two strata pass progressively from the Chellean to the Acheulean.

These four strata together seem to correspond to the two first Rainy periods with the dry phase separating them. Their deposition was followed by a long period of erosion and movements of the earth's crust. Then new deposits were laid down (No. 5), which contain a Capsian industry and reach up to the limestone soil of the plain.

Having lain in Stratum 2, which dates from the first Rainy period and is contemporary with a very archaic fauna, the human skeleton must be extremely ancient, a fact that is all the more astonishing because, as we shall see, it very closely resembles certain modern types. This would imply that the antiquity of *Homo sapiens* in East Africa and, more striking still, of one of the living races of *Homo sapiens*, is considerable. We can readily understand that, in view of the implications, the conditions of the deposit were submitted to minute investigation.

The fact that the skeleton, although mineralized, was less so than those of the mammals in the same stratum itself aroused some surprise. It also seemed curious that such an ancient fossil should be absolutely intact, and the exaggeratedly squatting position in which it was found resembled that seen in recent burials. But the decisive argument was furnished by Boswell,[47]

[45] Weinert, H., 'Über die neuen Vor- und Frühmenschenfunde aus Afrika, Java, China und Frankreich' (*Ztschr. für Morph. und Anthr.*, XLII, 1950).

[46] Reck, H., 'Erst vorläufige Mitteilung über den Fund eines fossilen Menschenskelettes aus Zentralafrika' (*Sitzungsber. der Ges. naturforschender Freunde zu Berlin*, 1914); *Oldoway, die Schlucht des Urmenschen* (Leipzig, 1933).

[47] Boswell, P., 'The Oldoway Human Skeleton' (*Nature*, August 13, 1932. See also March 18, 1933).

the geologist, who observed that the gangue of the skeleton contained elements from the upper strata. Oldoway Man was, therefore, not *in situ*. The true facts were established by an examination of the deposit: at the point where the skeleton was found Stratum 2 had been laid bare by erosion, and the bones were only just below the surface of the soil. There had been a burial, and this dated from the period during which Stratum 5 was formed; the skeleton is therefore contemporary with the Capsian of Kenya; it is the same age as the skeletons from Gamble's Cave, to which we shall refer later.

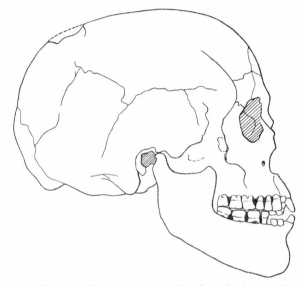

275 The Oldoway Skull, seen in profile. One-third natural size
(After T. Mollison)

After a long delay, the Oldoway Man was studied by Gieseler and Mollison.[48] He is a man of advanced age and tall stature (5 ft. 11 ins. ?). The skull, which is very long and narrow, has an index of 66, denoting very pronounced dolichocephaly (Fig. 275). The vault is very developed, with an oval forehead. The face is remarkably long and narrow. The nose is mesorrhinian, but bordering on leptorrhinia and hence rather narrow. The orbits are very high; the palate is narrow and long. There is slight alveolar prognathism, but the chin is clearly marked and very prominent. The teeth are of the classic type of modern Man; the front faces of the incisors have been filed down in a manner found nowadays only among the Indonesians.

Reservations have been expressed concerning the reconstruction of the skull. At all events, by the sum total of its characters it exhibits a close resemblance to the skulls of the Semi-Hamitic peoples of East Africa,

[48] Gieseler, W. and Mollison, Th., 'Untersuchungen über den Oldoway-fund' (*Verhandl. der Ges. für physische Anthrop.*, III, 1928).

especially the Masai, who now occupy the same region. Such a likeness is enough to show that it cannot be very old.

KANAM AND KANJERA

Just when the discussions aroused by the Oldoway Man were beginning to die away, Dr. L. S. B. Leakey recorded the discovery at Kanam and Kanjera, two localities near Kendu, north-east of Lake Victoria Nyanza, of human remains of early Pleistocene date.[49] They nevertheless belonged to *Homo sapiens*, so that the problem of the latter's very high antiquity in Africa and his priority over the other species of fossil Men, in particular Neandertal Man, was once more raised.

The deposits at Kanam and Kanjera were formed at a time when Lake Victoria extended over a very wide area. At Kanam, Leakey claimed to have found the front portion of a human lower jaw in a travertine containing two species of *Mastodon*, a *Dinotherium* and Pre-Chellean artefacts. Such deposits are contemporary with Stratum 1 at Oldoway and would date from the base of the Pleistocene.

At Kanjera, an incomplete skull and the elements of two other skulls, along with a piece of femur, lay in more recent travertines containing *Elephas antiquus recki*, a *Mastodon* and possibly *Hipparion*; they correspond to Stratum 2 at Oldoway, that is to say to the Chellean period.

These specimens were examined by a conference which met at Cambridge.[50] In spite of their antiquity they differed hardly at all from modern Man. The Kanam mandible is slightly thicker than those of today, but, by an unfortunate coincidence, the chin was the seat of an exceedingly rare type of bone tumour which seriously obscures the true morphology of this region. Enough is still visible, however, to show that its structure was that of the primitive types of modern Man and that, while not pronounced, the mental protuberance existed.

As for the fragments of skull, they are all shaped in the same way and correspond to long, narrow heads with foreheads like those of modern Man and show not the slightest trace of a brow visor. Their only peculiarity is the thickness of the calvarium, which does not, however, exceed that of other known fossil Men.

In sum, the Cambridge conference concluded, all these specimens indisputably belong to *Homo sapiens*. This did not prevent Leakey, a few months later, from creating for the mandible a new species, *Homo kanamensis*, which he claimed as the immediate ancestor of modern Man.

The Kanam and Kanjera discoveries are therefore of considerable interest. Unfortunately, investigations made shortly afterwards in the Kendu district by Boswell[51] have cast doubt on their value. Not only was the British geolo-

[49] Leakey, L., 'The Oldoway Human Skeleton' (*Nature*, May 14, 1932).
[50] 'Early Human Remains in East Africa' (*Man*, April 1933).
[51] Boswell, P., 'Human Remains from Kanam and Kanjera, Kenya Colony' (*Nature*, March 9, 1935).

gist unable to find the deposits from which the bone-remains had been extracted—the Leakey expedition having failed to mark them either on the
ground or on the map—but the photographs that were believed to be of
these deposits corresponded to sites of a totally different geological structure.
Excavations carried out by Boswell at points which appeared to be close to
those in which the discoveries had been made showed that the formations
of the whole of this region had been frequently reshuffled by landslides.
Under these circumstances the age of the human remains from Kanam and
Kanjera no longer offer the rigorous certainty we have a right to demand
from specimens giving rise to such important conclusions. Until more
ample information is available, they are best disregarded.

NAKURU AND ELMENTEITA

Other fossil human remains have aroused less dispute. But these are comparatively recent, contemporary with industries homologous to our Upper
Palaeolithic or even later. The majority were the outcome of Leakey's
explorations in the basins of Lake Nakuru and Lake Elmenteita. They
were made the subject of an important study by this author.[52]

The oldest are five skeletons found near Elmenteita, 600 feet above the
lake of the same name, in the small grotto known as Gamble's Cave II.
Here, superimposed at regular intervals, there were a series of deposits
running from the Capsian to the Mesolithic. The skeletons were discovered
in the surface section of the Capsian, buried in a contracted position and
covered with ochre. In type they were the same as the Oldoway Man: tall
(5 ft. 11 ins.), very dolichocephalic, with a long and not prognathous face,
and a narrow nose (Fig. 276). They are certainly not true Negroes in the
usual sense of the word, but men comparable to the Nilotics of the region
of the great lakes, or else to the fairer skinned peoples—Hamites and Semi-
Hamites—of these regions. A skeleton found recently at Naivasha[53] belongs
to the same type.

The same human type is met with at the Mesolithic level in the Bromhead
bed, a sort of alluvial deposit at the foot of a small cliff close to Lake Elmenteita, and also in the burials south of Lake Nakuru. But here it is accompanied
by a second type, of shorter, almost pygmy stature, with a mesocephalic
skull and broader face. Leakey compared it with the Springbok Man of
South Africa. A third type, with a relatively narrow skull, broad, convex
forehead, small face and massive limb bones, found in the kitchen middens
on the shores of Lake Tanganyika, recalls the prehistoric Bushmen or
Strandloopers of South Africa.

Numerous skeletons have been found near the River Makalia and Lake

[52] Leakey, L., *The Stone Age Races of Kenya* (London, 1935). Also Leakey, M., 'Report on
the Excavations at Hyrax Hill, Nakuru, Kenya Colony, 1937–1938' (*Trans. Roy. Soc. S.
Africa*, XXX, 1945).
[53] Leakey, L., 'The Naivasha Fossil Skull and Skeleton' (*J. East Africa Nat. Hist. Soc.*,
XVI, 1942).

Nakuru in Neolithic deposits corresponding to the second Post-Pluvial Period. Others have come from the Hyrax and Njoro Cave deposits. Others, discovered by Kohl-Larsen near Lake Eyasi, must undoubtedly be attributed to the same period.[54] Here again we see the ancient Gamble's Cave type persisting alongside certain more Negroid types directly resembling the Bantus. Some of the skulls have had the middle incisors removed, a mutilation observed among peoples still living in the same region.

To sum up, we see that, *Africanthropus* apart, the human remains so far discovered in East Africa do not differ from the present inhabitants of this

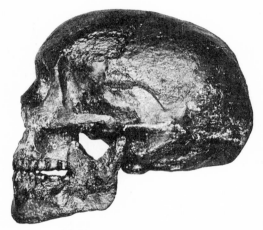

276 Skull of one of the individuals from Gamble's Cave, seen in profile
One-third natural size. (Photograph of a cast)

and neighbouring areas. From the Upper Palaeolithic onwards, we meet representatives of the tall, dolichocephalic type with more or less dark skin which still predominates in the region. In the Mesolithic it is accompanied by Men of short stature, possibly Proto-Bushmen, and in the Neolithic by more Negroid forms, related to the Bantus.

The 'recent' appearance of all these Men cannot surprise us, for the archaeological periods to which they correspond are undoubtedly far less ancient than those which bear the same names in Europe. Prehistorians have repeatedly emphasized the lateness in time of the African industries in comparison with ours.[55] The Upper Palaeolithic and Mesolithic in Kenya are certainly much closer to our own day than their homonyms in Europe. It is therefore not surprising that the skeletons from Oldoway, Gamble's Cave and Elmenteita should be almost identical with those of their present-day successors. But there is an enormous morphological gap between all these

[54] Bauermeister, W., 'Neue paläolithische Funde aus dem ehemaligen Deutsch-Ostafrika' (*Ztschr. für Morphol. und Anthrop.*, XXXIII, 1939).
[55] See in particular Vaufrey, R., 'La colonisation préhistorique de l'Afrique' (*L'Anthropologie*, XLV, 1935, p. 710).

forms, which are sub-fossil rather than fossil, and *Africanthropus*, about
which so little is yet known. It will take more than one discovery to fill it.

SOUTHERN AFRICA

The prehistory of South Africa has made great strides since 1855, when
Col. Baker found dressed stones there at a depth of 15 feet below the surface
of the soil. The investigations of many authors[56]—among whom we must
mention in the first place those of Péringuey, Johnson and Goodwin in Cape
Province, van Riet Lowe in the Orange Free State and Transvaal, and
Neville Jones in Rhodesia—have drawn attention to the incomparable rich-
ness of these states in archaeological material, and at the same time, to the
complexity of their prehistory.

This complexity is explained by their position. The immense territory
south of the Zambezi forms a vast blind alley into which the most ancient
and least developed peoples have been thrust back. Over a long period of
time, a series of invasions piled up in this area the relics of successive cultures
and produced hybrid industries that are difficult to interpret. Minute study
has been necessary in order to understand them, and even now many points
remain obscure. Stratigraphical and archaeological observations have
nevertheless made it possible to establish the main lines of a classification
parallel to that of Europe.

One important difference must, however, be noted: there is no true
Neolithic in Southern Africa. The Dressed Stone Age extends down to
our own day, and the present culture of the Bushmen represents its last
survival. Three periods have been distinguished by South African prehistorians, who call them by the names *Old Stone Age*, *Middle Stone Age* and
Late Stone Age. But the various industries covered by these terms can be
more or less exactly grouped under the classic headings employed in Europe.

The Old Stone Age corresponds approximately to our Lower Palaeolithic.
As in East Africa, an entirely primitive industry of worked pebbles has been
regarded as Pre-Chellean, but it has been found on the surface in old gravels.
Its exact age cannot be established. The industries that succeed it are characterized by numerous 'hand-axes' of Chellean and Acheulean type, generally of
quartzite (Fig. 277), some of which, with a cutting edge, have been termed
bezels; they are accompanied by discs made from large flakes. These artefacts
have been encountered in incredible quantities all over South Africa, but especially in Cape Colony and the diamond-bearing gravels of the 60- to 70-foot

---

[56] The bibliography of works on the Stone Age in South Africa is extremely vast. A detailed
list is contained in Goodwin, A., 'A Commentary on the History and Present Position of
South African Prehistory, with Bibliography' (*Bantu Studies*, IX, 1935). The following are
the principal books or memoirs published after this date: Sohnge, D., Visser, L., Van Riet
Lowe, C., 'The Geology and Archaeology of the Vaal River Basin' (*Mem. Geol. Survey S.
Africa*, XXXV, 1937). Cooke, H., 'A Preliminary Survey of the Quaternary Period in
Southern Africa' (*Union of S. A. Arch. Survey, Arch. Series*, No. 4, 1941). Goodwin, A.,
The Loom of Prehistory (Capetown, 1946). Breuil, H. and Van Riet Lowe, C., 'Early Man in
the Vaal Basin' (*Union of S. A. Arch. Survey, Arch. Series*, No. 6, 1948). Jones, N., 'The
Prehistory of South Rhodesia' (*Museum Memoirs*, No. 2, Cambridge, 1949).

terrace of the Vaal Valley, where they form enormous industry-centres of unparalleled abundance. Other deposits have been recorded by Felden in the high terraces of the Zambezi Valley, below the celebrated Victoria Falls. The alluvials that make up these terraces were laid down before the gorge was cut, at a time when the river flowed 430 to 500 feet above its present bed. This proves them to be extremely ancient. The dressed stones met with in these terraces, of rather crude workmanship, comprise Chellean types of lava, Acheulean types of chalcedony, and occasionally Mousterian types.

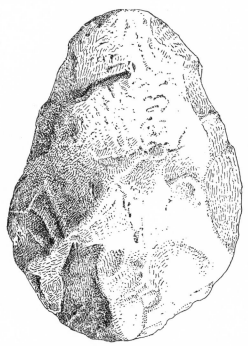

277 Quartzite dressed in the Chellean manner, from the Orange River. (After Hamy)

The Old Stone Age seems to have lasted a very long time. Yet the fauna corresponding to it was not very different from the present-day fauna: it comprised, *inter alia*, a primitive Elephant and a large Horse, *Equus capensis*. The climate was probably damper than today.

The Middle Stone Age presents a complex of industries in which we find Mousterian-type artefacts as well as others of Aurignacian, Capsian or even Solutrean type. The archaeological intricacy of this period is such that South African prehistorians have not yet been able to distinguish clearly between what is the outcome of a general evolution and what are only local facies. This confusion, the cause of which must be sought in the 'blind alley' character of Southern Africa, has so far prevented the establishment of subdivisions that can be correlated with those of the Middle and Upper Palaeolithic in Europe. But the stratigraphic position of the Middle Stone Age between the other two South African periods is constant.

Among the industries that characterize the Middle Stone Age, one of the most widespread is that called Still Bay, which is distinguished by beautiful wide, flat points, shaped like a laurel leaf, of Solutrean type, side by side with Mousterian-type points devoid of retouching and others called oak-leaf points. There are also discs and round stones for throwing or use with a bolas. This industry is found *in situ* in caves, sand dunes and alluvial deposits. It extends beyond the northern confines of Southern Africa and is observed as far as Abyssinia. The fauna which accompanies it is very similar to that of the present day, and it does not seem to date from very remote times, any more than the other facies of this period.

The Late Stone Age embraces the industries of the most superficial layers, which bear a likeness to both the Capsian and the Mesolithic, but with modifications due to the presence of a certain number of other elements which, in Europe, do not appear until the Neolithic culture. All of them share a special method of striking, along with small 'thumb-nail' scrapers, pallets of schist, pierced spheres—the *kwe*, used with digging sticks—and finally ostrich egg beads. Pottery is present, and there are also observed artefacts of bone and ivory, which are particularly well preserved in the deposits of caves and rock-shelters.

In the Cape region, an industry of Tardenoisian type frequently occurs in the caves and numerous kitchen middens along the coast. It was produced by a people of whom we possess many skeletons, the Strandloopers, the probable ancestors of the Bushmen. The latter continued to employ these implements, which they retained in spite of invasion by the iron-using Bantus, until very recently.

PAINTINGS AND ENGRAVINGS

Dressed stones are not the only products of prehistoric Man in Southern Africa. As in a large part of this continent, we find here paintings and engravings on the rock walls. And here these representations attain a technique and a degree of realism very much higher than that seen in the rest of Africa.

For a long time they were thought to be recent—the work of the Bushmen or their immediate ancestors. The investigations of various authors[57] have shown that they vary greatly in age and style.

[57] Numerous publications. See chiefly: Obermaier, H. and Keuhn, H., *Bushman Art: Rock-Paintings of S. W. Africa* (London, 1930). Breuil, H., 'The Palaeolithic Art of North East Spain and the Art of the Bushmen: A Comparison' (*Man*, Sept. 1930). Bleck, D., *Rock-Paintings in South Africa. . .*(London, 1930). Wilman, M., *The Rock-Engravings of Griqualand West and Bushmanland, South Africa* (Cambridge, 1933). Frobenius, L., *Matsimu Sangara* (Südafrikanische Felsbilderchronik, I) (London, 1933). Breuil, H., 'Les roches peintes d'Afrique australe, leurs auteurs et leur âge' (*L'Anthropologie*, LIII, 1949, p. 377). Van Riet Lowe, C., 'L'âge et les origines des peintures rupestres d'Afrique du Sud' (*L'Anthropologie*, LIV, 1950, p. 421).

Some of the engravings are recent in appearance, but others are deeply patinated; and as many as five superimposed layers of painting have been observed. Generally speaking, paintings and engravings are here superior in quality from the aesthetic point of view. Sometimes they are arranged to form a picture (Fig. 278), or assume a conventional, hieratic and possibly ideographic aspect.

The most recent of these representations are certainly the work of the Bushmen. There can be no doubt that most of the others belong to the Late Stone Age. According to Breuil this rupestrine art goes back still farther: he believes that it began in the Middle Stone Age and developed through

278 Red and black painting in a cave in Baroaland, representing Bushmen engaged in hunting being attacked by Kaffirs. Length of the picture 5 feet. (After Hamy)

subsequent periods. Proof of its antiquity is to be found in the fact that these paintings and engravings represent extinct species, including a Horse and a Great Buffalo. On the other hand, in Bambata Cave, Southern Rhodesia, an archaeological level overlying a Mousterian stratum and containing an industry analogous to that at Still Bay also contained numerous pieces of ochre and haematite, which had manifestly been used in painting the frescoes in the cave.

The resemblance of all these works of art to these of the Upper Palaeolithic in French and Spanish caves has often been noted: there are the same preferences in the choice of subject, animals being the most common, the same realism, the same fidelity of attitude, the same skill in reproduction, the same technique, and even the same weakness in drawing the human figure. All this has been invoked in support of the theory that the Bushmen were the ancestors of our Aurignacians and Magdalenians. Certain similarities between the industries of the two groups have been advanced in corroboration of this idea, which has been discussed at greater length in Chapter VIII of this work (see p. 318) and to which it would be pointless to return here.

HUMAN BONE-REMAINS:

TELANTHROPUS

It was in 1911, at Boskop in the Transvaal, that the first fossil human remains were discovered in South Africa. The interest aroused by these fragments had not died down when the discovery in Rhodesia of a human skull with even more primitive characters than those of Neandertal Man was announced in 1921. Although the age of this skull could not be precisely established, and although subsequent study revealed that it was scarcely fossilized in the strict sense of the word, it nonetheless casts fresh light on the evolution of the human race in this part of Africa. Its value from the standpoint of human palaeontology is indisputable.

The discovery of *Australopithecus* in 1925 increased still more the interest taken in South Africa, since many authors believed the new creature to be a direct ancestor of Man. We know now (see p. 87) that this assertion is far too categorical and that *Australopithecus*, like the related forms found later in the same region, is undoubtedly still an Anthropoid. But Broom and Robinson have recently discovered in the deposit at Swartkrans, which contained this fossil, some human remains—an almost complete lower jaw with five molars and the fragment of another lower jaw with two molars.[58]

The lower jaw, found in a more recent breccia than that containing the *Australopitheci* and which filled a pocket in the latter, resembled the Heidelberg jaw but with smaller dimensions. The very thick symphysis is receding, but the body of the bone is not exceptionally thick. The molars are definitely human, of a primitive type, and they increase in size from the first to the third. Basing their opinion on this character together with certain features of the mylo-hyoid groove, the value of which is disputed by Strauss,[59] the authors are convinced that this is a new form, intermediate between Heidelberg Man and *Australopithecus*, and have named it *Telanthropus capensis*. It is certainly more recent than the *Paranthropi* from the same deposit and may date from the Lower Pleistocene.

In the absence of stratigraphic data, it is very difficult to express an opinion on the exact value of these specimens, of which Broom and Robinson assert that they cannot represent a variation of *Paranthropus* but are definitely human. They reveal the existence in Southern Africa, at what is certainly a very ancient period of the Pleistocene, of exceptionally primitive human types as old as certain Australopithecidae, and this is an extremely important discovery. We cannot, for the time being, deduce more precise conclusions from them. Fortunately, other human remains have been brought

[58] Broom, R. and Robinson, J., 'A New Type of Fossil Man' (*Nature*, August 20, 1949); 'Man contemporaneous with the Swartkrans Ape-Man' (*Amer. J. Phys. Anthr.*, VIII, 1950, p. 151).
[59] Strauss, Jr., W., 'On the Zoological Status of Telanthropus capensis' (*Amer. J. Phys. Anthr.*, VIII, 1950, p. 495).

to light which furnish more complete data. Belonging essentially to the Middle Stone Age, they represent a physical type different from that of the present-day natives of the region. Their number is already quite considerable.

RHODESIAN MAN

For their anatomical characters, if not for their geological antiquity, the bone-remains from Rhodesia must be examined first. They come from Broken Hill, which stands in the part of this colony that extends north of the Zambezi. This hill was long mined for the minerals lead and zinc. It is tunnelled at its base by a cavern known for the extraordinary abundance of fossilized and mineralized animal bone-remains which it contains. But this cavern, almost completely filled with osteological deposits and clay, had only been explored along a very short distance of its total length.

The work of mining, carried out in the open air, had already partially demolished the hill, thus exposing the great subterranean recess. Towards the end of the summer of 1921, at the further end and lowest depths of this cave, a skull and other human remains were found in association with stone and bone implements and broken bones of animals which had evidentally been used as food. The implements hardly differ from those of modern Bushmen. The broken bones all belong to species still living in Rhodesia. Their appearance is very fresh, although the surface is encrusted with a fine layer of silicate of zinc (hemimorphite).

The human remains consist of a skull, unfortunately lacking the lower jaw, a portion of the upper jaw of a somewhat smaller skull, a sacrum, and portions of femora and of a tibia. They present exactly the same physical characters as the animal bones found along with them; they have not lost their organic matter and are not fossilized. The skull was covered by a layer of stalactite. All the specimens, together with the relics by which they were accompanied were made the subject of a detailed report by the experts at the British Museum.[60]

The skull is totally different from that of any Southern African whatsoever. On the contrary, it resembles to an extraordinary degree the skulls of the Neandertal Man of our old Europaen Palaeolithic. It has an even more brutish or simian aspect (Figs. 279 and 280).

Its length is 206 mm., its greatest breadth 145 mm. It is therefore elongated in form, dolichocephalic. The height of the cranial vault is 130 mm. These various figures agree remarkably closely with those of the skull of the Neandertal Man from La Chapelle-aux-Saints. But the brain must have been much smaller. Dubois estimated the cranial capacity of the skull

[60] Pycraft, W. P., Smith, G. Elliott, and others, *Rhodesian Man and associated Remains* (London, 1928). The study of the human skeleton in this report is by Pycraft. See also: Hrdlička, A., *The Skeletal Remains of Early Man*, p. 98, and Keith, A., *The Antiquity of Man*, p. 377. Morant, G. M., 'Studies of Palaeolithic Man, III: The Rhodesian Skull and its Relation to Neanderthaloid and Modern Types' (*Ann. of Eugenics*, III, 1928). Bonin, G. von, 'Studien zum Homo Rhodesiensis' (*Ztschr. f. Morphol. und Anthrop.*, XXVII, 1930).

from Broken Hill at 1,400 cubic centimetres.[61] Elliot Smith made it only 1,280 c.c. These figures are low.

The orbital arches are even more prominent than in Neandertal Man: the torus they form exceeds that of the Gorilla. The forehead is also very receding. In its lower region, the occiput presents a flattening that more closely resembles what we see in modern Australians than the ridge visible in Neandertal Man. The face, which is remarkably long, greatly resembles that of the Man of La Chapelle-aux-Saints: it has the same large flat maxillary bones, without canine fossae, and consequently the same *muzzle-like*

279 The Broken Hill Skull, seen in profile. (After A. Smith Woodward)

appearance, still further accentuated by the size of the sub-nasal space. The orbits are very high and the cheek-bones strongly developed. The wide nasal aperture merges insensibly into the face, as in the Gorilla.

The palate is immense, both wide and deep; its dimensions exceed even those of Neandertal Man. Nevertheless, the dentition is quite human; the canines are normal; the wisdom teeth are reduced in size. Most of the teeth are affected with caries; this pathological phenomenon has never so far been observed in truly Palaeolithic European skulls. The lower jaw must have been very massive.

According to Elliot Smith, who studied an endocranial cast, the brain of this Man is of quite a low type; its prefrontal and lower temporal regions are reduced in size, but it shows an unexpected prominence of the auditory region. The front part of the lateral cerebral fissure is relatively open, as in the Great Apes.

[61] Dubois, E., 'On the cranial form of *Homo Neanderthalensis* and of *Pithecanthropus erectus* determined by mechanical factors' (*Proc. Acad. Wetenschappen te Amsterdam*, XXIV, 1922).

The limb bones display little or no special characters, but it is not certain that they belong to the skull, a number of very different versions of their origin having been given. The sacrum is very human. The iliac bone, according to Pycraft, exhibits features that are incompatible with an erect carriage; but later study has disposed of this view. The femur and tibia are very

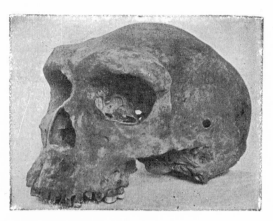

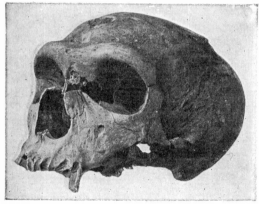

280 Skulls from Broken Hill (above) and La Chapelle-aux-Saints (below), seen three-quarters face at approximately the same angle to facilitate comparison

different from those of Neandertal Man and very similar to those of modern Man.

What significance are we to attribute to Broken Hill Man? A glance at Fig. 280 is enough to show that this skull is more like *Homo neandertalensis* than any race or variety, living or fossil, of *Homo sapiens*. Morant, like Smith Woodward recognized these points of resemblance; but the latter nevertheless gave this Man a special name, *Homo rhodesiensis*, because, while in Neandertal Man the foramen magnum occupies a more backward position at the base of the skull than in modern Man—which is in keeping with the general attitude of the body, still not absolutely upright—in *Homo rhodesiensis* the foramen magnum occupies a more forward, more central position, so that the skull must have rested with perfect ease and in perfect equilibrium on the vertical column.

Pycraft disputed this view. He was convinced that Broken Hill Man walked bent forward with flexed knees, and even created for him a new generic name—*Cyphanthropus rhodesiensis*. He based his opinion on the characters of the pelvis. But there is nothing to prove that this pelvis belonged to the skull, and von Bonim's researches have demonstrated that the features on which Pycraft based his case were illusory. Both the skull and the pelvis, as well as the femur and tibia, bear witness to a perfectly upright carriage. In spite of his coarse and bestial appearance, *Homo rhodesiensis* walked erect.

According to Dubois, the resemblance borne by the Broken Hill skull to Neandertal skulls is only superficial. There are numerous differences. The points of resemblance, according to him, are rather with the Australians, in which case *Homo rhodesiensis* would represent a type of *Homo sapiens* akin to the Australian type, but even more primitive than it. Even more than the Australoid skull from Wadjak (see p. 397), the Broken Hill skull deserves the title of 'Proto-Australian'.

In an attempt to draw any conclusion from the structural details, the age of the relics obtained from the Broken Hill Mine must be taken into account. The depth at which the discovery was made, and on which so much stress has been laid in the newspapers, has not in the present case any great value, as the human skull was taken from a cave into the depth of which it might have found its way in various ways and at any period.

The skull was contained in a superficial deposit covering the floor of the cave, which had yielded 'tons' of animal bones. Now these bones, accompanied by rude implements of stone and bone, resemble, as we have said, species still living in the country. One might conclude from this that the occupation of the cave by these animals and the filling up of the opening by bone-bearing deposits could not date very far back. But the palaeontologist Hopwood has pointed out that a study of the fossil mammals of the South African caves cannot serve the same purpose as in Europe, because of the very prolonged persistence of faunas in this region. The high antiquity of the human remains at Broken Hill cannot be denied on the basis of the modern appearance of the animals associated with them. Nor is an examination of the few stone artefacts found in the cave conclusive, although they have been compared to the implements of the living Bushmen. Recent research by Clark[62] tends to show that these specimens, which include round stones analogous to bolas, are of a type than can be attributed to a primitive Middle Stone Age. The Broken Hill deposits therefore date from the Upper Pleistocene, a view which agrees with certain affinities noted by Hopwood in the fauna. A chemical examination of the faunal remains, carried out by

[62] Clark, D., Wells, L., Oakley, K., and McClelland, J., 'New Studies on Rhodesian Man' (*J. Roy. Anthr. Inst.*, LXXVII, 1947).

Oakley and McClelland, has shown that their zinc and lead content is considerable. The same is true of the animal bones. All these remains are, therefore, more or less contemporary.

How can these facts be reconciled: on the one hand, the likeness between *Homo rhodesienis*, *Homo neandertalensis*, and modern Australian Man; on the other hand, the presence in Africa, almost in the centre of the Dark Continent, 560 miles from the nearest shore, of a human being of relatively recent age (in the geological sense of the word, be it understood), so different from all the races and varieties of African Negroes? The following conclusion may be drawn, at least provisionally.

Neandertal Man, Rhodesian Man, and the modern Australian race present a common stock of primitive characters. In spite of differences which distinguish them, it may be admitted that the three forms have a common origin; they must have spread and lived for a long period over vast extents of territory. In Europe, Neandertal Man seems to disappear somewhat abruptly after the Glacial period, but perhaps it was not total extinction. He may have continued to live in other regions. Indeed, it seems that *Homo rhodesiensis* reveals to us the persistence in Africa of a human type, long since become fossil in France. This type seems to have preserved in his skull and in his face the primitive features of brutishness, but, in the course of ages, he seems finally to have attained a perfectly upright attitude; in this direction he evolved further than his ancient European brother. We are thus led to think that he must have survived for a long time in the Dark Continent, as the last representative of a very ancient human form, now obsolete, in the midst of the modern black races, several of whom are themselves archaic in type and on the point of extermination.

Even if Rhodesian Man did not die very long ago, his presence need not particularly surprise us. His discovery is not more extraordinary than was that of the Okapi, the large and strange ruminant whose ancestors we have long known from bones obtained from the Miocene deposits of Europe and whose surviving representatives still live in a region quite close to Rhodesia.

SALDANHA MAN

The foregoing theory supposed that the type to which the Rhodesian Man belonged had already lived in Africa for a considerable period, but, until quite recently, this was no more than an unconfirmed hypothesis. Three years ago, the discovery at Saldanha in South Africa of a skull almost identical with that from Broken Hill afforded the awaited confirmation.

Seventy-five miles north of Capetown and about 8 miles from Saldanha Bay on the Atlantic coast, near the little township of Hopefield, there rises a group of recent dunes covering a much older and partially consolidated dune formation. Sweeping across the superficial dunes, the wind has laid bare the deeper formation, the surface of which is pitted with numerous hollows from which have been obtained heavily fossilized bone-remains and artefacts. Over several years Professor Drennan of Capetown University has collected from this site a fauna which, without being particularly archaic, nevertheless contains a certain number of extinct types. Amongst others, there have been found a Buffalo with a massive skull, a 'mammoth-toothed' Elephant, *Palaeoloxodon*, a large extinct Giraffe, *Griquatherium*, a giant Pig and the extinct Horse *Equus capensis*. The industry is characterized by large hand-axes of the final Acheulean type; it belongs indisputably to the Old Stone Age.

In June 1953, Mr. Keith Jolly discovered in this deposit fragments of a human skull. When joined together these fragments, 24 in number and

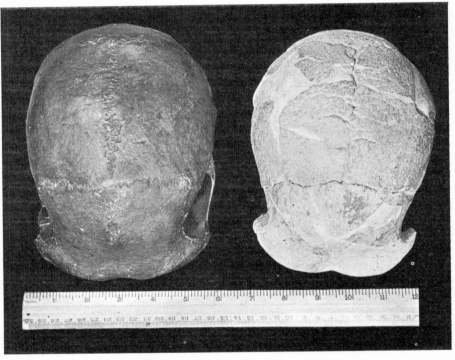

281 Saldanha Skull (right) compared with the Rhodesia Skull (left). View from above.
(After R. Drennan)

scattered over a wide area, formed an almost complete cranial calotte. This specimen was studied by Mr. Singer.[63] Corresponding to a strikingly thick skull, with a flattened vault and a powerful frontal torus, the Saldanha skull-cap displays an extraordinary resemblance to that of Rhodesian Man (Fig. 281): the dimensions are almost the same, the shape of the supraorbital ridge is so much alike that at this level the two skulls may be almost exactly

[63] Singer, R., 'The Saldanha Skull from Hopefield, South Africa' (*Amer. J. Phys. Anthr.*, XII, 19 54). Drennan, R., 'The Special Features and Status of the Saldanha Skull' (*Ibid.*, XIII, 1955).

superimposed. The only difference, and it is very slight, lies in the occipital region, where the torus is rather less pronounced than in the Broken Hill specimen, while the latter's post-parietal depression is lacking in the South African subject. The cerebral capacity seems also to be slightly lower: only 1,200 cubic centimetres as against 1,280 in Rhodesian Man.

A fragment of lower jaw was subsequently found in the same deposit. No detailed study has yet been published, but it clearly presents many primitive features.[64]

The importance of these discoveries is evident. Hitherto the sole representative of his type, the Rhodesian Man was of comparatively recent date and contemporary with a present-day fauna. The Saldanha skull, which belongs to the same type, is correlated with a far more ancient industry and contemporaneous with a partially extinct fauna. Its discovery shows that the archaic form know as *Homo rhodesiensis* occupied South Africa for a very long time: at least during the two periods in which first the Old Stone Age and then the Middle Stone Age developed. It provides the first fossil Man belonging to the earlier of the two periods who has yet come to light. There seems to be no doubt that this is the Man to whom is due the Acheulean civilization of Southern Equatorial Africa, and this is an extremely interesting fact.

THE BOSKOP SKULL

In 1914 a communication from L. Péringuey, Director of the Cape Museum, announced the discovery, made the previous year at Boskop near Pochefstroom, Transvaal, of fragments of a fossil human skeleton, consisting of a skull-cap (Fig. 282), the major portion of the right temporal bone, a segment of the lower jaw and some fragments of the long bones. These bones, deeply impregnated with mineral matter, were found at a depth of about 4 ft. 3 ins. during the digging of a drainage trench in a field. The soil in the field merges gradually into a laterite sub-soil containing no other fossils. The exact bed of the skull-cap can no longer be definitely ascertained, and explorations subsequently carried out by the Cape Museum have yielded no bone-remains *in situ*. The exact geological age of the Boskop fragments cannot, therefore, be determined, but their degree of fossilization argues in favour of considerable antiquity.

These relics were first studied by Haughton.[65] The brain-pan is remarkable for its flatness and great size. The reconstruction attempted by this author gives it a length of 205 millimetres and a breadth of 154 millimetres. Its cephalic index is about 75. The total capacity of the whole skull is estimated at about 1,830 cubic centimetres, which is enormous. According to

[64] Drennan, R. and Singer, R., 'A Mandibular Fragment probably of the Saldanha Skull' (*Nature*, Feb. 1955).

[65] Haughton, S., 'Preliminary Note on the Ancient Human Skull-Remains from the Transvaal' (*Trans. of the Roy. Soc. of S. Africa*, VI, 1917–1918), followed by a note by Elliot Smith on the endocranial cast of the Boskop skull-cap.

Broom,[66] even these figures are too small: he estimated the length at 220 mm., the breadth at 160 mm., and the height at 148 mm., which would bring its capacity up to 1,950 c.cm. A later reconstruction by Pycraft[67]

282 Skull-cap from Boskop, seen in profile and from above. About one-third natural size. (After Haughton)

produced very different figures: length 205 mm., breadth, 150 mm.; basion-bregma height, 137 mm.; giving a cephalic index of 73 and a capacity of no more than 1,717 c.cm.

The very thick skull-cap closely resembles in character the Cro-Magnon type: the form as a whole is pentagonal, with slight superciliary ridges, prominent glabella, straight forehead, the same kind of anteroposterior curve, and strong occipital prominence. From the Cro-Magnon type it

[66] Broom, R., 'The Boskop Skull' (*Amer. Mus. of Nat. Hist. Anthropological Papers*, XXIII, 1918).

[67] Pycraft, W., 'On the Calvaria found at Boskop, Transvaal, in 1913, and its Relationship to Cromagnard and Negroid Skulls' (*J. of the Roy. Anthrop. Inst.*, LV, 1925).

differs mainly in possessing a depression, a kind of hollow, in the inter-parietal region, which we have noted on several Negro skulls in the Anthro-pological Gallery of the National Natural History Museum in Paris, especially on the Namaqua skull, well known to all specialists.

The frontal bone is very narrow. The larger portion of the right temporal bone has been preserved; the mastoid apophysis is small but well separated; the petrous region is strongly developed; the glenoid cavity is large and shallow; and there is a post-glenoid apophysis. The most striking feature of this bone is the marked development of the supra-mastoid crest. Here we have a simian structure, resembling that of Neandertal Man, although, in its general form, the skull-cap may be compared to the Negroid, Bantu, and Cro-Magnon types.

The Boskop find includes also the two horizontal rami of a lower jaw, unfortunately in poor state of preservation. Their principal characters are their great strength, the presence of a slight chin and of small digastric fossae. Only one tooth is in position, the second left true molar. Its crown is badly preserved, so that it cannot be decided whether or not it possessed the posterior cusp characteristic of many primitive types. This jaw is already of the reduced dimensions which occur in modern Man; it is more highly evolved than the skull, and may be compared with that of the Bantus or Bushmen.

Examination of the portions of shafts of long bones, which are deeply impregnated with a kind of lateritic cement and much mutilated, yields no interesting results.

Professor Elliot Smith has examined an intra-cranial cast. Its flattened shape and certain other characteristics suggests resemblances between the Boskop Man and the Neandertal type. But the appearance and great develop-ment of the frontal protuberances point to closer relationship with the fossil Men of the Upper Palaeolithic in Europe, of whom the Boskop type might seem to be an immediate ancestor.

Some pieces of sandstone, with sharp edges, found in the laterite in the vicinity of the human bones have been examined by Péringuey. In spite of a few signs which seem to support the idea, no real trace of intentional working can be recognized.

Interpretation of such incomplete finds as this is always rash. In any case, we cannot share the opinion of Broom, who wished to attribute these relics to a new species, *Homo capensis*. The Boskop Man is certainly a *Homo sapiens*. South African anthropologists are agreed in acknowledging certain points of resemblance between this skull and the Cro-Magnon type; it also bears a likeness to the skulls of the Bushmen. Pycraft considered it a true inter-mediary between the two, a Proto-Bushman of Cro-Magnoid origin. This view was to all intents and purposes shared by Keith.

The problem of Boskop Man's significance was renewed some thirty-five years ago by the discovery of other human remains of the same type. Their study afforded a more exact knowledge of the characters of this fossil Man and, at the same time, established his archaeological age.

In 1921 five skeletons in very bad condition were found by Fitzsimmons
in a rock-shelter at Tzitzikama, a region of Port Elizabeth, 500 miles south
of Boskop (Fig. 275), at a depth of 15 feet beneath layers containing the
burials of Strandloopers. They were made the subject of a study by
Dart.[68]

Another skeleton was discovered in 1927 in the Skildergat Cave, near
Fish Hoek, some ten miles south of Capetown. This skeleton lay in a bed
containing a Still Bay industry and was therefore regarded as dating from the
Middle Stone Age. Certain recent observations,[69] however, seem to suggest
that it may be much later—Mesolithic at most. First studied by Drennan,
who considered it a primitive Bushman, it was later re-examined by Galloway.[70]

Another series of skeletons comes from a large rock-shelter at the mouth
of the River Matjes, near Knysna. Here there was a kitchen midden whose
upper layers contained burials of Strandloopers, while below, at a depth of
6 to 8 feet, burials of a different type contained skeletons placed on their
sides and accompanied by round funerary stones and pieces of ochre. There
were some dressed stones attributable to a Middle Stone Age industry. A
good description of these bone-remains was published by A. Keith.[71]

Yet another skeleton was found in 1929 during road building on the Springbok plateau, in the Northern Transvaal, not far from Pretoria. It was
embedded at a depth of 3 feet in a sort of limestone tufa, produced by
disintegration of the basalt forming the sub-soil of the plateau, and was
associated with the bones of a large buffalo of extinct species (*Bubalus bainii*).
It seems also to have been contemporaneous with the Middle Stone Age,
the industry of which abounds on the plateau, where it is the only one found.
The skull, which was badly damaged and lacked most of the face, was
reconstructed first by Broom[72] and then by Galloway.

Although not absolutely alike, all these fossil Men share a certain number
of common features with the Boskop subject. The skull is massive, pentagonal in *norma verticalis*, and tends towards dolichocephaly. Its dimensions
are considerable: the cranial capacity is large, almost always over 1,500
cubic centimetres. The bones of the vault are thick and the vault itself low.
The forehead is low and almost vertical; it is narrow and often displays a
'keel' along the centre line. Frequently, also, there is an inter-parietal depression. The face is short and broad, typically orthognathous. The limb bones
are thick and strong; their length shows the stature to have been notably
taller than that of the present-day Bushmen.

[68] Dart, R., 'Boskop Remains from the South East African Coast' (*Nature*, October 27,
1923).

[69] Goodwin, *Loc. cit.*, 1946.

[70] Galloway, A., 'Characteristics of the Skull of the Boskop Physical Type' (*Amer. J. of
Phys. Anthrop.*, XXIII, 1937).

[71] Keith, A., 'A Descriptive Account of the Human Skulls from Matjes River, Cape Province'
(*Trans. Roy. Soc. of S. Africa*, XXI, 1934).

[72] Broom, R., 'The Transvaal Fossil Human Skeleton' (*Nature*, March 16, 1929).

The Boskop type thus appears to be well defined, localized in the Middle Stone Age, and very much earlier than the Strandloopers. But its characters foreshadow those of the Strandloopers. Since the latter were themselves the ancestors of the Bushmen we can see that South Africa was the scene of a progressive evolution, in the course of which a human group of tall stature and very large skull was gradually transformed into a race of small stature, the last survivors of which are still living. During this transformation, which seems to have taken place as a result of the persistence in the adults of juvenile characteristics, a sort of neotenia,[73] the brain retained its relatively large volume, so that the Bushmen, despite their small proportions, recall in this character their Boskop ancestors. As for the relation of the latter to the fossil Men in the European Upper Palaeolithic, this does not seem yet to have been proved, despite the statements of South African palaeontologists. The question demands more ample research.

THE FLORISBAD SKULL

The Boskop type was not the only one to occupy South Africa during the Middle Stone Age. A distinctly different form is attested by a skull discovered in 1933 by T. Dreyer at Florisbad, Orange Free State, 25 miles from Bloemfontein.[74] This skull was embedded in a sandy deposit derived from an ancient spring. It was accompanied by numerous bone-remains of animals, many of which belonged to extinct species, such as a giant Buffalo (*Bubalus antiquus*) and two Horses (*Equus helmei* and *E. lylei*). There was also an industry belonging to the Middle Stone Age, but with obvious Mousterian affinities. Florisbad Man must, therefore, date from an early phase of this Age.

The skull is very incomplete, being limited to the major portion of the frontal bone, the front segment of the parietals and an important section of the right half of the face. It therefore presents serious gaps, and the reconstruction carried out by T. F. Dreyer (Fig. 283) is partly hypothetical. We can, however, say that this skull was of large proportions, with a low, flat vault displaying an interparietal concavity; the cephalic index must have been slightly dolichocephalic. The eyebrow arches are very developed but do not form a visor. The orbits are low and quadrangular; the nose is wide; the face is very prognathous and has deep canine fossae; the cheek-bones project outwards.

The endocranial cast of the fronto-parietal system has been studied by Ariens Kappers: it differs little from that of modern Man.

The majority of the characters of Florisbad Man mark him as a primitive

[73] This is what some authors refer to as 'pedomorphism'. On this subject, see Drennan, M., 'Pedomorphism in the Pre-Bushman Skull' (*Amer. J. of Phys. Anthr.*, XVI, 1931).

[74] Dreyer, T. F., 'A Human Skull from Florisbad, Orange Free State, with a note on the endocranial cast, by Ariëns Kappers' (*Kon. Akad. van Wetenschappen te Amsterdam, Proceedings*, XXXVIII, 1935); 'Further Observations on the Florisbad Skull' (*Soöl. Nav. Nas. Mus. Bloemfontein*, No. 1, XV, 1947).

type. First Dreyer and then Drennan[75] classed him with Neandertal Man, and the former was initially disposed to see in him a distinct human species. But the skull is incontestably that of a *Homo sapiens*: not only do the eyebrow ridges of Florisbad Man not form the visor characteristic of European Mousterians, but the low position of the orbits and the presence of well developed canine fossae are other important differences.

In the opinion of Galloway,[76] it is not so much towards Neandertal Man that the resemblances of this South African fossil skull tend as towards Boskop Man, with whom it shares its massiveness and the interparietal

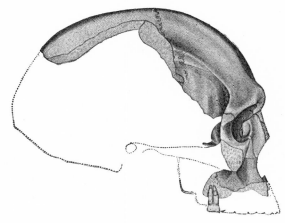

283 The Florisbad Skull, seen in profile. One-third natural size
(After T. Dreyer)

concavity, while the facial characters bear a great likeness to the Australians. It is therefore a generalized form, related to the primitive types of both South Africa and Australia. Keith, who accepts this view, adds that certain characters typical of Rhodesian Man may also be observed. Hence the latter, he thinks, is no longer an isolated specimen, and the Florisbad skull shows how the Broken Hill skull evolved and was continued by certain forms of *Homo sapiens*.

However conjectural these notions may be, it is certain that the most striking aspect of the Florisbad skull is the presence of characters typical of primitive human types although different, in their totality, from those of the Boskop skull. Now, these features are also seen, though to a lesser degree, in some skulls previously discovered in South Africa which it had already seemed justifiable to term 'Australoid'.

[75] Drennan, M. R., 'The Florisbad Cranium and Brain Cast' (*Trans. of the R. Soc. of S. Africa*, XXV, 1937).

[76] Galloway, A., 'The Nature and Status of the Florisbad Skull, as revealed by its non-metrical Features' (*Amer. J. of Phys. Anthr.*, XXIII, 1937).

The first of these skulls was exhumed at Bayville, near Port Elizabeth, and studied by Broom.[77]

A second was found at Mistkraal, in Cape Province, about 70 miles west of Bayville.[78]

More recently Broom described[79] a very fragmentary brain-box unearthed from an alluvial deposit at Barkley West, near Kimberley; while Drennan made a detailed study[80] of a fourth skull, found in a sand-pit at Cape Flats, in the immediate vicinity of the Cape (Fig. 284).

The exact age of all these specimens is not known. They do not seem to

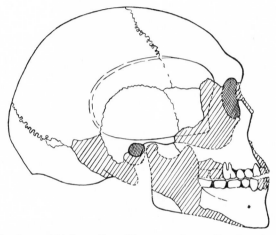

284 Skull of the Australoid from Cape Flats, seen in profile. One-third natural size
(After M. Drennan)

be very ancient. But they are all of a type that differs from the Bushmen and the Bantus. The cranium is long and the forehead very oblique. The eyebrow arches are remarkably developed. The face seems to be long and is slightly prognathous.

In the Border Cave, near Ingwavuma in Zululand, a human skeleton was recently found in deposits containing an industry of the Middle Stone Age type accompanied by a fauna much the same as that of the present day.[81] Very dolichocephalic and belonging to an adult of tall stature, it too has pronounced superciliary arches and is notable for the width of its brow.

[77] Broom, R., 'A Contribution to the Craniology of the Yellow-Skinned Races of South Africa' (*J. of the Roy. Anthr. Inst.*, LIII, 1923).

[78] Allen, A., 'A Report on the Australoid Calvarium found at Mistkraal, C. P.' (*S. African Journal of Science*, XXIII, 1926).

[79] Broom, R., 'Australoid Element in the Korannas' (*Nature*, Oct. 5, 1929).

[80] Drennan, M., 'An Australoid Skull from the Cape Flats' (*J. of the Roy. Anthr. Soc.*, LIX, 1929).

[81] Cooke, H., Malan, B. and Wells, L., 'Fossil Man in Lebombo Mountains South Africa. The "Border Cave", Ingwavuma District, Zululand' (*Man*, March, 1945).

These two characters give it a resemblance to Florisbad Man, with which it may be classed, in spite of certain points of likeness to Springbok Man.

The South African Australoid type has been grouped by Broom with the prehistoric Cro-Magnon race. This is an even more audacious hypothesis than that which attaches the Boskop Man to this race. The resemblance of the Australoids to the Florisbad Man is, on the contrary, obvious. This shows that there once existed in South Africa a type which differed from the Boskop type, with which it was no doubt contemporary, and which was characterized by very marked eyebrow arches. Perhaps this type has not entirely vanished. Broom has claimed that the Hottentot Koranna tribe has the same development of the eyebrow arches and is its last survival. This assertion also requires proof.

To sum up, we see that, if the discoveries made during the last forty years or so in South Africa do not yet tell us anything definite about the Men of the most ancient times, they show the existence of at least three human types when we come to the Middle Stone Age.

First, there is a very primitive Neandertalian type, closely related to the Mousterians of Europe, but certainly more recent. This is undoubtedly the last survival of a very old Neandertalian stock that occupied Africa at an extremely early period.

The other two types, which belong indisputably to the *Homo sapiens* group and which centre around the two fossil Men of Boskop and Florisbad, may be called respectively the *Boskopoid type* and the *Australoid type*. Their evolution seems to have taken place *in situ* and eventually to have terminated in the Bushmen and Hottentot races, now in the process of disappearing. Thus light is beginning to fall on the prehistory of Man in this region. It reveals, in particular, the curious fact that, among all these ancient forms, there is no Negro properly so-called. The same fact has been noted in North and East Africa. It raises a problem that has not yet been solved.

CHAPTER TWELVE

THE FOSSIL MEN OF AMERICA

THE history of the New World begins only in the 16th century, but, on the other hand, it has an immense prehistory stretching far in time as well as in space. Apart from a few traditions, we find indications of it in monuments of all kinds distributed over vast areas. To the scientist, however, America still remains as great a mystery as it was at the time of the Conquistadores. In spite of considerable efforts, American anthropology, ethnography and archaeology—which taken together now constitute a special group, Americanism—have not so far been able to elucidate any but minor points and matters of detail. None of the great problems they discuss has been definitely solved.

Have we to deal with one or with several great American races? Were the populations of the New World before its discovery indigenous or immigrant? And if the latter, where did they come from? Must we suppose that in America there existed one or several centres of origin and evolution for a section of Mankind, or must we believe that the country was peopled from the Old World? If that be the case, at what period did this settlement take place?

We cannot here discuss these important problems, to the solution of which geology, palaeontology, archaeology, the study of language and ethnography must all lend their aid. The literature on these various branches of the subject already forms a bulky library. We shall touch only on such of it as deals with fossil Man, but we think it may be useful, as a preliminary, simply to enumerate a few theories which, without being actually established as fact, are shared by the majority of students of American history.

From the anthropological point of view, we may say that it is all but unanimously agreed that the prehistoric populations of America, that is those now known as the *Amerindians*, belonged to the main stem of the Yellow Races. And there is no doubt that all these peoples came from the Old World. But their distribution, which took place at such a remote period of time, over the whole extent of the two Americas, the physical, linguistic, and social differences they exhibit or which they previously exhibited, lead one to think that the stocking of the New Continent from the Old must necessarily date from a very remote period.

Archaeology teaches us indeed that the indigenous peoples, the Indians or Amerindians, who lived in such numbers in America at the beginning of the 16th century, must have descended from a long series of ancestors more or less distant, to whom all sorts of monuments must be attributed: the shell heaps and kitchen middens which are strewn upon the sea shore everywhere, and sometimes occur even inland: the earthworks, tumuli, and ramparts known as 'mounds', scattered over all the great plains of the United States; the strange habitations of the 'cliff-dwellers', hollowed out or perched on the great steep cliffs of Colorado, Arizona, and New Mexico; the *pueblos*, stone or mud towns or villages of the same regions and also of Central America; and the wealthy cities of Central America and of Peru rich in monuments.[1] The skulls and human skeletons exhumed from these various sources present the chief characters of the 'Indians' of the same regions.

We now know that the general civilization of these Amerindians, which, if a comparision must be drawn, may be likened to that of our Neolithic (with many polished stone implements, finely dressed arrowheads, very varied pottery and an absence or scarcity of such metals as copper), lasted a very long time, for everywhere it has left behind countless traces; and some shell-heaps and mounds are of such large size, or are found in such topographical circumstances, that they must date from a very ancient period.

Away beyond this period reigns the darkness of geological times. Here, as in the Old World, the question becomes a geological and palaeontological problem, connected only with the natural sciences; thus it comes within the scope of this work. We cannot describe individually the great number of discoveries or finds brought forward to prove the existence of fossil Man in America. Many, indeed, are unworthy of note; we shall, therefore, describe only some of the most important, those which are worth discussing.

It is curious to note that in 1840, even before it had been definitely settled in Europe, the question of the co-existence of Man with the large extinct animals, such as the Mastodon, had already been broached in the two Americas.

NORTH AMERICA

GENERAL DESCRIPTION

During Pleistocene times, North America curiously resembled Europe. Glaciers, originating from three main centres, the first in Labrador, the second to the west of Hudson Bay, and the third on the ridge of the Cordilleran Highland from Alaska in the north to Montana in the south, coalesced to form an immense continental ice-sheet, covering the whole of Canada and the north of the United States almost as far as lat. 37° N. (Fig. 285).

[1] For general works on the subject, see: Moorehead, W. K., *The Stone Age in North America* (1910). Beuchat, *Manuel d'archéologie américaine* (Paris, 1913). Homes, W. H., 'Handbook of Aboriginal American Antiquities. Part I: Introductory' (*Smiths. Inst., Bureau of Amer. Ethnol.*, Bull. 60, 1919). Pericot, L., *América indigena* (I. Barcelona, 1936). Martin, P., Quimby, G. and Collier, D., *Indians Before Columbus* (Chicago, 1947). Canals Frau, S., *Prehistoria de América* (Buenos Aires, 1950).

The thickness of the ice varied in different regions from 4,000 to 10,000 feet.

The Rocky Mountains, the Cascade Mountains, and the Sierra Nevada had also their own glaciers, the advanced moraines of which reached sometimes as far as the plains, just as in the case of the glaciers of the Alps or the Pyrenees.

In many places, the moraine formations alternated with deposits of different origin containing fossils. As in Europe, so too in America several

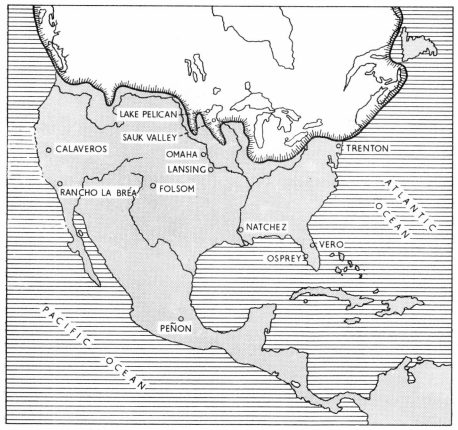

⎣⎡⎤⎦ LIMIT OF THE WISCONSIN GLACIATION

285 Map of the chief prehistoric sites in North America that have yielded human remains.

phases in the advance and withdrawal of the glaciers are to be observed. According to different authors these phases varied in number from three to six: the majority acknowledge four, the last of which, the 'Wisconsin' is virtually synchronous with the Würmian in Europe.

Thus Pleistocene times in America present a physical aspect akin to that of Europe. Does the same hold good in relation to the biological, and especially the human side? Let us note first of all that the fauna of large animals is very different in the two continents, except in the northern regions inhabited by circumpolar animals such as the Mammoth. Elsewhere, we meet with a Mastodon (Fig. 286), with several genera of large Edentata, *Megatherium*, *Megalonyx*, and *Mylodon* from South America, and other mammals, such as the Horse, Camel and Bison, differing generically and specifically from

286 Skeleton of *Mastodon americanus*. Frankfurt Museum

European forms. These differences make it difficult to correlate the divisions of Quaternary times in European countries with those which American geologists and palaeontologists have attempted to establish in their own country.

As regards Man himself, discoveries put forward in support of his geological antiquity are very numerous. But many have no scientific value, and even with reference to those which seem to have been found under the best conditions, opinion is far from unanimous. American fossil man long had many confirmed opponents, but discoveries made during the last twenty-five years are now gaining him an increasing number of very firm supporters. Let us examine the principal material evidences.

ARCHAEOLOGICAL OBSERVATIONS

Appeal was first made to archaeological evidence. Beside innumerable stone objects of Indian manufacture, strewn all over the surface of the soil of the United States, there are some objects of ruder manufacture and more ancient

THE FOSSIL MEN OF AMERICA

appearance, which are much more like the most ancient Palaeolithic implements of the Old World. At first it was thought that they were of the same
antiquity. Wilson[2] was convinced of the truth of this theory, basing his
belief on an important collection of objects of this nature which he had
gathered together at the Smithsonian Institution. The geologist Winchell[3]
came to the same conclusion after studying the 'palaeoliths' from Kansas,
which he regarded as belonging to four successive periods, two of which
were Palaeolithic. These distinctions he based mainly on his study of the
patina. Extending his investigations to the whole of South-West America,
Renaud[4] showed the existence of many deposits containing artefacts of
'Pre-Chellean, Chellean, Acheulean, Clactonian and Mousterian type'.
Along with points, blades, scrapers, and so on, there is an industry of quartzite pebbles resembling analogous specimens from the terraces of the
Garonne.

All these finds are interesting, but they do no more than indicate possi-
bilities. Only discoveries made in undisturbed geological layers can provide
conclusive evidence. For a very long time such discoveries were almost
entirely lacking. Numerous objects resembling the current products of
Indian manufacture were collected from the auriferous gravels of California.
Dressed stones have been found in various formations of clearly Pleistocene
age, such as the ancient alluvials of Mexico, the deposits of the ancient Lake
Lahontan in Nevada, the gravels and silts of Minnesota, Indiana, New
Hampshire, Ohio, New Jersey and elsewhere. But all these discoveries have
been made under very unsatisfactory stratigraphic conditions and their
antiquity has been vigorously disputed. They cannot be accepted as
evidence.[5]

There is even less reason to place any credence in the alleged 'bone
industry', which H. J. Cook claimed to have found in the Pliocene level
containing the famous tooth of 'Hesperopithecus'.[6] American prehistorians
gave it short shrift, as they did the so-called Anthropoid with which it was
supposed to be contemporary.

THE TRENTON ALLUVIALS

But there is a Pleistocene deposit at Trenton in New Jersey, upon which
we must dwell at greater length, for it was the subject of great discussion
and provided the partisans of the antiquity of Man in America with arguments

[2] Wilson, T., 'La période paléolithique dans l'Amérique du Nord' (*Congrès intern. d'Arch.
et d'Anthrop.*, Meeting at Paris, 1889).

[3] Winchell, N. H., (*Ibid.*, Meeting at Geneva, II, p. 365, and *Minnesota Historical Society*,
XVI, 1913).

[4] Numerous memoirs, in particular Renaud, E., 'Les plus anciennes cultures préhistoriques
du Sud-Ouest américain' (*L'Anthropologie*, XL, 1930). *The Archaeological Survey of the
High Western Plains*, 10th Report: *The Black's Fork Culture* (Denver, 1938).

[5] Wright, F., *The Ice Age in North America* (New York, 1889. Supplement to the 3rd Ed.,
1891). *Man and the Glacial Period* (New York, 1912). Homes, W. H., 'Handbook. . .'

[6] See p. 87.

that were not wholly valueless. In the year 1875, Dr. Charles Abbott[7] collected, in the ancient alluvial deposits of the Delaware River, stone implements (quartzite and argillite) rudely worked in forms often similar to those of European Palaeolithic flints (Fig. 287). The Trenton gravels have been formed by the re-sorting of the moraines of the last glacial extension; they contain bones of fossil mammals; and they are therefore undoubtedly

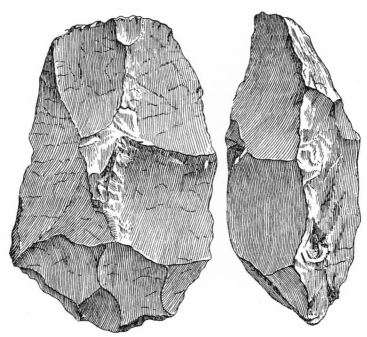

287 Front and side view of an implement of argillite found in the Trenton Alluvials, 6½ feet below the surface of the soil. Natural size. (After Wilson)

Pleistocene. The presence of dressed stones in the depth of these alluvial deposits proves the reality of the existence of an American Palaeolithic Man. This result at which Abbott arrived seemed conclusive, and it was at first generally accepted.

Various anthropologists, however, quickly pointed out the resemblance between the supposed implements of Palaeolithic Man, including those from Trenton, and the discarded products of manufacture found in enormous heaps around old quarries worked by the Indians. They thus denied, at one and the same time, the antiquity of the dressed stones and the authenticity of the deposit in which they were found.[8] In 1897 the geologist

---

[7] Abbot, C. C., *The Stone Age in New Jersey* (1877); *Primitive Industry* (1881) etc.

[8] McGee, W. J., 'Palaeolithic Man in America' (*Popular Science Monthly*, 1888). Holmes, W. H., 'Are there Traces of Man in the Trenton Gravels?' (*Journal of Geology*, 1893); *Science*, 1892, 1893, *passim*. Boule, M., 'L'antiquité de l'Homme dans l'Amérique du Nord' (*L'Anthropologie*, IV, 1893).

Chamberlin went so far as to say that the existence of Palaeolithic Man on American soil was not worthy of the honour of a discussion.

But Abbott's theory was supported by certain loyal partisans, first among whom must be ranked the late F. W. Putnam, Director of the Peabody Museum, Cambridge, Mass.[9] Interested from the first in Abbott's researches, he commissioned one of his fellow workers, E. Volk, to make observations and excavations, which were carried out during a period extending over twenty-two years, and the results of which have been published in a large volume which appeared in 1911.[10] Abbott himself published a work summarizing the results of ten years' work in the deposit.[11] The two observers, independently of each other, arrive at practically the same conclusions, less simple than those first broached, but no less explicit.

The later geological formations of the Delaware valley are of three kinds:

1. A superficial black deposit or vegetable soil (*black soil*), containing very abundant traces of the Neolithic culture of the Lenâpe Indians.

2. This black earth covers a yellow deposit (*yellow drift*), clayey and sandy in character, containing dressed quartzites and particularly dressed argillites characteristic of this level, which corresponds to a *Pre-Lenâpian* culture. The peoples associated with these remains may already have been Indians, but they had no polished axes.

3. Below the 'yellow drift' come the true and much discussed 'Trenton Gravels', of fluvio-glacial origin and Pleistocene age. Here there are no more argillites, but only quartz and quartzites of very rude manufacture, manufacture so rude as to be in itself open to question, although the presence of these objects *in situ* can no longer be a matter for doubt. Abbot gives the name *Homo delawarensis* to the Man who manufactured these implements.

The question of American fossil Man has not yet been settled by these explorations, however, since the problem of whether the quartzites of Stratum 3 are or are not artificial remains unresolved. In any case, the existence of a well characterized industry in Stratum 2 shows that the forerunners of the Indians lived for a long time in this region and that they must date from very far back in the Holocene Period. Those writers, therefore, who considered the problem closed, and who refused to allow the Indians an antiquity of more than 2,000 to 3,000 years before our era, were going too far. In 1930, with the discovery of the Folsom culture, the question arose afresh, and this time under much more favourable circumstances. But first we must say a few words about a certain number of finds of a different nature.

CONTEMPORANEITY OF MAN WITH EXTINCT ANIMALS

On several occasions traces of human industry were found, or thought to

[9] Putman, F. W., Numerous articles in his *Reports* as Curator of the Peabody Museum of Harvard University, 1876 to 1910.

[10] Volk, E., 'The Archaeology of the Delaware Valley' (*Papers of the Peabody Museum*, V 1910, and Cambridge, 1911, with bibliography).

[11] Abbott, C. C., *Ten Years' Diggings in Lenâpe Land* (Trenton, 1912).

have been found, in association with the bone-remains of extinct animals believed to be of Pleistocene age.[12] Such associations, if they were not the result of chance, seemed to provide positive proof of the antiquity of Man. But here again there has been much discussion.

The first observation of this nature was made by A. Koch in 1839 and involved the discovery of arrow-heads beside a mastodon skeleton. Comtemporary with the first finds of Boucher de Perthes, this observation raised the problem of the coexistence of Man with large extinct animals in America at the very moment when the same problem had arisen in France under similar circumstances. But whereas in France a few years were enough for the truth to gain acceptance, in the New World it was to take nearly a century.

A certain number of observations, which it is very difficult to evaluate today, followed Koch's without enjoying any great success.[13] On several occasions, notably in 1896, human relics were found mingled with bone-remains of *Megalonyx*, a large Edentate now extinct, in Big Bone Cave, Tennessee. While exhuming skeletons of *Bison occidentalis* from a Quaternary deposit, H. Martin, of the University of Kansas, collected a flint arrowhead from under and against the right shoulder-blade of one of them. Somewhat later, in 1903, Clarke recorded bone-remains of the Mastodon in association with traces of fire and pottery. All these finds have, however, been disputed.

A series of more recent investigations extending over a wide area of North America, from Nebraska to Texas, have furnished evidences found under much more carefully checked conditions.[14]

In 1925 J. Boyes discovered several arrowheads in contact with the skeleton of a flat-horned Bison, very different from the existing species, *in situ* in a fossiliferous deposit in a locality of Texas. The same formation contained the Mammoth, Horse and Camel—in other words a Pleistocene fauna since vanished. A similar find was made shortly afterwards in an Oklahoma quarry, where the fauna also included large Edentates. But the most interesting facts are those arising from the discovery by J. Figgins at Folsom, New Mexico, of a stone industry completely different from any so far known in North America and accompanied by extinct animals.

---

[12] A parallel argument is the representation of these same animals in drawings made by Man. In fact drawings of elephants (or mammoths?) on bones, stones, cave walls and also on certain ancient monuments in Central America have been reported on several occasions; but the identity of the animal portrayed, not to mention the authenticity of all these finds is very dubious. On this subject, see Eiseley, L., 'Myths and Mammoths in Archaeology' (*Amer. Antiquity*, XI, 1945).

[13] See: Wilson, Th., 'La haute ancienneté de l'Homme dans l'Amérique du Nord' (*L'Anthropologie*, XII, 1901). Osborn, H., *The Age of Mammals* (1910) p. 495.

[14] Renaud, E., 'L'antiquité de l'Homme dans l'Amérique du Nord' (*L'Anthropologie*, XXXVIII, 1928). Roberts, F., 'The Folsom Problem in American Archaeology' (*Smithsonian Report for 1938*, Washington, 1939). Bryan, K., 'Geology of the Folsom Deposits in New Mexico and Colorado' (in *Early Man*, Philadelphia, 1937). Bryan, K., and Ray, L., 'Geologic Aniquitty of the Lindenmeier Site in Colorado' (*Smithsonian Miscellaneous Collections*, CXIX, No. 2, Washington, 1940).

FOLSOM

What is known today as the 'Folsom point' (Fig. 288) is a flat point, finely retouched at the edges, and having a deep longitudinal fluting or groove on either face. At Folsom itself, points of this kind were recorded in direct contact with various bones of *Bison occidentalis* (Fig. 289). But this was not the only place at which they occurred. Folsom points have been found at Clovis, Dent, Lindenmeier and other places, in geological positions and

288 Different types of Folsom points. Three-fourths natural size. (After F. Roberts)

associated with large Pleistocene animals such as the Elephant, Mastodon, Horse, Camel, *Mylodon*, etc. At several places the bones were charred or showed traces of dismemberment and lay in immediate proximity to charcoal and beds of cinders. The Folsom points were accompanied by various stone tools, but never by polished axes. There can be no doubt that these are the vestiges of camping-places of hunters in pursuit of the great Quaternary mammals on which they fed.

The Folsom industry has been found along the whole of the western slope of the Rocky Mountains, from Canada to the Mexican border. It is very much earlier not only than the pre-Columbian Indians, but also than their forerunners in the western territories, the 'Basket-Makers'. Detailed exploration of certain deposits has established a precise stratification and shown the relations between the archaeological beds and the formation of the terraces dating from the end of the last Ice Age. The fauna indicates that at this time the climate was cold and wet.

Stimulated by the Folsom discovery, numerous excavations have been carried out since 1930 in the whole of the south-west of the United States.

In Sandia Cave, New Mexico, in deposits underlying those containing
Folsom points, Hibben[15] found an even older industrial complex comprising,
along with carinate scrapers, slotted points resembling those of the Solutrean
in Europe: these are the Sandia points. The fauna includes the Mastodon,
Mammoth, Camel and large Edentates. Undisturbed archaeological beds in
the 'sulphur spring' deposits of.Arizona revealed the existence of a relatively
sedentary people, who collected grains and pounded them in sandstone

289 Folsom point *in situ* against the rib of a fossil bison. (After F. Roberts)

mortars. This is the first stage in the 'Cochise culture', the development of
which has been traced over a very long period down to the Neolithic proper.[16]
The deposits of the Gypsum Cave (Nevada), Lake Mohave (California),
Lake Borax (California), among many others, have also yielded industries
of primitive workmanship associated with extinct beasts.

What age can we attribute to these first manifestations of human presence
in North America? Their existence side by side with large extinct mammals
initially suggested that they dated from the end of the Pleistocene. But the
most recent researches of American palaeontologists seem to show that,
contrary to what happened in Europe, the majority of these large mammals
now no longer extant persisted for an appreciable time after the end of the
Ice Age. They did not disappear until the Holocene Period, and perhaps

[15] Hibben, F., 'Evidence of Early Occupation of Sandia Cave, New Mexico. . .' (*Smithsonian Miscellaneous Collections*, XCIX, No. 23, 1941).

[16] Sayles, F. and Antevs, E., 'The Cochise Culture' (*Gila Pueblo, Medallion Papers*, XXIX, 1941).

their extinction was the work of Man.[17] Their presence in the archaeological layers would not imply that the latter are more than 5,000 to 6,000 years old.

Other deductions have been drawn from a study of the beds themselves. At Lindenmeier, a study of their relations with the river terraces and moraine deposits of the Rocky Mountains led Bryan and Ray to ascribe to the archaeological layer an age of 10,000 to 12,000 years, and perhaps much more. Antevs, employing the varve method (see Chap. II), arrived at similar figures for the Folsom point deposits as a whole: 12,000 to 13,000 years. Working on the disintegration of Carbon 14, Arnold and Libby give rather lower figures,[18] which nevertheless testify to an indisputable antiquity—5,900 years before our era for the first Cochise culture, 7,000 years for the Folsom culture, and 8,200 for the Gypsum Cave deposit. Man was, therefore, present throughout the whole of the Post-Glacial period. It would, however, be rash to assign him an antiquity of more than 10,000 to 12,000 years. This may be less than some authors hoped; but it is much more than the great majority of anthropologists and archaeologists believed only twenty-five years ago.

OSTEOLOGICAL EVIDENCE

Examination of the bone-remains is a difficult and complicated task,[19] in the elucidation of which the general studies of Hrdlička[20] will be of special assistance. This anthropologist has devoted himself to the re-examination of all the discoveries. None of them has been spared his criticism; in some cases it is the deposit which is questioned, sometimes the bones themselves are obviously modern; often the evidence is unsatisfactory in every respect.

As regards the oldest discoveries, we shall do no more than simply remind the reader of their existence, for to us they are lost evidence, since it is now impossible to estimate their value with full knowledge of the facts. Such, for instance, is the human skeleton from New Orleans (1884); the iliac bone

[17] For the controversies on this subject, see: Colbert, E., 'The Pleistocene Mammals of North America and their Relations to Eurasian Forms' (in *Early Man*, Philadelphia, 1937). Eiseley, L., 'Archaeological Observations on the Problem of Post-Glacial Extinction' (*Amer. Antiquity*, VIII, 1943).

[18] Arnold, J., and Libby, W., 'Radiocarbon Dates' (*Science*, CXIII, 2 Feb. 1951). Johnson, F., 'Radiocarbon Dating' (*Memoirs of the Soc. for Amer. Arch.*, VIII, 1951). In their first researches, Arnold and Libby gave the Folsom culture an age of only 4,300 years. It was later recognized that the sample they had studied came from a more recent deposit. A charred bone taken from the bed containing Folsom points in the Lubbock formation gave a figure of $9,883 \pm 350$ years.

[19] We shall leave aside so-called proofs of the antiquity of Man based on the existence of footprints attributed to Man. These were long since proved to bear only a very crude resemblance to the imprints of human steps. See Flint, Dr., in Putnam's *Report of Peabody Museum*, 1883, and *Science*, March 7, 1884.

[20] Hrdlička, A., 'Skeletal Remains suggesting or attributed to Early Man in North America' (*Smithsonian Institution, Bureau of American Ethnology*, Bull. 33, Washington, 1907); 'Recent Discoveries attributed to Early Man in America' (*Ibid.*, Bull. 66, Washington, 1918); 'Early Man in America: What have the Bones to say?' (In *Early Man*, Philadelphia, 1937). These works contain the history and complete bibliography of each discovery.

from Natchez (Mississipi), which came from a deposit containing bones of Pleistocene animals, but which the distinguished English geologist, Lyell, after examining it *in situ*, attributed to an Indian burial. The same thing applies to a skeleton found by miners at a depth of 22 feet at Soda Creek in Colorado; to a few human bones exhumed at Charleston in South Carolina; to a skull found in a crevice filled with earth and pebbles at Rock Bluff in Illinois, and so on. Although it falls into the same category, the Calaveras skull is too famous for us to pass it over without a few words.[21]

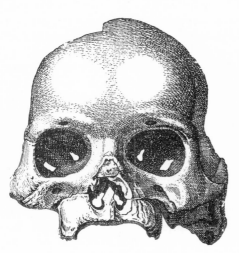

290 The Calaveras Skull

It is said to have been found in 1866, at a depth of 30 feet in the pit of a mine dug through super-imposed lavas and auriferous gravels of Pliocene age, in the Bald Hill near Altaville, in Calaveras County, California. This origin is more than doubtful. All the circumstances suggest that some hoax was perpetrated—'a practical joke of the miners', as the geologist Marcou declared.

The incomplete skull (Fig. 290) now belongs to the Peabody Museum in Cambridge, U.S.A.: it is partially fossilized and covered with a thin calcareous concretion. But the various American scientists who have studied it are unanimous in affirming its resemblance to the skull of the modern Indians of that region. Its resemblance to a skull found in a Californian cave, likewise covered with a limy coating, are such that the anthropologist Hrdlička declares we can ascribe both remains to a single race, and what is more, to the same tribe. It is very probable that they have a similar origin, and that, like the other, the Calaveras skull also came from a cave. It cannot be very ancient in the geological sense of the word.

TRENTON, PEÑON

There is first the series of bone remains collected at Trenton between 1879 and 1899 by Abbott and Volk. Some of them seem to come from a nearby Indian burial-place and are consequently of no interest. Only two skulls have been examined in any detail.

The first, described as from Burlington County, was accidentally found in a field, and seems to have come from a superficial alluvial deposit. The

[21] The bibliography is large, for this discovery was much discussed. The original report is by Whitney, *Auriferous Gravels of the Sierra Nevada* (Cambridge, U.S.A., 1879). A detailed account is contained in A. Vayson, *Les fraudes en Archéologie préhistorique* (Paris, 1932).

second, labelled 'from Riverview Cemetery', was recovered by a grave-digger at a depth of 3 feet, in a part of the cemetery still unused. The circumstances of the discovery are, to say the least of it, unsatisfactory. Now, these two skulls are equally remarkable from a morphological point of view. Not large, much depressed, with narrow face and large orbits, they indicate a human race very different from the Indians. Hrdlička has shown that they closely resemble the 'Batavian' skulls described by various German authors, which have sometimes been compared with Neandertal skulls; he does not hesitate to ascribe them to two old immigrants of Dutch origin. In Sarasin's view they are merely Indians whose skulls have been artificially deformed.[22]

In 1899, Volk himself took from the gravels a human parietal bone and a femur. If these bones are really contemporary with the gravel, as Volk affirms, they must belong to the dresser of the quartzites; they do not, however, present any noteworthy structural features.

In 1884, a piece of skull and some other fragments of a skeleton were found in calcareous tufa at Peñon, a valley in Mexico. By some this tufa is looked upon as of Pleistocene date, while to others it appears to have been recently formed by the hot springs which rise in the neighbourhood.

THE 'LOESS MEN'

In 1902, there were discovered at Lansing, in Kansas, the skeleton of an adult man and the jawbone of a child, lying in a silt 20 feet below the surface soil. The locality has been examined by many expert geologists, some of whom regard the silt as a true Pleistocene *loess*; others consider it of recent formation due to the flooding of the neighbouring river. The bones are, moreover, identical with those of modern Indians in this part of the United States.

In 1894 and 1906, an earth mound at Omaha in Nebraska also yielded numerous human bones. The discoveries of the latter year, much the most important, comprise the remains of a dozen individuals. They were examined by the originator of the excavations, Gilder, and by various scientists, including Barbour the geologist, Osborn the palaeontologist, and Hrdlička the anthropologist. The bones are derived from different levels, ranging from 2 ft. 6 ins. to 6 ft. 6 ins. in depth. According to Professor Barbour those from the upper level belong to a burial, but the others must be as old as the mud in which they were embedded. They represent 'Loess Man'.

Hrdlicka combated these conclusions. The conditions of the deposition of the skeletons, several of which retained their anatomical relations, indicated burials. At all the levels the bones showed the same coloration, consistency, and surface scratches. None present the slightest trace of fossilization. All exhibit, and at the same spots, incisions denoting certain funeral rites, such as have been found on similar specimens from the tumuli in the region. It is true that certain skulls have somewhat unusual characters: great thickness

[22] Sarasin, F., 'Zur Frage von der prähistorischen Besiedelung von Amerika, . . .' (*Mém. Soc. helvétique des Sc. naturelles*, Vol. LXIX, 1928).

of the bones, strong orbital arches, and low and receding foreheads, features which have caused them to be compared, mistakenly however, to the Neandertal and *Pithecanthropus* skulls. These characteristics certainly led to their being regarded as of very high antiquity. But Hrdlička has shown that such skulls are fairly frequent in the mounds or tumuli of the region, and that in all the remaining features of their morphology the Omaha skulls are the skulls of Indians.

RANCHO LA BREA

At Rancho la Brea, near Los Angeles in California, there is a curious bed of Quaternary animals, probably the richest in the United States. This deposit is formed of beds of asphalt, pure or mixed with alluvial products. For several years, Professor Merriam, of the University of California, made in that spot rich palaeontological collections of the skeletons of animals of extinct species, especially of *Smilodon* (an animal akin to our Sabre-Toothed Tiger, *Machairodus*), skeletons of which are found there in thousands.

In 1914, the American newspapers made a great fuss about the discovery of a human skeleton in the asphalt deposits at Rancho la Brea. The news caused a lively sensation, for a human skeleton, contemporary with *Smilodon* and other extinct mammals, seemed to be a relic of the first importance capable of throwing much light on the still hotly disputed question of fossil Man in America. But soon after, a paper by Professor Merriam focussed the matter in its true light. Once more scientists were faced by a fact without satisfactory geological backing. Owing to the viscosity of asphalt, layers of this material cannot really be accurately placed from a stratigraphical point of view. The human remains were found at a depth of between 6 and 10 feet, in a sort of chimney filled with asphalt, originating from a great subterranean mass of the same substance, and opening upon the surface. Such infiltrations of cavities or of spaces, in the upper layers of the detritus of the region, may have happened at various periods, and may date from very different ages.

From the palaeontological point of view, the facts are just as unsatisfactory. The numerous animal remains, found at the same time as the human bones, do not belong to the now classic Pleistocene fauna of Rancho la Brea, but to the Californian fauna of the present day. From the anthropological point of view, the high antiquity of the skeleton is not confirmed, for it does not differ from skeletons of Indians from Southern California. In this instance again, therefore, there can be no question of a fossil Man of the Pleistocene Period.

DISCOVERIES IN FLORIDA

Finally, the most recent discovery, announced in 1916, and still much discussed, was that at Vero, in Florida.

This is not the first time that the presence of fossil Man in Florida has been canvassed. A whole series of finds of human bone-remains were made, from 1852 to 1886, on the shores of Lake Monroe, and on the west coast of the peninsula, to the south of Sarasota, particularly in the neighbourhood of the little town of Osprey.

The majority of these bone-remains were embedded in a hard rock, a kind of ferruginous sandstone, rich in limonite; and chemical analysis indicates that they are deeply impregnated with mineral matter. But the geologist Vaughan has shown that, in spite of their appearance, the fossil-bearing deposits are post-Pleistocene, that the special conditions of fossilization are of no significance in this case, for they are due to the action of numerous iron springs, which consolidate recent sands and rapidly petrify all kinds of objects, particularly Indian pottery. Further, the bones, examined by Hrdlička, do not differ from those of the Indians.

The latest discovery, made by the State geologist Sellards at Vero on the east coast, has formed the subject of numerous reports by the most qualified specialists in the United States.[23]

The subsoil of the town and neighbourhood of Vero is composed from below upwards of the following components:

(1) Marls of marine origin, containing Pleistocene shells. These marls bear: (2) a marly sand, of river origin, with plant remains and bones of Pleistocene land animals, notably of an Elephant (*Elephas colombi*). Above comes (3) a superficial layer, likewise alluvial, but richer in organic matter (humus) and clearly separated from the two preceding ones. In excavating an irrigation canal through all these layers, the bone remains of two skeletons were discovered, at a depth of 2 ft. 6 ins. in the middle layer and at the base of the upper layer. The middle layer also yielded a blade of flint and some bones which seemed to be worked. The upper superficial layer is rich in shards of pottery and objects worked in bone or stone. According to Dr. Sellards, the contemporaneity of Man and a Pleistocene fauna in Florida is definitely established by these discoveries. The palaeontologist Hay entirely agrees with this opinion, while other specialists combat it more or less energetically.

This discussion has lost much of its significance now that we know that such a contemporaneity does not necessarily imply great antiquity on the part of Man, all the more so since the temperate climate of Florida would have enabled the great Pleistocene beasts to survive longer than elsewhere. But were the skeletons *in situ*? Hrdlicka was definitely negative on this point. He does not believe in the antiquity of the human bones. Chemical analysis shows that they are still rich in organic matter: the conditions of the deposit support the theory of burial far better than any other theory: and in their anatomical characters the bones do not differ from the bones of Indians. Hrdlička admits, however, that they may date from the early times of the Indian occupation of Florida.

[23] See in particular Sellards, E., 'The Vero Finds in the Light of Present Knowledge' (in *Early Man*, Philadelphia, 1937).

Hrdlička is no less emphatic about a very incomplete skull, found in 1923 near Melbourne, a small town to the north of Vero, in the same geological layer as the skeletons from this latter locality. The presence in its vicinity of arrowheads and pottery shows that it is a burial, says Hrdlička, who states that the skull belongs to a modern Indian of the type now native in Florida.

Certain facts, however, suggest that these judgments may be too severe. One of Hrdlička's chief arguments was that the Vero and Melbourne skulls exactly resemble those of the present-day Indians. Now, Stewart, who recently studied them afresh,[24] has established that the reconstruction of the Melbourne skull was very defective. Far from being brachycephalic, as Hrdlička believed, this skull is strongly dolichocephalic, and the Vero skull is almost the same shape. Both are thus completely different from the skulls of the Florida Indians: they belong to another, exceedingly archaic type, which this writer—as we shall see later—has found in other ancient or supposedly ancient deposits.

MINNESOTA MAN

In 1931 workmen digging up a road in the State of Minnesota, in the northern United States, brought to light a human skeleton from soil corresponding to an ancient Pleistocene lake, the 'glacial Pelican Lake'. It was only 27 inches from the surface, but if we take into account the earth removed during the building of the road this would be 10 feet below the original level. Professor Jenks has devoted a large memoir to it.[25]

To his mind there is no doubt about the skeleton's great age. Embedded in silts which filled up the lake, and already more or less mineralized, it belongs to an individual who fell or was thrown into the water. Now, the lake itself dates from the Glacial epoch. It was formed 15,000 to 20,000 years ago at the foot of the great Canadian glacier, at the moment when the latter was beginning to retreat towards the north. The skeleton must, therefore, be of Pleistocene age.

This skeleton, which lay on its left side with all its bones in anatomical connexion, was that of a young woman, not quite adult, and of small stature, about 5 ft. 1 in. It is incontestably a *Homo sapiens*, but Professor Jenks sees in it primitive characters. According to him it is 'a precocious Mongoloid type, in the process of evolution, and already displaying tendencies towards the contemporary Amerindians, especially the Eskimoes, rather than towards the peoples of Asia today'. It is a representative of one of the groups of hunters that had just arrived in America.

These conclusions have been disputed. No geologist was present at the extraction of the skeleton, and the fact that a gulley was found above the

[24] Stewart, D., 'A Re-examination of the Fossil Human Skeletal Remains from Melbourne, Florida, with further Data on the Vero Skull' (*Smithsonian Miscellaneous Collections*, CVI, No. 10, 1946).

[25] Jenks, A., *Pleistocene Man of Minnesota: a fossil Homo sapiens* (Minneapolis, 1937).

deposit suggests that it may have been simply a burial. This is quite certainly the case, according to Hrdlicka,[26] who points out that if the body had been immersed in a lake the anatomical connexions of the bones would not have been preserved, while the position of lying on the side is the one observed in the various Indian burials in the region. As regards the skeleton itself, the Washington anthropologist declares that he is unable to find in it the slightest primitive feature. In his view there is no doubt that it belongs to a Sioux, a group which lived in this district and whose physical type is particularly characteristic: a comparison of the Minnesota skull with those of Sioux women in the Washington Museum is conclusive in this respect.

The antiquity of the so-called Browns Valley skeleton, found two years later close to the site of 'Minnesota Man', appears to be equally dubious. It was interred in a gravel of Pleistocene age, but this gravel and with it the burial were covered by a thick layer of deposits to which E. Jenks, without any really convincing reason, attributed an age of 8,000 to 10,000 years; this would date the skeleton from the beginning of the Holocene Period. A few points found beside the skeleton are regarded by this writer as being derived from the Folsom points. The skull, which is dolichocephalic and exhibits marked superciliary ridges, is thought by him to belong to a primitive Mongol type. The Sauk Valley skeleton, discovered shortly afterwards in the same region, also represents an interment.[27] In the absence of any accurate geological or archaeological data, Jenks takes the fact that it exhibits more primitive characters than the Browns Valley skeleton as sufficient grounds to assert that it must be older. This argument is quite inadequate.

Other human remains have been unearthed in the United States during recent years, but always in dubious circumstances. Howells has described several skulls found in Wyoming.[28] In 1935[29] Figgins recorded the discovery a short distance from Folsom, at a depth of about 15 feet, of a skeleton of which he thought to make a special type, 'Homo Novus Mundus'. It was supposed to be the bearer of the Folsom culture. But this skeleton, which was embedded in an alluvial deposit of indeterminate age, displays, in the opinion of all who have examined it, the typical characters of the Indians of the South-West. It cannot be regarded as ancient.

The same attitude must be adopted towards a skull discovered the following year by Bowden and Lopatin near Los Angeles, California: no serious anthropological or stratigraphical argument has been advanced in favour of its antiquity.

[26] Hrdlička, A., 'The Minnesota Man' (*Amer. J. of Phys. Anthr.*, XXII, 1937).

[27] Bryan, K., Jenks, A., and others, 'The Sauk Valley Skeleton' (*Bull. of Texas Archaeological and Paleontological Soc.*, 1938).

[28] Howells, W., 'Crania from Wyoming resembling Minnesota Man' (*American Antiquity*, III, 1938).

[29] Figgins, J., 'New World Man' (*Colorado Museum of Nat. Hist.*, 1935).

TEPEXPAN MAN

The uncertainty surrounding all the foregoing discoveries explains the interest aroused by the finding, in 1947, of a fossil Man unearthed near the little township of Tepexpan, slightly to the north of Mexico City, in stratigraphic conditions declared this time to be indisputable:[30]

The human skeleton, exhumed by H. de Terra, was embedded at a depth of 4 feet in a deposit composed of foliated marls and silts corresponding to an ancient lake. This deposit was divided into two sections, one above the

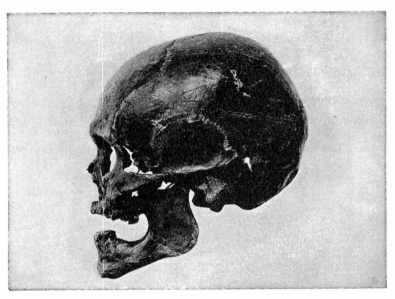

291 The Tepexpan Skull. View of the left side. About one-third natural size
(After J. Romero)

other, by a layer of calcareous nodules mixed with volcanic fragments formed during a phase when the lake was temporarily dried up. The skeleton was in the lower of these two sections, beneath the calcareous layer, the unbroken condition of which proved that the skeleton was *in situ* in the sediments. The same sediments elsewhere yielded remains of the Elephant, large Edentates and a Horse known to be Pleistocene. The Tepexpan Man was therefore contemporary with this extinct fauna.

De Terra endeavoured to obtain a more precise dating. By comparing the phenomena responsible for the ancient variations in the levels of the lake with data collected in the United States concerning climatic changes during the Pleistocene, he estimates that the human skeleton dates from the end of the Wisconsin Ice Age, that is to say from about 20,000 years before our

[30] Terra, H. de, Romero, J. and Stewart, D., 'Tepexpan Man' (*Viking Fund Publ. in Anthropology*, XI, 1949).

era. This is a very great age. Examination of the organic deposits contained in the nodule layer overlaying the skeleton by the Carbon 14 method gave a much lower figure—4,100 years. But the skeleton was underneath this layer, so that this is only a minimum age, certainly far less than the real age. The latter cannot, however, under these circumstances, exceed 8,000 to 10,000 years.

The bone remains were studied by J. Romero. They belong to a man of fairly tall stature and include a large mesocephalic skull with a lofty, rounded vault (Fig. 291). The superciliary arches are undeveloped. The face is broad with prominent cheek-bones and is not prognathous. The nasal aperture is rather wide and the teeth are extraordinarily worn. None of these characters is appreciably different from those of contemporary Indians. Indeed, the Tepexpan skull so closely resembles the male skulls of what is called the Archaic period of Mexico, and which dates from a few centuries before our era, that Romero declares that, if we did not know its stratigraphic origin, we should unhesitatingly attribute it to this period. In spite of the hopes it aroused, in spite of the exceptional guarantees it offers, the evidence afforded by the Tepexpan discovery therefore differs little from that furnished by more recent deposits.

CONCLUSIONS

Such is the picture, almost complete, though summary, of the facts brought forward in support of the existence of fossil Man in North America. As we have just seen, according to certain scientists the matter is proved, from the anthropological as well as from the archaeological point of view. According to others, not one of the facts adduced can be regarded as conclusive: all the osteological material must be attributed to the indigenous populations before the Conquest.

Between the exaggerated enthusiasm of the former and the excessive scepticism of the latter there is, however, rocm for an intermediate attitude. Since the earlier editions of this book, the discoveries made in the United States have been submitted to exhaustive examination; carefully checked excavations have been carried out; the problems raised by the Quaternary glaciations have been studied at length by geologists. A certain number of findings have resulted from all these investigations.

The first, and by no means the least, is that Man existed in America before the present period. The dressed stones found in the Trenton gravels already offered serious grounds for presuming his antiquity. The discovery of the Folsom and Sandia industries leave no further doubt about it: Man was present at the moment the last Ice Age ended. Archaeological, geological and palaeontological data agree in affirming this fact.

A second point, equally well established, is the contemporaneity of these early Americans with the great mammals then living in the plains of the West. They knew the Mammoth, the Mastodon, the Camel, the Horse and the large Edentates: they hunted them and fed upon them. But it must not

be supposed that this contact with a Pleistocene fauna places the advent of
Man beyond the last glaciation. It seems, in fact, to be proved that all these
great mammals lived on for a considerable time after this period. Their
coexistence with Man is no evidence that his antiquity was greater than is
indicated by archaeological findings.

The question of the human remains is more complicated. Many of the
skeletons unearthed are certainly not worthy of consideration: the conditions
under which they were obtained were not such as must be demanded for
finds of this importance. But there are others which seem to be ancient.
They have been disputed on the grounds that the human types to which
they belong appear to be the same as those observed among the Indians of
these territories, while many writers state that, according to the laws govern-
ing the general evolution of mammals, fossil Man must differ from living
Man.

Without absolutely condemning this view of the matter, we must recognize that it should not be carried to extremes. It is not necessary that Man
or any other creature, in order to be regarded as fossil, should no longer be
represented in living nature. This fact, indeed, is certain, that not the least
trace of a Man differing structurally from modern Man has been found in
America, and yet this should not surprise palaeontologists, who know very
well that America is not the land of origin of the higher Primates; but the
resemblance of the old skeletons already discovered to the skeletons of
Indians does not prove that these old skeletons date from Recent or Holocene
times. Do we not know that in Europe there are regions where certain
inhabitants have retained the features of Cro-Magnon and Chancelade Man,
who date from the last glaciation?

Besides, do these ancient skeletons so closely resemble those of living
Indians? One of the most constant characters of these Indians is the possession of a rounded, brachycephalic or strongly mesocephalic skull. Now,
the American anthropologist Stewart[31] has drawn attention to the fact that
the great majority of the 'prehistoric' skulls of America have a long, dolichocephalic or mildly mesocephalic skull. This is particularly true of the
subjects from Lansing, Pelican Lake, Browns Valley, Melbourne, Vero, the
two crania from Wyoming, and 'Homo Novus Mundus'. There seems,
therefore, to have been a primitive type with a long head, a type that is also
characterized by a lofty vault, very pronounced superciliary arches, a long
face, high-set orbits and a rather broad nose. This type cannot be considered identical with that of the great majority of Indians, and its frequency
in ancient deposits is certainly not due to chance.

There is no reason to be more exacting towards America than we are
towards our own continent. From the resemblances noted by United States
anthropologists we can only conclude that the 'ancient' skeletons of that
country do not belong to a period far removed from the Quaternary. But
some of them may be contemporary with the end of the Wisconsin. The

[31] In *Tepexpan Man* (1949).

conclusions furnished by a study of the human remains do not, therefore, contradict those reached through archaeology and stratigraphy.

The various orders of evidence therefore agree in showing that the peopling of America, while it is less recent than was at one time supposed, cannot date very far back in the Pleistocene. The most ancient traces of Man seem to go back to the closing period of this epoch, something like our Upper Palaeolithic, or like our transition period between Palaeolithic and Neolithic. This would mean 10,000 or 12,000 years, possibly 15,000 at the very most. On this hypothesis, the arrival of Man from Asia may be explained without difficulty. The Bering Strait is not deep, and a drop in the sea level of 120 feet would be enough to turn it into dry land. According to Daly's calculations, the level of the water fell 280 feet during the last glaciation. The investigations of geologists, on the other hand, have shown that as soon as the glaciers began to retreat they freed a corridor from the centre of Alaska, along the eastern edge of the Rocky Mountains, and down towards the centre of the North American plains: Man might have followed this corridor in pursuit of the great mammals he hunted. Was he at this time still at the stage of Dressed Stone? Hrdlička has pointed out that, if so, we ought to find deposits belonging to this period in Eastern Siberia. Perhaps the industries on the banks of the Angara and Lake Baikal, at Ulan-Khada and Rasputino, which, in their deepest levels, present certain biface points bearing a singular resemblance to those of ancient North American deposits, may provide the key to the problem when they are better known. Archaeological exploration of North-East Asia is still only in its infancy. We must wait and see.

However that may be, we must not expect to find in America fossil Men belonging to any other species than *Homo sapiens*, nor even races very different from those which today form the great Amerindian stock. At most we may encounter primitive forms of the latter. Thus the study of American fossil Man is not so much the concern of the palaeontologist proper as of the anthropologist. It is nonetheless of great interest, since it will bring us the solution to the great problem of the first peopling of America.

SOUTH AMERICA

GENERAL REMARKS

SOUTH America, with its very ancient Central Massif or Brazilian Plateau, with its immense river basins, with the Cordillera mountain range 5,000 miles long, beaconed and crowned by enormous active volcanoes, forms, from the physical point of view, a very special and highly autonomous continental unit.

This autonomy is no less marked from the point of view of living things. South America constitutes one of the chief biogeographical divisions of the globe, the *Neo-Tropical Region*. Its virgin forests and grassy plains show special plant associations extended over vast areas; it has also its particular forms of insects, fishes, and reptiles; it is the home of a multitude of birds of gorgeous plumage, such as humming-birds, parrots, cocks-of-the-rock, and so on. It is the almost exclusive home of the marmosets, of monkeys with prehensile tails, vampire bats, opossums, peccaries, llamas, and particularly of the edentates—ant-eaters, sloths, and armadilloes.

This special feature is a legacy of the past, a fact which we see confirmed when we retrace our steps through the geological ages. During Quaternary and Tertiary times, there were, besides enormous edentates such as *Megatherium* (Fig. 292), *Mylodon*, and *Glyptodon*, so amazing to the early palaeon-

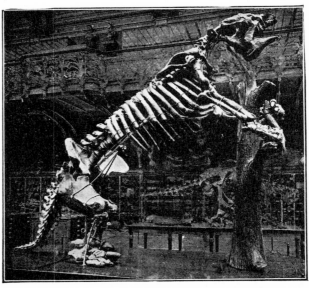

292 Skeleton of *Megatherium*. True height 12 feet. Palaeontological Gallery of the French National Museum of Natural History

tologists but in reality only giant forms of modern sloths[32] and armadilloes, a crowd of other mammals, so different from those of the northern hemisphere that special orders had to be created for them; such are *Typotherium*, *Toxodon*, *Macrauchenia*, and still earlier, *Astrapotherium*, *Pyrotherium* and others. On the other hand, there has never been found in the rich Tertiary fossil-bearing beds of Patagonia, the least trace of animals which could be likened to our proboscidians, artiodactyls, ruminants, perissodactyls, placentary carnivores and higher monkeys. Towards the end, during Pliocene and Pleistocene times, there were, however, mastodons, tapirs, horses, deer,

[32] It was the great French scientist Cuvier who recognized the true nature of *Megatherium* on examining a skeleton sent to Madrid in 1789. The King of Spain, Charles III, then ordered officials in the colony to send him one of these animals alive or at least stuffed. It goes without saying that the royal command went unfulfilled.

and large felines, but these were not native animals; they had come from elsewhere, mainly from North America. Albert Gaudry was able to state that, after the beginning of the Tertiary Era, the evolution of mammals did not proceed in these regions as in the northern hemisphere.

This is a fact of considerable importance from the point of view of the palaeontological history of Man. Since South America has always lacked highly developed Primates and higher Monkeys, we cannot expect to discover in this continent representatives of early Man or of his immediate ancestors. We shall see, however, that a naturalist of great merit, Ameghino, adopting exactly the opposite view, constructed a whole system of human genealogy.

South America was never buried beneath Quaternary ice-sheets. Even in the southern part of the continent they remained localized in the chain of the Andes or in the neighbouring regions. But the great climatic changes of the later geological periods have, none the less, played their part and left well-marked traces. First, there originated from the breaking down of the Cordillera range, and spread out around the base of the range, great deposits laid down by glacial rivers and torrents. These gradually merge into formations which cover all the lower portions of the continent with an immense coat of detritus: sands, clays, silts and so on, produced sometimes by streams, sometimes by the rushing waters of floods, sometimes by the aerial transport of volcanic cinders, or by temporary encroachments of the sea, and often by the combined action of these different factors.

THE PAMPAS FORMATIONS

The formations to which belong the Pampas deposits, very similar to our silts or loess, are of special interest to us since they have yielded the majority of the anthropological discoveries of which we must give an outline.

All these deposits are rich in fossils. Unfortunately, because of differences in the faunas, which have in this region a special character of their own, it is difficult to establish any time correlations or synchronisms with North America, and still more difficult to establish them with Europe. Palaeontologists were at first deeply impressed by the curious character and giant forms of the fossil animals discovered in the superficial deposits of South America, and, through remote analogy with Europe, they were led to regard these deposits as very ancient. This was the line followed by the Argentine scientist Ameghino. Nowadays the tendency is rather to regard them as more recent, and this is consistent with purely geological data. Many curious fossil beasts from the sub-soil of the Pampas may have lived up to a period relatively not far distant from our own times. In the case of some of them this seems even to have been proved, as we shall see directly.

The Pampas formations were at first regarded as a unitary mass. Then an attempt was made to divide them, based on the one hand on their physical characters, and on the other, on their palaeontological content. Some writers carried this division to excess. Nowadays we are content to make small numbers of divisions in the thickness of the Pampas formations, and there is general agreement in regarding them as ranging from the Pliocene to the present Period. Thus the superficial deposits of the Pampas may be divided into four stages, the characters of which are indicated below.[33]

Holocene or Recent	. . . .		*Post-Pampean*
Pleistocene	Pampean	Upper,	*Bonarean*
		Lower,	*Ensenadean*
Pliocene	Pre-Pampean	Upper,	*Chapadmalean*
		Lower,	*Hermosean*

Below these are to be found in Patagonia more ancient formations belonging to Miocene and Oligocene times.

The *Pre-Pampean*, which is localized in the coastal region, contains deposits of virtually the same structure as those of the overlying Pampean,

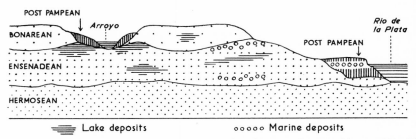

293 Diagrammatic section of the Pampas Formations between Buenos Aires and La Plata. (After Outes and Bruch)

from which they are separated by a very distinct erosion surface. The best known is the *Hermosean*, readily seen at Monte Hermoso near the Bay of Bahia Blanca, which is formed of sandy or clayey layers of a ginger-bread-brown colour. Ameghino regarded it, and with it the *Chapadmalean*, as Miocene. Most geologists attribute it to the end of the Pliocene.[34]

The true Pampas or *Pampean* deposit is superimposed upon the Hermosean, and almost everywhere forms the covering of the Argentine plain. Ameghino attributed it to the Pliocene, but there can be no doubt that it belongs to the Quaternary. It is essentially of terrestrial or sub-aerial origin, is warm brown in colour, and represents, with its calcareous concretions (*tosca*), a formation similar to our loess; but occasionally there are to be

[33] The bibliography is large and too specialized to be given here. The following may usefully be consulted: Outes and Bruch, *Los Aborigenes de la República Argentina* (Buenos Aires, 1910). Windhausen, A., *Geologia Argentina* (Buenos Aires, 1931). Frenguelli, J., 'El problema de la antigüedad del Hombre en la Argentina' (*Congrès Int. des Américanistes*, 25th Meeting, La Plata, 1932); *La serie geologica de la República Argentina en sus relaciones con la antigüedad del Hombre* (Buenos Aires, 1939).

[34] Simpson, G., 'Review of the Mammal-Bearing Tertiary of South America' (*Proc. Amer. Phil. Soc.*, LXXXIII, 1946).

observed fresh-water deposits, beds of volcanic ash, and, towards the shore, intercalated beds of marine sediments. It may be fairly easily divided into two stages.

The lower stage, or *Ensenadean*, is formed of plastic clays, compact, light brown in colour, containing calcareous concretions with concentric layers or branched. It is from 50 to 70 feet deep in the region of La Plata.

The upper or *Bonarean* stage is formed by a less compact unstratified clay, a true air-borne loess, of yellow colour, containing concretions of fantastic shapes ('fairy stones' or *'poupées'*). This portion of the Pampas formations is most easily observed, as it crops up everywhere from under the humus. It, likewise, sometimes attains a depth of 70 feet.

Above the Bonarean at some points are to be seen certain deposits which Ameghino regarded as still Pleistocene, but which may be correlated with the European Holocene, for they really represent modern times. They are sedimentary, grey in colour, formed in depressions of the soil, chiefly on the banks of water-courses. Some deposits show signs of slight encroachments of the sea; and there are also coastal dunes.

Palaeontology shows an imperceptible transition between the different stratigraphic series, from the Pliocene fauna of the Hermosean to the exclusively modern fauna of the Post-Pampean. It is during this period that we observe the progressive arrival of a certain number of North American mammals, while various forms peculiar to South America become extinct.

After these general statements, we may now enter upon our main subject; and continuing the method we have hitherto followed, we will first examine the archaeological discoveries and the discoveries of human bone-remains.

ARCHAEOLOGICAL EVIDENCES

The whole of South America is rich in archaeological relics. From the Antilles to Cape Horn, it is covered with ancient monuments, more or less imposing in character, or strewn with objects of all kinds indicating a long period of human occupation. Here, as in North America, it is very difficult to separate what relates to the native tribes at the time of the Conquest from what belongs to their distant ancestors.

We shall leave aside certain human settlements such as the *paraderos*, the sites of the villages and burial mounds of the ancient Patagonians, or the *samb aquis*, shell mounds and kitchen middens that have been found in large numbers on the shores of the Atlantic and the Pacific. All these relics of occupation are very much later in date than Pleistocene times: some of the *sambaquis* are still in the process of formation.

A deposit that occurs particularly frequently in the Pampean strata is a mingling of scoriae with hard red rock resembling brick or terracotta, which is found in many localities at all levels of the Pampean and even of the Hermosean. These pieces of baked earth, which are sometimes associated with burnt or striated bones, were held by Ameghino to be relics of ancient human hearths, witnessing to the presence of Man at an extremely early period. The Argentine palaeontologist devoted numerous articles to the defence of this theory.

Ameghino's view has been vigorously disputed. Enquiries by various geologists and mineralogists have not favoured it.[35] The extraordinary abundance and extent of these deposits and the regularity of their stratification are not at all in keeping with the hypothesis of a human origin. All these baked earth formations have exactly the same chemical composition as the Pampean silts, and they closely resemble the re-sorted volcanic products of the Central Massif. They are quite different in nature from what we find in the floors of occupation in Palaeolithic or Neolithic beds in the Old World. To whatever causes they may be due, human agency must be ruled out.

STONE RELICS

Speaking generally, stone objects are rare in the depths of geological layers more ancient than the Post-Pampean or recent deposits. And this is a significant fact, when we contrast it with the abundance of human bones exhumed from the same deposits. Outes[36] tells us that superficial layers containing stone implements of Palaeolithic manufacture are fairly numerous in Patagonia. Ameghino is said to have taken two dressed pieces of quartz from a rather deep bed in the gravels of the brook Observación (Fig. 294), a fact which justifies one in attributing to the Pleistocene (Upper Pampean) the generality of this industry, with its oval stones, dressed on both surfaces and greatly resembling those from Trenton in the United States. The objection may be made that the Pleistocene age of the gravels has not yet been proved, and that similar objects are numerous in Post-Pampean deposits.

In addition to these facts, there have been recorded a great number of isolated finds of quartzites and flints, apparently showing signs of deliberate dressing, and sometimes even of real implements, in the Upper Pampean, the Lower Pampean, and even in the Hermosean. All this proves little: either we are dealing merely with formless stones, split by natural agencies, or with simple flakes, or even with objects identical with those of the Indians. Nowhere has there been found *in situ* a collection of stone objects belonging to a settlement or factory.

Ameghino recorded an extremely primitive industry of 'broken stone, the simplest that could possibly be imagined' from the Lower Pampean and Hermosean. Examinations made on the spot by Hrdlicka and Willis showed that these pebbles were simply the waste products of manufacture left by

---

[35] Among the copious literature on this subject the following, in particular, may be read: Ameghino, F., 'Productos piricos de origen antrópico' (*Anales del Museo de Buenos Aires*, XIX, 1909); 'Énumération chronologique et critique des notices sur les terres cuites et les scories anthropologiques' (*Ibid.*, 1910). Outes, F., Ducloux, E. H. and Bucking, H., 'Estudio de las supuestas escorias y tierras cocidas. . .' (*Revista del Museo de La Plata*, XV, 1908). Hrdlička, A., *Early Man in South America* (Washington, 1912).

[36] Outes, F., 'La edad de la piedra en Patagonia' (*Anales del Museo de Buenos Aires*, 1905).

the Indians and more or less buried in recent sand-dunes. They were barely a century old! Ameghino also recorded facts of the same kind from much more ancient deposits dating, according to him, from the Oligocene and even from the Eocene. He claimed that they were rudimentary implements

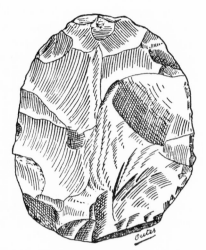

294 Dressed quartz from the Arroyo Observación. Four-fifths natural size. (After Outes)

manufactured and used by the small apes of these remote periods, the supposed ancestors of the human kind. These statements are not even worthy of discussion.[37]

BONES OF FOSSIL ANIMALS: USED, WORKED, OR CUT

The whole long series of bones, burnt, split, striated, engraved, polished, or dressed, which have been collected from the different levels of the Pampas formations, even from the Hermosean, and have been figured or described at length by Ameghino, do not seem to have any greater value as proof, and may in general be accounted natural objects.[38]

A certain number of observations have been advanced in support of the contemporaneity of Man with vanished species. About seventy years have passed since Ameghino and Roth spoke of the carapaces of glyptodons buried in an inclined or inverted position, which could only be explained by human intervention. We shall see that a human skeleton was found under one of the carapaces.

On several occasions there have been collected, in more or less close association with the bones of large extinct animals, such as *Glyptodon*,

[37] Ameghino, F., 'Une nouvelle industrie lithique' (*Anales del Museo de Buenos Aires*, XX, 1910).

[38] See Lehmann-Nitsche, R., 'Nouvelles recherches sur la formation pampéenne et l'Homme fossile de la République Argentine' (*Revista del Museo de La Plata*, XIV, 1907).

Mylodon, and *Toxodon*, stones which might have been used to slay them, or teeth of these fossils shaped as implements. The majority of these finds, chiefly due to Ameghino, are of doubtful value. One of them, which caused a great sensation, is, however, worth describing.

In 1914, Carlos Ameghino,[39] brother of the late palaeontologist, while exploring a Chapadmalean layer near Miramar, found a femur of *Toxodon* which retained, actually in the body of the bone at the level of the great trochanter, a quartzite point which must have transfixed it. This point of the modern form known as 'willow leaf', might have been the head of a lance used to attack the animal from behind. Shortly after, and not far from the spot of his first find, C. Ameghino and Dr. Keidel found a portion of the vertebral column of *Toxodon*, with two dressed quartzite arrow-heads embedded between the vertebrae. These discoveries were disputed. Reliable geologists affirmed[40] that the objects came from the upper beds, which formed the site of a *paradero* or ancient Indian settlement, and that they were found today in the Tertiary bed only as a consequence of disturbances and re-sortings which that bed had suffered. The archaeological data support this conclusion, for the same Tertiary bed yielded dressed and polished stones, *bolas* and *boleadoras*, identical with those used as missiles by the Indians. An excellent ethnographer, Boman,[41] recording these facts, wrote: 'The chief difficulty lies in this: without exception, all the objects exhumed from the Chapadmalean bed at Miramar are absolutely identical with similar objects found everywhere on the surface and in the upper beds of La Plata and Patagonia. Could it be possible, then, that Man lived in the Pampas, from the Miocene to the Spanish Conquest, without changing his habits and improving his primitive industry in any way whatsoever?'

The Miramar relics were, therefore, much less ancient than was first thought. But there remains the archaeological fact that arrow-heads were found embedded in the bones of *Toxodon*. Similar finds have been made since. Thus Castellanos[42] described hearths with the bone remains of animals —*Toxodon*, *Glyptodon*, *Macrauchenia*, *Equus*, etc., etc., intentionally broken and more or less burnt—from the Upper Pampean. We shall see later that two skeletons have been found in caves—one at Punin, the other at Confins—in levels containing the Horse, Camel and Mastodon. That Man was contemporaneous with the extinct South American beasts seems, therefore, to have been definitely proved. The discoveries made in the extreme south of Patagonia, which we shall now discuss, reveal identical facts.

[39] Ameghino, Carlos, 'El femur de Miramar' (*Anales del Museo de Buenos Aires*, XXVI, 1915). Articles in *Physis*, II and IV, etc.

[40] Romero, A., 'El *Homo pampaeus*' (*Anales de la Soc. científica Argentina*, LXXXVI, 1918).

[41] Boman, E., 'Encore l'Homme tertiaire dans l'Amérique du Sud' (*J. de la Soc. des Améri-canistes de Paris*, Vol. IX, 1914–1919).

[42] Castellanos, A., 'El Hombre prehistorico en la Provincia de Cordoba, Argentina' (*Rev. de la Sociedad 'Amigos de la Arqueologia'*, VII, 1934).

NEOMYLODON

About 1889, various explorers, including Ramon Lista, Moreno, Nord-jenskiöld and Hathal, found at Ultima Speranza, in a cave named *Ceuva Eberhard*, large shreds of skin full of ossicules and covered with the hair of an animal (Fig. 295) to which various names have been given (*Glossotherium* and *Grypotherium*), but which really seems to be the descendant of the *Mylodon* of former times, that is to say a *Neomylodon*.[43]

Even its excrement has been collected. All these remains are so well preserved that they can only have belonged to animals quite recently dead. They were associated with human bone-remains in a layer of 'manure' more than a yard thick, which led to the belief that *Neomylodon* was domesticated. Furthermore, the Indians have preserved in their legends the tradition of a great shaggy animal armed with strong claws, and contemporary hunters allege that they have seen and followed it in its nocturnal wanderings. If so, the monster may be still alive! One thing appears to be certain, that its bones bear traces of the hand of Man: 'It would seem that the

295 Piece of skin of *Neomylodon* with hair and dermic ossicules. Natural size. Palaeontology Gallery, French National Museum of Natural History.

animals had been killed by blows upon the head, dealt with large stones. They would then be cut up and eaten, and this would explain the very broken condition of their bones.'

The same cave yielded burnt bones and pieces of skin of a horse belonging to an extinct species, *Onohippidium*. Finally, Outes declares that in the neighbourhood of the river Salado and of the brook Tapalqué, the bones of a sort of Glyptodon (*Doedicurus*) and of the large Tiger, *Smilodon*, are found in a state of remarkable preservation.

Some of the foregoing facts were disputed. The investigations carried out by J. Bird, between 1932 and 1937, at the southern tip of South America produced still more telling arguments.[44]

[43] Hauthal, R., Roth, S., and Lehmann-Nitsche, R., 'El mamifero misterioso de la Patagonia' (*Revista del Museo de La Plata*, IX, 1899). Lehmann-Nitsche, R., 'Zur Vorgeschichte der Entdeckung von *Grypotherium*' (*Naturwissenschaftliche Abhandlungen*, Vol. 29, 1901). With bibliography.

[44] Bird, J., 'Antiquity and Migrations of the Early Inhabitants of Patagonia' (*Geographical Review*, XXVIII, 1938).

Bird excavated several caves. The chief of these, Fell Cave, contained deposits 8 ft. 3 ins. thick showing evidence of human occupation. Five archaeological levels have been recognized. The most recent yielded an industry identical with that of the Ona Indians now living in the region. The second level contained a different industry, with rounded stones or bolas, resembling that of the Patagonians. After the next two archaeological levels came a sterile stratum probably correlated with ancient seismic disturbances accompanied by volcanic eruptions. Beneath this a final layer presented an industry of archaic appearance, very different from that of all the recent Indians and vaguely reminiscent of the Sandia industry in North America. There were also hearths containing charred bones of the Horse, Guanaco and Mylodon.

Basing his opinion on certain geological phenomena, notably the existence of raised beaches, Bird attributed to the lowest level of Fell Cave an age of about 5,000 years. Using the Carbon 14 method on fragments of charcoal from the neighbouring cave of Palli-Aiké, which presents an identical association of fauna and virtually the same stratification, Libby and Arnold arrived at an age of 8,700 years. Thus Man, at this remote period, had already reached the Strait of Magellan and lived there side by side with an extinct fauna.

Such facts are in striking agreement with what we have noted for North America. Without in any real sense post-dating the Pampean formations, they show that the fauna of large Mammals found there may have persisted well into the Holocene period. Hence the contemporaneity of human remains or a human industry with this fauna does not necessarily imply that there were fossil Men here. This explains many of the facts which seem to be contradictory, and helps to reconcile to a certain extent the most divergent opinions.

HUMAN BONES:

LAGOA-SANTA

Almost all the palaeo anthropological discoveries in South America have been made either in caves in Brazil, or in the Pampas formations of the Argentine Republic.[45] We shall study them in order.[46]

Lund, a Danish naturalist, devoted forty-eight years of his life to the study of the fossil fauna of Brazil. He claimed to have explored more than 800 caves in the province of Minas Geraes. Between 1835 and 1844 he exhumed human bones from six of these caves. One of the caves, situated

---

[45] In this study we shall leave out of account two finds made respectively in a Cuban cave and near Cuzco in Peru. They both date from a period little earlier than the present epoch and are of no interest from the standpoint of human palaeontology.

[46] Hrdlička, A., 'Early Man in South America' (*Smithsonian Institution, Bureau of American Ethnology*, No. 52, Washington, 1912). In this work will be found the history and complete bibliography of all the discoveries, edited and critically reviewed with the collaboration of distinguished specialists, the archaeologist Holmes, the geologist Bailey Willis, and the mineralogists Wright and Fenner.

on the shore of Lake Sumidouro, near Lagoa-Santa, yielded the remains of about thirty individuals, young and old, lying mingled together with the bones of animals of living and extinct species. Lund at first regarded these discoveries as affording little proof of the contemporaneity of Man with the extinct species; the cave is subject to periodical flooding by the waters of the lake, which might have resulted in the intermingling of deposits, and furthermore really ancient layers, seemingly undisturbed, contained no human bones. He thought that the cave had served as a burial-place. Later, he became less hesitant. By 1844, he had become almost convinced: 'The occupation of South America by Man *probably* dates back to geological times.' An examination of the skulls enabled him to add: 'The race which then occupied this part of the world was already that which Europeans found here at the time of the discovery [of the continent].'[47]

With the exception of a skull left in the Historical and Geographical Institute of Rio de Janeiro, the greater part of the human remains collected by Lund were sent to Copenhagen, where they may still be seen. These relics have been examined by many anthropologists.[48] De Quatrefages[49] regarded the Sumidouro skull as the type of a particular race, the *Lagoa-Santa race*, clearly characterized by the shape of the head, which was both long and high. The present day Botocudos originate from this type, which also enters into the constitution of many of the South American peoples. Its presence was noted in the *sambaquis* of Brazil, and in the old cemeteries of Tierra del Fuego and of Patagonia (Verneau). It was again met with in Ecuador and even among the Indians of Lower California. It must have played a great part in the early peopling of South America.

Hansen thus summarizes the distinguishing features of the Lagoa-Santa type: thick, dolichocephalic skull, ovoid in shape and very highly vaulted; face short and prognathous, forehead exceptionally broad, nose and orbits medium. Seen in full face, the skull presents a characteristic pyramidal appearance, due to the widely separated zygomatic arches (Fig. 296).

According to Hrdlička, the presence of thirty individuals in a single bed seems to prove that it was a case of burial. But in spite of the special characters of these skulls he does not admit that they can be separated from the 'American race': they form one of the types of the latter, nothing more. The idea of a relationship with the Papuans was advanced by de Quatrefages. This is a purely theoretical conception without any serious anthropological foundation. It has been categorically refuted by American scientists.[50]

A skull found in 1923 at Punin, Ecuador, in a bed of volcanic origin

[47] Lund, P. W., 'Lettre à Rafn, March 28, 1884' (*Mém. de la Société royale des Antiquaires du Nord*, 1845). Reproduced in part in *Matériaux*, XVII, 1882–1883.

[48] In particular Hansen, S., 'Lagoa-Santa Racen' (*Museo Lundii*, I, Copenhagen, 1888). See also Poech, H., 'Beitrag zur Kenntnis von den fossilen Funde von Lagoa Santa und Fontezuelas' (*Mitteil. anthropol. Ges. in Wien*, LXVIII, 1938).

[49] Quatrefages, A. de, *Introduction a l'étude des races humaines* (Paris, 1887).

[50] See in particular Hrdlička, A., 'Melanesians and Australians and the Peopling of America' (*Smithsonian Miscellaneous Collections*, XCIV, No. 11, 1935).

again containing bones of the Horse, Camel and Mastodon, must surely be attributed to the same type.[51] Very dolichocephalic and with a low, prognathous face, this skull has been compared with the Australians. Despite certain differences, however, its general characters seem to be those of the Lagoa-Santa race.

It is also to the latter that we must ascribe a skeleton discovered in a new cavern in the province of Minas-Geraes, the Confins Cave. This skeleton,

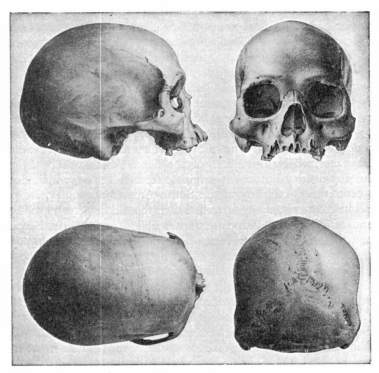

296 One of the human skulls from the Sumidouro Cave, seen in profile, full face, from above, and from behind. One-fourth natural size. (After S. Hansen)

8 ft. 3 ins. down beneath a stalagmitic floor, was embedded in a bone-bearing level which likewise included the Horse and Mastodon.[52]

All these facts show that a certain antiquity must be granted to the Lagoa-Santa race, whose importance as an ethnical stock is beyond doubt. This race lived in South America at a time when there existed in this continent a fauna which has today wholly vanished. By its anthropological characters

[51] Sullivan, L. and Hellman, M., 'The Punin Calvarium' (*Anthrop. Papers of the Amer. Mus. of Nat. Hist.*, XXIII, 1925).

[52] Walter, A., Cathoud, A. and Mattos, A., 'The Confins Man: A Contribution to the Study of Early Man in South America' (in *Early Man*, Philadelphia, 1937).

it perhaps belongs to the primitive dolichocephalic type whose existence we have noted among the most ancient inhabitants of North America. This would establish the first link in the chain showing the common origin of the most ancient human groups of the New World.

Discoveries in the Upper Pampean

Discoveries made in the Argentine Republic by different investigators are numerous, and still more numerous are the works published about these discoveries, particularly by Ameghino, Roth, Lehmann-Nitsche, Outes, Mochi, Hrdlička, and others. They have given rise to keen discussion and, on the part of the first of these scientists, were the subject of a theory of the origin of Man from minute Tertiary monkeys in Patagonia[53]—a theory which enjoyed a brief hour of celebrity, but which had no serious foundation and has long since fallen into oblivion.

The deposits of the Upper Pampean or *Bonarean* which, as we have said, spread over almost the whole surface, yielded numerous discoveries of human bones.

In 1864, a naturalist-traveller, Séguin, found on the banks of the Rio Carcaraña, to the north of Rosario, in the province of Santa-Fé, the remains of four skeletons which, together with a collection of fossil bones of animals from the same source, he sold to the Paris Museum. Gervais[54] described and figured nine separate human teeth and some dressed stones, identical, however, with those of Indians. This find is open to criticism. Its only real interest lies in the fact that it was the first of this kind to be made in the Argentine.

The succeeding discoveries, due to Ameghino, were made, in 1870 and 1873, in a terrace of the little valley of the Arroyo de Frias, near Mercedes. They consisted of human bones in a state of great deterioration, found in company with the remains of *Glyptodon*, and with pierced and incised bones of animals, dressed stones, charcoal, etc.

In 1876, Santiago Roth first observed a human skeleton at Saladero near Pergamino, in circumstances which suggest a burial. Five years later, in 1881, Carl Vogt[55] announced that Roth had just taken from deposits at Fontezuelas or Pontimela, near the Rio Arrecifes in the Province of Buenos Aires, an almost entire skeleton, of small stature, which lay under a well-preserved glyptodon carapace, or at least close by. The skull belongs to the Copenhagen Museum. S. Hansen attributes it to the Lagoa-Santa race, and declares that we cannot regard as absolutely proved the contemporaneity of the Man and the Glyptodon, as stated by Roth.[56] This opinion, shared by

[53] Ameghino, F., *La antigüedad del Hombre en el Plata* (2 vols., Paris, Buenos Aires, 1880–1881). See also Castellanos, A., *Homenaje a Florentino Ameghino* (Rosario, 1937).

[54] *Journal de Zoologie*, II, 1873.

[55] Vogt, C., *Bull. de la Soc. d'Anthrop. de Paris*, 1881.

[56] This account, both the original text and a French translation, is to be found in Lehmann-Nitsche's *Nouvelles recherches. . .*

Hrdlička, is not that of Lehmann-Nitsche, who believes in the antiquity of the Fontezuelas skeleton.

In 1889, Ameghino recorded the discovery, in the same region and in the same deposit, of a skull known as the Arrecifes skull. The circumstances of its deposit are insufficiently established; the skull, somewhat impregnated with mineral matter, is of the same type as the preceding.[57]

In the same year, Ameghino described the so-called Samborambón skeleton, found by a naturalist-traveller from the Museum of Buenos Aires in a lake deposit interbedded in the Pampean formations. At a higher level, the remains of a large fossil edentate, *Scelidotherium*, were collected. For no valid reason Kobelt named it *Homo pliocenicus*.

The skeleton from Chocori, described by Lehmann-Nitsche in 1907, was found nineteen years previously by an assistant from La Plata Museum, near the Arroyo Chocori on the Atlantic coast. The only point, and that not a definite one, favouring a certain degree of antiquity, is the presence of some calcareous incrustations.

Several series of human bones, collected from various places in the neighbourhood of Ovejero, in the province of Santiago del Estero, belong, according to Ameghino, to two distinct races, of which one is a pygmy race (4 ft. 3.2 ins. high) akin to the Negritos of Africa and Asia. From an examination made on the spot by Hrdlička and Willis, in the course of which the scientists themselves found another skeleton, it appears that these are burials of Indians whose descendants are still living in the same spots. The bone-remains do not represent two races, and do not in any way resemble the Negritos. The deposit which contained them is a windborne formation of recent date.

It was in the same spirit that Ameghino interpreted two finds made on the Atlantic shore of the province of Buenos Aires: the Villanueva skeleton, of which he made a new species to include the Samborambón skull—*Homo caputinclinatus*; and the skeletons from the Arroyo del Moro, which he attributed to the species *Homo sine mento*. None of these appellations has any value. The Villanueva skeleton is a child's skeleton artificially deformed; those from the Arroyo del Moro are the skeletons of Indian women with a chin that is weak but nevertheless present. Willis has shown that these skeletons are in every case recent.

Finally, a skeleton was discovered in 1919 at Speranza, a small hamlet some distance from Santa Fé on the banks of the Rio Salado. Although badly damaged, the skull, which is dolichocephalic like that from Fontezuelas, which it much resembles, shows the general characters of the Lagoa-Santa race.[58] The conditions of deposit are unfortunately not well established, and it is only on *a posteriori* data that it has been attributed to the Upper Pampean.

[57] A bibliography of this, and also of the following discoveries in the Pampas formations, will be found in the works of Lehmann-Nitsche and Hrdlička.

[58] Vignati, M., 'El Hombre fosil d'Esperanza' (*Notas preliminares del Museo de La Plata*, III, 1934).

THE LOWER PAMPEAN:

PROTHOMO

The Lower Pampean or *Ensenadean* is less rich in anthropological evidences, due evidently to the fact that its outcrops are much less extensive.

We must first record the skeleton exhumed by Roth in 1887, near Baradero, a locality on the Parana, about 80 miles upstream from Buenos Aires. This poorly preserved skeleton is in the Polytechnic School at Zurich. R. Martin finds that it does not differ from the skeletons of modern Man in South America. The fact that its various parts have retained their anatomical relations favour the theory of a burial.

Returning again to the Atlantic shore, we have to record the later discoveries which enabled Ameghino to establish still another new species of fossil Man, *Homo pampaeus*. There is first a skull found accidentally in 1888 near Arroyo de la Tigra, south of Miramar. Next there are three skulls, accompanied by other bones, which were lying at no great depth near Necochea, in a deposit regarded by Ameghino as belonging to the Lower Pampean (and therefore Pliocene). *Homo pampaeus*, characterized by a very low receding forehead, a character in which he differs greatly from *Homo sapiens*, was, according to Ameghino, a true *Prothomo*.

Examination of these relics by expert anthropologists, Lehmann-Nitsche, Mochi, and Hrdlička, revealed nothing of the sort. The skulls, artificially deformed after the fashion of recent Patagonian and Peruvian skulls, in other respects resemble those of Lagoa-Santa. They still contain much organic matter; their position in the layer rather indicates burials, and, according to Willis, these burials were carried out in a deposit of recent age, not Pampean at all. *Homo pampaeus* has never existed except in Ameghino's imagination.

There is no cause to attach any great importance to remains found near Miramar in deposits of Chapadmalean age, that is to say in the Pre-Pampean —a fragment of lower jaw unearthed in 1921[59] and two teeth discovered twenty years later.[60] Although Vignati considers these fragments the most ancient human remains yet discovered in South America, and although Castellanos subsequently created for them the designation *Homo chapadmalensis*, no proof has been put forward of their contemporaneity with the formations in which they were found.

DIPROTHOMO AND TETRAPROTHOMO

Ameghino's imagination created further forms, about which a few words will suffice.

In the course of work carried out in 1896 in the port of Buenos Aires,

[59] Boman, E., 'Los vestigios de industria umana encontrados en Miramar y attribuitos a la epoca terciaria' (*Rev. chilena de Hist. y Geog.*, XXXIX, 1921).

[60] Vignati, M., 'Descripción de los molares humanas fósiles de Miramar' (*Rev. Mus. de La Plata*, New Series, *Antropologia*, I, 1941).

the workmen found several human skulls. One of them, consisting of a portion of the vault only, was sent after a long delay to Ameghino. The deposit
from which it had been taken seemed to belong to the extreme base of the
Pampean, and would thus, according to Ameghino, date from the Lower
Pliocene. As to the bone fragment, it appeared to the Argentine palaeontologist's eyes so different from the types already known, that he saw in it the
representative, not only of a new species, but even of a new genus, which he
immediately made the ancestor of his *Prothomo* and consequently named
Diprothomo platensis.[61] He later artificially united an atlas bone, which had
long been exhibited in a glass-case in the La Plata Museum and was supposed
to have been taken from the cliff at Monte Hermoso (Miocene according to
Ameghino), with a small femur obtained from the same locality and made
of them a new genus, of Miocene age and the forerunner of his *Diprothomo
platensis*, which he called *Tetraprothomo argentinus*.[62]

All these conceptions are pure figments of the imagination. The skull-cap
of the alleged *Diprothomo*, the exact age of which cannot be ascertained,
possesses all the characters of modern Man. Numerous anthropologists[63]
have had no difficulty in proving this, and Schwalbe demonstrated that the
frontal bone of *Diprothomo* can be exactly superimposed on that of an inhabitant of Alsace! The Monte Hermoso atlas bone has no primitive characters, and Hrdlička was able to show that it falls completely within the limits
of variation to be observed in the atlas bones of modern Indians. As to the
femur, it could be attributed neither to a man nor even to an ape. It belongs
to a small mammal, very probably one of the Procyonidae.[64]

CONCLUSIONS

What conclusions may be drawn from the mass of facts we have described?
Ought we to believe in the presence in South America, during the Pleistocene
period, of fossil Men who preceded the living Indians and were in a way
their ancestors? No, is the decided reply of many scientists, notably, as we
have seen, of Hrdlička and his co-workers. According to them, nothing,
absolutely nothing, gives us any ground for affirming the existence of Fossil
Man in South America. There is no more proof of it here than in North
America.

There are serious reasons for this negative attitude. How can one but
be struck by the contrast between the abundance of human skeletons in the
Pampas formations and the poverty of the archaeological finds made *in*

[61] Ameghino, F., 'Le *Diprothomo platensis*' (*Anales de Museo de Buenos Aires*, XIX, 1909).

[62] Ameghino, F., 'Notas preliminares sobre el *Tetraprothomo argentinus*, un precursor del
Hombre' (*Ibid.*, XVI, 1908).

[63] See particularly: Mochi, A., 'Nota preventiva sul *Diprothomo*' (*Rev. de Museo de La
Plata*, XVII, 1910); 'Appunti sulla Palaeontologia argentina' (*Arch. per l'Antrop. e la Etnol.*,
XI, 1910).

[64] Bordas, A., 'La posición sistematica del *Tetraprothomo argentinus* Ameghino' (*Relaciones
Soc. Arg. Antropologia*, III, 1942).

situ in the same deposits? This is exactly contrary to the case in Europe, where true fossil bone remains are most rare in comparison with the innumerable archaeological relics. And how can one but be unfavourably impressed by the discovery that, apart from a few broken and splintered pebbles, and a few split or striated bones without any conclusive value, the industry of the alleged fossil Men is identical with that of modern Indians? Such a fact seems incompatible with our knowledge of those other regions of the globe which have been most thoroughly studied, and in which industrial evolution seems to follow a general law throughout the ages.

But, along with so many finds that are devoid of any real palaeontological value, it must be acknowledged that there are some among those of the last twenty to thirty years which have come to light under stratigraphic conditions that are to be taken seriously. These afford more reliable scientific facts and are vouched for by true scientists. They agree with the discoveries made during the same period in North America in showing that Man is an older inhabitant of the New World than many anthropologists believe, and that the peopling of America must be dated from at least the dawn of modern geological times. If there were no American fossil Men in the sense in which we understand the word, there were certainly 'sub-fossil' Men.

---- CHAPTER THIRTEEN ----

GENERAL CONCLUSIONS

We have just completed an inventory of the main contributions to knowledge made by human palaeontology and prehistoric archaeology. It is now our duty to summarize these facts and try to construct from them a provisional synthesis, so that we may see how far they illumine the great questions of the origin and evolution of Mankind.

MAN'S PLACE IN THE CLASSIFICATIONS

Naturalists, from Aristotle onwards, recognized at a very early stage that the human body showed great resemblances to the bodies of other mammals, and especially to those of the Apes; they had no hesitation in classifying Man along with the latter, while affirming that he is superior to all his fellows in the same zoological class, that he is premier amongst the Primates, that is to say, the very 'First of the First'.

Some scientists, it is true, regarding such company as humiliating, have desired, on the ground of the attributes of his intelligence and his religious nature, to place Man not only above but even quite apart from all other living beings, and create for the protection of his 'threatened dignity' the 'nebulous sphere' of a *Human Kingdom*. But it was easy to prove that nothing could be more irrational, and with Darwin one may say, that 'if Man had not been his own classifier, he would never have thought of founding a separate order for his own reception'. Even the less exclusive view of those who have confined themselves to making of Man a special type of zoological organization, parallel to those of the various orders of mammals, does not stand up to serious examination.[1]

With the progress of zoology and comparative anatomy, the morphological relationships between Man and the other Primates have become more accurately known. Buffon first taught us that, in his physical structure, Man differs less from the Anthropoid Apes than these differ from lower Monkeys. This view, clearly expressed by Huxley a century later, and renewed

[1] On this subject, see L. Vialleton's book *L'Origine des êtres vivants* (Paris, 1929), and the refutation of this writer's theory concerning Man's position in relation to the other vertebrates in R. Anthony's 'Une récente critique de l'évolutionnisme' (*Revue générale des Sciences*, XXXV, 1924). Also Westenhoefer, M., *Die Grundlagen meiner Theorie vom Eigenweg des Menschen* (Heidelberg, 1948).

and developed by Broca in his excellent work on *L'Ordre des Primates*, has since been confirmed by numerous investigations, bearing not only on the skeleton, but also on the soft parts of the Primates, their muscular and nervous systems, their sense organs, viscera, dentition, genital organs, spermatozoids, hair arrangement, papillary lines of the extremities, and so on.

It has become possible to estimate numerically the relative affinities of their various groups, and to establish a scale based on the number of human characters presented by each group. According to Keith, the Chimpanzee presents the greatest number of points of resemblance to Man. The Gorilla closely follows the Chimpanzee. According to some writers it is even closer to us. Then comes the Orang and after it the Gibbon, but at greater distance. The other Apes end the procession.

Embryological studies, contributing their share, accentuate these resemblances and show that many differences shown by adult men and apes are much less marked or may even be absent in the embryo.[2] Thus we are led to admit descent from common ancestors.

Other phenomena can be similarly explained only by admitting more or less direct genealogical relationships. There are, first, certain *anomalies*, that is, certain structural arrangements which are occasionally found in Man, but which are, in the normal course of things, present in related animals. At first regarded simply as curiosities, they now appear, in the light of the theory of evolution, to be marks of retrogression, or, to put it otherwise, atavistic characters, that is to say, abnormal relapses to an ancient state of things which was normal in the case of the common ancestors. These anomalies are countless, and concern all the organic systems; they have furnished anatomists with matter for many important works.

Such are the true 'rudimentary organs', structural arrangements which, normal and well-developed in other mammals where they fulfil a more or less important function, are reduced in Man to the point of becoming physiologically useless. The significance and importance of these rudimentary organs have been clearly brought out by Darwin. They furnish the strongest arguments that comparative anatomy, on its own authority, can bring forward in support of the transformist theory in general, and of the animal descent of Man in particular.

Physiology likewise contributes its evidence. There is now a science of comparative bio-chemistry, according to which each group of beings possesses a specific chemical constitution accompanying its specific morphology, and distinguishing it, like the latter, from neighbouring groups. The very striking experiments made in recent years by the method of serum precipitation by numerous physiologists have enabled an accurate estimation to be made, in

[2] To take only one example, such is the inter-maxillary bone, the existence of which in Man has for long been misunderstood, and which might pass for a distinctive character; but embryology shows it to be present, with its simian features, in the human embryo less than two and a half months old. It is hardly necessary to recall that, if adult Humans, and with them the Anthropoids, have no caudal appendix, their embryos possess one.

a marvellously delicate manner, of the degree of consanguinity between the different Primates. Even the curious phenomenon of so-called blood groups is found among the higher Apes. The relationship of Man with the Anthropoids, especially the Chimpanzee and Gorilla, has been confirmed. With other Monkeys of the Old World, such as the Macaque, his relationship is much less close and is still more distant with the Flat-Nosed (Platyrrhine) Monkeys of the New World.

Comparative pathology also testifies in the same sense: it is those creatures most closely akin to us, from the morphological point of view, which take our infectious illnesses with the greatest readiness.

So much for the physical or bodily aspect. There is yet the moral or spiritual side, the extreme importance of which cannot be doubted, and regarding which some explanation must be given.

Since psychology has lost its scholastic character and become scientific, that is to say physiological, the great barrier it sought to erect between Man and 'the beasts' has indeed been demolished. It can no longer be maintained that the mental faculties are essentially different in the various kinds of living beings. They exhibit only differences of degree, and their mechanism is everywhere the same. We now speak of 'comparative psychology', 'animal psychology', and even of 'cellular psychology' in a way which would have startled the majority of the professors of philosophy who prepared young people of past generations for their Arts degrees. Most interesting books on the origin of intelligence, on the psychic life of animals, and on mental evolution have appeared. We can observe the progressive development of psychical phenomena in each of the great zoological groups, and this development takes place parallel with that of the nervous centres, the real psychic machinery. We can see a continuous chain of phenomena, from the first manifestations of a vague consciousness to the most complicated mental operations.

Just as the human brain is much larger than the brain of the highest Anthropoid so human intelligence is greatly superior to that of the Ape, yet all the manifestations of the former are to be found, merely in less degree, in the latter. And these differences become still less when our comparison is made between the most intelligent of modern apes and children of two to four years old. The researches of experimental psychology carried out during recent years[3] have shown the existence in the large Anthropoids, especially in the Chimpanzee, of a whole series of intellectual processes that might

[3] These studies, which have been carried a very long way, were made in laboratories in which apes lived under conditions as closely as possible resembling their natural state. The most important are those of Yerkes and his pupils at Yale University in the U.S.A. Those of Köhler at Teneriffe and of Kohts at the Darwinian Institute, Moscow, must also be mentioned. The results obtained went far beyond what had been expected and are of much greater value than the acts due merely to training observed in apes exhibited in circuses. See Koehler, W., *The Mentality of Apes. . .* Trans. E. Winter (2nd Ed., London, 1927). Yerkes, R. and A., *The Great Apes* (New York, 1929). A good review of the problem is contained in Guillaume, P., 'La psychologie des Singes' in Dumas's *Nouveau Traité de Psychologie*, Vol. VIII, Paris, 1941).

have been thought peculiar to Man. They really possess an intelligence related to our own, capable of distinguishing the possible from the impossible, perceiving the external world in terms of aspects and relationships that resemble the human world, able to employ implements whose use poses geometrical and mechanical problems which it succeeds in solving, and so on. The Anthropoids' principal inferiority in comparison with ourselves consists, according to Guillaume, in the relatively limited development of their memory and imagination; but this is a difference of degree, not of kind, and it now seems certain that human reason is not a special creation, that it made no sudden appearance, but came gradually into being. Here again, in the kingdom of the spirit, as well as in the kingdom of the body, the close ancestral relationship between Man and the other Primates reappears.

It has not gone so far as an articulate language, though the rudiments of such are to be found amongst many animals, particularly amongst birds, which are capable of associating certain sounds, that is to say certain vocal signs, with certain acts or objects. And in the case of our neighbours, the Monkeys, the constitution of their brain, larynx, genio-glossal and genio-hyoid muscles is such that it may be safely affirmed that very little more is necessary, from the organic point of view, to secure the exercise of a function whose origin in ourselves must probably be ascribed to the extraordinary development of our imaginative life, and which was gradually perfected according to a mechanism which physiologists and linguists are now beginning to understand and reconstruct. It was animal intelligence that prepared the way for the birth of language, and it is language that has made possible the wonderful development of the human intelligence.

To sum up, the facts relating to modern Primates which have been acquired by the different branches of biology, may be expressed thus:

1. Man is a Primate, the highest of the Primates. He is much more akin to the Anthropoid Apes than the latter are to other Monkeys.

2. The individual development of Man shows that his various systems and organs pass through transitory phases corresponding, if not to the final stage of lower animal forms, at least to one of the embryonic stages of these forms (ontogeny repeats the stages of phylogeny).

3. The *anomalies* of his various anatomical systems are very often reappearances of morphological features of these lower types, and many *organs* called *rudimentary* can only be explained by the theory of evolution; they represent relics of ancestral states.

4. Man is much superior to the highest apes in the size and organization of his brain. As a result, the highest physiological product of this brain, that is intelligence, is likewise much higher in Man. But the difference is only one of degree and not of kind. We may say, paraphrasing and completing the sentence with which Darwin ends his admirable work on *The Descent of Man*, that Man still retains, in his spirit as well as in his body, the indelible seal of his lowly origin.

Embryologists have sought to go still further; they have made an attempt to reconstruct the different stages of evolution in Man, on the basis of the parallel between ontogeny and phylogeny. Haeckel made himself notorious by the daring with which he launched upon and followed this course, which led to the production of his *Anthropogenia*. But such an attempt was more than foolhardy. The investigations of embryologists have shown that the individual development of living beings presents numerous modifications as compared with the probable stages of their phyletic evolution. We see in ontogeny the repetition of certain embryonic or adult phases of the ancestors, but there is certainly no parallelism in the strict meaning of the word.[4] Moreover, palaeontologists know, from the genealogical history of other zoological groups, how easy it is to err in attempting such reconstructions in the absence of sufficient material evidences.

Further it must be noted that opinions expressed on the subject have themselves been very diverse. First, on the question of our knowledge as to whether Man's origin be single or multiple: as to whether the genus *Homo* comprises only one species originating from a single ancestral form, or whether it comprises several species each one of which must have had its particular line of descent.[5] And, secondly, on the degree of relationship which exists between the human branch, whatever may be its degree of ramification, and the other branches of the great stem of the Primates.[6]

Differences of opinion even among equally expert scientists are very considerable. They evidently show that, in respect to the establishment of human genealogy, as in respect to everything relating to the evolution of organized beings in general, the last word must lie with palaeontology when that science is in a position to give a clear pronouncement. The finest anatomical studies, the most detailed comparisons, the most subtle, the most ingenious theories of the structure of living creatures, cannot have the conclusive value of relics extracted from the rock where they were deposited and embedded in their actual chronological order. Such evidences from a new kind of archive, such anatomical specimens, preserved for thousands or hundreds of thousands of years, represent in concrete, tangible, and measurable forms the transitory stages, the different links of a chain uniting a

[4] On this subject, see Vialleton, L., *Un problème de l'évolution. La théorie de la récapitulation des formes ancestrale au cours de l'évolution embryonnaire* (Montpellier, 1908). Beer, G. de, *Embryologie et évolution* (Paris, 1933); *Embryos and Ancestors* (London, 1951).

[5] This theory is known as polyphyletism. It has been advanced on various occasions and its principal advocates during the last thirty or forty years were G. Sergi, H. Klaatsch and G. Sera. The arguments on which it rests are inadequate from the standpoint both of palaeontology and anthropology. See Vallois, H., 'Y a-t-il plusieurs souches humaines?' (*Revue générale des Sciences*, XXXVII, 1927); 'Les preuves anatomiques de l'origine monophylétique de l'Homme' (*L'Anthropologie*, XXXIX, 1929).

[6] Is it still worth while mentioning that the idea of a direct genealogical relationship between Man and modern Apes has long since been abandoned, if indeed such an idea was ever entertained, by all true naturalists? It is now found only among writers totally ignorant of science, or in the sermons of a few country curates. But, of necessity, a common origin must be attributed to Apes and Man. Differences of opinion are confined only to modes of regarding the branching of the human stem.

series of organized types, the extreme terms of which appear at first sight to be, and indeed are, so very different.

The discovery of the remains and the study of ancestral fossil forms constitute the precise end of palaeontology, and particularly, in the present case, of human palaeontology. It cannot be too often repeated that *the origin of Man is a problem the solution of which can only be expected from palaeontology*. The prime importance of the study of fossils and the advantages to be derived from it are made evident by the fine results which have crowned the science of animal palaeontology.

THE ORIGIN OF MAN

It is true, as we have seen, that anthropology owes a great deal to zoology, but it must be confessed that the latter science shows Man's place in Nature in a false light, since it presents him as a creature almost isolated among the Primates, in the same fashion as, though in a less degree than, the Horse among Perissodactyles, the Elephant among Proboscidians, the Camel among Ruminants, and so on. Since Palaeontology has broken down the isolation of these animals by relating them to others through intermediate forms, and by discovering their genealogy from generalized forms, there was reason to hope that it would also break down, or at least likewise diminish the isolation of Man, and that it would also enable us to discover the main evolutionary stages in human genealogy. Have these hopes been realized?

Towards the end of last century, the naturalist-philosophers who studied the mystery of human origins derived little help from the study of fossils. Relics of the kind were too rare and too incomplete: only a few remains of Apes closely akin to living species, a larger number of human remains which revealed no difference of importance from modern Man, and only one human brain-box which, indeed, showed a few simian characters, but the antiquity of which was questioned, as well as its very nature, for by some it was regarded as normal and by others as pathological.

Since then our palaeontological knowledge has increased. But even now does it reveal to us the principal evolutionary stages of the human branch? To reply to this question, we must first recall the conclusions reached in the chapter in this book dealing with fossil Monkeys.

First we have seen the order of the Primates take its rise, like all the other orders of mammals, at the commencement of the Tertiary Era. The zoological group to which Man belongs is not, then, the slow and splendid crowning of a unique, and indeed imaginary, series in the whole range of the mammals. In the Lower Eocene its early representatives break away from a crowd of related creatures, which, however, themselves show tendencies towards other orders of mammals. It is not, as was long believed, because they are, taken as a whole, the most intelligent of the mammals that the Primates necessarily appeared latest. Their early differentiation, which took place in a particular direction, dates as far back into the past as the early differentiations, in different directions, of the Pachyderms, Ruminants, Perissodactyls,

Carnivores, and so on. And this fact is of the greatest interest from the point of view of a philosophy of nature.

We have next seen the representatives of the different modern groups succeed each other in chronological order, in an order conforming to their places in the animal kingdom: first the Lemurs, then the tailed Monkeys followed by the Anthropoids. Unfortunately, the scarcity and the fragmentary state of the palaeontological relics have not allowed, so far, of a comparative study sufficiently detailed to determine the ties of relationship which link together the various fossil Apes. Certain preliminary indications on this point have, however, been gained. It would seem that the different branches of the tree of the Primates had very ancient origins, that they began to differentiate early, at least from Oligocene times. *Propliopithecus* from Fayum may be taken as a generalized type of Anthropoid, related to, if not in very truth, that synthetic form which theory demands should be placed at the base of the branch of the Great Apes, and from which present-day Gibbons seem to descend almost directly, through the intermediary of the Miocene *Pliopithecus*.

While tailed Monkeys in their various kinds increase till they spread over vast areas of the Old World, the anthropoid branch in its turn split into several branchlets, at first so close to one another as to be difficult to distinguish, judging by the few fragments we possess, and then becoming more and more distinct and increasing so as to produce, on the one hand, forms which are manifestly the ancestors of modern types, and, on the other, special forms, sometimes greatly differentiated and very large, which have died out without leaving any descendants. The relative frequency of their remains in the fossil-bearing deposits of Uganda and the Siwalik Hills leads us to believe that East Africa and Southern Asia were, if not the sole centres, at least two of the chief centres of habitation, of multiplication, and of differentiation of those ancient anthropoids, some of which show affinities with modern Orangs, others with the Gorilla-Chimpanzee group, whilst others again represent independent and extinct forms.

In this complex, certain forms, both in Africa and Asia, are noteworthy for certain peculiar features which suggest a resemblance to the human group. But the resemblance abruptly becomes much greater when we pass to the Australopithecinae of South Africa, which possess a characteristic previously considered absolutely peculiar to Man—upright carriage. But for the probably recent geological age of these Primates, they could be placed in our direct line of descent. It may be seen that, in spite of the relatively limited number of fossil Anthropoids known, and in spite of their extremely fragmentary state, it has been possible to draw up a table of relationships. If we do not know those which were at the very root of our family tree, at least we may observe in certain fossil forms an indisputable tendency towards human structure, a tendency which, in one group, almost reaches actual humanity, and this observation is of tremendous interest.

The discovery of *Pithecanthropus* and *Sinanthropus* provided no less cogent data. These two fossils, in fact, possess characters which fall so curiously in between those of the Hominians and those of the Anthropoids that they have been regarded by turns as belonging to the former of these two groups, to the latter, or to an intermediate group. We now know that they must be classed with the first, of which they represent if not the ancestral type, at least a form very close to this type. The name Prehominians marks their position from this point of view. The Australopithecinae of South Africa greatly lessen the morphological gap separating living Apes from living Men. The Prehominians fill another part of what remains.

The history of fossil Man helps in the same way to show a closer relationship between the human and the simian branches. Although it is but in its first youth, human palaeontology has already made noteworthy progress. We now know at least two types of fossil Man which, on account of their osteological characters, clearly take their place at a lower level than modern types, and which exhibit a combination of structural features separating them less markedly from the Apes than from the generality of modern Men.

There is first the Heidelberg Man, *Homo heidelbergensis*, who dates from the dawn of Quaternary times. His lower jaw, the only relic known to us, exhibits an extraordinary mixture of human and simian characters. Had only the teeth of this jaw been found, they would certainly have been attributed to a man not differing, in any important character, from certain races of *Homo sapiens*. If, by some accident, the jaw had been found without its teeth, there would have been no hesitation in making it the type of a new genus of Anthropoid Ape. This example of the miscarriage of Cuvier's famous law of the correlation of characters is particularly instructive, since it relates to a palaeontological relic representing, in an almost ideal way, a form intermediate between the structure of an ape and of a human being. Unfortunately, these remarks refer only to the merest fragment of the skeleton. When the day comes for the discovery of a complete skull or limb-bones, palaeontologists will be called upon to make investigations and verifications of the greatest interest, perhaps with results entirely unforeseen.

The so-called *Homo dawsoni* was held to represent a second extremely primitive type, not because of his skull, which seemed hardly different from the skull of a modern Man, but because of his lower jaw with its exceedingly simian characters. We now know that it is devoid of all palaeontological value. But other fossils have been brought to light which, in spite of their very great age, have a skull curiously similar to that of modern Man. We have designated these various forms by the name *Presapiens*. Whatever their position in relation to modern Man, there is little doubt that it is at least very close to the stock which gave birth to the latter.

Further, and most important of all, there is Neandertal Man, *Homo neandertalensis*, descended perhaps from Heidelberg Man, perhaps from an unknown and still more archaic form. We know a great deal about his structure. We know that, in the organization of his skeleton and of his brain, he combined not only the majority of the various simian characters distributed among certain representatives of modern Man, but also several features of inferiority unknown in the latter.

Human Beings, the Hominians or Hominids, have always been regarded as forming a family or an order, or even a class or separate kingdom, placed much higher in the scale than the other Primates. Up to the present time this group of high degree corresponded to the genus *Homo* alone, and this genus itself comprised, in the opinion of many anthropologists, only the single species *Homo sapiens*.

Palaeontological discoveries have lessened the distance separating Man from the animals most closely related to him, and in so doing have lessened the isolation in which some have always been inclined to place him. This isolation, which was looked upon as not the least of his attributes, seemed to augment his greatness and nobility in the eyes of those who regarded him from a religious or metaphysical point of view.

At the present day, apart from the new genera formed by the Prehominians *Pithecanthropus* and *Sinanthropus*, there has been created the genus *Palaeoanthropus* for the Heidelberg jaw, while the Neandertal type likewise, according to several naturalists, represents a special genus. In any case, it is difficult to deny nowadays that there may have been several species of the genus *Homo* and that *Homo heidelbergensis* and *Homo neandertalensis* may not be very distinct from the main mass of *Homo sapiens*, fossil or living.

This conclusion should not be surprising to naturalists who, believing in the theory of evolution, cannot refuse to apply it to all living beings, to Man as well as to his neighbours the apes and other mammals. But it is not theory that we are dealing with here. These are facts of conclusive value. Palaeontology contributes new *concrete* data to the natural history of the human zoological group, and these data clearly show that the evolution of this group proceeded in the same way as the evolution of other groups of mammals.

The origin of Mankind must be relegated to a much more distant geological past than was long supposed. General palaeontology hints as much, for the problem of the origins of the different forms of life is much oftener relegated than solved. Human palaeontology teaches us, moreover, that as early as Lower Pleistocene times there existed other human types than those of Heidelberg and Neandertal, and that these types already in striking degree resembled *Homo sapiens*. These fossil types perhaps represent the direct ancestors of modern Man; from times so remote they have formed an individual branch of which the European *Homo neandertalensis* represents the now withered end.

The fact that Neandertal Man existed at the same time as the ancestors of certain types of *Homo sapiens*, and the additional fact that, at least in Europe he seems to have become extinct without leaving any posterity, agree with what is tending to become a palaeontological law, namely that the development of creatures is not accomplished as simply as was believed in the early days of the science; that unilateral series appear to us as more and more rare; that, if they exist, it is extremely difficult to discover them or trace them for any distance.

Each grouping of beings related to one another in the generality of their structural characters, whether it be a family, a generic, or a specific group, may be compared to a tree or a bush more or less branched, of which each branch, branchlet, or twig represents either a genus, a species, or a race. The development of each of these offshoots has been more or less vigorous, its duration more or less long. Modern forms are only the flores-cence, the latest blossomings of certain terminal twigs, the majority of which are dead and fossilized.

The human group is no exception. At an early stage it must have divided into several branches, which must have borne branchlets, and these in their turn twigs. In terms of the polygenist theory, it might be said that several of these branchlets or twigs have survived up to the present period; according to the monogenist theory, it is claimed that the mass of *Homo sapiens*, with its various races, forms but one single branchlet. Yet even a few years ago we did not know, and it was palaeontology that taught us, that side by side with these branchlets which are still vigorous and full of sap, the human branch formerly gave rise to branchlets which are now withered, and of which we are just beginning to discover the fossilized blooms in the depths of the geological layers.

So the original stock of the Hominids must plunge its roots deep into a much more ancient past than was supposed, *a priori*, and there is no doubt that a being, already in possession of some of the physical if not even the psychical attributes of Man, must have existed somewhere during the Pliocene period. But did this being already deserve the name of Man? And have we the right to speak of a 'Tertiary Man'? We have seen that none of the concrete discoveries brought forward as evidence of his existence is conclusive and that, moreover, it is most often impossible to distinguish stones splintered, dressed and 'retouched' by purely physical forces from certain products of deliberate but rudimentary manufacture. We have like-wise seen that no discovery of bones made in an alleged Tertiary deposit has yet been able to withstand criticism, a point on which, it must be acknow-ledged, everyone is virtually agreed. To carry conviction in such a case, the evidence ought to be absolutely demonstrative. Now, up to the present day, no solid proof of the existence of a human being in our regions before the dawn of Quaternary times has been brought forward. We may doubt whether it ever will be.

GENEALOGICAL RELATIONSHIPS

So far we have singled out for consideration only certain intermediate structural forms. Can we, in the present state of our knowledge, form a reasonable and accurate opinion regarding the palaeontological origin of the human group? Or to put it otherwise: What genealogical relationships can we establish between the human branch and the other branches and trunk of the tree of the Primates? Replies to this new question are not lacking, but, from all that has previously been said, it is not difficult to foresee that they must be hesitating and incomplete.

Of late years, several naturalists have drawn up 'genealogical trees' of the Primates, living and fossil, according to their morphological and chronological relationships. We would mention in particular the attempts of Gregory, Keith, Pilgrim, Abel, Le Gros Clark, Schultz, Hooton, and R. Gates. A

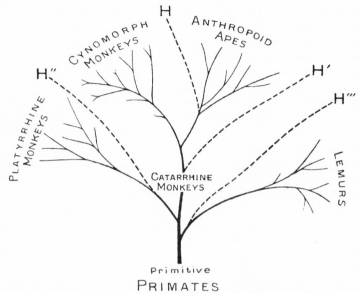

297 Diagram showing the different theories of the genealogical relationships of Mankind with the other groups of the Primates. For explanation see text

comparison of their diagrams is calculated to increase, if possible, our caution, for between the various diagrams there are great, sometimes even fundamental differences. The human group is shown as having relationships so different that the wisest plan is to conclude that this group is still 'in the air', and that we do not know exactly the place where the human branch should be inserted among the branches or twigs round about it. The more authors, the more theories.[7]

[7] See particularly: Miller, G., 'Conflicting Views on the Problem of Man's Ancestry' (*Amer. J. of Phys. Anthrop.*, III, 1920). Gregory, W., 'Studies on the Evolution of the Primates' (*Bull. Amer. Museum Nat. Hist.*, XXXV, 1916). Giuffrida-Ruggeri, V., *Su l'origine dell'-Uomo*, (Bologna, 1921). Mendes Correa, A., *Homo: Os modernos estudos sobre a origem do Homen* (Coimbra, 1926). Elliot Smith, G., *The Evoluion of Man* (London, 1927). Wood Jones, F., *Man's Place among the Mammals* (London, 1929). Abel, O., *Die Stellung des Menschen im Rahmen der Wirbeltiere* (Jena, 1931). Weinert, H., *Ursprung der Menschheit* (Stuttgart, 1932). Arambourg, C., *La genèse de l'humanité* (Paris, 1943). Hooton, E., *Up from the Ape* (2nd. Ed, New York, 1947). Keith, A., *A New Theory of Human Evolution* (London, 1948). Gates, R., *Human Ancestry* (Cambridge, 1948). Straus, Jr., W., 'The Riddle of Man's Ancestry' (*Quarterly Review of Biology*, XXIV, 1949).

Together with Gaudry, Dubois, Schlossen, Schwalbe, Osborn, Pilgrim, Weinert, Abel, Elliot Smith, Arambourg, Keith, Gregory, Schultz and others, the majority of naturalists would place Men in close relationship with the Anthropoids, both together forming a common branch, which has long been distinct from the neighbouring branch of the tailed Monkeys (Fig. 297, H.). We know that Darwin and Haeckel regarded the human group as forming an autonomous branch, early detached from the mother branch of the Catarrhinians or Dog-Faced Monkeys (Fig. 297, H'.) Carl Vogt, Ameghino, Aëby, and Sera preferred to attach it to the older branch of the Platyrrhinians or Flat-Nosed Monkeys (H''). Cope wished to place it still lower, at the level of the most ancient of the Primates, the Lemurs (H'''), and the anatomists Hubrecht and Wood-Jones do not hesitate to regard the curious monkey, Tarsius, as the living animal most akin to Man.

Each of these theories has been supported by good arguments, for the arguments are based on more or less common generalized structural features, which give a marked unity to the whole primate group. According as the stress is laid on one or other special character, insistence on a particular comparison becomes necessary.

Morphology and physiology, including physiological psychology, obviously support the first theory and are strongly reinforced by recent facts in biochemistry.[8] But there is room for discrimination.

Some anthropologists have felt that the human branch could even be placed inside the Anthropoid group. Either they attached it more directly to certain of these Apes, like Pilgrim, who accepts a common origin for Man and the Gibbon, or Schultz and Weinert, who trace Man, the Chimpanzee and the Gorilla back to the same stock; or else they associate the various types of Quaternary Man with particular genera of modern Anthropoids, like Klaatsch, who imagined a group which he called the 'Orang-Men of Aurignac', along with another group, the 'Gorilla-Men of Neandertal'. All these notions are extremely dubious. They take account of certain points of resemblance, but ignore the manifest unity of the Anthropoids and their overall difference from ourselves, and must therefore be dismissed.

Of greater interest are the views of the many naturalists who, while attaching the human group to the anthropoid group so as to form a single whole, clearly separate the human branch from the neighbouring branch of the Great Apes, and only attribute to them a very distant common origin (dating from the Pliocene or even Miocene) from which they must have diverged. This is the view most easily vindicated, and we have seen that, to the weight of anatomical arguments in its favour, may be added the biochemical argument, the value of which is apparently undeniable.

This view is, however, open to serious objections, and we may wonder if

[8] It would, however, be important to know whether we cannot accept the existence of convergence phenomena of biochemical characters, analogous to the convergence phenomena of a morphological order. There is no reason why a similar morphological evolution in two different groups should not be accompanied by a parallel evolution of phenomena ascribable to biochemistry. It seems that naturalists have not given their attention to this point.

it would not be reasonable to reconcile it with the second theory, that of a more ancient origin, starting from the great Catarrhinian stock. For this purpose it would be enough to admit that the anthropoid form leading up to Man very early became separated from the neighbouring forms leading up to modern Anthropoid Apes; that its point of insertion on the ancestral parent-branch of the Catarrhine Monkeys was independent of the points of insertion of those other forms which led by evolution to the fossil or modern types of Anthropoid Apes.

Zoologists who are specialists in the comparative anatomy of the Primates, have long since observed that many human characters cannot be explained by direct descent from one single stock of large Apes. 'It would be necessary to merge in one', said Carl Vogt, long ago,[9] 'the anthropoid characters of the *three* Anthropoid Apes and *even of several other Monkeys*, to obtain the combination from which Man could have descended.' This is the view which palaeontology seems to confirm.

A study of Neandertal Man, especially of the skeleton of his limbs, show that, in many osteological characters, it is easier to associate this fossil Man with lower Monkeys than with the various forms of living Anthropoids. Without encountering too serious difficulties, then, we may place the insertion point of the human branch upon the branch of the Dog-Faced Catarrhinians, at a lower level than the starting-point of the anthropoid branch.

It would perhaps be wiser, without going so far as the Lemurs, as Cope proposes, to descend still lower, even to the common stem of the Monkeys. Palaeontology, indeed, teaches us that the various types of modern Monkeys are very ancient, and that the independence of each of the groups massed about these types has been acquired at a very early period.[10] The same must have been the case with the human group, the ancestral forms of which must have possessed, from the catarrhinian stage and perhaps even from the platyrrhinian stage, certain features of organization different from those of neighbouring types; and the progressive development of these forms must have attained to a quite distinct anthropoid stage, the actual forerunner of the prehuman and human stages. The recent discoveries at Fayum to a certain extent confirm this view, for *Propliopithecus* seems to present a mixture of characters both very archaic and yet specialized in the direction of a higher evolution.

Palaeontology and zoological palaeogeography also teach us that if our very remote ancestors must have passed through a Platyrrhinian stage, at least as regards their dental formula, it would be impossible to maintain now, like Aëby and Ameghino, that the human branch only represents an exceptional development of certain elements of the Platyrrhinian branch. From

---

[9] *Congrès internat. d'Anthrop. et d'Archéol. préhist.*, 2nd Meeting, Paris, 1867, p. 442.

[10] Do we not find, even in the Lower Eocene, that quite small-sized Primates, *Anaptomorphus* for example, exhibit the main characters of the modern Tarsius, remarkable for the development of its brain-pan, its shortened face, its combination of lemurian and simian features, and even for some human characters?

Upper Eocene or Oligocene times, the latter have been confined to South America; there they developed and diverged, but their progressive evolution seems to have stopped at an early stage.

These preliminary conclusions are not purely imaginary conceptions; they are scientific theories, having the advantage of being based on palaeontological observations, or of being in agreement with these observations.

We must not deceive ourselves, however. We are still far from knowing accurately the main stages of the human line, from its commencement with the original lowly forms. If the various phases leading from the Prehominians to modern Man are now apparent to us in general outline, it is so far impossible to establish a progressive series, based on concrete evidences, as has already been done for many mammals, such as the Horse, the Elephant, the Bear, and others.

It is very probable that our most distant ancestors early became distinguished from the mass of other Primates by certain characters, which we may describe as fundamental, characters which already exhibited a tendency towards human superiority and by which these distant ancestors are recognizable. But it is only by slow degrees that the relationship can be established and traced with certainty. The solution of the problem of our origin and especially the accurate determination of the different elements in our descent, demands fresh discoveries of fossils, and indeed of many fossils.

We must confess then, however damaging the confession may be to our pride, that we are still too ignorant to give a direct answer to Huxley's 'supreme question', or to solve in full the perplexing problem of our origin. And this ignorance, we cannot refrain from repeating, is due to the great blanks in our palaeontological evidence, those blanks which Darwin deplored, which made the old Gaudry say that palaeontology was at once splendid and poverty-stricken, and which can be filled in only with painful slowness. The discoveries of recent years, however, give us the right to place great faith in a future perhaps not far distant.

It must be recognized, indeed, that science has made real progress since the last discoveries of human palaeontology were made. Alongside of all that we are yet ignorant of, we must place all that we have already learned, all that we have securely laid hold of.

The human type is no longer isolated. We know that there have been several species, and probably several genera of the human kind, and that these ancient Hominians were structurally much lower in type than living Men; that they exhibited numerous characters in which they were less distantly related than we are to the other Primates, particularly to the highest representatives of these, the Anthropoid Apes. Between the latter and Humans properly so-called we now know two new groups, the Australopithecine group and the Prehominian group, the characters of which are in almost every feature intermediate between those of Man and of the living Great Apes. In our museums we possess actual remains of all these extinct forms. Before these discoveries were made, such intermediate forms were only imaginary or theoretical.

We know that there was a human *branch*, and that this branch was divided into many more branchlets than had been supposed; the human branch now assumes in our eyes the same character as the other branches of the Primates or of other groups of mammals. Its evolution, as we are now beginning to perceive, in every way resembles the evolution of these groups. The science of palaeontology is one and the same, whether it concerns itself with Men or with animals.

So much then we know today, with certain knowledge. It is, indeed, little in comparison with what still remains to be learned; but it is a great deal in comparison with our former ignorance, or our very imperfect knowledge of not so long ago.

THE BIRTHPLACE OF MANKIND

The unsatisfactory nature of palaeontological evidence still makes it difficult to decide exactly in what countries the human kind originated.[11] The first idea to occur quite naturally to the minds of anthropologists, was that the present habitat of the races which we call 'primitive' must be regarded as their place of origin; and hence arose an extraordinary number of 'centres of creation' or 'appearance'. This was the convenient solution, naturally suggested by such adherents of the polygenistic theory as Agassiz. But de Quatrefages rightly pointed out that this *initial* cosmopolitanism was opposed to the general facts of zoological distribution. It is also contrary to our present understanding of the conditions and causes of the migrations of mammals in general, as palaeontology has revealed them. Although various authors have recently sought to restore this view to favour in a modified form,[12] it cannot be regarded as more than a mere speculative hypothesis.

Next there have been suggested in turn the northern countries, the central massif of Asia, Central or Southern Europe, intertropical regions, Africa, South America, the Antarctic continent, and Australia. These propositions are, for the most part, mere conjectures. It is likely that this new problem is also much more difficult and more complex than we suppose; that the immediate ancestors of the human kind, or the first of the human beings, were often displaced in the course of their long evolution corresponding to geological ages the vicissitudes of which, along with the other mammals, they must have kept pace with and endured. The main fact which palaeontology seems to have firmly established is that, starting from very primitive stages, the lemurian and platyrrhinian stages, the evolution of the group which potentially comprised the human branch did not take place either in North America, whence all Primates seem to have disappeared since the Upper Eocene, nor in South America, where the platyrrhinian branch has

[11] On this subject, see Vallois, H., 'Le berceau de l'humanité' (*Scientia*, 1946).

[12] This is Rosa's theory of ologenesis. See Rosa, D., *L'ologénèse. Nouvelle théorie de l'évolution et de la distribution géographique des êtres vivants* (Paris, 1931).

dominated exclusively. It is therefore in the Ancient Continent that we must seek our 'cradle'. Mankind is a product of the Old World.

Does the present state of our knowledge enable us to make a more definite statement? The part played by Asia, and especially by Southern Asia, must have been considerable. The Siwalik fossils show that in that region, about the Upper Miocene and Lower Pliocene Periods, there was a most extraordinary flux of life, especially among the higher Primates. In view of the number and diversity of form of the great fossil Apes already described, the impression arises that, at this time, Asia was the laboratory where the differentiation of the ancestors of Mankind must have been in process of elaboration. And India appears more and more to have been a very old centre of prehistoric culture.

The American palaeontologist Matthew,[13] in a very suggestive memoir, stated the reasons which led him to believe that the centre of dispersal of Mankind should be placed farther to the north, towards the great Central Asian Plateau. This theory was revived and developed by Black.[14] It is based on the fact that the geographical distribution of the various groups of Lemurs, Apes—Cynomorphs and Anthropomorphs—and Men show that they are orientated around Central Asia. The palaeographic distribution of the Primates, during Eocene and Oligocene as well as Miocene and Pliocene times, presents exactly the same situation (Fig. 298). Such a phenomenon, which, moreover, is repeated as regards other groups of mammals, is only to be understood if the forms in question radiated from the centre of Asia.

This region of the continent underwent great seismic disturbances in the course of the Tertiary Era. At the beginning of the latter, the Himalayas did not exist. The site of these mountains was occupied by a depression, to the south of which extended the ancient plateau of Gondwana. To the north it was bordered by a vast pre-Tibetan plain, a well watered region at a moderate altitude and washed on the west by the prolongation of the primitive Mediterranean. This ancient equivalent of Tibet had long enjoyed a climate favourable to the development of a terrestrial fauna, and this is where the first Primates are thought to have lived.

During the Miocene Period, climatic conditions in this region were changed by the upheaval of the Himalayas and the Tibetan plateau together with the retreat of the sea. The temperature of Central Asia, originally warm and humid and subtropical in character, became colder and drier and temperate. This change had an effect on the autochthonous fauna. It seems that at this period the pre-human stock was already separated from that of the Anthropoid Apes, which had themselves been differentiated from the Cynomorphs since the end of the Eocene.

[13] Matthew, W. D., 'Climate and Evolution' (*Annals of the New York Acad. of Science,* XXIV, 1915).

[14] Black, D., 'Asia and the Dispersal of Primates' (*Bull. of the Geol. Soc. of China,* IV, 1925). See also Griffith Taylor's curious book, *Environment, Race and Migration* (Toronto, 1937).

In order to keep to a favourable environment, the ancestors of the Anthropoids are thought to have emigrated towards the Siwalik Hills and gradually reached their present habitats. Man's ancestors, being more progressive and perhaps endowed with a mental capacity that enabled them to adapt themselves better to the new environmental conditions, stayed where they were and continued to become further differentiated. The evolution of the prehuman stock therefore took place in the region corresponding to what is

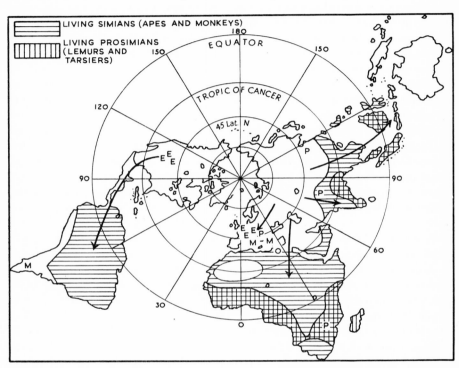

298 Geographical distribution of living and fossil Primates. (After W. Matthew, modified)

E, Lemurs and Eocene Tarsiers; O, Oligocene Simians; M. Miocene Simians; P, Pliocene and Quaternary Simians

now Tibet. It was from here, under the pressure of new generations, that successive human groups are supposed to have diverged in a series of concentric waves.

One proof of these phenomena is seen in the fact, which has frequently been pointed out, that the living human races regarded as the most primitive are found in regions farthest from this centre: the Australians, Andamans, Veddahs, Negritos, African Negrillos, Bushmen, and the Fuegians in the extreme south of South America. It may also be remarked that, whereas Africa, America and Europe shelter only one or two of the great basic races, Asia is at the crossroads of all of them: the White, Black and Yellow races live there side by side, and in a manner of speaking they are centred upon the Pamiro-Tibetan region like so many outflows diverging from a single centre of formation.

The hypothesis of Matthew and Black is based on engaging arguments, but is manifestly no more than a hypothesis. De Terra has recently noted[15] that a certain number of facts of a geological and palaeontological order contradict the idea that Man might have been born in Central Asia, and that his evolution is more likely to have taken place somewhere on the periphery of India. But other writers are not even certain that the scene of the ultimate transformation from the pre-human anthropoid stage into the human stage was in the continent of Asia at all. The discovery of the great Miocene Apes of Kenya and of the Australopithecinae has led some palaeontologists to return to the old view held by Darwin that not Asia, but Africa, a continent in which climatic conditions have changed little since the Tertiary Era, was the cradle of Mankind.

Possibly, too, this cradle was less localized than we suppose. Maybe we ought to think, with Mendes Corrêa, of the whole Afro-Asian shore of the Indian Ocean, the area which the Portuguese anthropologist calls the 'Indian anthropo-phyletic arc'. Perhaps this is part of some continent now buried beneath the ocean waves. The answer to this fascinating problem is still far from having been discovered.

THE DIFFERENTIATION OF HUMAN TYPES

Prehistoric anthropology is still too poor in osteological evidences to be able to reconstruct the genealogies and migrations of the human beings who have peopled the different continents, starting from the centre of development and dispersal of the genus *Homo*. The rare skeletons of our most distant ancestors which we possess have been exhumed from the soil of Western Europe. Now this region, we cannot too often repeat, is but an advanced point of Eurasia, a sort of cul-de-sac, into which successive waves of many human tides have broken; it is in no respect a continental centre where, any more for Man than for the other mammals, we may watch the scene of an unbroken evolution.

The great antiquity of the Heidelberg jaw obliges us to admit a still more unbelievable antiquity for the first representatives of Mankind, and this view agrees with those geological observations which lead to the belief that certain layers in India containing dressed flints perhaps date from the Tertiary Era. It is impossible to relate Heidelberg Man to one of the great human types, from which it entirely differs, judging at least from the jaw-bone, the only relic of it we possess. We are obliged to make of it a special species, the ins and outs of which so far we do not know, but which is still very simian.

Countless centuries separate Heidelberg Man from Neandertal Man, for geology and palaeontology teach us that the archaeological periods called by

[15] Terra, H. de, 'Geology and Climatology as Factors of Human Evolution in Asia' (*Studies in Physical Anthropology*, No. 1: *Early Man in the Far East*, 1949).

prehistorians Pre-Chellean, Chellean, and Acheulean correspond to a long series of physical and biological events, and, in consequence, to an immense lapse of time—much greater than that of all the more recent archaeological periods added together.

The distribution of amygdaloid implements and related forms extends not only in the direction of Europe; it occurs also over the whole of Africa, as well as in Asia, Australia and America, and this presupposes a past of vast duration, provided we admit the single origin of these primitive industries rather than the spontaneous and independent origin in every continent, a possible but improbable occurrence. The suggestion has been made that this origin was African, but the antiquity of dressed stones in India is perhaps as great as that of the oldest artefacts in Africa, and the Indian Archipelago has yielded extremely ancient implements. All we can say at present is that America and Australia are ruled out; for the time being, this is as far as we can go.

As regards the Men who manufactured these implements, we know little or nothing about their bodily structure. This long period corresponds to one of the biggest gaps in human palaeontology.

On the other hand, we have good grounds for affirming that Neandertal Man, the successor in Western Europe of these Men, is still an isolated type compared with the various representatives of modern Mankind. Perhaps he is descended from Heidelberg Man, perhaps he represents a new type, entirely different from those of the warm fauna, a type which may have come to us from the North with the glaciers and the cold fauna which accompanied him. In any case, he represents a peculiar species, the terminal bloom of a twig, now withered and dead, of the human branch.

In spite of their fragmentary nature, the discoveries at Swanscombe and Fontéchevade suggest that there lived in Europe alongside Neandertal Man, and no doubt also before him, other primitive forms, more human than the Neandertalians in some of their characters, more archaic in others. Are these, perhaps, the forms that gave birth to modern Man? At all events, there can be no doubt that the origins of the latter go back to a still more distant past.

Only when we come to the Upper Pleistocene, the Reindeer Age, relatively much less distant in time, can we affirm, positively and indisputably, that there existed on our soil human forms higher in every respect and now readily comparable to living types in various parts of the globe. And it is interesting to observe that even if these Men, grouped around the type known as 'Cro-Magnon', are already Whites, they occasionally exhibit many points of resemblance, on the one hand, with the Yellow, and on the other with the Black races.

The differentiation of human types was, then, already far advanced before the end of Quaternary times, but this differentiation was less complete than it is today; we can still observe the existence, among the Men of this period, of various synthetic characters. Evidences collected by prehistoric anthropology enable us, very imperfectly it is true, to follow the progress of this differentiation under manifold influences, first of a physical and geographical and later of a political kind, and to see it result in the extraordinary medley of ethnical groups which correspond to prehistoric, protohistoric, and modern times.

Sparse and fragmentary as they are, our European evidences may be looked upon as rich compared with those of the other great regions of the earth's surface. And no attempt at synthesis, even of a rudimentary kind, can be essayed until Asia and Africa reveal some of the secrets they now withhold.

In the former of these continents the discoveries of human palaeontology have greatly increased during recent years. They have shown us the existence of very primitive types, still simian in many of their characters and constituting in many aspects of their structure those intermediate forms between ourselves and the Great Apes that were so long sought in vain. Our knowledge of these Prehominians is still very incomplete. Thanks to them, however, the veil is beginning to lift on the beings which immediately preceded true Men in the evolution of the Primates.

On the other hand, we know that Neandertal Man existed in Asia as he did in Europe, and no doubt he lived there at the same period as in our own continent. But there he no longer appears in isolation; some of his forms are linked with the Prehominians, others with the Men of the Upper Palaeolithic. Thus, whereas the Neandertal Man of Europe occupies the position of a type apart, of whose origin we are ignorant and which seems, according to all the evidence, to have vanished without issue, the little we know about this type in Asia shows it as included within a regular evolutionary sequence. The significance of this extinct species thus appears in a new light.

Finally we know that, in the Upper Pleistocene, Asia presented forms comparable to living types but, as in Europe, possessing a certain synthetic character. Thus there is a visible parallel between the two continents, and it may be that, when we have a more detailed knowledge of the fossil Men in both of them, we shall find that the fundamental events in the evolution of Mankind took place in Asia, and that what we see in Europe is only the outcome of modifications brought about on the neighbouring continent.

The facts are less clear as regards Africa. The discovery of the Australopithecinae, however, confronts us with a fact of capital importance which is, in a way, the counterpart of what the Prehominians show us: namely, the existence of fossil Anthropoids that are already human in certain of their characters. It seems, on the other hand, that in this continent too there lived Prehominians which were succeeded by Neandertal Men, the last of whom, in a very specialized form, persisted down to a period very close to the present. In the Upper Palaeolithic, Men resembling modern Man appeared all over the continent—in North Africa, in the Sahara, and in East and South Africa. With these forms we are already in the presence of distinctly African types, but still possessing that synthetic character which the first representatives of *Homo sapiens* seems to have had in every continent.

Can we form an overall picture from these relics, so few in number, so scattered, so widely separated from each other? Any hypothesis on this subject is still very rash. Nevertheless, a comparison between archaeological and anthropological facts leaves one with the impression that successive human waves covered the surface of the earth one after the other.

Throughout most of the Old World, we see a first great layer, remarkably uniform, which corresponds to the Chellean and Acheulean industries. But we know little or nothing about the Men of this epoch, of whom the only remains that have come down to us are those of Heidelberg Man. As may be seen, they amount to very little.

The industry which in Europe we call Mousterian represents a second wave. We know its author: Neandertal Man, an extinct species whose area of distribution appears larger and larger as our knowledge increases. Long vanished from our continent, this species seems to have persisted much longer in other parts of the world, notably in South Africa. Certain living peoples, localized in peripheral regions, appear to have retained some of its characteristics, for example the Fuegians, Veddahs, Australians, Melanesians and Korannas.

A third archaeological layer extends everywhere above the foregoing. It corresponds to our Upper Palaeolithic. The Men who produced it were now *Homo sapiens*, and we can recognize among them the first signs of the great races which we distinguish today. The differentiation of Mankind into its principal types had, therefore, already begun, and the geographical distribution of these types was becoming established.

First with the Mesolithic, and then with the Neolithic, new waves succeeded the earlier ones, associated with more diversified human groups that were close to those of today and constituted true Yellow, Black and White races, and so on. This brings us to the dawn of modern times, from which we are separated by only a tiny interval from the standpoint of palaeontology.

Thus Mankind appears immensely old. And its development is bound up with a great series of events whose major lines are beginning to emerge, but whose exact sequence we cannot yet establish in all its extraordinary anthropological and archaeological complexity.

INTELLECTUAL EVOLUTION

Our knowledge of the physical evolution of Mankind is still very rudimentary; and here care must be taken to distinguish physical evolution from moral and intellectual evolution. The study of the latter is rather more advanced, owing to the vast accumulation of facts revealed by prehistoric archaeology in every country. In this case also, however, only partial or regional syntheses can be attempted. As J. de Morgan[16] has said, 'The unfortunate thing is that the majority [of countries] where the first civilizations developed present conditions which make research there particularly difficult.'

[16] Morgan, J. de, *Les premières civilisations* (Paris, 1900), p. 39. See also the same author's *L'Humanité préhistorique* (Paris, 1921).

In Western Europe, which is specially favoured in this respect, it is possible to trace a general and fairly accurate picture, at least so far as the foreground is concerned, that is to say so far as concerns the prehistoric ages which lie nearest to us. Thus, away beyond the times corresponding to the ancient history of historians, which is in reality only ultra-modern history to the prehistorian and even more so to the palaeontologist, we are fairly well acquainted with the habits of Neolithic Man and of the Men of the Reindeer Age.

Their intellectual and moral development and their culture can be readily compared with the state of certain peoples still living, or but lately living, in more or less pronounced conditions of savagery. Parallels can be drawn even in a great number of details relative to their psychic and moral life as well as to their material life. A whole series of ethnographical facts clearly reveals the same mentality and the same level of intellectual development. Mankind in the Reindeer Age of Europe was already a superior Mankind essentially resembling modern Mankind, and endowed with the same intelligence, the same inventive genius, and the same sentiments.

Our Mousterian Men, much more ancient, lived in a state more primitive in every respect. Nevertheless it is possible to compare them, if not from the physical aspect, at least from the moral point of view, with some specially retrograde peoples in certain parts of the globe, which lead a life extraordinarily like that which *Homo neandertalensis* must have led. Already, in spite of the structural inferiority of his brain, the latter is a Man, a *Homo*, and in no sense a pre-Man, for accompanying his skeleton lie in confusion the stone implements which he knew how to make, along with charcoal and cinders from the hearth-fires he knew how to light and feed. Already his methods are those of certain modern savages. And were naturalists, abandoning their general methods, to give prominence to intellectual characters in classifying the creatures they study, there would be no occasion to separate *Homo neandertalensis* from Modern Man in a specific sense, although, as we have seen, we cannot refuse him this distinction on account of his physical characters.

We know very little of the ethnography of the peoples who for so long a time, in the Acheulean and Chellean periods, occupied our own land and a great part of the surface of the globe. We can, however, affirm that they also were true Men, in the full sense of the word, in habit as well as in physique; for with selected materials, they knew how to make implements, indeed very fine implements; already an aesthetic feeling accompanied their spirit of invention, for the elegant shapes of the Saint-Acheul flints represent an initial quest for art. They knew how to make fire, that distinctive human accomplishment which lay at the foundation of all future progress, which contained the potentiality of all civilization, and the discovery of which 'constitutes the most characteristic act of genius of which Mankind can boast'.[17]

[17] Rémy de Gourmont, *Promenades philosophiques* (2nd Series, 1908) p. 11.

Indeed, the invention of primitive implements and the production of fire result from intellectual qualities as marvellous as the greatest modern inventions they made possible of achievement. And in this respect we cannot but admit Rémy de Gourmont's law of the intellectual constant and, up to a certain point, the doctrine of 'psychic unity' held by certain philosophic anthropologists.

Heidelberg Man, although in comparison with Neandertal Man he was only a very distant forerunner, undoubtedly already spoke an articulate language and knew how to light a fire and dress flints, so that he already represented Bergson's *Homo faber*.[18]

Can the same be said of *Sinanthropus* and *Pithecanthropus*? As we have seen, this is still an open question. Here we are probably very close to a cardinal point in the evolution of Mankind: the moment when the pre-human Anthropoid, attaining at a single bound the dignity of the human status for which his physical and mental evolution had prepared him, on the one hand learned how to kindle a fire, and on the other, passed from the habit of using rude stones to the manufacture of an implement. But how are we ever to fix such a moment?[19]

Regarding the invention of fire, we have only very vague ideas. The oldest archaeological cave deposits, beds in which only Acheulean and even Chellean industries are represented, already contain pieces of charred wood and cinders. But we are not sure that certain still more ancient deposits, likewise attributed by prehistorians to their Chellean or pre-Chellean, do not afford similar evidences. The invention of the first implements constitutes a problem of which the scientific explanation may still perhaps be long delayed, for reasons we have explained in connexion with the fascinating 'eolith' theory.

The Progress of Mankind

Such it seems, are the principal conclusions to be drawn at the present time from our knowledge of human palaeontology. The day will come when much more abundant material, collected from all parts, will make the history of early Man less obscure and less discontinuous. At the present moment, it is possible to state that the human group is more branched and more diversified than had been supposed, and that the evolution of this group obeyed the biological laws regulating all creatures, from the lowliest to the highest.

Already certain writers have been able to disentangle, from the mass of historical facts, certain causes of a general character, independent of and dominating the more artificial factors. Dimly they have perceived the link between

[18] 'Were we able to divest ourselves of all pride; were we, in order to define our species, to adhere strictly to what history and prehistory show to be the constant characteristic of Man and of intelligence, perhaps we should not say *Homo sapiens*, but *Homo faber*' (Bergson, H., *L'évolution créatrice*, 22nd Ed., 1920, p. 151).

[19] On this subject, the reader may consult the audacious book by E. Le Roy, *Les origines humaines et l'évolution de l'intelligence* (Paris, 1931). See also Teilhard de Chardin, P., *Le groupe zoologique humain, structure et directions évolutives* (Paris, 1950).

human history and natural history, the close relations between the laws of empire and those of organized beings. As Edgar Quinet in particular remarked: 'There are points in common between the revolutions of the globe and the revolutions of the human kind, as if they both belonged to one single plan which unfolds from age to age. . . All the elementary laws of Palaeontology are to be found and can be verified over great fields in the history of human society. Words change, but the principle remains the same in fossil nature and in the world of Mankind.'[20]

In showing that Mankind has steadily progressed during the few thousands of years which it records, history has taught us that this progressive evolution is not effected in a continuous manner, that is to say, it is not brought about by the whole of Mankind acting simultaneously or at the same points, but by various and successive groups acting in different countries. From history we have likewise learnt that the purely ethnographical groups have, like the more natural groups, only a limited duration of life; that they are born, grow, and die, and that often, if not always, their final decline follows very soon after the climax of their development has been reached. Such disappearances, however, do not entail the stoppage of the progressive movement of Mankind as a whole. The movement is renewed by other groups, which have hitherto remained in the background, and which, taking advantage of the results acquired by their predecessors, develop more or less rapidly, and in their turn add riches to the common intellectual treasure, before succumbing like the rest. The general perfection of the Human Race, in historic times, may be represented as the sum total of the partial advances made through the repetition of this kind of cycle.

This succession of relays in time and space, which, once again, confirms the great solidarity of Mankind (a familiar idea in history), is not peculiar to history alone. Human palaeontology teaches us that it acted in the same manner in prehistoric and even in geological times. It is only a special aspect of the mechanism of evolution which general palaeontology reveals in its construction of the genealogy of any group of animals.

Obvious progress has indeed been made from the Lower to the Upper Palaeolithic, thence to the Neolithic Age, from the Neolithic to the Ages of Metals, and from the latter to historical times. But this progress is the collective work of peoples very different from each other and inhabiting various countries.

The continuity of the gradual perfecting of Mankind, since the use of the first flints and the use of the first fire, cannot, therefore, be represented by a straight ascending line, but by a succession of broken lines, the different segments of which are joined together like the branchings of certain plants. This continuity is thus only the apparent result of partial and discontinuous progress, which projects itself into the terminal branch, the highest of all. This branch, to continue the metaphor, is formed as a succession of different components, each of which has served as a basis of progress at a given

[20] Edgar Quinet, *La Création*, Vol. II, p. 227.

moment, but not one of which can claim to have been the exclusive factor. At all periods and in every group of creatures, there are individuals which have advanced and others which have been left behind. The latter yield under pressure from the former, awaiting the time when these new masters of the moment shall undergo the same fate. How striking are the examples of this truth which the great events of prehistory reveal to us: the quick succession from the Reindeer Age to the Mousterian, from the Neolithic to the Reindeer Age, and so on.

In the long series of changes and transformations, the final result of which is to raise higher and higher the terminal twig of our branched system, many components of the system have disappeared never to return. There has been the extinction of certain groups, such as that of Neandertal Man. Their place has been taken by other groups, whose development, until then latent, suddenly sprang into fresh life and vigour.

This is true, not only of the successive representatives of the genus *Homo*, but also of those forerunners of his who link Mankind genealogically to the great trunk of the Primates. The ramifications of the latter took place in the same way, by divisions into branches, branchlets and twigs; some of these simply vegetated before dying, while others gave rise to finer products and then withered in their turn, to be replaced by new shoots still higher in the scale, whose vigour, nevertheless, lasted or will last only for a time.

Man, in spite of his superior attributes, thus takes his place in the scheme of general organization, and forms no exception among living creatures. In stepping backwards from history to prehistory and from prehistory to geological times, we see that always he is subject to the laws which regulate the evolution of every living thing. And it is because of this that human palaeontology and general palaeontology are alone found to be capable of guiding us to a full understanding of the true place of Man in nature. His true superiority, of a purely intellectual order, gradually acquired in the course of a slow and laborious evolution, now enables him to raise a corner of the veil which conceals from him both the lowliness of his origin and the glory of his ascent.

INDEX